The Good Launch Guide

Geoffrey Campbell

www.boatlaunch.co.uk

The Good Launch Guide Copyright © 2010 Boatlaunch

Data supplied by www.boatlaunch.co.uk

Published by Boatlaunch
42 Half Moon Lane
London SE24 9HU
Tel 020 8133 1745

Maps provided by OpenStreetMap & contributors
Creative Commons by Share Alike

Cover by Words and Pictures
25-27 Westow Street, London, SE19 3RY

Cover photo by Sandra Campbell

Printed by Europa
72 New Bond Street
London W1S 1RR

Distributed by Boatlaunch
42 Half Moon Lane
London SE24 9HU

ISBN: 978-0-9566056-0-3

Welcome to the fourth edition of The Good Launch Guide with detailed coverage of slipways in and around Great Britain and contact details for marinas.

For over 10 years Boatlaunch has been committed to producing comprehensive and up to date information on slipways for trailer boaters. In 2001 we produced our first "book" on the office photocopier, complete with plastic bindings and since then the project has gone from strength to strength. We now list 940 slipways and 365 marinas with all the information you need to ensure that you have the best start to a great day on the water.

This year we have included better maps showing place names and major roads to help you locate the slipways. (You are still going to need your trusty road atlas or SatNav.) We have also included latitude and longitude so that you can use SatNav to help to get you to the right spot.

There is a wealth of detail about the slipways and we are extremely grateful to the thousands of people who have contributed new sites and updated our existing information. A book like this simply would not be possible without the amazing support that we get from the boating community. On top of the information about the actual slipway, you will find details of charges, how to get there, local facilities, and information about navigational hazards.

Every effort is made to ensure that the information is as up to date as possible but things do change. We suggest that you phone ahead whenever possible to check the slipway is available and not being used as race control for the local regatta on the day you want to use it.

If you do spot any errors or you know of things that have changed please log onto www.boatlaunch.co.uk and make the necessary changes to the information. We will make sure that it is incorporated into the next edition.

We hope that The Good Launch Guide will prove to be a handy addition to the glove box and get you from the driveway to the slipway. Last but not least, have a great time on the water.

Geoff Campbell

Contents

Using This Book

The listings are divided into 7 rectangular sections with Section 1 being the North East of England. From there we travel clockwise around the coast with Section 7 finishing in Scotland. Within each section we have listed the coastal slipways and marinas clockwise along the coast. The inland slipways are listed alphabetically by nearest place name.

Symbols used on the map

Slipways ◼

Marinas ▦

Terms used in the listings

SUITABILITY – This refers to the size of boat that can be launched.

Large trailer needs a car – RIBS, sportsboats and large sailing boats

Small trailer can be pushed – Inflatable boats, dinghies

Portable only – Canoes and small inflatables

ACCESS – This is that state of the tide when you can use the slipway. On average the tide take 12 hours to go from low to high and back to low tide again. A slipway that is accessible for ¼ tidal is typically available 3 hours in 12, 1 ½ hours either side of high tide.

UPPER AREA and LOWER AREA – These are descriptions of the land surrounding the upper and lower areas of the slipway.

Latitude and Longitude notation

We have opted for decimal notation; the most computer friendly and easiest to key in to a SatNav. Negative longitude is west and positive longitude is east. I'm sorry if this upsets the purist who would like to see degrees, minutes and seconds, but you can blame it on computers in general and Google maps in particular.

Other useful sources of information

There is a lot more than knowing about slipways for a fun and safe day on the water. Two web sites in particular are worth looking at:

www.rnli.org.uk

Lots of excellent information on safety.

www.rya.org.uk

Good for advice, information on training courses and general boating.

Successful launch and recovery make for a great day out

Many would-be trailer boaters are put off by the potential difficulties of launching and recovering a boat, their fears no doubt reinforced by watching some poor soul make a complete hash of putting his boat in the water in front of an appreciative crowd around the slipway. However launching and recovering do not have to be stressful experiences. The following tips will ensure a smooth start and finish to your day.

The first tip is to plan ahead. The slipway is the start and finish point of your journey and therefore needs to be just as much of your passage plan as any other part of the journey. First of all make sure that the slipway is suitable for your boat. Check out the information on **www.boatlaunch.co.uk** or use this book to check the details of slipways in and around the UK. Slipway suitability is more than checking that your trailer will fit on the ramp. Many slipways can only be used at certain states of tide so make sure that the tide will be high enough for when you intend to launch (and recover). Is there secure overnight parking at the slipway if you are planning an overnight journey on your boat? Trailers make easy targets for thieves and it's very difficult to recover your boat without one. It is a good idea to phone ahead if possible. You don't want to drive hours to discover that your chosen slipway is closed for repairs.

When you get to the slipway, park up out of the way and take a look around, don't be in a rush to get onto the water. This will give the trailer wheel bearings a chance to cool down before going in the cold water. If not, the contraction of the warm air in the bearings will suck salt water deep into the bearings and cause serious long term damage. I always check the wheels on the trailer whenever we stop the car and if I have been using the brakes a lot, they can be hot to the touch. Now is a good time to sort out who will do what, and where you are going to park the car and trailer, and how the person parking the car and trailer will get onto the boat. Walk over to the slipway and have a look around. If someone else is launching, go down and have a look, you may pick up some useful tips. Walk down the slipway to check if it's slippery or muddy and you may wish to wade in a way to check for potholes, rocks, old bikes and trolleys. Talk to the harbourmaster if available, pay any charges due and get all the local advice that you can. Some slipways offer assisted launches where a tractor will launch your boat for you. This is well worth taking advantage of when launching across sand or shingle beaches that can bog down even the toughest four wheel drive cars.

Get everything ready before you get onto the ramp. Take off the trailer board and prop bag. Remove safety straps off the rear of the boat if you use them. Take the outboard off the tilt support lever. Put all your gear into the boat, put the keys in the ignition and the kill cord in place. Check fuel and oil if necessary and prime the fuel pump, check the GPS and radio. In short, you should be ready to go to sea, including wearing lifejackets, before you put your boat onto the ramp. One last check that everything is ready and only then head off to the ramp.

Reversing a trailer down the ramp is not something you can learn about in books, you just have to try it, but don't let a crowded ramp on a Sunday morning be your practice ground. Try reversing in an empty car park or driveway. If you have an off-road vehicle with low ratio, this is a good time to use it. Going slowly and not having to slip the clutch makes life a lot easier.

Some slipways are just too slippery and steep to risk taking a car onto. I will never forget the experience as my Land Rover Discovery, trailer and boat slid gently down the slipway at Helensburgh with all four wheels locked. Cars have been lost in this way. The heart-stopping solution was to release the brakes until the wheels started to turn and then very gently re-apply them. To avoid this nerve racking experience in these slippery circumstances, lower your trailer down the ramp by means of a long rope attached to the car so that your vehicle stays well above the slime. Be careful when unhitching a trailer near the top of a ramp. I saw the result of a RIB that had careered out of control down a slipway and rammed a concrete post. The engine was a write-off, the boat was badly damaged and they were very lucky that no one was injured. When using a length of rope between the car and trailer, the person at the trailer will not be able to see the person in the car and to avoid a lot of shouting and confusion a couple of cheap walkie-talkies can be very handy. Most slipways will not require the use of a rope, especially if you have a four wheel drive car, but it is a useful trick to know, especially if launching or recovering at low tide.

Reverse the trailer until the transom is in the water and, if you are a power-boater, lower your engine and get it started. If there are any problems with the engine you can abort your trip without having to get your boat back onto the trailer. Assuming the engine is running fine, switch off and bring the engine back up. That way, if there are any unseen obstructions in the water you won't damage your engine when you launch.

Now you should be ready to launch and there are as many different ways to get a boat off a trailer as there are trailer boaters. The important thing is to use a method that is safe and that you feel comfortable with. What follows are methods that have worked well for me over the years launching a variety of boats off different trailers and the details will change for different boats and different trailers.

If you have a roller trailer, it should be possible to roll your boat off the trailer into the water, keeping your precious trailer wheel bearings out of the water. When launching into a harbour or lake where there is no cross-current, my preferred method is to reverse the trailer until the trailer wheel hubs are just above the water. I attach one end of an 8 metre rope to the bow of the boat and the other end to the trailer with the slack neatly coiled in the boat. I then undo all the straps holding the boat onto the trailer. Our boat is a 6 metre, one tonne RIB and putting your shoulder under the bow and pushing up causes the boat to gently slide off the trailer into the water. And since we remembered to tie the boat to the trailer you can pull the boat back to the ramp and climb aboard.

If you are launching into a cross-current or on a steep ramp, you may want to use a more controlled approach and lower your boat into the water by means of the trailer winch. In this case, keep the boat attached to the trailer winch and with one person pushing, the other can lower the boat on the winch. Once the boat is in the water, but being held with the winch, one person can get aboard, get the engine going and be ready to go. However, be extremely careful when using the trailer winch. If you lose your grip on the handle and it starts to spin, DO NOT try to catch it. You will not be able to stop it and more likely than not, you will end up with a broken wrist. Just let it run. Alternatively, tie a rope onto the bow eye of your boat and take a few turns around the trailer winch post. Take up the strain on the rope and slowly release the trailer winch and unhook it from the boat. Then lower the boat by slowly letting the rope out.

If your trailer does not have rollers, but has carpet bunk pads instead, a different technique is required. Get everything ready as before and take off all the trailer straps and either attach a long rope between boat and trailer or put someone in the boat. Then, starting with the trailer wheels just in the water, smartly reverse the car and trailer until the rear of the car is at the water's edge and hit the brakes. Your boat should glide off the trailer. If not, it is probably still attached to the trailer. You won't believe how many people attempt to launch a boat while it is still strapped onto the trailer!

To recover the boat, you have to put someone ashore to get the car and trailer. Many slipways do not have the luxury of a pontoon and a walkie-talkie to keep contact between the car and the boat is useful if you are hanging around in the boat wondering where on earth the car has got to. For a roller style trailer, reverse the trailer until the trailer wheels hubs are just above the water and slowly drive the boat up to the trailer and, with the engine ticking over in forward gear, clip the trailer winch strop onto the boat. Turn the engine off and winch the boat onto the trailer. With a carpet type trailer, put the trailer deeper into the water and drive the boat onto the trailer. You may want to experiment with the best speed for your approach, but I have found that tick-over speed is best for getting the boat onto a carpet style trailer. As soon as you have got the boat onto the trailer, attach a safety line in case the winch strop breaks. We use a length of chain with a snap shackle. Boats can roll off the back of trailers as they are pulled up the ramp causing damage and injury. Park up away from the ramp and get your boat and trailer ready for the road.

If you are using a slipway in a river you may have to recover your boat in a cross-current which can make life difficult as your boat will be swept sideways over the trailer. Try and avoid this if possible by timing your recovery at slack tide. If you have to recover in a cross current, the trick is to start your approach upstream of the trailer. Drift down towards the trailer with your boat aligned with the trailer and control your approach with the throttle. If you get it right you will arrive at the trailer and be in-line with the trailer so that you can just drive onto it. If not, reverse out and try again. Avoid the temptation to approach the trailer with the boat pointing upstream to counteract the effect of the current. When you get to the trailer you find that the boat is pointing in a different direction to the trailer, it won't go on and you end up with expensive scratch marks on your gel coat and lots of shouting, much to the amusement of the crowd that will have gathered to watch.

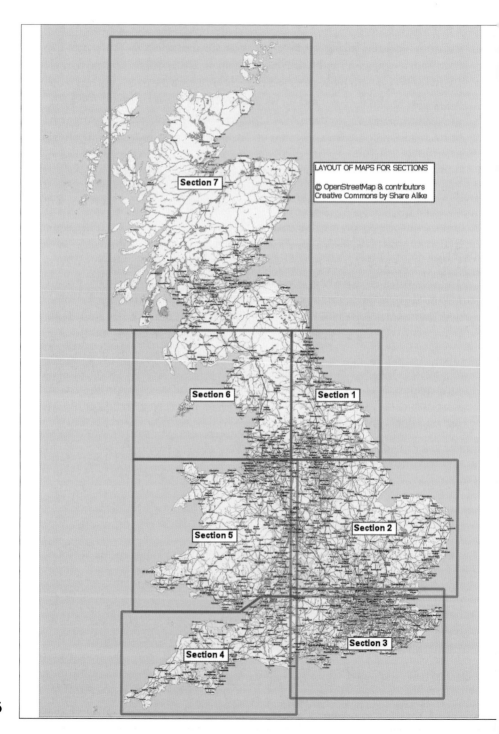

LAYOUT OF MAPS FOR SECTIONS

© OpenStreetMap & contributors
Creative Commons by Share Alike

Section 7

Section 6

Section 1

Section 5

Section 2

Section 4

Section 3

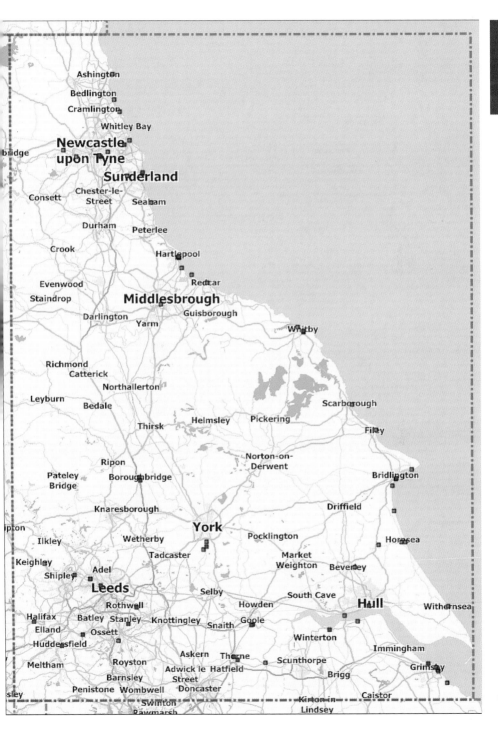

1

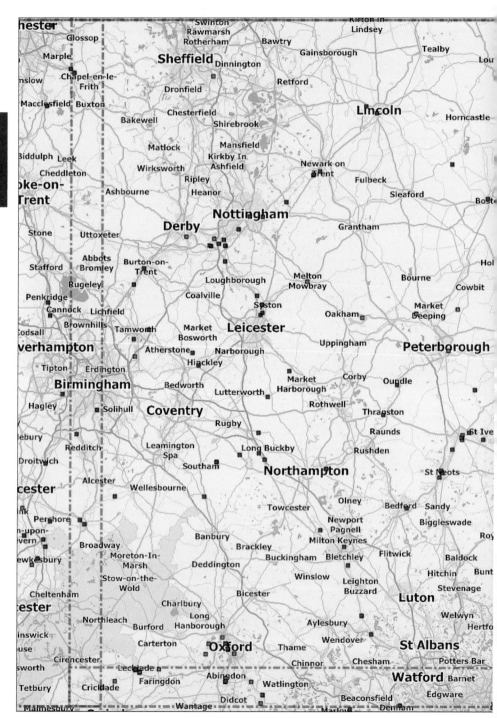

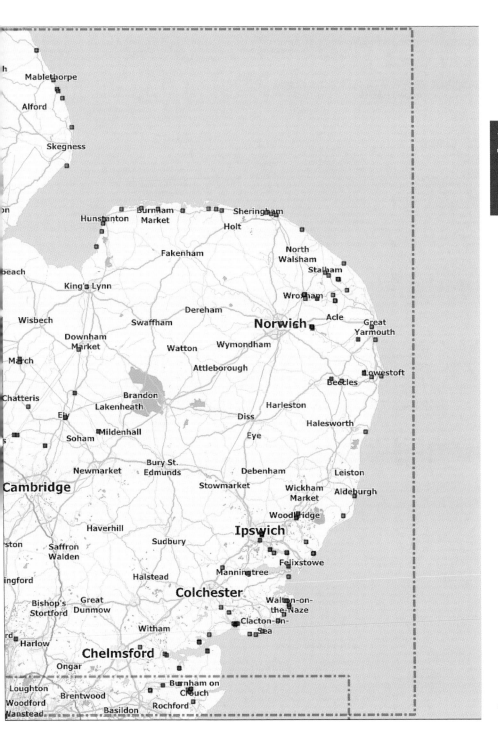

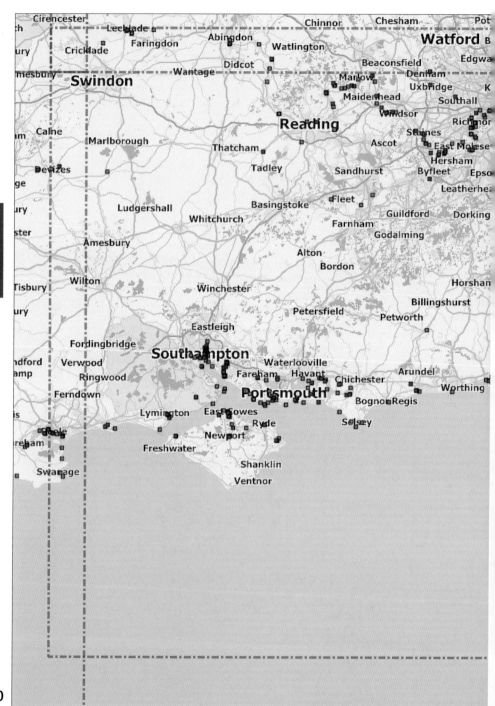

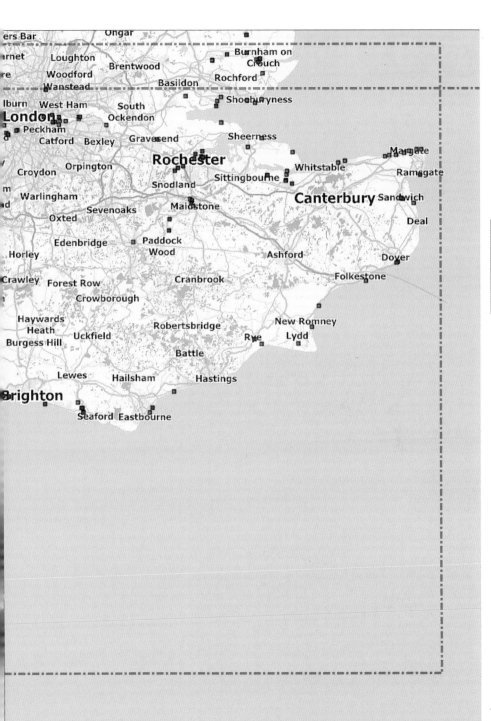

3

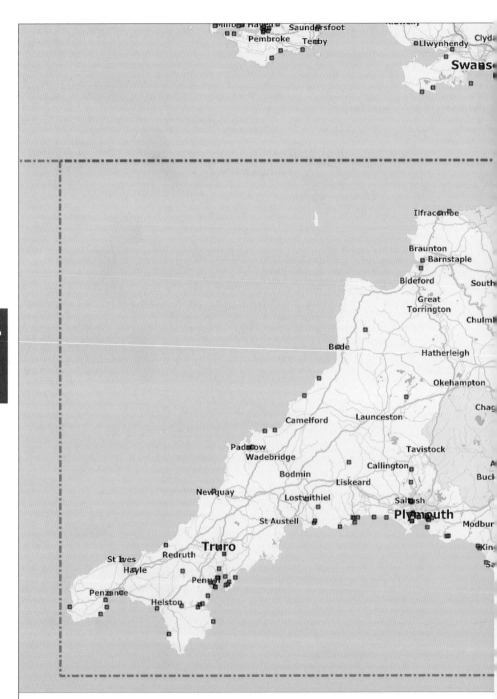

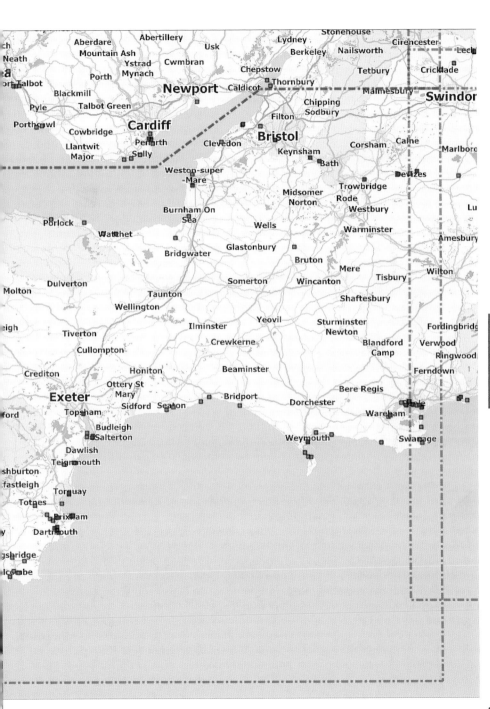

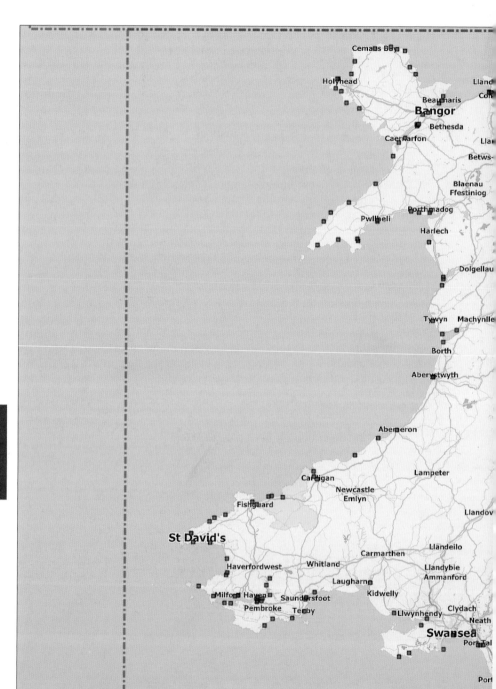

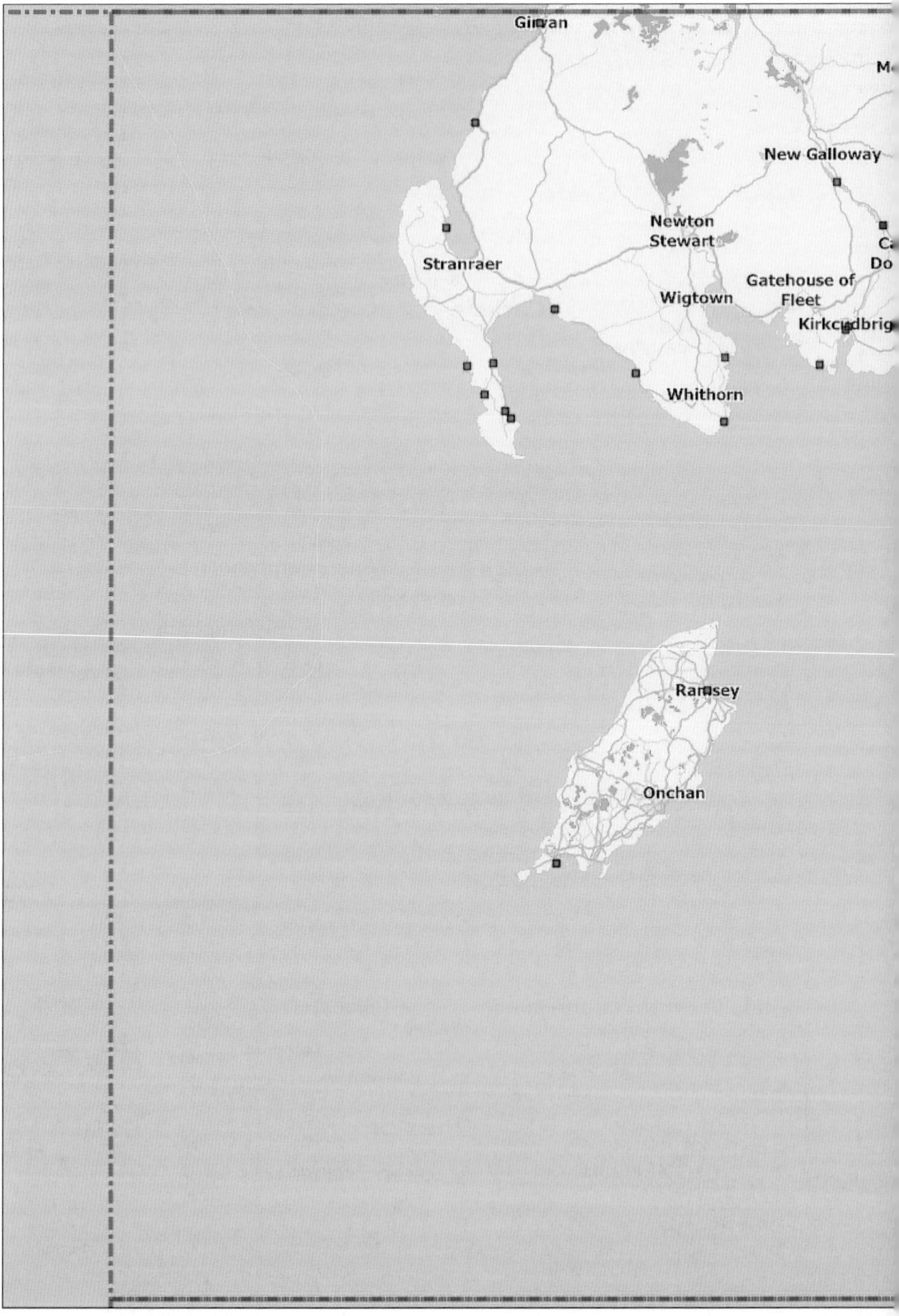

Girvan

M

New Galloway

Newton
Stewart

C
Do

Stranraer

Gatehouse of
Fleet

Wigtown

Kirkcudbrig

Whithorn

Ramsey

Onchan

6

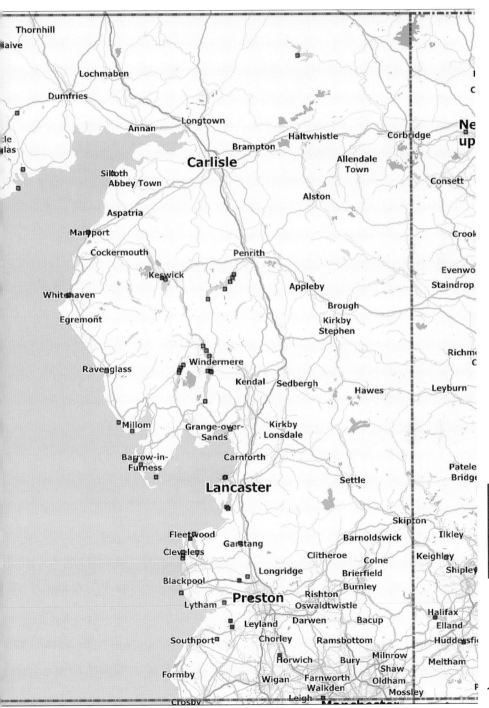

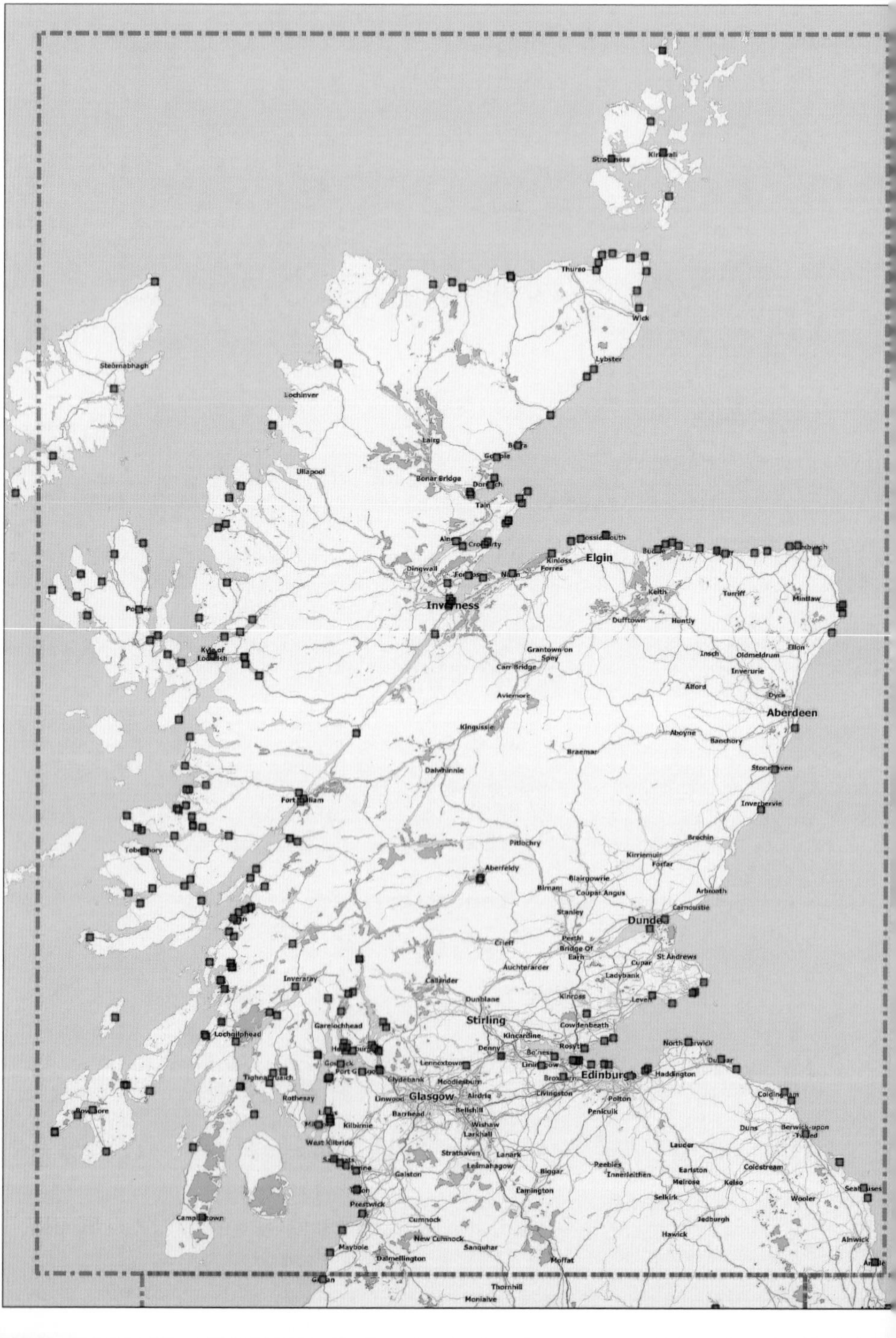
Thurso
Wick
Lybster
Steòrnabhagh
Lochinver
Lairg
Ullapool
Bonar Bridge
Tain
Dingwall
Elgin
Kinloss
Forres
Inverness
Keith
Turriff
Mintlaw
Dufftown
Huntly
Grantown on Spey
Carr Bridge
Insch
Oldmeldrum
Ellon
Inverurie
Alford
Dyce
Aviemore
Aberdeen
Kingussie
Aboyne
Banchory
Braemar
Dalwhinnie
Pitlochry
Brechin
Kirriemuir
Forfar
Aberfeldy
Blairgowrie
Coupar Angus
Arbroath
Carnoustie
Stanley
Crieff
Perth
Bridge Of Earn
St Andrews
Cupar
Auchterarder
Ladybank
Inveraray
Callander
Kinross
Dunblane
Stirling
Garelochhead
Lochgilphead
Kincardine
Denny
North Berwick
Lennoxtown
Haddington
Clydebank
Moodiesburn
Edinburgh
Tighnabruaich
Rothesay
Linwood
Glasgow
Airdrie
Livingston
Polton
Penicuik
Barrhead
Bellshill
Kilbirnie
Wishaw
Larkhall
West Kilbride
Duns
Berwick-upon Tweed
Lauder
Strathaven
Lanark
Lesmahagow
Biggar
Peebles
Innerleithen
Earlston
Coldstream
Galston
Melrose
Kelso
Lamington
Selkirk
Wooler
Prestwick
Campbeltown
Cumnock
Jedburgh
Hawick
New Cumnock
Sanquhar
Alnwick
Maybole
Dalmellington
Moffat
Thornhill
Moniaive

1 North East England

Ashington to Grimsby

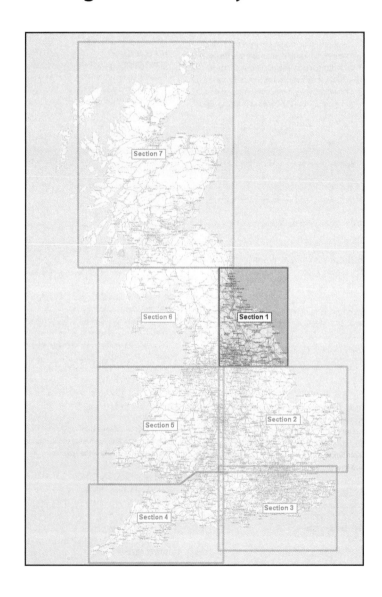

COASTAL SLIPWAYS
clockwise around the coast

Promenade Slip, Newbiggin by the Sea
Lat. 55.1855, Long. -1.5051.
SUITABILITY: Large trailer needs a car.
ACCESS: All of tidal range. **TYPE OF RAMP:** Slip onto hard sand.
UPPER AREA: Sand. **LOWER AREA:** Sand.
DIRECTIONS: Public ramp is next to the car park onto the beach.
RAMP DESCRIPTION: There are 2 options: Down lifeboat ramp onto beach or down public ramp (recommended) next to car park onto beach. Public ramp (concrete) is flat and extends over top of beach to the Spring high water level only, and then you are onto sand. The top 5-10 metres of beach is often soft sand, especially in summer and with Neap tides. Loose sand tends to blow and build up. Hard sand in the intertidal zone. 4 × 4 recommended for anything heavier/ bigger than small sailing dinghy. Occasionally local boat owners with tractors will assist visitors (especially anglers) but cannot rely on this. Launch and recovery easiest for powered boats with 2.0 metres of tidal height (or greater), due to flat seabed at low water, (i.e. use high water +/- 4 or 4½ hours generally). Lifeboat ramp is steep and straight onto soft sand, also used by local cobles, and access around back of lifeboat house is narrow with sharp turns. After new development of beach area, the sand is very soft especially at water level. Please check first.
FACILITIES: Plenty of car parking space or park trailers on beach. Petrol and shops in town.
HAZARDS: Site can be exposed to southerlies as well as south easterlies.

Sluice Harbour, Seaton Sluice
Lat. 55.0844, Long. -1.4727.
01670 542346
CHARGES: £7
SUITABILITY: Large trailer needs a car.
ACCESS: ¼ tidal. **TYPE OF RAMP:** Concrete **UPPER AREA:** Harbour.
LOWER AREA: Unknown.
DIRECTIONS: The slipway is situated off the A193 between Blyth and Whitley Bay. Slipway leads into the harbour.
RAMP DESCRIPTION: Access by prior arrangement. Note that the harbour is not manned. The road to the slipway is narrow. Good wide and steep slipway into harbour usable about two hours either side high water. Entry into the harbour is difficult on a beam sea. Upstream of the bridge, launching is possible over a concrete ramp where there is an existing boat park. All launching under licence.
FACILITIES: Good parking near to the harbour slipway and close to town of Seaton Sluice.
HAZARDS: 5 knot speed limit in harbour.

Royal Quays Marina, North Shields
Albert Edward Dock, Coble Dene Rd, North Shields, Tyne & Wear, England NE29 6DU
Lat. 54.9947, Long. -1.4526.
0191 272 8282

St Peters Marina, Newcastle-upon-Tyne
St Peters Basin, Newcastle-upon-Tyne, Tyne & Wear, England NE6 1HX
Lat. 54.9664, Long. -1.5733.
0191 265 4472

Waterski Club, Newburn
Lat. 54.9819, Long. -1.7446.
Paul 0191 264 7029
CHARGES: £100/year.
SUITABILITY: Large trailer needs a car.
ACCESS: ¼ tidal. **TYPE OF RAMP:** Concrete **UPPER AREA:** Concrete.
LOWER AREA: Mud.
DIRECTIONS: Ramp is at the Tyne Riverside Country Park, Grange Road. From A69 take the A6085 for Throckley / Newburn. Turn off in Newburn into Grange Road and follow signs.
RAMP DESCRIPTION: Fairly steep concrete slipway. Available to club members only. No Jetskis and only 6 boats on the water at one time. Site has a locked barrier.
FACILITIES: Leisure Park nearby with toilets and vending machine. Café next to the ramp.
HAZARDS: Speed zone for use of club members only.

Powerhouse Marina, Derwenthaugh
Lat. 54.9642, Long. -1.6833.
0191 4140065
CHARGES: £8/day or £110/year
SUITABILITY: Large trailer needs a car.
ACCESS: ¾ tidal. **TYPE OF RAMP:** Concrete **UPPER AREA:** Mud.
LOWER AREA: Mud.
DIRECTIONS: From the A1 follow signs to Blaydon (A65) and look for blue building with ACRO. Follow narrow road past this building to the marina. This will take you under the Scotsdale Bridge and along the river bank to Powerhouse Marine.
RAMP DESCRIPTION: Two medium sized concrete ramps. All craft launching must have third party insurance. Jetski zone close to the ramp and an unrestricted speed area runs for approximately 1½ miles downstream of the slipway. Slipway gets muddy from use and may need a 4 × 4 for larger Jetskis and powerboats in wet conditions.
FACILITIES: Plenty of parking. Toilets and shower are for annual members only and you get your own key so you can use the slipway out of hours. Jetski hire available at the marina. Pub nearby and fast food outlets.
HAZARDS: 6 knot speed limit upstream. Fast water zone downstream. With the river speed restrictions it's a 2 hour journey to the mouth of the Tyne

Friar's Goose Club, Gateshead
Lat. 54.9635, Long. -1.5675.
Clubhouse 0191 4692545 or Sec 0191 262 2617
CHARGES: £5
SUITABILITY: Large trailer needs a car.
ACCESS: ½ tidal. **TYPE OF RAMP:** Concrete **UPPER AREA:** Unknown.
LOWER AREA: Unknown.

1

DIRECTIONS: Ramp is at the Friar's Goose Water Sports Club, Felling. Follow the A6127 from A1(M) into Gateshead. The club is situated on the banks of the River Tyne adjacent to Gateshead International Stadium and just off the Felling bypass.
RAMP DESCRIPTION: Large slipway.
FACILITIES: The excellent clubhouse is open every day except Tuesday with bar and catering available. All welcome, our friendliness is legendary. It is a RYA Recognised Teaching Establishment for power. The club has facilities for sorts of craft and a large slipway, travel hoist, pontoon landing, deep water, workshop, and facilities for restoration and building projects.
HAZARDS: 6 knot speed restriction in the river.

Hebburn Marina, Hebburn
Lat. 54.9763, Long. -1.5321.
CHARGES: FREE
SUITABILITY: Large trailer needs a car.
ACCESS: Unknown. **TYPE OF RAMP:** Ramp is concrete, of average condition. At low tide the ramp is very steep anything larger than a small dinghy would need a car. Local knowledge advised that the way is even steeper underwater at low tide. **UPPER AREA:** Concrete.
LOWER AREA: Concrete.
RAMP DESCRIPTION: Free slipway plenty free parking. The slipway is steep at low water and a little tight for large boats. There are no facilities to moor boats after launching. At high tide the slipway is bounded by wire-mesh encased stone walls. At low tide either side of the way is weed covered mud. Way is only really suitable for PWC or small dinghy.
FACILITIES: None other than ramp and free parking.
HAZARDS: Beware of logs/driftwood in the river.

Groyne Launching Ramp, South Shields
Lat. 55.0069, Long. -1.4275.
Tourist Office 0191 4546612
CHARGES: £21/day (22 August 2009) + £5 deposit for barrier electronic key.
SUITABILITY: Large trailer needs a car.
ACCESS: All of tidal range. **TYPE OF RAMP:** Concrete
UPPER AREA: Sand. **LOWER AREA:** Sand.
DIRECTIONS: Ramp is at Little Haven Beach. Follow the A6115 south from Newcastle or A1 then A194 to South Shields and follow the signs to the sea front. Slipway is near the junction of Harbour Drive and River Drive.
RAMP DESCRIPTION: Concrete slipway. Not accessible at Spring low tide. Must have permit to use the ramp and car park, permits are available from Tourist Information Centre, Sea Road or from Central Library, Prince George Square. You will get a sticker for the boat and one for the car. Certificate or 3rd Party insurance for £1,000,000 is required in order to get a permit. Site gets very busy during peak periods. Two adjacent sailing clubs and divers use this site. Jetskis can use this site.
FACILITIES: Boat storage available at the adjacent sailing clubs for members. Local club members can buy a season ticket for £26 and non club members pay £36.
HAZARDS: 6 knot speed limit. Keep clear of large ships in the shipping lane.

Sunderland Marina, Sunderland
Marine Activities Centre Sunderland Marina, Sunderland, Tyne & Wear, England SR6 0PW
Lat. 54.9200, Long. -1.3674.
0191 514 4721

Sunderland Marina, Roker
Lat. 54.9166, Long. -1.3685.
0191 5144721
CHARGES: £100 per annum
SUITABILITY: Large trailer needs a car.
ACCESS: All of tidal range. **TYPE OF RAMP:** Concrete
UPPER AREA: Concrete. **LOWER AREA:** Sand.
DIRECTIONS: From the A1 take the A690 and A19 north. Turn right onto A1231 east to Roker following signs to the seafront and National Glass Centre. Address is North Dock, Roker, Sunderland, SR6 0PW.
RAMP DESCRIPTION: Concrete ramp into the river, regularly cleaned. Annual pass only, no day passes. There is a locked barrier onto the slipway; you get a key in exchange for your pass. Site gives access to the river Wear 10 minutes from the open sea. Jetskis welcome.
FACILITIES: Parking area at top of slipway ramp.
HAZARDS: 6 knot speed limit in harbour and river. Waterskiing permitted only in designated areas. Signage with zoning areas and Harbour rules at top of slipway.

Claxheugh Rock, Claxheugh Rock
Lat. 54.9113, Long. -1.4395.
SUITABILITY: Large trailer needs a car.
ACCESS: ½ tidal. **TYPE OF RAMP:** Concrete **UPPER AREA:** Concrete.
LOWER AREA: Mud.
RAMP DESCRIPTION: Half tidal slipway. Need car for heavy boats
HAZARDS: 6 knot limit

Slipway, Seaham Harbour
Lat. 54.8382, Long. -1.3268.
CHARGES: £50 per year plus £12 to join the club. £2M 3rd party liability insurance and compliance with RNLI SEACHECK required. (2007)
SUITABILITY: Large trailer needs a car.
ACCESS: Unknown. **TYPE OF RAMP:** Concrete - Requires a 4 wheel drive only if launching over the sand at low water
UPPER AREA: Concrete. **LOWER AREA:** Sand.
DIRECTIONS: Seaham harbour north Dock entrance. Barrier key and card required from Club.
RAMP DESCRIPTION: Ramp refurbished October 2009. Slope now 1 in 8 and extended to 37.5 metres.
FACILITIES: Being upgraded to provide workshops, toilets café and marina office plus 70 berths. Work expected to be completed by early summer 2010.
HAZARDS: Rocks show in front of the slip at Spring lows. 1.2 metres of water at low tide required to launch safely up to 20 foot trailed boats.

Hartlepool Marina, Hartlepool
Lock Office, Slake Terrace, Hartlepool, Teeside,
England TS24 0RU
Lat. 54.6912, Long. -1.1987.
01429 865744

Hartlepool Marina, Hartlepool
Lat. 54.6893, Long. -1.2055.
01429 865744

CHARGES: £15/day
SUITABILITY: Large trailer needs a car.
ACCESS: ½ tidal. **TYPE OF RAMP:** Concrete **UPPER AREA:** Shingle.
LOWER AREA: Sand.
DIRECTIONS: The ramp is on the south side of the marina in Hartlepool on Maritime Avenue off Marina Way (A179). It is next to the Museum ship and car parking area.
RAMP DESCRIPTION: Short flat concrete ramp at the edge of marina. There needs to be enough water in the marina to use this ramp as there is a steep drop off into 4+ metres of water. Approach to the ramp with a medium size boat is extremely difficult, as the ramp has just a very narrow access gate. Care needed on ramp - according to the loch keeper a Land Rover & boat/trailer tipped in and floated off, (8/2002). Jetskis and boats use marina - but need to go through the lock to reach the sea, for which there is a charge. Second ramp outside the lock gates to the north is not in use due to construction work, hopefully to clean up all the rubbish which normally blocks the slip.
FACILITIES: Diesel, parking and boat storage, toilets, showers and food.
HAZARDS: 4 knot speed limit.

Tees and Hartlepool YC, Hartlepool
Lat. 54.6885, Long. -1.1973.
01492 265400

CHARGES: Club membership
SUITABILITY: Large trailer needs a car.
ACCESS: ½ tidal. **TYPE OF RAMP:** Concrete **UPPER AREA:** Harbour.
LOWER AREA: Sand.
DIRECTIONS: Slipway leads into the West Harbour, just to the south of the marina lock gates.
RAMP DESCRIPTION: Visitors are welcome and must phone ahead and arrange temporary membership if you want to use the slip. Launch 2 hours either side high water but possible other times with light boat. Phone club house for permission well in advance (01429-274931), no steward at club, members answer. Slip can be busy with water skiers. This is a sheltered harbour giving access to a good bay with good sailing except in strong southeast winds.
FACILITIES: Car parking near top of ramp. Fresh water in clubhouse if open. New club house on site.
HAZARDS: Beware 10,000 ton ships in narrow entrance and a watchful pilot vessel.

Seafront, Seaton Carew
Lat. 54.6606, Long. -1.1856.

CHARGES: None
SUITABILITY: Small trailer can be pushed.

ACCESS: ¾ tidal. **TYPE OF RAMP:** Concrete **UPPER AREA:** Unknown.
LOWER AREA: Sand.
DIRECTIONS: Follow the A19 from Teeside then A689 and B1276 to seafront.
RAMP DESCRIPTION: Concrete slipway with slope onto soft sand. Suitable for small power boat approximately 4 hours either side of high water by prior arrangement. Vehicles allowed only on beach with permission. Exposed conditions in onshore wind.
FACILITIES: Parking and boat storage.
HAZARDS: All craft must keep clear of shipping channels.

Tees Barrage, Teeside Park
Lat. 54.5634, Long. -1.2883.
Tees Barrage 01642 633273

CHARGES: Registration fee for powered boats.
SUITABILITY: Large trailer needs a car.
ACCESS: Non-tidal. **TYPE OF RAMP:** Concrete **UPPER AREA:** Harbour.
LOWER AREA: Harbour.
DIRECTIONS: Tees Barrage is signposted off the A66 west of the A19. The ramp is 500 metres upstream of the A19 bridge on the south bank. Good access from A19/A66. Adjacent to a large retail park.
RAMP DESCRIPTION: Shallow concrete slipway. All power craft must be registered with Tees Barrage Ltd and have proof of 3rd party liability insurance £3.10/metre/week for non club members. Craft intending to enter the tidal waters downstream of the lock must register with Tees Harbour Office (01642 277205). Jetskis can launch here but must be club members.
FACILITIES: Plenty of parking, 12 tonnes boat hoist. Close to shops and fuel. Waterski and Jetski areas nearby are for local clubs only and use is allocated on a time slot basis. Barrage operators very friendly and helpful.
HAZARDS: 5mph restriction on the river. Waterskiing and PWC are permitted for club members only in designated areas.

South Gare Marine Club, Redcar
Lat. 54.6387, Long. -1.1404.

CHARGES: £10/launch
SUITABILITY: Large trailer needs a car.
ACCESS: ¾ tidal. **TYPE OF RAMP:** Concrete **UPPER AREA:** Shingle.
LOWER AREA: Shingle.
DIRECTIONS: Follow the A1085 from Middlesbrough to Coatham taking Sea Front Road at traffic lights by Cowies Garage and turning left at roundabout. Club will be seen on left after 3 miles. Access is via single track private road with passing places which may be shut at odd times and locked barrier at entrance to club.
RAMP DESCRIPTION: Open at weekends and Bank Holidays only. Concrete slipway available all times except 1 hour either side of low water. There is always someone around at the weekend, make sure you agree your return time before you go or the gate may be locked. All craft must register with the harbour office telephone; 01642 277205 and will be expected to carry basic safety equipment.
FACILITIES: Parking, boat storage and toilets and café. Old wartime buildings.
HAZARDS: Tides may be strong at the river mouth. 6 knot speed limit in river.

1

Seafront, Redcar

Lat. 54.6202, Long. -1.0645.
SUITABILITY: Small trailer can be pushed.
ACCESS: All of tidal range. **TYPE OF RAMP:** Concrete
UPPER AREA: Unknown. **LOWER AREA:** Sand.
DIRECTIONS: Follow the A1085 from Middlesbrough.
RAMP DESCRIPTION: Three wide concrete slips onto firm sand.
Available all states of tide, but best to use 2-3 hours either side of high
water. Exposed conditions in onshore wind, local knowledge is essential.
FACILITIES: Petrol, parking and toilets.

Slipway, Upgang slipway

Lat. 54.4954, Long. -0.6402.
SUITABILITY: Small trailer can be pushed.
ACCESS: ¼ tidal. **TYPE OF RAMP: UPPER AREA:** Concrete.
LOWER AREA: Sand.
DIRECTIONS: Get key for bollards from Whitby Golf Club bar (£5
deposit)
RAMP DESCRIPTION: Concrete ramp

Whitby Harbour, Whitby

Whitby Harbour Office, Endeavour Wharf, Whitby,
North Yorkshire, England YO21 1DN
Lat. 54.4842, Long. -0.6128.
01947 602354

Whitby Marina, Whitby

Lat. 54.4818, Long. -0.6128.
01947 600165 (Harbour Dept.)

CHARGES: £18.00 includes parking as at August 2009.
SUITABILITY: Large trailer needs a car.
ACCESS: ½ tidal. **TYPE OF RAMP:** Concrete **UPPER AREA:** Harbour.
LOWER AREA: Concrete.
DIRECTIONS: The site is off Langbourne Road follow A171 east from
Middlesbrough or A64 / A169 from York, turn right in centre of town past
Co-op Supermarket. Go straight ahead to the marina.
RAMP DESCRIPTION: Shallow concrete ramp. Council owned, not
shared with club. Whitby marina is off Langbourne Road.
FACILITIES: Diesel nearby, no petrol, parking for car and trailer on-site,
toilets and chandlery on-site, diving supplies and outboard repairs
nearby.
HAZARDS: Speed limit in force. Water skiing prohibited in the
harbour.

Harbour Slipway, Scarborough

Lat. 54.2834, Long. -0.3916.
01723 373 530 (Harbour Dept.)
CHARGES: £9.40/day, £133/year.
SUITABILITY: Large trailer needs a car.
ACCESS: All of tidal range. **TYPE OF RAMP:** Concrete
UPPER AREA: Harbour. **LOWER AREA:** Mud.
DIRECTIONS: Located in Scarborough Harbour. Follow the A64 from
York to Scarborough. Site is off the Harbour Side Road.

RAMP DESCRIPTION: Shallow concrete ramp. PWC are prohibited.
Slipway has a locked barrier - contact the Harbour Dept. Remove trailers
from the slipway.
FACILITIES: Trailer compound may be closed due to work on cliffs
above. Petrol, chandlery and parking. Close to the centre of town.
HAZARDS: Speed restrictions in harbour.

Coble Landing, Filey

Lat. 54.2134, Long. -0.2817.
01723 373 530 (Harbour Dept.)

CHARGES: £7.58/day, £76/year
SUITABILITY: Small trailer can be pushed.
ACCESS: All of tidal range. **TYPE OF RAMP:** Concrete and stone.
UPPER AREA: Sand. **LOWER AREA:** Sand.
DIRECTIONS: Follow A64 and A1039 from York. Site is at the north end
of the sea front.
RAMP DESCRIPTION: Shallow slipway of concrete and stone leading
onto sand. Suitable for sailing and small powered craft. No PWC.
Accessible all states of tide for smaller craft, but only 2 hours either
side of high water for larger craft. Boats with an engine capacity of over
12.5hp are prohibited. Not suitable for car launches, can be used in any
tide but could walk miles if tide is out so avoid low water Spring tides
due to soft sand and mud.
FACILITIES: Fresh water at toilet block, food at stalls by car park or
in town. Car park and ramp on to a flat beach. A very good, quiet
launching place in early spring or late summer. Very crowded in season
when cobles and fishermen's cars park on ramp. Impossible to park car
unless you're there before 8 am.
HAZARDS: Speed limit within 200 metres of shore. Water skiing
permitted outside this area. Easterlies bring in strong surf.

Flamborough, South Landing

Lat. 54.1038, Long. -0.1179.

CHARGES: None advertised.
SUITABILITY: Large trailer needs a car.
ACCESS: ¼ tidal. **TYPE OF RAMP:** Concrete and beach.
UPPER AREA: Concrete. **LOWER AREA:** Sand.
DIRECTIONS: In Flamborough you will see signs for the Lifeboat
Station, follow these and it will take you down the lane where you will
find Pay and Display Car parking and toilets. By continuing past these
you will drive down to the ramp, signs explain that you need to seek
permission before launching.
RAMP DESCRIPTION: Permission needed - ask in Lifeboat Station. Not
the best slipway in the area, best to use Filey and Bridlington. South
Landing tends to be used by locals with very heavy boats and they use
tractors. Visiting divers use it where they have a lot of man power to
manoeuvre the boat. Tractors are not always available to hire. The sand
can be soft and even a 4 × 4 can get stuck. There are rocks at low water
and large chalk stones up to 1foot across at high water. It can have quite
an awkward little sea with a strong southerly wind. Not an easy site.
Bridlington is close and always has tractors available.
FACILITIES: Pay and display car park with toilets.

Bridlington Harbour, Bridlington
Gummers Wharf, West End,, Bridlington, East Yorkshire, England YO15 3AN
Lat. 54.0809, Long. -0.1914.
01262 670148

South Shore, Bridlington
Lat. 54.0791, Long. -0.1948.
East Yorkshire BC 01262 678255

CHARGES: Launch fee £10.50, tractor assistance £12.00
SUITABILITY: Large trailer needs a car.
ACCESS: All of tidal range. **TYPE OF RAMP:** Concrete
UPPER AREA: Concrete. **LOWER AREA:** Sand.
DIRECTIONS: Enter Bridlington on the A165. Take the first right in Bridlington and then turn right at the traffic lights. Ramp is at the end of this road.
RAMP DESCRIPTION: Need tractor as beach can be soft. There are several which can be hired and will tow you down and back up. Seasonal access. Ramp operated by East Yorkshire BC (foreshore / car parks office. Tel:01262 678255). Open April 1st to 28th October, 9am to one hour before dusk. Pay security man for launch and recovery, Tel 01262 673761. Exposed coast. Harbourmaster 01262 670148, Royal York's YC 01262 672041. Site gets busy and offers excellent service.
FACILITIES: All normal facilities, toilets, water, changing rooms. Pay and display car park. Car parking free for slipway users.

Bridlington Boat Launch, Bridlington
Lat. 54.0613, Long. -0.2118.
01262 400841

SUITABILITY: Large trailer needs a car.
ACCESS: Unknown. **TYPE OF RAMP: UPPER AREA:** Concrete.
LOWER AREA: Sand.
DIRECTIONS: We have moved half a mile to the south of the old compound. Access is from the A165 at the new roundabout to the park and ride.
RAMP DESCRIPTION: 200 boat capacity compound with tarmac slipway leading to beach. Jetskis welcome.
FACILITIES: Toilets, showers, boat wash area, tractors.

Beach Bank, Hornsea
Lat. 53.9936, Long. -0.2074.

CHARGES: £10 for launch with a tractor
SUITABILITY: Large trailer needs a car.
ACCESS: ½ tidal. **TYPE OF RAMP: UPPER AREA:** Concrete.
LOWER AREA: Sand.
FACILITIES: Water

Hornsea launch, Hornsea
Lat. 53.9086, Long. -0.1584.
01964 533116

CHARGES: Single day launch and recovery at Hornsea for 2009 is £25.00 by tractor driven by compound staff berths available with discounted launches
SUITABILITY: Large trailer needs a car.

ACCESS: All of tidal range. **TYPE OF RAMP:** Purpose built concrete onto sand. **UPPER AREA:** Sand. **LOWER AREA:** Sand.
DIRECTIONS: 15 miles northeast of Kingston-Upon-Hull. Boat compound is at the southern end of Hornsea at the car park on South Promenade.
RAMP DESCRIPTION: Purpose built compound with wash down bays and access ramp to the beach. All types of boats and skis are welcome. Jetskiers and power boats must keep 300 metres offshore. Launching has to be done by our tractor due to several customers vehicles getting stuck in the sand.
FACILITIES: Brand new purpose built facility in a boat compound. Toilets, showers, tractor launches available April-October. The tractor has a power winch making easy recovery. Purpose built facilities for washing down boats, short and long time storage berths available

Slipway, Withernsea
Lat. 53.7315, Long. 0.0345.

CHARGES: £10.00 to launch and retrieve.
SUITABILITY: Large trailer needs a car.
ACCESS: ¼ tidal. **TYPE OF RAMP:** Concrete **UPPER AREA:** Concrete.
LOWER AREA: Sand.
RAMP DESCRIPTION: Ramp can only be used with a tractor. However tractors are not always there in which case you will not be able to launch.

Hull Marina, Kingston upon Hull
Warehouse 13, Kingston Street, Kingston upon Hull, East Yorkshire, England HU1 2DQ
Lat. 53.7397, Long. -0.3392.
01482 330505

Humber Rescue, Kingston-upon-Hull
Lat. 53.7145, Long. -0.4530.
Humber Rescue 01482 648200

CHARGES: £30 annual fee.
SUITABILITY: Large trailer needs a car.
ACCESS: All of tidal range. **TYPE OF RAMP:** Hard shingle.
UPPER AREA: Shingle. **LOWER AREA:** Shingle.
DIRECTIONS: Just upstream of the Humber Bridge at the Humber Rescue station.
RAMP DESCRIPTION: The £30 annual fee gives you a key to open the locked chain giving access to the hard pebble and sand beach. Launch is possible at all states of the exception of very low water. Humber Rescue is manned at the weekend during the day. Probably the best launching site in the area. Popular with Jetskis.
FACILITIES: Parking available. Pub and restaurant nearby. Hot drinks at the club house.

Goole Boathouse, Goole
Lat. 53.6957, Long. -0.8796.
01405 763985

CHARGES: £5 each way.
SUITABILITY: Large trailer needs a car.
ACCESS: Non-tidal. **TYPE OF RAMP:** Concrete **UPPER AREA:** Concrete.
LOWER AREA: Concrete.

1

DIRECTIONS: Ramp is on the Dutch Riverside. From junction 36 on the M62, head into Goole. Turn right at the first traffic lights then follow signs to Waterway Museum. Sobriety Centre is adjacent to site.
RAMP DESCRIPTION: Concrete ramp 1:8. All concrete ramp that leads into the canal. Assistance is required if no 4 × 4, ramp always to be kept clear. Assisted launch is £15 each way.
FACILITIES: Diesel, toilets, pub parking for car and trailer, boat yard facilities. Chandlery and pump out facilities.
HAZARDS: 6mph limit on the Aire and Calder canal.

Goole Boathouse, Goole
The Timber Pond, Dutch Riverside, Goole, North Humberside, England DN14 5TB
Lat. 53.6948, Long. -0.8861.
01405 763985

South Ferriby Marina, Barton On Humber
Red Lane South Ferriby, Barton On Humber, North Lincolnshire, England DN18 6JH
Lat. 53.6775, Long. -0.5249.
01652 635620

Barrow Haven Boatyard, Barton-upon-Humber
Lat. 53.6982, Long. -0.3935.

CHARGES: A charge is made for use of the slipway
SUITABILITY: Large trailer needs a car.
ACCESS: ½ tidal. **TYPE OF RAMP:** Concrete slipway extends to bottom of tidal creek. Ramp is fairly steep. **UPPER AREA:** Concrete.
LOWER AREA: Mud.
DIRECTIONS: Go through Barrow Haven village, over humpback bridge, past pub, over level crossing, boatyard is on left hand side (blue gates).
RAMP DESCRIPTION: Private slipway in boatyard is available for public use by prior arrangement only. Concrete ramp 10 feet / 3 metres wide usable for a maximum of 3 hours each side of high water. Slip is suitable for RIBs; unfortunately no Jetskis as there is a nature reserve opposite.
FACILITIES: Hard standing for vehicles/trailers, water for wash down. Craneage also available for larger boats up to 10 tonnes. Secure boat storage. Moorings.
HAZARDS: No specific hazards as the entry to Barrow Haven is straight forward and there is plenty of water in the middle of the channel. The Humber Estuary is strongly tidal and has large areas which dry, not recommended for novice boaters.

Humber Cruising Association, Grimsby
Meridian Quay, Fish Docks, Grimsby, North East Lincolnshire, England DN31 3RP
Lat. 53.5787, Long. -0.0698.
01472 268424

Wonderland slip, Cleethorpes
Lat. 53.5676, Long. -0.0340.
01472 698828

CHARGES: None
SUITABILITY: Large trailer needs a car.
ACCESS: ¼ tidal. **TYPE OF RAMP:** Concrete **UPPER AREA:** Concrete.
LOWER AREA: Sand.
DIRECTIONS: Follow A46 from Lincoln or M180 / A180. Site is next to pier. Instead of going direct to Cleethorpes Pier slip at the end of Sea Road, just before the pier slip turn left along the sea front, go to the very end and you will see on your right a concrete slip , same facilities as Cleethorpes slip but will give you longer as this slip gets the water first.
RAMP DESCRIPTION: Keep clear for emergency rescue access. Water safety restrictions are displayed at all slipways and further information is available at the beach safety /first aid office based on the central prom opposite the pier (including free tide tables). Used by local fishermen, ski boats and holiday makers. Most park on the beach with 4 × 4s. At low tides sand is not suitable for normal cars. The rescue services regularly pull cars out of the soft sand so take care. Jetskiers are permitted but there have been reports of near misses with swimmers on the beach.
FACILITIES: Parking can be difficult, especially in the summer.
HAZARDS: No powered craft within 200metres except at designated launch / recovery areas.

Pier Slipway, Cleethorpes
Lat. 53.5614, Long. -0.0267.
01472 698828
CHARGES: None
SUITABILITY: Large trailer needs a car.
ACCESS: ¼ tidal. **TYPE OF RAMP:** Concrete **UPPER AREA:** Sand.
LOWER AREA: Sand.
DIRECTIONS: Follow A46 from Lincoln or M180 / A180. Site is next to Pier at the end of Sea Road.
RAMP DESCRIPTION: Keep clear for emergency rescue access. Water safety restrictions are displayed at all slipways and further information is available at the beach safety /first aid office based on the central prom opposite the pier (including free tide tables). There is a second slip to the right of the pier, both are free of charge. A lot of launches take place from the beach at the end of Wonderland Market, the sand will support a car, and the launch window is then extended by about 2 hours. Jetskiers are permitted but there have been reports of near misses with swimmers on the beach.
FACILITIES: Parking can be difficult, especially in the summer.
HAZARDS: No powered craft within 200metres except at designated launch / recovery areas.

Brighton Street, Cleethorpes
Lat. 53.5572, Long. -0.0228.
01472 698828
CHARGES: None
SUITABILITY: Small trailer can be pushed.
ACCESS: ¼ tidal. **TYPE OF RAMP:** Concrete **UPPER AREA:** Sand.
LOWER AREA: Sand.
DIRECTIONS: Follow A46 from Lincoln or M180 / A180. Launch ramp is in Brighton Street, south of the pier and next to the coastguard and inshore lifeboat station.

RAMP DESCRIPTION: Take care not to obstruct the slipway which must be kept clear for the lifeboat. Every year the rescue services are hindered by inconsiderate parking. A lot of launches take place from the beach at the end of Wonderland Market, the sand will support a car (in places), and the launch window is then extended by about 2 hours.
FACILITIES: Parking can be difficult, especially in the summer.
HAZARDS: 8 knot speed restriction within 200 metres of shore. Waterskiing is permitted but only in designated areas with access to the channel.

Humber Mouth YC, Humberston
Lat. 53.5252, Long. 0.0169.
Club Secretary 01472 329788
SUITABILITY: Small trailer can be pushed.
ACCESS: ¼ tidal. **TYPE OF RAMP:** Concrete **UPPER AREA:** Sand.
LOWER AREA: Sand.
DIRECTIONS: Follow the A18 and signed route to holiday attractions. Site is at the small creek at the south end of Humberston Fitties.
RAMP DESCRIPTION: Ramp onto the beach. No vehicles on the beach so really only suitable for smaller boats. Please obtain permission from the Yacht Club before using the ramp.
FACILITIES: Parking. Toilets in the club house may be locked.
HAZARDS: 8 knot speed restriction inshore.

INLAND SLIPWAYS
alphabetical by place name

Slipway, Beverley Weel
Lat. 53.8445, Long. -0.3995.
CHARGES: None
SUITABILITY: Large trailer needs a car.
ACCESS: Non-tidal. **TYPE OF RAMP:** Stone and mud.
UPPER AREA: Mud. **LOWER AREA:** Mud.
DIRECTIONS: Slip is just north of small iron bridge and junction of Beverley Weel road on east side of river. This slip is kept locked, you need a key from the Environment Agency (annual membership fee) to get access.
RAMP DESCRIPTION: Fairly rough ramp into the river.
FACILITIES: Limited parking at the top of the slipway. There have been reports of stolen trailers, so make sure you lock up.

Hainsworth boatyard, Bingley
Lat. 53.8669, Long. -1.8509.
01274 565925
CHARGES: £20 for the weekend inc. parking
SUITABILITY: Large trailer needs a car.
ACCESS: Non-tidal. **TYPE OF RAMP:** Concrete **UPPER AREA:** Concrete.
LOWER AREA: Concrete.
DIRECTIONS: Near Crossflats. 26, Fairfax Rd, Bingley West Yorkshire BD16 4DR.
RAMP DESCRIPTION: Gradient is gentle. Day licence also required from British Waterways offices keys to open swing bridges and locks also from BW.

FACILITIES: Parking charges- £20 inc. launch. Secure overnight parking available. Launch from boatyard into Leeds - Liverpool canal. Water, diesel and Calor gas available. Sanitary station nearby. 15 minute walk into town.

Boroughbridge Marina, Boroughbridge
Boroughbridge Marina Limited Valuation Lane, Boroughbridge, North Yorkshire, England YO51 9LJ
Lat. 54.0971, Long. -1.4009.
01423 323400

Calder Valley Marine, Bradford
Apperley Bridge Marina, Waterfront Mews, Apperley Bridge, Bradford, West Yorkshire, England BD10 0UR
Lat. 53.8357, Long. -1.7104.
01274 616961

Fosse Hill Jet Ski, Brandesburton
Lat. 53.9030, Long. -0.2852.
Janet and Tony Butterfield, 01964 542608
CHARGES: Summer £20, winter £10.
SUITABILITY: Large trailer needs a car.
ACCESS: Non-tidal. **TYPE OF RAMP:** Concrete
UPPER AREA: Unknown. **LOWER AREA:** Unknown.
DIRECTIONS: From Hull follow A165 north for half an hour until you get to Brandesburton. Then follow signs for Jet Ski Centre which will be on your right. Windsurfing lake in on the right hand side of the bypass.
RAMP DESCRIPTION: Concrete ramp into 15 acre lake. Water-skiers can use the lake if not being used by Jetskiers. Phone ahead. Lake on the other side of the by-pass has facilities for the sailors and windsurfers.
FACILITIES: Buoyed course. Hot and cold food. Clubhouse and bar. Camping for tents and caravans. Permanently manned. Changing rooms. Showers and toilets, parking. Pro shop, workshop and second hand sales. You can also hire Jetskis and lifejackets and wetsuits.

Seven Lakes Park, Crowle
Lat. 53.5921, Long. -0.8242.
01724 710 245 / 01724 711 814
CHARGES: £22 per day, £16 for 3 hours.
SUITABILITY: Large trailer needs a car.
ACCESS: Non-tidal. **TYPE OF RAMP:** Concrete slipway.
UPPER AREA: Unknown. **LOWER AREA:** Unknown.
DIRECTIONS: 2 miles north of junction 8 on the M180. Cross over the A18 and the canal and take the first left.
RAMP DESCRIPTION: Water ski boats are allowed during the week day but Jetskis only during the summer weekends. You will have to show insurance in order to use the facility.
FACILITIES: Showers, changing room, pub restaurant, motel. Static and touring caravan park, children's play area. Jetski show rooms.

The Good Launch Guide

Staniland Marina, Doncaster
Thorne Lock Marina Ltd. Staniland Marina Lock Hill Thorne, Doncaster, South Yorkshire, England DN8 5EP
Lat. 53.6100, Long. -0.9719.
01405 813150

Blue Water Marina, Doncaster
South End, Thorne, Doncaster, South Yorkshire, England DN8 5QR
Lat. 53.6017, Long. -0.9543.
01405 813165

Hornsea Mere Slip, Hornsea
Lat. 53.9089, Long. -0.1762.
01964 533277

CHARGES: £10 per day.
SUITABILITY: Small trailer can be pushed.
ACCESS: Non-tidal. **TYPE OF RAMP:** Concrete
UPPER AREA: Unknown. **LOWER AREA:** Unknown.
DIRECTIONS: Slipway is on the eastern bank of Hornsea Mere
RAMP DESCRIPTION: Gradient is gentle. This is a dinghy only launch site and no boats with engines or cabins are allowed. The launch area is on the south side of the lake.
FACILITIES: Free parking. No overnight parking. Parking space is ample. Slip water tap available. Hornsea Sailing Club who is based at this location has several Mirrors owned and sailed by members on this excellent stretch of water - though watch out for the shallows! There is an excellent little café and a small chandlery for those last minute bibs and bobs.

Aspley Wharf Marina, Huddersfield
Aspley Basin, Huddersfield, West Yorkshire, England HD1 6SD
Lat. 53.6449, Long. -1.7742.
01484 514123

Ripon Race Course Marina, Hull
Hull Marina, Warehouse 13, Kingstone Street, Hull, Yorkshire, England HU1 2DQ
Lat. 54.1119, Long. -1.5016.
01482 609960

Aire Valley Marina, Leeds
Redcote Lane, Leeds, West Yorkshire, England LS4 2AL
Lat. 53.8063, Long. -1.5891.
0113 279 8997

Lemonroyd Marina, Leeds
Fleet Lane Methley, Leeds, Yorkshire, United Kingdom LS26 9EU
Lat. 53.7466, Long. -1.4234.
01482 609960

Fallwood Marina, Leeds
Lat. 53.8248, Long. -1.6372.
0113 258 1074

CHARGES: £12 same day in and out for customers, £15 for visitors.
SUITABILITY: Large trailer needs a car.
ACCESS: Non-tidal. **TYPE OF RAMP:** Concrete
UPPER AREA: Unknown. **LOWER AREA:** Unknown.
DIRECTIONS: Pollard Lane, Leeds, LS13 1ER.
RAMP DESCRIPTION: Gives access to the Leeds and Liverpool canal.
FACILITIES: Crane can be brought on site for larger boats. Diesel and gas. Toilets and showers. Good security on site.

Fallwood Marina, Leeds
Pollard Lane, Leeds, West Yorkshire, England LS13 1ER
Lat. 53.8248, Long. -1.6372.
0113 258 1074

Shepley Bridge Marina, Mirfield
Huddersfield Road, Mirfield, England WF14 9HR
Lat. 53.6745, Long. -1.6757.
01924 491872

Shire Cruisers, Sowerby Bridge
The Wharf, Sowerby Bridge, West Yorkshire, England HX6 2AG
Lat. 53.7101, Long. -1.9035.
01422 832712

Stanley Ferry Marina, Wakefield
Ferry Lane, Stanley Ferry, Wakefield, W Yorks, England WF3 4LT
Lat. 53.7021, Long. -1.4634.
01924 201800

Pugneys, Wakefield
Lat. 53.6572, Long. -1.5101.
01924 302360

CHARGES: Basically £6/8 single/multi dingy and £6 for windsurfers hire prices vary and limited to 1.5 hour session times. Car park charges are unknown as the barrier has been broken more times than I can remember, but on the odd day that it is working using the water facilities gives you a refund on parking.
SUITABILITY: Large trailer needs a car.
ACCESS: Unknown. **TYPE OF RAMP: UPPER AREA:** Concrete.
LOWER AREA: Unknown.
DIRECTIONS: From M1 junction 39 head towards wakefield at second roundabout take 3rd exit, its signposted from just after the first roundabout. once you enter the park head back towards the exit and left before the exit barrier. For windsurfers head from the far corner of the car park for the grass over flow car park, then park near the ridge to be that bit closer to the water.
RAMP DESCRIPTION: Moderate angle ramp, can feel quite steep after a full day on the water, has an annoying lip step on the end of the

concrete where it hits the lake bed. For windsurfers and canoeist its possible and recommended to launch from the lake side Park opens at 9am and lake opens at 10am lake closes about an hour before the park does, with the park shutting 30-40 minutes before dark

FACILITIES: Toilets, showers, café, vending machines and a small train to take you part way around the lake

HAZARDS: Shallow area surrounding a duck platform in the lake, normally marked off with buoys, about 1-2 feet deep. Area to right of pontoon has boats moored for hiring and is the area for pedalos, if the wind picks up they are not allowed out anyway so not much of a hazard

Acaster Malbis, York
Lat. 53.9005, Long. -1.1035.

CHARGES: Yes
SUITABILITY: Large trailer needs a car.
ACCESS: Non-tidal. **TYPE OF RAMP:** Concrete
UPPER AREA: Unknown. **LOWER AREA:** Unknown.
DIRECTIONS: Site on River Ouse 4miles south of York. Connects to River Humber and North Sea.
RAMP DESCRIPTION: Wide concrete slipway into the river with adjacent pontoon.
FACILITIES: Overnight parking is possible. Need River Ouse licence.

Naburn Marina, York
Naburn, York, North Yorkshire, England YO19 4RW
Lat. 53.9083, Long. -1.0893.
01904 621021

York Marine Services, York Bishopthorpe
Lat. 53.9215, Long. -1.0886.
01904 704442

CHARGES: Use of slip £10 River licence £6.50 day or £11 weekend. Assisted launch. It's all done for you with their Landover and you just step onto your boat from the pontoon. £15 River licence £6.50 day or £11 weekend.
SUITABILITY: Large trailer needs a car.
ACCESS: Non-tidal. **TYPE OF RAMP:** Concrete **UPPER AREA:** Concrete.
LOWER AREA: Concrete.
DIRECTIONS: Ferry Lane Bishopthorpe, York, North Yorkshire, YO23 2SB.
RAMP DESCRIPTION: Slip is at end of Ferry Lane. Can go up river to Ripon (via locks) or down to River Humber. No locks in York area. Gradient is very steep.
FACILITIES: Launch fee includes daytime parking. Overnight parking available for a fee. Parking space is OK busy in summer. Toilets, chandlery and showers are on-site. Pubs, food and shops are 5 minutes walk away. The guys who run York Marine Services are excellent and very helpful to first-time boaters. "They fixed a problem with my trailer at a very reasonable rate. While they were doing the repair, they looked after my boat, slipping it and out of the river as necessary, leaving it moored for my use as and when while the steel was being delivered and all at no extra charge. I cannot speak highly enough of the friendly and organised way in which they operate." (Bill Allerton).

HAZARDS: SPEEDING ON THE RIVER! Watch out for the patrol boats and also the cruise boat people who are quite happy to shout subtle words of 'encouragement' from the quayside if they think you are creating a wake!

1

2

East England and Midlands

Mablethorpe to Burnham on Crouch

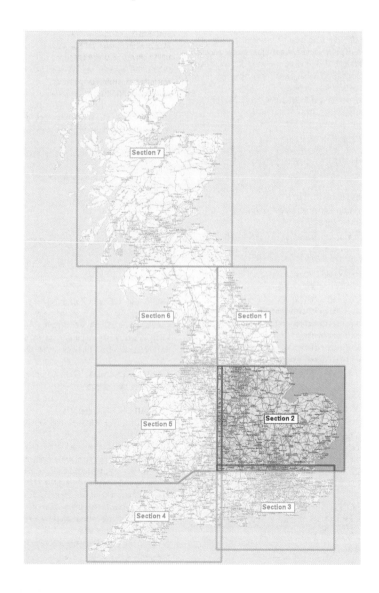

COASTAL SLIPWAYS
clockwise around the coast

Slipway, Saltfleet Haven boat club
Lat. 53.4179, Long. 0.1954.

CHARGES: Slipway ticket £ 65.00
SUITABILITY: Large trailer needs a car.
ACCESS: All of tidal range. **TYPE OF RAMP:** Concrete ramp
with a large winch and parking area **UPPER AREA:** Concrete.
LOWER AREA: Concrete.
RAMP DESCRIPTION: All boats using the club moorings or slip must
have at least 3rd party insurance cover and skippers must be competent
to handle their craft. All skippers will have to agree to the Safety Officers
'Minimum Equipment' list and may have to show competency.

Seaholme Road Pullover, Mablethorpe
Lat. 53.3341, Long. 0.2715.

CHARGES: None
SUITABILITY: Small trailer can be pushed.
ACCESS: All of tidal range. **TYPE OF RAMP:** Pullover
UPPER AREA: Unknown. **LOWER AREA:** Unknown.
DIRECTIONS: Follow A52 north from Skegness.
RAMP DESCRIPTION: Pullover onto a sandy beach. Water-skiing and
PWC prohibited.
FACILITIES: Toilets, parking, boat storage and restaurant.

Church Lane Pullover, Sutton-on-Sea
Lat. 53.3079, Long. 0.2873.

CHARGES: None
SUITABILITY: Small trailer can be pushed.
ACCESS: Unknown. **TYPE OF RAMP:** Pullover onto sandy beach.
UPPER AREA: Unknown. **LOWER AREA:** Unknown.
DIRECTIONS: Follow the A52 north from Skegness. The site is
approximately 3 miles south of Mablethorpe. Look out for the signposts
which will direct you to the site.
RAMP DESCRIPTION: Available at all states of the tide over the beach.
Motor vehicles are not allowed on the pullover.
FACILITIES: Toilets, parking, boat storage and restaurant.

Sea Lane Pullover, Sandilands
Lat. 53.3026, Long. 0.2919.

CHARGES: May be a charge for tractor.
SUITABILITY: Small trailer can be pushed.
ACCESS: All of tidal range. **TYPE OF RAMP:** Pullover onto sandy beach.
UPPER AREA: Sand. **LOWER AREA:** Sand.
DIRECTIONS: Simply follow the A52 and minor roads north from
Skegness. The site is well signposted so you should not have a problem
finding it.
RAMP DESCRIPTION: Pullover onto sandy beach. Tractor assistance
may be available from local fishermen. Available at all states of tide.
FACILITIES: Toilets and parking.

Huttoft Boat Club, Huttoft
Lat. 53.2826, Long. 0.3109.
SUITABILITY: Large trailer needs a car.
ACCESS: No Ramp. **TYPE OF RAMP:** Beach **UPPER AREA:** Sand.
LOWER AREA: Sand.

Skegness Watersports, Ingoldmells
Lat. 53.2011, Long. 0.3498.
07768 933934

CHARGES: £10
SUITABILITY: Large trailer needs a car.
ACCESS: All of tidal range. **TYPE OF RAMP:** Foreshore
UPPER AREA: Sand. **LOWER AREA:** Sand.
DIRECTIONS: Situated at Jackson's Corner to the north of Ingoldmells
near to the Butlin's Holiday camp off Roman Bank.
RAMP DESCRIPTION: Tractor launch across the foreshore. The site
is controlled by Skegness Watersports Club - contact the secretary for
permission and advice. You must have third party liability insurance and
operate 200 metres from the shore. Approach and leave at low speed.
Jetskis are welcome.
FACILITIES: Toilets and parking and wash down facilities.

Gibraltar Point, Skegness
Lat. 53.0944, Long. 0.3196.
Skegness Yacht Club 01754 890209

CHARGES: Nominal.
SUITABILITY: Large trailer needs a car.
ACCESS: ¼ tidal. **TYPE OF RAMP:** Concrete **UPPER AREA:** Mud.
LOWER AREA: Mud.
DIRECTIONS: Follow minor road approximately 3 miles south from
town centre. Site is at the entrance to Wainfleet Creek on Lincolnshire
Trust Nature Reserve.
RAMP DESCRIPTION: Sailing boats only at this site, no Jetskis. Please
make arrangements with the Yacht Club before using this site. Limited
tidal access, so not really suitable for day sailing.
FACILITIES: Toilets and parking in the Nature Reserve car park.
HAZARDS: Details of pilotage notes on the clubs website.

Common Staithe Quay, Kings Lynn
Lat. 52.7566, Long. 0.3922.
01485 535150
SUITABILITY: Large trailer needs a car.
ACCESS: ½ tidal. **TYPE OF RAMP:** Concrete **UPPER AREA:** Mud.
LOWER AREA: Mud.
DIRECTIONS: Ramp is in the car park at the end of Ferry Street.
RAMP DESCRIPTION: Gradient is moderate to steep and mud does
sometimes get washed onto the slipway. Tidal currents are VERY
STRONG. Quay is 2 miles from open sea (the Wash). Slipway is closed off
with a locked bollard. Key available from Norfolk Leisure Services 01485
535150, Hunstanton. Access is currently under suspension (9th June
2002) due to local residents complaining about the noise from Jetskis. It
will be closed until further notice.
FACILITIES: Pay and display car park at the head of the ramp. Town
centre location.

2

Snettisham Beach SC, Snettisham

Lat. 52.8676, Long. 0.4450.

CHARGES: Free to S.B.S.C. sailing members. Day membership available.
SUITABILITY: Portable Only.
ACCESS: ¼ tidal. **TYPE OF RAMP:** Concrete **UPPER AREA:** Shingle.
LOWER AREA: Shingle.
DIRECTIONS: From King's Lynn, take the A149 towards Hunstanton. Turn left at the roundabout before Dersingham and after approximately 2½ miles turn left at the Snettisham Beach sign. Continue for about 2 miles and after a sharp right bend the road will go over a bank. After the bank turn left just before the shops. Take the right fork and follow the concrete road around the sailing lake. Continue and you will see the Clubhouse on the right.
RAMP DESCRIPTION: The ramp is owned by the club and it therefore can only be used by sailing members or by paying the current day sailing membership fee.
FACILITIES: The club also has an inland lake ideal for junior sailing. The clubhouse has shower, toilet and changing facilities. There is a bar open at weekends from Easter to October. Parking available.
HAZARDS: None. Due to the tide access is high water +/- 1½ hours. See website for sailing programme details. www. snetbeach.co.uk.

North Beach, Heacham

Lat. 52.9088, Long. 0.4726.

CHARGES: No charge.
SUITABILITY: Large trailer needs a car.
ACCESS: ½ tidal. **TYPE OF RAMP:** Concrete **UPPER AREA:** Sand.
LOWER AREA: Sand.
DIRECTIONS: Take the A149 north from Kings Lynn to Heacham. Turn left at Heacham and follow your nose to the sea.
RAMP DESCRIPTION: Concrete ramp onto the sand. For use by power boats. Sailors should go to the Hunstanton Sailing Club slipway.
FACILITIES: Car park and toilets 100 yards from slipway is £2.20 all day for both car and trailer.
HAZARDS: Tricky coastline due to sandbanks and currents. There are strict byelaws on the use of the slip and the water around it. These byelaws are clearly indicated on a sign at the slipway itself. They include, amongst many other things, that flares, a red flag, a yellow flag, a paddle and a fire extinguisher must be carried on all powered craft.

South Beach, Hunstanton

Lat. 52.9308, Long. 0.4807.

CHARGES: £40 includes day membership and use of facilities.
SUITABILITY: Large trailer needs a car.
ACCESS: ½ tidal. **TYPE OF RAMP:** Concrete **UPPER AREA:** Sand.
LOWER AREA: Sand.
DIRECTIONS: South of the Sea Life Centre in Hunstanton which is at the southern end of Hunstanton. Slipway is off South Beach Road.
RAMP DESCRIPTION: Adequate insurance is mandatory and launching will be refused if that is not in place. Excellent wide concrete ramp leading onto sand at low tide. For use by power boats only. Sailing boats should go to the Sailing Club. Concrete ramp onto the beach. It

is possible to launch at lower tides, but it is a long way out to the sea. Power boats only. Sailors should go to the sailing club.
FACILITIES: Day membership to use the tractor launch facility, (club member only to drive), is now £40.00. This includes the use of our new facilities, bar, showers and parking. The car parking space soon fills up when the sun shines and on club event days we prioritise the available space for club members and visiting clubs. The car park has an attendant 8.30am - 5pm May to Sept who will gladly relieve day members of their fee....this swells the club coffers and helps us to maintain the facilities. We have incorporated a café on the ground floor of the café and this is open to the general public. Another option for campers/tourers is to stay at Searls Holiday Camp and get day/weekend/weekly membership from there and this gets you even more.....you can use Searles facilities and the clubs, (Hunstanton and District Watersports Club)
HAZARDS: Tricky coastline due to sandbanks and currents.

Hunstanton Sailing Club, Hunstanton

Lat. 52.9421, Long. 0.4868.
01485 534705

CHARGES: Parking charges apply.
SUITABILITY: Small trailer can be pushed.
ACCESS: ½ tidal. **TYPE OF RAMP:** Concrete to sand.
UPPER AREA: Sand. **LOWER AREA:** Sand.
DIRECTIONS: Hunstanton is North of King's Lynn on the A149.
RAMP DESCRIPTION: Ramp off promenade to beach next to old pier. Can launch at any state of tide if prepared to pull boat over sand far enough. Hunstanton is a very busy holiday centre. Get advice from sailing club near ramp and from Tourist Information Office next to The Golden Lion Hotel on the Upper Green. Sailing boats only from this site. Power craft should use South Beach or Hencham North Beach.
FACILITIES: Council parking for cars, trailers and motor caravans on promenade / sea front. Street parking restricted.
HAZARDS: Hazardous sandbanks and fast tides make this a tricky coast.

Thornham, Hunstanton

Lat. 52.9682, Long. 0.5708.

CHARGES: None
SUITABILITY: Small trailer can be pushed.
ACCESS: ¼ tidal. **TYPE OF RAMP:** Gravel / mud. **UPPER AREA:** Mud.
LOWER AREA: Mud.
DIRECTIONS: Off A 149, ¾ mile access road west end of Thornham village.
RAMP DESCRIPTION: Public slipway, open 24 hours. Gradient is steep. Only possible to launch 1 hour +/- high water. But gives good access to the Tope fishing in June/July.
FACILITIES: Parking space is limited on the roadside. Beware high water flooding on road.

Slipway, Brancaster Staithe

Lat. 52.9688, Long. 0.6641.
Contact 01485 210638 (HM)

CHARGES: National Trust donation box located in disused fairway buoys £5 donation.

SUITABILITY: Small trailer can be pushed.
ACCESS: ½ tidal. **TYPE OF RAMP:** Hard gravel, mud at bottom.
UPPER AREA: Shingle. **LOWER AREA:** Mud.
DIRECTIONS: At Brancaster Staithe turn left down short approach road off the A149.
RAMP DESCRIPTION: Public slipway, open 24 hours. Moderate gradient.
FACILITIES: No parking on hard, very busy during peak periods. Restricted parking in sailing club car park (by arrangement). Hard floods on Spring tides.
HAZARDS: Bar at entrance to Brancaster Bay. Inlet dries to firm sand. Refer to harbour safety sign located on village green or contact National Trust Warden for a copy of General Directions. NT warden Dial House Brancaster Staithe King's Lynn Norfolk PE31 8BW

Slipway, Burnham Overy Staithe
Lat. 52.9647, Long. 0.7434.
Boathouse 01328 738348

CHARGES: £10/year licence fee.
SUITABILITY: Small trailer can be pushed.
ACCESS: ½ tidal. **TYPE OF RAMP:** Concrete **UPPER AREA:** Sand.
LOWER AREA: Mud.
DIRECTIONS: Near the centre of the village of Burnham Overy Staithe.
RAMP DESCRIPTION: Gentle gradient slipway and you can also launch from the car park about 50 metres to the west. Floods on very high tides. Exposed to bad swell in northerly winds. Brancaster or Morston are easier. Pay at the Boathouse. There is an 8 knot speed limit in the harbour, and visitors are made very welcome.
FACILITIES: Parking space is limited. Small village with pub, a one way system and not much room to park. Very crowded in summer.
HAZARDS: Strong currents when the tide is flowing and shifting sand banks.

Public Slip, Wells-Next-Sea
Lat. 52.9571, Long. 0.8599.
Harbourmaster 01328 711646

CHARGES: £5 payable to harbourmaster.
SUITABILITY: Large trailer needs a car.
ACCESS: ½ tidal. **TYPE OF RAMP:** Concrete **UPPER AREA:** Shingle.
LOWER AREA: Sand.
DIRECTIONS: Slip is on east end of Wells front promenade.
RAMP DESCRIPTION: 3 slipways, all run by the harbourmaster. Wells is a busy commercial port and holiday resort, crowded in season. There is also a ramp (approximately TF 915 455 52 58.31 'N 00 51.12 'E) at the end of Beach Road, usable only near high water and unsuitable for car.
FACILITIES: Speak to the harbourmaster about parking. He will find you a slot. Toilets at the harbour and plans for showers and laundrette in 2003.
HAZARDS: Beware of harbour bar in a northerly wind.

Morston Hard, Morston
Lat. 52.9595, Long. 0.9822.
SUITABILITY: Large trailer needs a car.

ACCESS: ½ tidal. **TYPE OF RAMP:** Hard clay and pebble.
UPPER AREA: Shingle. **LOWER AREA:** Shingle.
DIRECTIONS: At village turn left down lane as A149 takes sharp right turn. Sign indicates boat trips to see the seals.
RAMP DESCRIPTION: Leads into Blakeney Channel, large area of water sheltered by Blakeney Point which is a bird sanctuary. Probably wise to get in early on the tide.
FACILITIES: Large car park, appears to be plenty of space but only seen in September. No shops.

Town Slip, Blakeney
Lat. 52.9577, Long. 1.0178.
Harbourmaster, 01263 740362

CHARGES: None
SUITABILITY: Large trailer needs a car.
ACCESS: ½ tidal. **TYPE OF RAMP:** Concrete to sand.
UPPER AREA: Shingle. **LOWER AREA:** Sand.
DIRECTIONS: Stratton Long Marine, Blakeney, Norfolk.
RAMP DESCRIPTION: Launch on right at bottom of High Street opposite NT Car Park. The car park floods at high water Springs across the majority of the available hard standing. Take local advice. For local advice try Blakeney Point Sailing School (www.blakeneypointsailing.co.uk), or Blakeney Sailing Club (clubhouse adjacent to the Quay).
FACILITIES: Parking charges - unless you show NT membership. Lower end flood high water Springs. Slip is in car park at east end. Shops in village crowded in summer. Free harbour with no real restrictions; people seem to moor by agreement and tradition rather than anything else.
HAZARDS: Shallow water can kick up a bad sea especially in northerlies. Harbour speed limit is 8 knots east of the Lifeboat House on Blakeney Point - marked by yellow spherical bladder buoys.

Slipway, Cley next the Sea
Lat. 52.9531, Long. 1.0427.
CHARGES: None
SUITABILITY: Small trailer can be pushed.
ACCESS: ¼ tidal. **TYPE OF RAMP:** Concrete **UPPER AREA:** Mud.
LOWER AREA: Mud.
DIRECTIONS: Ramp is at Cley next the Sea, Norfolk. Take the A149 to Cley, then look for the turn off to Cley Mill.
RAMP DESCRIPTION: Only useable for an hour or so either side of high water. Needs tides of mid range or higher to be worth using. Really best used by small outboard powered dinghies to about 12 '.
FACILITIES: Limited free parking nearby
HAZARDS: Areas of shallow water, but the channel is buoyed.

West Runton Gap, Cromer
Lat. 52.9415, Long. 1.2515.
Cromer tourist office 01263 512497

CHARGES: None
SUITABILITY: Large trailer needs a car.
ACCESS: No Ramp. **TYPE OF RAMP:** Concrete onto the beach
UPPER AREA: Concrete. **LOWER AREA:** Sand.

DIRECTIONS: Take the A149 west of Cromer to West Runton. From West Runton there is only one road that takes you to the beach and the launch site.

RAMP DESCRIPTION: Very good concrete ramp that takes you onto a sand and shingle beach. A lot of large rocks to overcome before you can launch at this site (watch your prop). Sand may get washed away making it impossible to drive a boat onto beach as height of sand is below lowest point of slip. Even so it should be possible to launch and recover directly off slip.

FACILITIES: West Runton is a better launching place than East Runton, there is a large grassy car park at the top of the slip for leaving cars and trailers, but make sure you get a parking ticket before you set off. Access road down to the beach is a little narrow in places so care is needed with wide loads.

HAZARDS: Surf on the beach, especially in a northerly wind.

East Runton Gap, Cromer
Lat. 52.9376, Long. 1.2740.
Cromer tourist office 01263 512497

CHARGES: None
SUITABILITY: Large trailer needs a car.
ACCESS: ¼ tidal. **TYPE OF RAMP:** Concrete **UPPER AREA:** Shingle. **LOWER AREA:** Sand.
DIRECTIONS: East Runton is about 1 mile west of Cromer. Ramp is at the end of the road leading down to the beach by the large car park.
RAMP DESCRIPTION: Concrete ramp onto the beach. Vehicles are not allowed onto the beach. Unfortunately this slipway is often severely restricted by the fishing boats found parked at the bottom. It is only really suitable for the launching of windsurfers and canoes or any craft that can be tipped easily on its side and carried between the fishing boats.
FACILITIES: Large car park nearby and public toilets. Close to village of East Runton.
HAZARDS: Dangerous in onshore winds.

Seafront, Cromer
Lat. 52.9338, Long. 1.2974.

CHARGES: None
SUITABILITY: Small trailer can be pushed.
ACCESS: No Ramp. **TYPE OF RAMP:** Concrete ramp onto beach
UPPER AREA: Sand. **LOWER AREA:** Sand.
DIRECTIONS: Slipway leads off the Promenade on the Cromer Seafront
RAMP DESCRIPTION: A small slipway that can be found on the prom leading down onto the beach. Tight turn at the top of the slipway and only suitable for small craft that can be manhandled down onto the beach.
FACILITIES: Parking is only possible on the Prom for disabled badge holders. Parking will have to be in one of the town's large car parks which are quite a walk from the Seafront if you are carrying a lot of gear.

Public Slip, Trimingham
Lat. 52.8899, Long. 1.4141.

CHARGES: None
SUITABILITY: Large trailer needs a car.

ACCESS: No Ramp. **TYPE OF RAMP:** Track to beach.
UPPER AREA: Sand. **LOWER AREA:** Sand.
DIRECTIONS: The launch site is situated between Trimingham and Mundesley on the B1159. It is at the end of a track beside the hotel.
RAMP DESCRIPTION: Launch site is a track down to the beach and the sand is soft around the high tide area. Suitable for 4 × 4 only and be careful of the soft sand. Plans to have a tractor on site in the summer.
FACILITIES: Car park but little else. Downtide Marine, 10 miles away has Jetskis and chandlery. Phone Downtide Marine 01263 768813 for advice.

Beach Rock Leisure, Sea Palling
Lat. 52.7898, Long. 1.6022.
01692 598000

CHARGES: £10 daily (Jetskis) £145 annual (Jetskis).
SUITABILITY: Large trailer needs a car.
ACCESS: No Ramp. **TYPE OF RAMP:** Concrete **UPPER AREA:** Sand. **LOWER AREA:** Sand.
DIRECTIONS: Situated on the coast half way between Great Yarmouth and Cromer. Follow the road through South Palling to the sea and the facility is by the lifeboat station.
RAMP DESCRIPTION: Local inshore lifeboat station situated at top of ramp, also used by divers' boats, fishermen and Jetskiers. Tractor launches available, £15 for a boat and £10 for a Jetski. £145/year for as many launches as you require. Do not drive onto the beach as the sand is soft and even a 4 × 4 will get stuck.
FACILITIES: Shop, shower, parking, fast food café, pub next to ramp open during season, small amusement arcade next to ramp, camp site within sight of ramp, public toilets at bottom of ramp. Beautiful sandy beach.

Martham Boat Building and Development Company, Martham
Lat. 52.7151, Long. 1.6098.
01493740249

CHARGES: Slip £5 each way. (2006) Car plus trailer £2 per day (2006)
SUITABILITY: Large trailer needs a car.
ACCESS: Unknown. **TYPE OF RAMP:** Concrete. **UPPER AREA:** Concrete. **LOWER AREA:** Concrete.
DIRECTIONS: Not the easiest place to find. Follow Cess road out of Martham, on the right if aproaching from Potter Heigham. Follow road left and then right. A single track road takes you past a large boat shed associated with the yard. Carry on to boat yard car park.
RAMP DESCRIPTION: Not too steep ramp. Fairly narrow but plenty wide enough for boats which can get down Cess Road from Martham Village. It is tidal but there is minimum tidal range. The orange strap in the photo is 10 meters long. I just had a straight pull to get the trailer on the level at the top of the slip.
FACILITIES: Licences available. Fuel and toilet pump out. Motor boats, yachts and sailing dayboats for hire.
HAZARDS: Potter Heigham Bridge (one of the lowest on the Broads) is close to the west. Air draught to get under is 6´9˝ but depends on tide and weather.

2

Bure Marine, Great Yarmouth
Lat. 52.6101, Long. 1.7172.
014 9365 6996 or 07808 060152

CHARGES: Phone boatyard.
SUITABILITY: Large trailer needs a car.
ACCESS: All of tidal range. **TYPE OF RAMP:** Hoist and crane.
UPPER AREA: Harbour. **LOWER AREA:** Unknown.
DIRECTIONS: Entrance is in Breydons Road which is off Sto Road to the south of Breydons Bridge.
RAMP DESCRIPTION: Only crane and hoist in 2002.
FACILITIES: All the facilities of a working boatyard that welcomes pleasure users. Plans for 2003 include a slipway, showers and toilets, pontoons and dry berths. Very close to a brand new and large Tesco Store (ready Dec 2002). Well positioned to give access to the Broads and to open water. Opposite the railway station.

Harbour Slipway, Great Yarmouth
Lat. 52.5734, Long. 1.7321.

CHARGES: Free
SUITABILITY: Large trailer needs a car.
ACCESS: All of tidal range. **TYPE OF RAMP:** Concrete
UPPER AREA: Concrete. **LOWER AREA:** Concrete.
DIRECTIONS: The slip is situated next to the RNLI station in Gorleston (Great Yarmouth). Find your way to Somerfield; the slip is a few hundred meters east of that (on the eastern side of the lifeboat house).
RAMP DESCRIPTION: Slip is steep and narrow, off a fairly narrow street so is only suitable for small (-> 6m) craft.
FACILITIES: There is a good pay and display car park next to the slip. The RNLI station is next door, and may offer toilets.
HAZARDS: As soon as you're off the ramp you're in the River Yare just a few hundred meters before it meets the North Sea. There is a "slow" speed limit in the harbour, and craft should be aware of large commercial ships using the harbour. The slip has a steep drop off the end. A 4 × 4 is needed for anything above about 500kg due to the gradient. A rope may be needed for launching at low tide due to sea-weed. There can be a very strong current running past the slip so beware!

Royal Norfolk & Suffolk, Lowestoft
Lat. 52.4719, Long. 1.7507.
Harbour Control: 01502 572286, Yacht club 01502 566726

CHARGES: £7.50/day
SUITABILITY: Large trailer needs a car.
ACCESS: ¾ tidal. **TYPE OF RAMP:** Concrete **UPPER AREA:** Harbour.
LOWER AREA: Mud.
DIRECTIONS: Royal Norfolk & Suffolk Yacht Club, Lowestoft Harbour, Lowestoft, Suffolk.
RAMP DESCRIPTION: Get permission to use the site. Good slip, but narrow with high sides. A road legal RIB (2.5m) will fit down but needs skilful reversing. Jetskis can use the slipway provided they keep to the speed limit and do not interfere with any of the other vessels using the main navigation channel. Harbour navigation: bridge opening always by (greater than 20 minutes) prior permission (Lowestoft Harbour Control: 01502 572286 VHF 14) M-F 0700 0930 1100 1600 1900 2100, Sa Su BH

0745 0930 1100 1400 1730 1900 2100 (or with commercial shipping). Bridge central clearance high water Springs 2.2m (2.4m on tide gauge). Mutford Lock: day return charge £6.00, always by prior permission (01502 531778 / 523003 or VHF 9&14) 0800-1100 and from Apr-Oct 1330-1630 and from May-Sept Sa Su BH (notify before 1630) 1630-1930.
FACILITIES: Overnight parking by prior arrangement in secure club car park. Camilla's Restaurant: 12-2pm and 7-9pm, Bar: 11.30am to 11.00pm (Sun: 12.00noon to 10.30pm). Close to the centre of Lowestoft. Club offers accommodation to visiting yachtsmen (including those with trailers).
HAZARDS: Busy port and you must get permission from Harbour Control Ch14 to leave or enter port. Traffic light scheme operates at the harbour entrance.

Southwold Sailing Club, Southwold
Lat. 52.3202, Long. 1.6630.
Harbourmaster: 01502 724712

CHARGES: Harbour dues £4.60.
SUITABILITY: Large trailer needs a car.
ACCESS: All of tidal range. **TYPE OF RAMP:** Concrete and wood.
UPPER AREA: Mud. **LOWER AREA:** Mud.
DIRECTIONS: Enter Southwold on A1095 turn right at Kings Head to river. Left at river after hump-backed bridge. Ramp is next to the Harbourmaster's Office close to the Harbour Inn.
RAMP DESCRIPTION: Small boats can launch at all states of the tide, larger should leave an hour around low water. Can get slippery at bottom. Slip is straight and wide. There is a drop off by the height measurement post. Jetskis can use the slipway. Please speak to the harbourmaster first and head upstream to the waterski area. The river entrance is dangerous for small craft and you should not head downstream. Once on the water call the harbourmaster on CH 12.
FACILITIES: Do not park at the top of the slip but use the car park by the harbourmaster's office where you can pay harbour dues. Beware of unmade road flooding at very high Spring tides. Slip water tap available. Beautiful old world river side with great traditional pub. There are numerous other private slips in the area, which advertise that you can ask for permission to use them. There is a chandlery nearby, and boat yards with cranes, cradles and slings for large boats.
HAZARDS: Access for North Sea cruising, but not for the inexperienced. Avoid entering harbour on strong ebb tide, an outboard useful for upper reaches.

Slaughden Quay, Aldeburgh
Lat. 52.1438, Long. 1.5955.
RF Upson & Co 01728 453047

CHARGES: £5-10/day
SUITABILITY: Large trailer needs a car.
ACCESS: ½ tidal. **TYPE OF RAMP:** Concrete or firm shingle.
UPPER AREA: Shingle. **LOWER AREA:** Mud.
DIRECTIONS: Directions: Head for Aldeburgh town centre. At High Street T junction turn right to Slaughden Quay and Aldeburgh YC. Follow lower shingle track past Slaughden SC. At Upson's Boatyard turn right to slips.
RAMP DESCRIPTION: Check with the boatyard before turning up as the slipway may be busy.

2

FACILITIES: Plenty of parking spaces in the boatyard. Fresh water tap and hose. Small chandlery on site.

Orford Quay, Orford
Lat. 52.0905, Long. 1.5390.
Harbour Office 01394 459950.

CHARGES: As of 14/7/07 Sailing boats - £18 daily launch fee, annual launch permit £65 Moorings from £300 Speed boats - £60 daily, annual pass is £250. No Jetskis
SUITABILITY: Large trailer needs a car.
ACCESS: ¾ tidal. TYPE OF RAMP: Concrete UPPER AREA: Harbour. LOWER AREA: Mud.
DIRECTIONS: B1084 to Orford. At village centre turn left. Follow round to right. ½ mile to slip at end of road by Quay. No road access to Orfordness
RAMP DESCRIPTION: Private slipway, open 24 Hours. Slip is straight and wide. Office on seaward side of dyke between quay and sailing club. Do not place launch trolley wheels beyond mark written on side of jetty when launching / recovering, it is possible to drop off end of ramp.
FACILITIES: No parking on Quay. Good private car park nearby for car and trailer (£4 per day, extra charge for trailer). Overnight parking available. Car park entrance opposite Jolly Sailor pub. Attendant Martin Smith (Tel: 01394 459172). Telephone and toilets 150 yards, supplies in village. Slip water tap at northeast corner on top of pier head. Rubbish bins. VHF Ch 80
HAZARDS: Beware of fast currents up to 5 knots past quay. River exit to sea has bar which is dangerous in certain wind and tide conditions.

Bawdsey Quay, Woodbridge
Lat. 51.9904, Long. 1.3944.
Alexander's International School, 01394 411633

CHARGES: £10/day
SUITABILITY: Large trailer needs a car.
ACCESS: ¾ tidal. TYPE OF RAMP: Concrete UPPER AREA: Sand. LOWER AREA: Sand.
DIRECTIONS: Slipway is part of the Bawdsey Quay Watersports Centre near the Alexander's International School, Bawdsey Campus, Bawdsey, Woodbridge, Suffolk IP12 3AZ.
RAMP DESCRIPTION: Sand can drift onto the ramp and may have to be cleared off before use. Top of slip is closed off by a barrier. Key available by prior arrangement from School Office. Recovery- keep car off sand- use rope. End of ramp is exposed at low water. Sailing boats only please. You may have to show proof of insurance.
FACILITIES: Public car park 500 yards up road in small woods. Hostel accommodation available from school. Bawdsey Haven YC club house is behind large wooden gates and tall brick wall. All facilities available by arrangement. Land owned by Alexander's International School. Bawdsey village, 2 miles. Basic club house at Bawdsey Haven YC: Fees weekend £10, annual £20 Key deposit £6 Annual boat storage £25. Fresh water tap at Bawdsey Haven YC yard.
HAZARDS: NOTE: tides run fast, ferry comes and goes, top of slip is on a bus route.

Ramsholt Quay, Woodbridge
Lat. 52.0230, Long. 1.3613.
SUITABILITY: Small trailer can be pushed.
ACCESS: Unknown. TYPE OF RAMP: Concrete UPPER AREA: Shingle. LOWER AREA: Mud.
DIRECTIONS: Take the B1083 south from Woodbridge. Turn left after 6 miles for Ramsholt and follow the road down to the river.
RAMP DESCRIPTION: Small slipway. There have been reports of people being turned away from this slipway. Public access has been the subject of local rights of way committees. Still not totally sorted.
FACILITIES: Location of the well-known pub the Ramsholt Arms (voted 9th best British pub by the Independent).

Granary Yacht Harbour, Woodbridge
Dock Lane, Melton, Woodbridge, Suffolk, England IP12 1PE
Lat. 52.1029, Long. 1.3313.
01394 386327

Robertson's Boatyard, Woodbridge
Lat. 52.0929, Long. 1.3239.
01394 382305

CHARGES: £15/day
SUITABILITY: Large trailer needs a car.
ACCESS: ½ tidal. TYPE OF RAMP: Concrete, mud at bottom. UPPER AREA: Unknown. LOWER AREA: Mud.
DIRECTIONS: Robertsons of Woodbridge Boatbuilders Ltd, Lime Kiln Quay, Woodbridge, Suffolk IP12 1BD.
RAMP DESCRIPTION: This is a working boat yard and slip may be blocked. Always arrange beforehand. Drying mud channel leads to slip. Rail crossing to negotiate by road. No Jetskis.
FACILITIES: Parking is in busy small boat yard. Chandlery nearby.
HAZARDS: Speed limit on the Deben River.

Tidemill Yacht Harbour, Woodbridge
Tidemill Way, Woodbridge, Suffolk, England IP12 1BP
Lat. 52.0905, Long. 1.3211.
01394 385745

Felixstowe Ferry, Felixstowe
Lat. 51.9898, Long. 1.3913.
07917023987

CHARGES: £10/day, £50/year for 30HP and over. £6/day, £30/year for under 30HP.
SUITABILITY: Large trailer needs a car.
ACCESS: All of tidal range. TYPE OF RAMP: Cobble stones patched with concrete. UPPER AREA: Shingle. LOWER AREA: Concrete.
DIRECTIONS: From Felixstowe town centre / A12 head to Old Felixstowe (signposted golf club / water-ski club, drive through the middle of the golf course which will bring you to Felixstowe Ferry the home of East Suffolk Waterski Club and the slipway operated by them.
RAMP DESCRIPTION: The slipway is licensed to the East Suffolk Waterski Club which set the prices for launching and maintains the

slipway. Tickets can be purchased from the Ferry Café, our Slipway Wardens, and the Sailing Club barman or in advance by post. Please visit the website www.eswsc.co.uk for more details. Day rate; Powered craft (inc. PWCs) with engines 30HP and over £10. Lower then 30HP £6 Annual rate; £50 and £30 respectively.

FACILITIES: 2 pubs, café, sailing club, waterski club, parking £10/day at the Ferry Café, boat yard, toilets. Parking with trailers is a big issue here. Be prepared for difficulty finding somewhere.

HAZARDS: On the estuary outlet to the sea, care has to be taken for the sand banks; the tide race can be quite fast at times. Speed limit during summer in the area surrounding the slipway, details posted on signs near the slipway.

Suffolk Yacht Harbour, Levington
Lat. 51.9954, Long. 1.2714.
01473 659465

CHARGES: £10 for <6m boat and £20 for 6-8m
SUITABILITY: Large trailer needs a car.
ACCESS: All of tidal range. **TYPE OF RAMP:** Steep concrete.
UPPER AREA: Harbour. **LOWER AREA:** Concrete.
DIRECTIONS: A14 / A12 Junction East of Ipswich. Marina is well signposted.
RAMP DESCRIPTION: Ramp is steep. A cable and pulley system is provided and use is recommended if you don't have a 4 × 4 especially at lower tides when the ramp can be slippery. Do not put your wheel beyond the anchor chains of the steel support of the ramp. Once you have launched the boat into the marina there are two temporary mooring pontoons on either side. Long queues can form at peak times in the summer. No Jetskiers allowed at this site.
FACILITIES: Petrol, diesel, LPG, friendly chandlery, engineers, toilets, moorings and storage. There is no area set aside for car and trailer parking so you have to try and find room amongst the boats, trailers and cars on the hard standing. Also Bob Spalding Marine and Leisure on site selling sportsboats and lots of water toys including wake boards.
HAZARDS: Entry and exit from the marina itself is via a short dredged channel, marked at either end by a pair of stakes. Waterskiing area is just downstream of the harbour entrance. Orwell and Felixstowe Docks are very busy with commercial shipping.

Suffolk Yacht Harbour, Ipswich
Levington, Ipswich, Suffolk, England IP10 0LN
Lat. 51.9964, Long. 1.2707.
01473 659240

Neptune Marina, Ipswich
Neptune Quay, Ipswich, Suffolk, England IP4 1AX
Lat. 52.0526, Long. 1.1614.
01473 215204

Ipswich Haven Marina, Ipswich
New Cut East, Ipswich, Suffolk, England IP3 0EA
Lat. 52.0510, Long. 1.1602.
01473 236644

Debbage Yachting, Ipswich
The Quay New Cut West, Ipswich, Suffolk, England IP2 8HN
Lat. 52.0481, Long. 1.1599.
01473 601169

Fox's Marina Ipswich, Ipswich
The Strand, Wherstead, Ipswich, Suffolk, England IP2 8SA
Lat. 52.0338, Long. 1.1504.
01473 689111

Woolverstone Marina, Ipswich
Woolverstone, Ipswich, Suffolk, England IP9 1AS
Lat. 52.0067, Long. 1.1942.
01473 780206. Chandlery 01473 780172

Woolverstone Marina, Ipswich
Lat. 52.0066, Long. 1.1960.
Woolverstone Marina 01473 780206

CHARGES: £10-20/day depends on length.
SUITABILITY: Large trailer needs a car.
ACCESS: ½ tidal. **TYPE OF RAMP:** Concrete, mud at bottom.
UPPER AREA: Concrete. **LOWER AREA:** Mud.
DIRECTIONS: From A1375 south of Ipswich take B1456 to Woolverstone. Take track to marina from village.
RAMP DESCRIPTION: Good straight concrete slipway in the boatyard but it has a large flat concrete area at the lower end which is covered in 2-3 inches of wet very slippery mud. Usable around 2.5 hours either side of high tide. Fees are: up to 3m £10/day, up to 4.5m £15/day, over £4.5m £20/day.
FACILITIES: Fee includes parking. Overnight parking by arrangement. Ample parking space in marina boatyard. Park trailer on long drive or beyond restaurant car park. Usual marina facilities. Restaurant and chandlery. Land camping possible at extra cost. Slip water tap at top of slip.
HAZARDS: Large vessels, constrained by their draft, in the River Orwell between Ipswich and the North Sea.

Slipway, Pin Mill
Lat. 51.9970, Long. 1.2123.

CHARGES: Free
SUITABILITY: Large trailer needs a car.
ACCESS: ½ tidal. **TYPE OF RAMP:** Concrete onto a hard.
UPPER AREA: Shingle. **LOWER AREA:** Concrete.
DIRECTIONS: From B 1456 Ipswich / Shotley road take left at far end of Chelmondiston village. The road down to Pin Mill is narrow and twisty. Also gets busy at the weekends.
RAMP DESCRIPTION: There is a lot of mud here if you get the tides wrong. The ramp extends across the mud flat, but it is very shallow and only suitable for launching shallow draft craft up to about 3hrs each side of high water. A stream (known as the Grindle) runs down alongside the lengthy hard and helps to keep it clean.

2

FACILITIES: Excellent pub and a small boatyard nearby. Parking can be difficult especially at weekends.

Shotley Marina, Ipswich
Shotley Gate, Ipswich, Suffolk, England IP9 1QJ
Lat. 51.9578, Long. 1.2754.
01473 788982

Mistley Marine & Leisure, Manningtree
Northumberland Wharf, Anchor Lane Mistley, Manningtree, Essex, England CO11 1NG
Lat. 51.9435, Long. 1.0879.
01206 392127

Dovercourt Seafront, Harwich
Lat. 51.9291, Long. 1.2738.
Kevin Marsden Council office, 01255 253235

CHARGES: £10/year to register.
SUITABILITY: Large trailer needs a car.
ACCESS: No Ramp. **TYPE OF RAMP:** Ramp onto beach
UPPER AREA: Sand. **LOWER AREA:** Sand.
DIRECTIONS: Follow signs to Dovercourt and the seafront. Ramp is off Low Road adjacent to the Blue Flag beach and near to the boating lake.
RAMP DESCRIPTION: Ramp onto the beach. Not ideal for Jetskiers due to the proximity of the bathers on the beach. Council run site. You will have to show insurance documents to use this facility. You can pay and register on the day, but cheques only and no cash please. Best to register with the council first.
FACILITIES: Parking for car and trailer, on street parking and a large car park behind the swimming pool. Next to the swimming pool. Near to the town.
HAZARDS: 8 knot speed restrictions close the shore and on the approaches to the ramp.

Marina Slip, Titchmarsh
Lat. 51.8631, Long. 1.2578.
01255 672185

CHARGES: £16.00
SUITABILITY: Large trailer needs a car.
ACCESS: All of tidal range. **TYPE OF RAMP:** Concrete
UPPER AREA: Harbour. **LOWER AREA:** Mud.
DIRECTIONS: As you enter Walton, turn left by the church, entrance road to Marina is about ¼ mile on left. Easy to miss.
RAMP DESCRIPTION: Ramp is through the compound at Titchmarsh Marina. Pay in the marina office prior to launch. Bottom of ramp can be a bit muddy at low tide and a little shallow. Jetskiers not allowed.
FACILITIES: Excellent marina facilities. Diesel, large chandlery, moorings and storage, engineers, toilets, bar and restaurant. No petrol but LPG available and pontoons can be used for day and overnight mooring.
HAZARDS: Speed limit 8 knots until Stone Point. Numerous yacht moorings.

Titchmarsh Marina, Walton-on-Naze
Coles Lane, Kirby Road, Walton-on-Naze, Essex, England CO14 8SL
Lat. 51.8630, Long. 1.2583.
01255 672185

Public Slip, Walton-on-Naze
Lat. 51.8518, Long. 1.2688.
SUITABILITY: Small trailer can be pushed.
ACCESS: ¼ tidal. **TYPE OF RAMP:** Hard gravel. **UPPER AREA:** Shingle.
LOWER AREA: Mud.
DIRECTIONS: Once in Walton-on-Naze, follow the signs for Mill Lane Car Park.
RAMP DESCRIPTION: Wide gravel hard giving access into a muddy channel. Gives access to Swallows & Amazons inland sea - lots of mud low water. Slip is next to Frank Hall's Boatyard directly off Mill Lane off High Street.
FACILITIES: Car parking in adjoining streets only.

Slipway, Walton Seafront
Lat. 51.8460, Long. 1.2704.
SUITABILITY: Small trailer can be pushed.
ACCESS: All of tidal range. **TYPE OF RAMP: UPPER AREA:** Concrete.
LOWER AREA: Sand.
RAMP DESCRIPTION: Ramp is a long concrete ramp which goes onto sand. During the summer months they lock the gate between 9:00am - 5:30pm. So you need to launch before or after those time. But at least it's free.

Seafront, Frinton
Lat. 51.8251, Long. 1.2438.
SUITABILITY: Small trailer can be pushed.
ACCESS: No Ramp. **TYPE OF RAMP:** Concrete onto sand.
UPPER AREA: Sand. **LOWER AREA:** Sand.
DIRECTIONS: Ramp is at the southern end of the seafront off the Esplanade at the junction with Third Avenue. Access road goes across the Green to the beach. Access road has sharp turns.
RAMP DESCRIPTION: Steep concrete ramp down to the beach with sharp turn at the bottom. Jetskiers and small boats only. You must a member of Clacton Watercraft Club to use this site. See their web site for more details.
FACILITIES: Limited parking. Toilet nearby.
HAZARDS: 8 knot speed limit close to the shore.

Slipway, Gunfleet Boating Club
Lat. 51.8089, Long. 1.2158.
01255814318

CHARGES: £105 per year membership including use of all facilities.
SUITABILITY: Large trailer needs a car.
ACCESS: Unknown. **TYPE OF RAMP:** Long concrete ramp in a bay which reaches sand at low tide. Quite steep. Hand launching not recommended.
UPPER AREA: Unknown. **LOWER AREA:** Unknown.
DIRECTIONS: At the end of holland-on-sea seafront where the road heads inland, look for the signs to Holland Country Park. Follow the speed bumped road past the car park entrance, through the TDC gate

and turn right at the end of this access road opposite the two cottages. clubhouse is on the Promenade.

RAMP DESCRIPTION: Wide concrete ramp reaching sand at low tide which can be soft in places. Launching is with club Range Rover. Speed boats, fishing boats, and PWCs welcome. Slipway is managed by Gunfleet Boating Club so members only. Membership is £105 per year, which includes full use of the slip and clubhouse facilities. All craft must be insured to launch.

FACILITIES: Fully licensed bar, male and female showers and toilets, launch vehicle, car parking, flushing facilities.

HAZARDS: 8 knot speed limit within 200 meters of low water mark.

Martello Bay, Clacton
Lat. 51.7811, Long. 1.1415.

CHARGES: Members only, joining fee is £75.57

SUITABILITY: Large trailer needs a car.

ACCESS: No Ramp. **TYPE OF RAMP:** Concrete ramp onto beach.

UPPER AREA: Sand. **LOWER AREA:** Sand.

DIRECTIONS: Ramp is west of the Clacton Pier off Hastings Avenue near to the Martello Tower.

RAMP DESCRIPTION: Good facility with wide concrete ramp onto the beach which is very soft in places launching is with club tractor. Speed boats and PWCs are welcome here. Site is run by Clacton Watercraft Club so members only, £75 joining fee which includes car park permit. Must be able to prove insurance and data tag registration to become a member and agree to adhere to club rules.

FACILITIES: Members only car park and beach restaurant near by.

HAZARDS: 8 knot speed limit 200 meters of low water

Pullover, Jaywick
Lat. 51.7730, Long. 1.1108.

SUITABILITY: Small trailer can be pushed.

ACCESS: No Ramp. **TYPE OF RAMP:** Concrete ramp onto beach.

UPPER AREA: Sand. **LOWER AREA:** Sand.

DIRECTIONS: Go through Jaywick. Follow road along seafront. Pullover is just by the roundabout before the Sunset Amusement Arcade.

RAMP DESCRIPTION: A concrete ramp through the sea wall allowing access to the beach. Warning of soft sand on the beach. Site is popular with Jetskiers.

FACILITIES: Parking and shops close by.

Hutleys Beach, Seawick
Lat. 51.7752, Long. 1.0830.

CHARGES: £10 per annum to register then £6 Jetski/£15 boat launch fees

SUITABILITY: Small trailer can be pushed.

ACCESS: All of tidal range. **TYPE OF RAMP:** Shingle beach

UPPER AREA: Shingle. **LOWER AREA:** Shingle.

DIRECTIONS: Follow signs to Clacton and then St Osyths. Pass straight through St Osyth village following signs for Seawick and Hutleys Caravan sites. Drive into Hutleys site and carry straight on until you reach the sea wall.

RAMP DESCRIPTION: Beach launching with a tractor, not suitable for cars/4 × 4's. Launching is operated by Hutleys Caravan Park. Jetskiers are welcome

FACILITIES: Toilet, shop and bar/café next to beach. Parking on both sides of the sea wall (for a small fee).

HAZARDS: 8 knot speed limit within 250m of high water marker. Exposed rocks around the beach at low water.

Point Clear, St Osyths
Lat. 51.8026, Long. 1.0200.

CHARGES: None

SUITABILITY: Large trailer needs a car.

ACCESS: All of tidal range. **TYPE OF RAMP:** Hard sand.

UPPER AREA: Sand. **LOWER AREA:** Sand.

DIRECTIONS: Head towards Clacton from the A12. Follow signs to St Osyths. When at St Osyths bear right to Point Clear, and follow signs for Beach. Keep going through the caravan parks and head towards the Martello Tower.

RAMP DESCRIPTION: Two ramps in use. One for 2 hours +/- high water, one for other times. To get to the ramp you need to drive over the sea wall and non 4 × 4 vehicles may ground. Then drive onto the beach to launch. Popular with Jetskiers.

FACILITIES: Parking and toilets and pub close by.

Boatyard, Brightlingsea
Lat. 51.8055, Long. 1.0307.

Rick Morgan 01206 302 003

CHARGES: £30/day

SUITABILITY: Large trailer needs a car.

ACCESS: ½ tidal. **TYPE OF RAMP:** Wide concrete.

UPPER AREA: Harbour. **LOWER AREA:** Mud.

DIRECTIONS: From Brightlingsea Pubic hard, head east through and industrial estate and on to the boatyards along the Brightlingsea Creek.

RAMP DESCRIPTION: Wide concrete ramp in the boatyard. At low tide the slipway ends in soft mud with assorted rocks. Jetskis are not allowed.

FACILITIES: Part of the Brightlingsea boatyard facility. Offers a boat storage and park and ride at around £860/year plus vat.

HAZARDS: 4 knot speed restriction.

Brightlingsea Town Hard, Brightlingsea
Lat. 51.8055, Long. 1.0244.

Council 01206 303535.

CHARGES: Powered craft £15 per day Jetskis £13 per day

SUITABILITY: Large trailer needs a car.

ACCESS: All of tidal range. **TYPE OF RAMP:** Wide concrete.

UPPER AREA: Concrete. **LOWER AREA:** Concrete.

DIRECTIONS: Between Colchester and Clacton-on-Sea. At Thorrington Cross follow B1029 to Brightlingsea. Follow signs through Brightlingsea.

RAMP DESCRIPTION: Public slipway, open 24 Hours. Wide slipway with a gentle gradient. Can get muddy at low tide. Pay at the hut on the hard. Jetskiers and powered craft welcome.

FACILITIES: Public car parks close by. Trailer parking on Hard. NOTE: Hard and adjacent roads flood at high tide. Good chandlers and petrol nearby. Slip water tap. Fish and chips.

HAZARDS: 4 knot speed limit in harbour.

Brightlingsea Sailing Club, Brightlingsea
Lat. 51.8058, Long. 1.0128.

CHARGES: Free
SUITABILITY: Small trailer can be pushed.
ACCESS: ¾ tidal. **TYPE OF RAMP:** Concrete **UPPER AREA:** Unknown.
LOWER AREA: Unknown.
DIRECTIONS: Western Promenade, Brightlingsea, Essex.
RAMP DESCRIPTION: Get permission to use the site. Gradient is steep then gentle. Slip is tortuous and long. Note: slip starts with steep hump over sea wall.
FACILITIES: Free parking. Overnight parking by prior arrangement. Parking space is adequate. Security is adequate. Club car park available by prior arrangement.

The Ford, Alresford
Lat. 51.8379, Long. 0.9938.

SUITABILITY: Small trailer can be pushed.
ACCESS: ½ tidal. **TYPE OF RAMP:** Shingle hard.
UPPER AREA: Shingle. **LOWER AREA:** Shingle.
DIRECTIONS: From Alresford take Church Lane that runs into Ford Lane down to the waters edge.
RAMP DESCRIPTION: Shingle road that leads into the river. Suitable for small and portable craft. The slip gets covered in soft mud/silt from 1/3 way down. Up to 3ft deep.
FACILITIES: No parking and the tide covers the roadway at Spring tide.
HAZARDS: There is an 8 knot speed limit. Old cruiser moorings are a hazard for PWCs.

Public Hard, Rowhedge
Lat. 51.8530, Long. 0.9586.

CHARGES: None
SUITABILITY: Small trailer can be pushed.
ACCESS: ¼ tidal. **TYPE OF RAMP:** Track to the river.
UPPER AREA: Mud. **LOWER AREA:** Mud.
DIRECTIONS: From Rowhedge take the road south to Fingringhoe. Turn left at the church and take the next left down to the end of Ferry Road.
RAMP DESCRIPTION: Basically a track down to the river suitable for small boat and portable craft.
FACILITIES: Small jetty at the launch site. Opposite the Wivenhoe Quay, very beautiful with lots of pubs. Very limited parking.
HAZARDS: Site is above the tidal barrier which is closed at high Springs when a surge is expected so it may not be possible to proceed far downstream. Seldom a problem.

Public Hard, West Mersea
Lat. 51.7788, Long. 0.8988.

SUITABILITY: Large trailer needs a car.
ACCESS: ½ tidal. **TYPE OF RAMP:** Concrete **UPPER AREA:** Shingle.
LOWER AREA: Mud.
DIRECTIONS: Take the B1025 south from Colchester to West Mersea. Road to Mersea Island can flood on very high tides. The ramp is on the western end of West Mersea opposite the old Lifeboat house.
RAMP DESCRIPTION: Public slipway, open 24 hours. Gradient is gentle.

FACILITIES: Overnight parking is available but parking space is impossible in high season. Back street parking possible if prepared to walk. Extremely crowded summer weekends. Public car park by toilets gets full early. Moorings: available by arrangement with West Mersea YC ferry, call sign YC1. Beaching: firm muddy shingle by Life Boat Shed. Berthing: inside jetty for short periods. Water Taxi: CH37 / 80 Call sign 'YC1' £1.00 round trip (mooring buoy-shore) Runs: till 22.30. West Mersea Yacht Club: 01206 382947 Open: 1200-1500 1800-2300 Food: 1200-1345 1830-2045. Good slip with water available by arrangement. For more local Mersea Island Information visit http://www.west-mersea.co.uk

Woodrolfe Hard, Maldon
Lat. 51.7601, Long. 0.8490.

CHARGES: Free
SUITABILITY: Large trailer needs a car.
ACCESS: ¾ tidal. **TYPE OF RAMP:** Public hard and ramp
UPPER AREA: Shingle. **LOWER AREA:** Mud.
DIRECTIONS: From Maldon head to Tollshunt d'Arcy then to Tollesbury
RAMP DESCRIPTION: Stones and some mud but ok on middle to high tide
FACILITIES: Chandlery
HAZARDS: Look where you are going and you will be fine

Tollesbury Marina, Maldon
Lat. 51.7588, Long. 0.8504.
01621 868471

CHARGES: £5 in and £5 out.
SUITABILITY: Large trailer needs a car.
ACCESS: ½ tidal. **TYPE OF RAMP:** Concrete **UPPER AREA:** Mud.
LOWER AREA: Mud.
DIRECTIONS: From Maldon take the B1026 to Tolleshunt d'Arcy. Turn right to go to Tollesbury and take the left fork to follow the signs for the water front down Woodrolfe Road. Address is The Yacht Harbour, Tollesbury, Maldon, Essex, CM9 8SE.
RAMP DESCRIPTION: Good wide boatyard slipway. Slipway is available for all the tidal range but you can only get out of the creek 2-4 hours around high tide (depending on draught). Phone ahead to check slip is free. Tides: Southend -30min. VHF Ch80. Season tickets available. There is also a public slipway outside the marina suitable for small boats. It is a shingle ramp onto mud and can be used for 1½ hours around high tide. Often busy at peak season. Several sailing clubs nearby, limited parking for trailers. Beware Spring tides that cover the access road - a place that is also convenient for parking.
FACILITIES: Parking for car and trailer in the yard. Anyone taking an overnight berth can make use of the extensive club house facilities including swimming pool, laundry, showers and restaurant. Good chandlery on-site.
HAZARDS: Stick to the channel. Ask local advice for further information about the deep water route out. On leaving the slipway, stay close to the line of boats on the south side of the channel until you can head straight for the lightship. Once in the middle of the channel again, stay there until you reach the lateral marks at the entrance to Woodrolfe Creek. Stick between these marks and your route will gradually turn south.

Now follow the line of moored boats - beware that it is very shallow at the sides of the creek. After about 1/2 mile you will come across some withies. These mark the eastern side of the channel. Stay close to the west of them until you come across a new set of lateral marks. Stay close to the starboard marks until you meet the east cardinal mark (Note the lone port mark nearby - Keep north of this; it is VERY shallow to the south of it). For small boats, you are now in safe water. For deeper boats, follow the port hand buoys until you reach the Nass Beacon (also an East Cardinal).

Tollesbury Marina, Tollesbury

The Yacht Harbour, Tollesbury, Essex, England
CM9 8SE
Lat. 51.7581, Long. 0.8498.
01621 869202

Shipways Boatyard, Maldon

Lat. 51.7302, Long. 0.6877.
01621 854280

CHARGES: £5 in and £5 out.
SUITABILITY: Large trailer needs a car.
ACCESS: ¼ tidal. **TYPE OF RAMP:** Wide concrete. **UPPER AREA:** Mud.
LOWER AREA: Mud.
DIRECTIONS: Boatyard is situated at the end of North Street.
RAMP DESCRIPTION: A good boatyard ramp with good gradient. Check with boatyard before travelling. Gates are locked 6pm-8am. Lots of mud around and boats may be blocking the ramp.
FACILITIES: Limited parking for car and trailers. Marine store chandlery on-site, toilets and fresh water. Queen's Head Pub just down the road offers a very warm welcome.
HAZARDS: Mud everywhere.

Slipway, Maldon

Lat. 51.7262, Long. 0.6961.
Chris Reynolds-Hole 01621 856487

CHARGES: None
SUITABILITY: Small trailer can be pushed.
ACCESS: ¼ tidal. **TYPE OF RAMP:** Concrete onto mud.
UPPER AREA: Mud. **LOWER AREA:** Mud.
DIRECTIONS: Bottom of High Street, turn into Park Drive and turn left into Promenade car park. Toilets less than ¼ mile.
RAMP DESCRIPTION: Open during car park hours. Maldon SC has priority. Slip is steep at top and then shallow onto the mud. Approach road is quite twisty, small trailer only. Max engine size is 25hp, no Jetskis.
FACILITIES: Overnight parking available in nearby pay and display, other facilities in town. Car park open from 6am to 10pm in summer, so car may get locked in.
HAZARDS: 8 knot speed limit 250 metres offshore. Wardens have speed guns and will prosecute offenders.

Blackwater Marina, Maylandsea

Marine Parade, Maylandsea, Essex, England
CM3 6AN
Lat. 51.6888, Long. 0.7526.
01621 740264

Blackwater Marina, Maylandsea

Lat. 51.6889, Long. 0.7531.
01621 740 264

CHARGES: £5 in and £5 out.
SUITABILITY: Large trailer needs a car.
ACCESS: ½ tidal. **TYPE OF RAMP:** Concrete **UPPER AREA:** Mud.
LOWER AREA: Mud.
DIRECTIONS: From Maylandsea, turn north at the garage and follow the road to the boatyard.
RAMP DESCRIPTION: Always contact the boatyard before travelling. The slipway may not be available to visitors.
FACILITIES: Parking, fresh water and pontoons available plus boatyard facilities. The Horny Toad Pub is on-site.
HAZARDS: Mud banks everywhere.

Marina Slip, Bradwell

Lat. 51.7331, Long. 0.8865.
01621 776 235

CHARGES: £14 (03/06/07)
SUITABILITY: Large trailer needs a car.
ACCESS: ¾ tidal. **TYPE OF RAMP:** Long concrete ramp, can get slippery.
UPPER AREA: Concrete. **LOWER AREA:** Concrete.
DIRECTIONS: From South Woodham Ferrers, take B1017 / 1018. Signposted Bradwell Waterside. Marina is on your left as you get to Bradwell waterside.
RAMP DESCRIPTION: Very busy on summer weekends. Quite narrow. Cars and trailers must be removed from ramp. Call marina on VHF Ch80.
FACILITIES: Bradwell Marina. Petrol / LPG, toilets, bar, parking. Bradwell Quay Yacht Club welcomes visiting sailors (Club House: 01621 776539, Secretary: Chas Moore 01268 763679) Fri, Sat, Sun 7-11pm and Sun12-3pm. Green Man Pub and restaurant nearby. Local post office and grocers nearby. Day berths available.
HAZARDS: Submerged stump approximately 10ft from end of slip.

Bradwell Marina, Bradwell on Sea

Waterside, Bradwell on Sea, Essex, England
CM0 7RB
Lat. 51.7328, Long. 0.8864.
01621 776391

Bradwell Creek, Bradwell

Lat. 51.7344, Long. 0.8865.
01621 776256

CHARGES: £51.60/year or £15/day.
SUITABILITY: Small trailer can be pushed.
ACCESS: ¾ tidal. **TYPE OF RAMP:** Shallow concrete.
UPPER AREA: Shingle. **LOWER AREA:** Shingle.

DIRECTIONS: Head to Bradwell. Go past the marina on your left and follow the road to the water's edge.

RAMP DESCRIPTION: Shallow concrete ramp onto a wide hard. There is a locked barrier at the head of the slipway. Very crowded in summer. You must phone before using, really intended for small sailing and rowing boats only. Larger boats should use the marina next door.

FACILITIES: Small dingy park. Very restricted parking especially in the summer.

HAZARDS: No Jetskis or PWC.

Marina Slip, Burnham on Crouch
Lat. 51.6292, Long. 0.8025.

01621 782150

CHARGES: £10/day

SUITABILITY: Large trailer needs a car.

ACCESS: All of tidal range. **TYPE OF RAMP:** Wide concrete

UPPER AREA: Concrete. **LOWER AREA:** Mud.

DIRECTIONS: Drive in to Burnham on Crouch over the railway bridge. Immediately turn right (at Co-op) and follow road down to marina which is signposted. Ramp is in front of the main buildings.

RAMP DESCRIPTION: An easy comfortable launch on an excellent wide slipway. Open 24 hours. The bottom of the slipway can get muddy at very low tide but still usable. There is a restriction on launching speedboats but, ribs are exempt from the restriction. Check with the marina office before travelling if in doubt. Will need to pay Crouch Harbour Authority dues, can be paid in the marina office.

FACILITIES: Petrol, pub, good restaurant, toilets and changing rooms. Park close to slip or on raised car park at side of entrance drive. Slip water tap close by. Overnight berths available and a hoist for larger boats.

Burnham Yacht Harbour, Burnham-on-Crouch
Burnham Yacht Harbour Marina Ltd, Burnham-on-Crouch, Essex, England CM0 8BL

Lat. 51.6296, Long. 0.8029.

01621 782150, HM 01621 786832

Creeksea SC, Burnham-on-Crouch
Lat. 51.6281, Long. 0.7889.

CHARGES: For use by members only.

SUITABILITY: Small trailer can be pushed.

ACCESS: ½ tidal. **TYPE OF RAMP:** Rough concrete. **UPPER AREA:** Mud. **LOWER AREA:** Mud.

DIRECTIONS: West of Burnham-on-Crouch, follow the sign to Creeksea.

RAMP DESCRIPTION: The slipway is for use by members only and the slipway can not be accessed from the public road. Membership details and fees are on the website www.creeksea.org.uk. Fees are very modest and the club welcomes new member enquiries.

FACILITIES: Parking and clubhouse.

Bridgemarsh Marine, Althorne
Bridgemarsh Lane, Althorne, Essex, England CM3 6DQ

Lat. 51.6453, Long. 0.7512.

01621 740414

Fambridge Yacht Haven, Chelmsford
Church Rd, North Fambridge, Chelmsford, Essex, England CM3 6LR

Lat. 51.6431, Long. 0.6725.

01621 740370

Slipway, South Woodham Ferrers
Lat. 51.6310, Long. 0.6129.

Waterski Club 07940 519450. Crouch Harbour 01621 783602

CHARGES: None

SUITABILITY: Large trailer needs a car.

ACCESS: ½ tidal. **TYPE OF RAMP:** Mud and rocks (bumpy).

UPPER AREA: Shingle. **LOWER AREA:** Mud.

DIRECTIONS: From South Woodham Ferrers, follow the directions to Marsh Farm and then carry on towards the river. Ramp is at the old river ford.

RAMP DESCRIPTION: There is a public slipway and one that belongs to the waterski club. The public one is bumpy and muddy and in a poor state of repair. It is also shallow in places and runs at an angle to the river bank. The Ski club has a wide concrete ramp with a good gradient. Available to members only.

FACILITIES: Public car park next to the ramp. Neighbouring waterski club has club house and storage facilities.

The Ford, Hullbridge
Lat. 51.6296, Long. 0.6136.

River Crouch Harbour Authority, 01621 783602 9.30-11.30.

CHARGES: None

SUITABILITY: Large trailer needs a car.

ACCESS: ¼ tidal. **TYPE OF RAMP:** Concrete onto shingle.

UPPER AREA: Concrete. **LOWER AREA:** Mud.

DIRECTIONS: Either by A127 or A12 head for Wickford (Essex) junction on A130. Follow signs for Battlesbridge, then onto Hullbridge. Hullbridge town is quite small, turn left at the mini roundabout and follow road - this will lead onto the slipway.

RAMP DESCRIPTION: The ramp is where the ford used to go into the river. It is narrow and has a long reverse down the narrow road leading onto the slipway.

FACILITIES: Anchor Pub overlooking ramp, with garden down to river bank. At high tide it is possible to moore up alongside the riverbank (wall) at the end of the pub garden. Ideal for a swift half and there is parking nearby. Also various boatyards and yacht clubs. The ramp is opposite the Woodham Ferres Waterski Club.

HAZARDS: Situated in the middle of a trot of moorings, 8 knots speed limit until you reach the ski area. Skiing only permitted if you're a member of Burnham-on-Crouch ski club.

Essex Marina, Rochford
Wallasea Island, Rochford, Essex, England SS4 2HF
Lat. 51.6217, Long. 0.7962.
01702 258531

Paglesham Hard, Paglesham
Lat. 51.5942, Long. 0.8107.
Paglesham Boatyard 01702 258885

CHARGES: £10.00 payable to Paglesham Boatyard.
SUITABILITY: Large trailer needs a car.
ACCESS: All of tidal range. **TYPE OF RAMP:** Wide concrete hard, gently sloping to water. **UPPER AREA:** Mud. **LOWER AREA:** Mud.
DIRECTIONS: Paglesham is a village a few miles from Rochford which is a small town to the north of Southend on Sea, Essex. On approaching Paglesham take the turning to 'East End', not 'Church End'. Continue to the end of the lane where there is a pub, the Plough and Sail, on the left. Take an unmade track to the left of the pub which leads down to the Paglesham Boatyard where the hard is.
RAMP DESCRIPTION: Good wide gentle sloping concrete ramp. Lower extremity of ramp tails off into mud at extreme low Spring tide but slip is usable by very large trailers at all other tide states. Boat yard has tractor and cranes for launching heavy boats. Jetskis can launch here.
FACILITIES: Boatyard with large car park. (Check with boatyard office in Portacabin to left of slip before launching). One toilet in small cubicle somewhere in boatyard. A café based in a caravan in the boatyard operates most weekends in the summer. Pub is Plough and Sail a few hundred yards up the lane.

INLAND SLIPWAYS
alphabetical by place name

St Helens Warf, Abingdon
Lat. 51.6673, Long. -1.2823.

CHARGES: No charges
SUITABILITY: Small trailer can be pushed.
ACCESS: Non-tidal. **TYPE OF RAMP:** Cobble stones
UPPER AREA: Concrete. **LOWER AREA:** Mud.
DIRECTIONS: From the centre of Abingdon proceed behind the County Hall down East St.Helens Street. At the bottom of East St.Helens Street, carry on down past St.Helens Church and the slipway is straight ahead.
RAMP DESCRIPTION: Public slipway from the road. Fairly narrow and reasonably steep.
FACILITIES: Parking 200 yards in pay & display car park in West St.Helens Street. Pub with food 20 yards away on St.Helens Warf. Abingdon Boat Centre 50 yards upstream with chandlery and fuel available.
HAZARDS: ALL boats require a licence from the Environment Agency and 8kph speed limit.

Abingdon Marina, Abingdon
Lat. 51.6570, Long. -1.2837.
SUITABILITY: Large trailer needs a car.

ACCESS: Non-tidal. **TYPE OF RAMP:** Concrete **UPPER AREA:** Concrete.
LOWER AREA: Unknown.
DIRECTIONS: From the A34 Abingdon junction head toward Abingdon. Go straight over 2 roundabouts then turn right onto the B4017 toward Drayton. Straight over the roundabout then second left into Preston Rd. After road bends left turn right into Lambrick Way. Follow this road to slip. For parking return to Preston Rd and turn right to Wilsham Rd.
RAMP DESCRIPTION: Excellent wide concrete slipway.
FACILITIES: Excellent free slipway. Road access has height restriction of approx 7ft. This will be opened by the marina manager if he is on site. (Call for times). Parking is now available at the top of slip, no charge for launch or parking.
HAZARDS: ALL boats require a licence from the Environment Agency and 8kph speed limit.

Abingdon Marina, Abingdon
South Quay, Abingdon, Oxfordshire, England OX14 5TW
Lat. 51.6589, Long. -1.2812.
01235 536147

ABC Leisure Group, Alvechurch Marina, Alvechurch
Scarfield Wharf, Alvechurch, Worcestershire, England B48 7SQ
Lat. 52.3469, Long. -1.9724.
0121 445 1133

Carsington Water, Ashbourne
Lat. 53.0608, Long. -1.6413.
01629 540609

CHARGES: Sailing club charges: 1/2 day £10 full day £20 - this is for sailing boats and not motorised cruisers!
SUITABILITY: Large trailer needs a car.
ACCESS: Non-tidal. **TYPE OF RAMP:** Concrete and pontoons
UPPER AREA: Shingle. **LOWER AREA:** Shingle.
DIRECTIONS: Carsington Sports & Leisure, CarsingtonWater, Ashbourne, Derbyshire. DE6 1ST. Signposted from A6
RAMP DESCRIPTION: Straight, good access, shallow ramp with a pontoon reaching out into deeper water, 1metre deep about 8 metres out.
FACILITIES: Sailing club house. Toilets, showers, changing rooms, bar, car park. Purpose build reservoir with large sailing club and visitor centre. Onsite storage and berthing for trailer sailors. Very clean / clear water.

Old Ferry Slipway, Bablockhythe
Lat. 51.7351, Long. -1.3721.
Ferry Hotel 01865 880028

CHARGES: £4 each way.
SUITABILITY: Large trailer needs a car.
ACCESS: Non-tidal. **TYPE OF RAMP: UPPER AREA:** Unknown.
LOWER AREA: Unknown.

DIRECTIONS: Exit A40 at Witney junction. Head toward Abingdon on A415. after 4 miles turn left into Standlake. Turn right at T junction. After 2 miles turn right at T junction then 300 yards to slip.
RAMP DESCRIPTION: Nasty step just below waterline but passable. Cost £4 each way. Ample parking. Controlled by Ferryman Inn, Bablock Hythe, Northmoor, 01865 880028.
FACILITIES: Arrange parking with Ferry Hotel.
HAZARDS: ALL boats require a licence from the Environment Agency and 8kph speed limit.

Yacht Station, Beccles
Lat. 52.4640, Long. 1.5641.
01502 712225

CHARGES: Free
SUITABILITY: Large trailer needs a car.
ACCESS: ¾ tidal. **TYPE OF RAMP:** Concrete **UPPER AREA:** Concrete.
LOWER AREA: Sand.
DIRECTIONS: On A146 to Lowestoft turn off at roundabout by Safeway store, over river, 1st right and right again slip is on the right hand side. Car park is on the other side of the water.
RAMP DESCRIPTION: Public slipway. Flood defence board may be in place during winter months. Remove boards and replace them after launching.
FACILITIES: Free overnight parking in public car park 200 metres away where you can leave car and trailer. Showers, toilets and laundry available at the Yacht Station which is manned 8.30 to 18.00, April to October and 8.00-10.00 in the winter months. Broads Authority Information office on-site.

Waveney River Centre, Beccles
Lat. 52.4842, Long. 1.6703.
The Manager, Waveney River Centre, 01502 712538

CHARGES: Yes
SUITABILITY: Large trailer needs a car.
ACCESS: Non-tidal. **TYPE OF RAMP:** Concrete
UPPER AREA: Unknown. **LOWER AREA:** Unknown.
DIRECTIONS: Follow A143 from Gillingham (Beccles) towards Great Yarmouth, follow signs for Burgh St Peter and then signs for Waveney River Centre.
RAMP DESCRIPTION: Public slipway. Gradient is medium, slip is straight and narrow. Slip may be locked, requires prior notification.
FACILITIES: Overnight parking available. Parking space is adequate. Security is adequate. Park in Waveney Arms Hotel Park. Slip, moorings, camping, pub, restaurant, swimming pool, toilets, showers. Slip water tap.

Rowan Craft, Beccles
Wherry Dyke, Big Row, Geldeston, Beccles, Suffolk, England NR34 0LY
Lat. 52.4716, Long. 1.5163.
01508 518208

Priory Marina, Bedford
Barkers Lane, Bedford, Beds, England MK41 9DJ
Lat. 52.1316, Long. -0.4386.
01234 351931

Hoseason's boatyard, Benson
Lat. 51.6189, Long. -1.1145.
SUITABILITY: Large trailer needs a car.
ACCESS: Non-tidal. **TYPE OF RAMP: UPPER AREA:** Unknown.
LOWER AREA: Unknown.
DIRECTIONS: On the left bank going downstream.
RAMP DESCRIPTION: Get permission to use the site. Two slips.
FACILITIES: All boatyard facilities.

Nitrojet Action Sports, Berinsfield
Lat. 51.6565, Long. -1.1653.
01865 341115

CHARGES: Morning launch £20.00. Full day launch £30.00. Annual membership £400.00
SUITABILITY: Small trailer can be pushed.
ACCESS: Non-tidal. **TYPE OF RAMP:** Concrete slipway, with sand beach area. **UPPER AREA:** Shingle. **LOWER AREA:** Unknown.
DIRECTIONS: Nitrojet is between Reading and Oxford on the A4074. It is also easily reached from the M4 via the A34/A415. From the roundabout on the A4074/A415, take the road sign posted to Berinsfield. Follow the road for approx 1/2 mile, the turning will be on your right hand side and there is a sign for Oxford waterski and wakeboard club
RAMP DESCRIPTION: The lake is open 7 days a week from 10am to all watercraft - both stand up and sit-downs. Closing times vary to season, please call for full details. Day launch is £30. Half day launch is available from 10am - 2pm and is £20. Annual membership is £400.
FACILITIES: Changing rooms, café and excellent stocked showroom, workshop for servicing and repair.

Lyons Boatyard, Birmingham
Canalside, Limekiln Lane, Warstock, Birmingham, England B14 4SP
Lat. 52.4140, Long. -1.8770.
0121 544 1795

Boston Marina, Boston
5-7 Witham Bank East, Boston, Lincolnshire, England PE21 9JU
Lat. 52.9837, Long. -0.0320.
01205 364420

Lincoln Marina, Brayford Pool
James Kendall & Co Ltd, The Boatyard, Brayford Pool, Lincolnshire, England LN6 7GA
Lat. 53.2291, Long. -0.5478.
01522 526896

Waveney River Centre, Burgh St Peter
Staithe Road, Burgh St Peter, Norfolk, England
NR34 0BT
Lat. 52.4824, Long. 1.6697.
01502 677343

Shobnall Marina, Burton on Trent
Shobnall Road, Burton on Trent, Staffordshire,
England DE14 2AU
Lat. 52.8059, Long. -1.6545.
01283 542718

Barton Turns Marina, Burton-On-Trent
Barton Turns, Barton-under-Needwood, Burton-
On-Trent, Staffordshire, England DE13 8DZ
Lat. 52.7618, Long. -1.7027.
01283 711666

National Trust picnic spot, Buscot
Lat. 51.6839, Long. -1.6774.
SUITABILITY: Small trailer can be pushed.
ACCESS: Non-tidal. **TYPE OF RAMP:** Low bank.
UPPER AREA: Unknown. **LOWER AREA:** Unknown.
DIRECTIONS: On the right bank going downstream. National Trust
picnic spot. Low bank.
RAMP DESCRIPTION: Public slipway.
**HAZARDS: ALL boats require a licence from the Environment
Agency and 8kph speed limit.**

Red Lion Lawn, Castle Easton
Lat. 51.6608, Long. -1.7918.
SUITABILITY: Small trailer can be pushed.
ACCESS: Non-tidal. **TYPE OF RAMP: UPPER AREA:** Unknown.
LOWER AREA: Unknown.
DIRECTIONS: On the right bank going downstream. Lawn of Red Lion
pub.
RAMP DESCRIPTION: Get permission to use the site from the pub.
**HAZARDS: ALL boats require a licence from the Environment
Agency and 8kph speed limit.**

Grebe Canal Cruisers, Cheddington
Lat. 51.8353, Long. -0.6551.
Tel: (01296) 661920
CHARGES: £115 in and out plus £5/day
SUITABILITY: Large trailer needs a car.
ACCESS: Non-tidal. **TYPE OF RAMP: UPPER AREA:** Concrete.
LOWER AREA: Unknown.
DIRECTIONS: Pitstone Wharf, Cheddington, Bucks, LU7 9AD.
FACILITIES: Yard facilities to work on the boat. Crane can be brought
onto the site.

Jet Ski Centre, Church Wilne
Lat. 52.8873, Long. -1.3222.
SUITABILITY: Large trailer needs a car.
ACCESS: Non-tidal. **TYPE OF RAMP:** Concrete
UPPER AREA: Unknown. **LOWER AREA:** Unknown.
DIRECTIONS: Junction 24 on the MI. Take the A6 to Derby and then take
first turning to Long Eaton. Turn left at the Nags Head onto Sawley Road
and continue past the Severn Trent Water works onto the second lake.
RAMP DESCRIPTION: Strictly members only
FACILITIES: Club house with heated changing rooms, excellent
showers, bar and food available. Parking on site.

Colwick Park Marina, Colwick
River Road, Off Mile End Road, Colwick,
Nottinghamshire, England NG4 2DW
Lat. 52.9469, Long. -1.0941.
0115 987 0785

Belle Isle Marina, Coningsby
Dogdyke Rd, Coningsby, Lincolnshire, England
LN4 4UU
Lat. 53.0826, Long. -0.1955.
01526 342124

Crick Marina, Crick
West Haddon Rd, Crick, Northamptonshire,
England NN6 7SQ
Lat. 52.3478, Long. -1.1231.
01788 824034

Thames Lane Ford, Cricklade
Lat. 51.6430, Long. -1.8517.
SUITABILITY: Small trailer can be pushed.
ACCESS: Non-tidal. **TYPE OF RAMP: UPPER AREA:** Unknown.
LOWER AREA: Unknown.
DIRECTIONS: On right bank when going downstream. Ford at farm at
bottom of Thames Lane.
RAMP DESCRIPTION: Ask permission at farm.
**HAZARDS: ALL boats require a licence from the Environment
Agency and 8kph speed limit.**

Slipway, Crowland
Lat. 52.6797, Long. -0.1835.
CHARGES: License needed to navigate the Wellend
SUITABILITY: Large trailer needs a car.
ACCESS: Non-tidal. **TYPE OF RAMP:** Concrete **UPPER AREA:** Concrete.
LOWER AREA: Concrete.
DIRECTIONS: Exit through crowland on gravel causeway heading
towards market deeping, slipway is on the left at junction to wellend
bank near large white water tower.
RAMP DESCRIPTION: Recently built concrete slipway. Key needed for
barrier across slip

2

Welton Hythe and Welton Haven Marina, Daventry
Welton, Daventry, Northants, England NN11 2LG
Lat. 52.2909, Long. -1.1225.
01327 842282

Braunston Marina, Daventry
The Wharf, Braunston, Daventry, Northants,
England NN11 7JH
Lat. 52.2870, Long. -1.2108.
01788 891373

Whilton Marina, Daventry
Whilton Locks, Daventry, Northants, England
NN11 5NH
Lat. 52.2728, Long. -1.0959.
01327 842577

Slipway, Denver Sluice
Lat. 52.5836, Long. 0.3439.

CHARGES: Believed none but see note about Environment Agency.
SUITABILITY: Large trailer needs a car.
ACCESS: Unknown. **TYPE OF RAMP:** Concrete. **UPPER AREA:** Concrete.
LOWER AREA: Unknown.
DIRECTIONS: Turn off A10 at signpost Denver and then follow signs for
Denver Sluice.
RAMP DESCRIPTION: Concrete into deep water. Free car park but
locked height restriction barrier at entrance but Environment Agency
offices nearby who, I assume, have keys. Sign saying boats must be
registered (with E.A.) and bear prominent numbers.

Shardlow Marina, Derby
London Road, Shardlow, Derby, Derbyshire,
England DE72 2GL
Lat. 52.8672, Long. -1.3369.
01332 792832

Donnington Bridge Slipway, Donnington
Lat. 51.7359, Long. -1.2420.
01865 248673

CHARGES: £30 a year for a key to access slipway 24/7
SUITABILITY: Large trailer needs a car.
ACCESS: Non-tidal. **TYPE OF RAMP: UPPER AREA:** Concrete.
LOWER AREA: Concrete.
RAMP DESCRIPTION: Note: there is a new padlock on the gate to this
slipway. (Frustrating Sunday visit!) The Watersports centre's opening
hours are 09:00 to 16:00 weekdays.
FACILITIES: Above Donnington Bridge, good slip with nearby parking.
Oxford Riverside Centre, Donnington Bridge, Oxford, Oxon OX4 4AZ.
Opening hours 09:00-16:00 Monday to Friday. Contact Dave Holmes.
**HAZARDS: ALL boats require a licence from the Environment
Agency and 8kph speed limit.**

Slipway, Eastern Marine Sales
Lat. 52.2450, Long. -0.8128.
01604 408312

CHARGES: Slipway - £15
SUITABILITY: Large trailer needs a car.
ACCESS: Non-tidal. **TYPE OF RAMP:** Concrete slipway
UPPER AREA: Unknown. **LOWER AREA:** Unknown.
FACILITIES: Slipway, chandlery and all usual boatyard services

Twenty Pence Marina, Ely
Twenty Pence Road, Wilburton, Ely, Cambs,
England CB6 3PX
Lat. 52.3201, Long. 0.1718.
01954 251118

Cathedral Marina, Ely
Waterside, Ely, Cambs, England CB7 4AU
Lat. 52.3969, Long. 0.2704.
01353 664622

Ely Town Quay, Ely
Lat. 52.3953, Long. 0.2707.

CHARGES: None
SUITABILITY: Large trailer needs a car.
ACCESS: Non-tidal. **TYPE OF RAMP:** Firm but bumpy hard.
UPPER AREA: Unknown. **LOWER AREA:** Unknown.
DIRECTIONS: From Market St. turn down Fore Hill into Waterside,
leading to Quay Side, slip is alongside bridge over river to boatyards.
RAMP DESCRIPTION: Public slipway. Gradient is average. NRA licence
required.
FACILITIES: Free overnight parking in new car park. Toilets in the car
park, 100m behind the waterfront. Tescos store is at the station. The
slip water tap on the front. There is a boat chandler in Waterside approx
200m from the front. The Maltings Restaurant and Bar is situated on the
front near the ramp.

Boathaven Littleport, Ely
Lynn Road, Littleport., Ely, Cambs, England
CB6 1QG
Lat. 52.4632, Long. 0.3184.
01353 863763

Riverside Island Marina, Ely
1 KINGFISHER ISLEHAM Fenbank, Isleham, Ely,
Cambs, England CB7 5SL
Lat. 52.3544, Long. 0.4218.
01638 780663

Sankey Marine, Evesham
Worcester Road, Evesham, Worcs, England
WR11 4TA
Lat. 52.1076, Long. -1.9561.
01386 442338

Evesham Marina, Evesham
Kings Road, Evesham, Worcs, England WR11 3XZ
Lat. 52.0963, Long. -1.9350.
01386 768500

Friars Quay, Friars Quay
Lat. 52.6324, Long. 1.2964.
CHARGES: Free (although you will need a valid Broads Toll which can be obtained from the Broads Authority office just down the road)
SUITABILITY: Large trailer needs a car.
ACCESS: All of tidal range. **TYPE OF RAMP:** Concrete
UPPER AREA: Concrete. **LOWER AREA:** Concrete.
DIRECTIONS: Head towards Colgate.
RAMP DESCRIPTION: Slip is reasonably steep but most suitable for dinghies and small day boats.
FACILITIES: Slip is in the city centre off a residential road. There are no facilities although Norwich Yacht Station is only ten minutes down stream and offers good, free facilities.

Godmanchester Public Slip, Godmanchester
Lat. 52.3184, Long. -0.1753.
CHARGES: Free
SUITABILITY: Small trailer can be pushed.
ACCESS: Non-tidal. **TYPE OF RAMP:** Mud ramp
UPPER AREA: Unknown. **LOWER AREA:** Unknown.
DIRECTIONS: Off the causeway road in godmanchester. limited road side parking
RAMP DESCRIPTION: Mud ramp maintained by the EA
FACILITIES: None
HAZARDS: Quite shallow and weedy

Burgh Castle Marina, Great Yarmouth
Butt Lane, Burgh Castle, Great Yarmouth, Norfolk, England NR31 9PZ
Lat. 52.5771, Long. 1.6502.
01493 780331

Slipway, Griffin Marine
Lat. 52.6235, Long. 1.3606.
CHARGES: £7.50
SUITABILITY: Large trailer needs a car.
ACCESS: Non-tidal. **TYPE OF RAMP:** Mostly concrete.
UPPER AREA: Harbour. **LOWER AREA:** Mud.
DIRECTIONS: If you're coming off the A47 towards Norwich, take the 1st turning past the Griffin pub (signposted River Trips). If you're heading towards the A47 from Norwich, it's the 1st right after the rail bridge.
RAMP DESCRIPTION: Mostly concrete, mud nearer the bottom. Quite easy to use for smaller boats, slip is fairly shallow though, plenty of room to manoeuvre. Temporary mooring available, plenty of (free) parking.
FACILITIES: Small shop nearby.

Hickling Broad, Hickling Heath
Lat. 52.7471, Long. 1.5701.
Whispering Reeds Boatyard 01692 598314
CHARGES: £6.50 launch fee, trailer storage £5 per week. £11.50 day launch (launch, recover and park car and trailer). But they lock the gate a 5pm so you have to be out and gone by then. (Feb 2009) In 2008 it cost £9-00 each way to launch, plus £30-00 a week for parking car and trailer. As stated, slip is VERY awkward to use - need to leave towing vehicle at top of ramp and winch trailer up before driving off.
SUITABILITY: Large trailer needs a car.
ACCESS: Non-tidal. **TYPE OF RAMP: UPPER AREA:** Concrete.
LOWER AREA: Mud.
DIRECTIONS: From Norwich take A1151 north through Wroxham. Road continues as A149 After Stalham take left turn to Hickling Heath. Ramp is located in the boat yard on the North side of the broad adjacent to the Wherryman PH.
RAMP DESCRIPTION: It is in a boat yard, there is a building 10 feet away behind the ramp that can make reversing a little awkward but still possible. Boats over 16 ´ will have problems getting out as the slip is short and has a step at the bottom that is a real problem for larger boats to be retrieved. Obtain a Broad licence from the boatyard. Only relatively shallow draught yachts are able to use the slip due to the step at the end. It is not possible to get a trailer all the way down and a lifting keel really helps here. The yard does have a sling and hoist, so you can get you out if you find that it is impossible to recover via the slip.
FACILITIES: There is a pub called the Pleasure Boat to the west of the ramp. This serves food in season and has a pool table and some moorings outside. It can be popular in season and can be advantageous to moor on the broad and go in by tender. There is plenty of room to moor on the broad and it is very pleasant. Fixed deep keel boats should keep near the post markers in the centre of the broad. There is a good car park (public) behind the pub as well as public toilets that are well maintained. Very nice place to launch from and explore the broads, for deeper keeled boats, Horsey Broad, next one along offers excellent sailing over most of its area. Trailer storage is good and secure.
HAZARDS: Be aware of the navigation posts, these can be awkward in poor visibility and if you are a deep draught vessel you should stay close around the marking.

Hickling Broad, Hickling, Norfolk
Lat. 52.7464, Long. 1.5741.
SUITABILITY: Small trailer can be pushed.
ACCESS: Non-tidal. **TYPE OF RAMP: UPPER AREA:** Unknown.
LOWER AREA: Unknown.
DIRECTIONS: From Hickling village take Staithe road for about a mile - slip is just past pub on right, before reaching the boatyard. Contact details and charges are on board at entrance to site.
RAMP DESCRIPTION: Two small wooden ramps with step at end. Fixed winches make launch/recovery easy, though. £4-00 charge (in and out) No parking at site for car and trailer, though pub car park could possibly be used.

2

Furness Vale Marina, High Peak

The Moorings, Station Rd, Furness Vale, High
Peak, Derbyshire, England SK23 7QA
Lat. 53.3494, Long. -1.9875.
01663 742971

Trinity Marinas, Hinckley

Wharf Farm, Coventry Rd, Hinckley, Leicestershire,
England LE10 0NF
Lat. 52.5364, Long. -1.3989.
01455 896820

Westview Marina, Huntingdon

High Street, Earith, Huntingdon, Cambridgeshire,
England PE28 3PN
Lat. 52.3530, Long. 0.0297.
01487 841627

Hermitage Marina, Huntingdon

Earith Bridge, Earith, Huntingdon, Cambs,
England PE28 3PR
Lat. 52.3522, Long. 0.0442.
01487 840994

Hartford Marina, Huntingdon

Banks End, Huntingdon, Cambridgeshire, England
PE28 2AA
Lat. 52.3371, Long. -0.1428.
01480 454677

Buckden Marina, Huntingdon

Mill Road, Buckden, Huntingdon, Cambridgeshire,
England PE19 5QS
Lat. 52.2914, Long. -0.2214.
01480 812660

The Huntingdon Boat Haven & Caravan Park, Huntingdon

The Avenue, Godmanchester, Huntingdon,
Cambridgeshire, England PE29 2AF
Lat. 52.3235, Long. -0.1775.
01480 411977

Bill Fen Marina, Huntingdon

Mill Drove, Ramsey, Huntingdon, Cambridgeshire,
England PE26 2RD
Lat. 52.4552, Long. -0.1116.
01487 813621

Huntingdon Public Slipway, Huntingdon

Lat. 52.3306, Long. -0.1734.

CHARGES: Free
SUITABILITY: Large trailer needs a car.

ACCESS: Non-tidal. **TYPE OF RAMP:** Large concrete ramp
UPPER AREA: Unknown. **LOWER AREA:** Unknown.
DIRECTIONS: Just off the huntingdon ringroad
RAMP DESCRIPTION: Concrete ramp maintained by the EA
FACILITIES: Car park near by

East Midlands Boat Services, Kegworth

Willow Moorings, London Road, Kegworth,
Derbyshire, England DE74 2EY
Lat. 52.8241, Long. -1.2716.
01509 672385

Riverside Road, Kelmscot

Lat. 51.6866, Long. -1.6759.
SUITABILITY: Large trailer needs a car.
ACCESS: Non-tidal. **TYPE OF RAMP: UPPER AREA:** Unknown.
LOWER AREA: Unknown.
DIRECTIONS: On the left bank going downstream. Field at end of
Riverside Road leading from village.
**HAZARDS: ALL boats require a licence from the Environment
Agency and 8kph speed limit.**

Mill Marina, Kettering

Midland Road, Thrapston, Kettering, Northants,
England NN14 4JR
Lat. 52.3918, Long. -0.5412.
01832 732850

Kingsbury Jet Bike, Kingsbury

Lat. 52.5621, Long. -1.6976.
Jayne Crowther 01827 874815 or 07968 748734

CHARGES: £30 for a 3 seater and £25 for solo.
SUITABILITY: Small trailer can be pushed.
ACCESS: Non-tidal. **TYPE OF RAMP:** Concrete
UPPER AREA: Unknown. **LOWER AREA:** Unknown.
DIRECTIONS: J9 on the M42, follow signs for Kingsbury Water Park
(A4097). Go left at the first roundabout and then right before you cross
the motorway. This will take you to the park. Go past the visitor centre
to the Jet Ski centre.
RAMP DESCRIPTION: Concrete ramp. No water skiing.
FACILITIES: 600 acres of park with camping and caravans. Café,
showers, changing rooms, new and used PWCs clothing and accessories
for sale.

Fenny Marina, Leamington Spa

Fenny Compton, Leamington Spa, Warwicks,
England CV47 2XD
Lat. 52.1721, Long. -1.3752.
01295 770461

Recreation Ground Car Park, Lechlade

Lat. 51.6911, Long. -1.6976.
SUITABILITY: Small trailer can be pushed.
ACCESS: Non-tidal. **TYPE OF RAMP: UPPER AREA:** Unknown.
LOWER AREA: Unknown.

DIRECTIONS: On the right bank going downstream. Car park at recreation ground flanks an arm of the river.
RAMP DESCRIPTION: Public slipway.
HAZARDS: ALL boats require a licence from the Environment Agency and 8kph speed limit.

Riverside Cafe, Lechlade
Lat. 51.6929, Long. -1.6933.
Mr Meek 01367 252229

CHARGES: £7/day
SUITABILITY: Large trailer needs a car.
ACCESS: Non-tidal. **TYPE OF RAMP:** Concrete
UPPER AREA: Unknown. **LOWER AREA:** Unknown.
DIRECTIONS: Turn South off A417 onto A361. Turn right into Marina before bridge.
RAMP DESCRIPTION: Good wide concrete slipway leading into the marina.
FACILITIES: Riverside café, boatyard, and chandlery. Plenty of parking. Cost approximately £7 + £1 car park per day.
HAZARDS: ALL boats require a licence from the Environment Agency and 8kph speed limit.

Riverside Lechlade Marina, Lechlade
Park End Wharf, Lechlade, Gloucestershire, England GL7 3AQ
Lat. 51.6931, Long. -1.6940.
01367 252229

Nimbus Narrow Boats, Leicester
The Boat Yard, Mill Lane, Thurmaston, Leicester, Leicestershire, England LE4 8AF
Lat. 52.6803, Long. -1.1000.
01162 693069

Raynsway Marina, Leicester
Pinfold Rd, Thurmaston, Leicester, Leicestershire, England LE4 8AS
Lat. 52.6746, Long. -1.1085.
0116 260 6166

Debdale Wharf Marina, Leicester
Nr Smeeton Westerby Kibworth, Leicester, England LE8 0XA
Lat. 52.5179, Long. -0.9776.
0116 279 3034

Grebe Canal Cruises, Leighton Buzzard
Pitstone Wharf, Pitstone, Leighton Buzzard, England LU7 9AD
Lat. 51.8356, Long. -0.6554.
01296 661920

Burton Waters Marina, Lincoln
Burton Lane End Burton Waters, Lincoln, Lincolnshire, England LN1 2WN
Lat. 53.2489, Long. -0.5983.
01522 567404

Paper Mill Lock, Little Baddow
Lat. 51.7518, Long. 0.5750.
Office: 01245 223482 24hr answer phone: 01245 225520

CHARGES: Slip £12 and licence £8 /day +VAT.
SUITABILITY: Large trailer needs a car.
ACCESS: Non-tidal. **TYPE OF RAMP:** Concrete
UPPER AREA: Unknown. **LOWER AREA:** Unknown.
DIRECTIONS: The Lock Keeper, Chelmer and Blackwater Navigation Company. Paper Mill Lock, North Hill, Little Baddow, Chelmsford, Essex CM3 4BF. Head southwest out of Hatfield Peverel on B1137; long straight road dips and rises; turn left at end of long low brick wall, heading to Little Baddow.
RAMP DESCRIPTION: Quiet shallow, canal leading from Chelmsford Basin to Heybridge Basin, Maldon. Access via sea lock to River Blackwater by prior arrangement (lockmaster: 01621 853506). Lock key returnable deposit: £60.
FACILITIES: Free parking. Overnight parking available by prior arrangement. Parking space is adequate. Security is excellent. Slip water tap close by.

Sawley Marina, Long Eaton
Sawley, Long Eaton, Nottingham, England NG10 3AE
Lat. 52.8734, Long. -1.3001.
0115 973 4278

Sileby Mill Boatyard, Loughborough
Mill Lane, Sileby, Loughborough, Leics, England LE12 7NF
Lat. 52.7280, Long. -1.1244.
01509 813583

Hunters Yard, Ludham
Lat. 52.7039, Long. 1.5437.
Boatyard 01 692 678 263
SUITABILITY: Large trailer needs a car.
ACCESS: Non-tidal. **TYPE OF RAMP:** Yard slipway.
UPPER AREA: Unknown. **LOWER AREA:** Unknown.
DIRECTIONS: From Norwich take A1151-Hoveton. At Hoveton take A1062 to Ludham. Yard is at end of Horsefen Rd, signposted from east end of village, 1½miles from the road.
RAMP DESCRIPTION: It is very unlikely that the slipway will be available for use due to all the work taking place in the yard so speak to the yard before turning up with your boat. Donations to the charitable trust would be appreciated.
FACILITIES: Traditional boatyard, visitors are welcome to come down and see traditional boat building taking place. Boat hire offering an authentic 1930s sailing experience.

2

North Kilworth Wharf, Lutterworth
North Kilworth Wharf Station Road North Kilworth, Lutterworth, Leicestershire, England LE17 6JB
Lat. 52.4469, Long. -1.0785.
01858 881723

Fox's Marina, March
10 Marina Drive, March, Cambs, England PE15 0AU
Lat. 52.5633, Long. 0.0667.
01354 652770

C.T Fox Boatyard, March
Lat. 52.5544, Long. 0.0657.
01354 652770
CHARGES: Yes
SUITABILITY: Large trailer needs a car.
ACCESS: Non-tidal. **TYPE OF RAMP:** Concrete
UPPER AREA: Unknown. **LOWER AREA:** Unknown.
DIRECTIONS: From south, on A141 cross river. Hard left at roundabout. Left again after about 300 yards, and follow lane down to boatyard.
RAMP DESCRIPTION: You need permission to use the site and the ramp is within Fox's yard, who are narrow boat builders and is permanently blocked by their vessels.
FACILITIES: Overnight parking available. Parking space is OK. Security is good. Parking is by prior arrangement in boatyard marina. Slip water tap.

Slipway, Melton Mowbray
Lat. 52.7656, Long. -0.8898.
01664 563563
CHARGES: None
SUITABILITY: Small trailer can be pushed.
ACCESS: Non-tidal. **TYPE OF RAMP:** Concrete
UPPER AREA: Unknown. **LOWER AREA:** Unknown.
DIRECTIONS: On the A607 through Melton Mowbray, at the rear of the Cattle Market/bus station car park site.
RAMP DESCRIPTION: Built by volunteers 2001. Access to a loop of the River Wreake and the Melton Mowbray Navigation (under restoration).

Block Fen, Mepal
Lat. 52.4303, Long. 0.0997.
07748 030306
CHARGES: £30 per day launch for skis, membership is available
SUITABILITY: Large trailer needs a car.
ACCESS: Unknown. **TYPE OF RAMP:** Concrete
UPPER AREA: Unknown. **LOWER AREA:** Unknown.
DIRECTIONS: Between Ely and Chatteris
RAMP DESCRIPTION: Concrete slip. Two lakes available one mainly for stand up skis and smaller PWCs. Other larger lake available for boats and PWCs on alternating weekends, very good size, ideal for wakeboarding and towing.
FACILITIES: Not much, unfortunately toilets have been vandalized. But this is a really good clean lake that is usually fairly quiet.

Cosgrove Marina, Milton Keynes
The Lock House, Lock Lane, Cosgrove, Milton Keynes, Bucks, England MK19 7JR
Lat. 52.0747, Long. -0.8422.
01908 562467

Milton Keynes Marina, Milton Keynes
Waterside, Peartree Bridge, Milton Keynes, Bucks, England MK6 3BX
Lat. 52.0277, Long. -0.7317.
01908 672672

Willowbridge Marina LTD, Milton Keynes
Stoke Road, Bletchley MK2 3JZ, Milton Keynes, Buckinghamshire England
Lat. 51.9759, Long. -0.7154.
01908 643242

Newark Marina, Newark
26 Farndon Road, Newark, Nottinghamshire, England NG24 4SD
Lat. 53.0711, Long. -0.8229.
01636 704022

Farndon Marina, Newark
Lat. 53.0624, Long. -0.8520.
Tel: (01636) 705483
CHARGES: £10/day to launch and recover, £2/day to park for additional days. A BWB permit for the day for a 5m boat is £5-40 which can be obtained from the marina.
SUITABILITY: Large trailer needs a car.
ACCESS: Non-tidal. **TYPE OF RAMP:** Wide concrete ramp
UPPER AREA: Concrete. **LOWER AREA:** Unknown.
DIRECTIONS: North End, Farndon, Newark, Notts, NG24 3SX.
RAMP DESCRIPTION: Very good ramp that gives access to the River Trent. One of the few slipways in the area.
FACILITIES: Toilets and shower block with laundrette, £5 plus a £30 deposit for the key. Restaurant barge nearby which is open at the weekend. Sling lift available for boats up to 20 tonnes by arrangement only. Pontoon available. Ski club operates upstream during set times only.

Farndon Marina, Newark-on-Trent
North End, Farndon, Newark-on-Trent, Nottinghamshire, England NG24 3SX
Lat. 53.0623, Long. -0.8529.
01636 705483

Billing Aquadrome Marina, Northampton
Billing Aquadrome, Gt Billing, Northampton, Northamptonshire, England NN3 9DA
Lat. 52.2450, Long. -0.8115.
01604 408181/01604 784948

Brooms, Norwich
Riverside, Brundall, Norwich, Norfolk, England NR13 5PX
Lat. 52.6195, Long. 1.4382.
01603 712334

Horning Ferry Marina, Norwich
Ferry Road, Horning, Norwich, Norfolk, England NR12 8PS
Lat. 52.6961, Long. 1.4683.
01692 630392

Bell Boats, Norwich
Waterside, Brundall, Norwich, Norfolk, England NR13 5PY
Lat. 52.6196, Long. 1.4360.
01603 713109

Cove Marina, Norwich
Riverside Estate Brundall, Norwich, Norfolk, England NR13 5PL
Lat. 52.6191, Long. 1.4387.
01603 713663

Brundall Bay Marina, Norwich
Brundall, Norwich, Norfolk, England NR13 5PN
Lat. 52.6148, Long. 1.4394.
01603 716606

Eastwood Marina, Norwich
Riverside Estate Brundall, Norwich, Norfolk, England NR13 5PT
Lat. 52.6191, Long. 1.4387.
01603 715573

Nottingham Castle Marina, Nottingham
Marina Road, Castle Marina Park, Nottingham, Nottinghamshire, England NG7 1TN
Lat. 52.9482, Long. -1.1545.
0115 941 2672

Gunthorpe Marina, Nottingham
Trentside, Gunthorpe, Nottingham, Nottinghamshire, England NG14 7FB
Lat. 52.9867, Long. -0.9825.
0115 966 4283

Beeston Marina, Nottingham
Riverside Road, Beeston, Nottingham, Notts, England NG9 1NA
Lat. 52.9131, Long. -1.2068.
0115 922 3168

Long Eaton Marina, Nottingham
Sheet Stores Ind Est, Long Eaton, Nottingham, Nottinghamshire, England NG10 1AU
Lat. 52.8844, Long. -1.2771.
0115 946 1752

Red Hill Marina, Nottingham
Red Hill Marine Limited, Ratcliffe On Soar, Nottingham, Notts, England NG11 0EB
Lat. 52.8676, Long. -1.2707.
01509 672770

The Ashby Canal Centre, Nuneaton
Willow Park Marina, Upton Lane, Stoke Golding, Nuneaton, Warwickshire, England CV13 6EU
Lat. 52.5714, Long. -1.4265.
01455 212636

Oulton Broad slip, Oulton Broad
Lat. 52.4711, Long. 1.7043.

CHARGES: Free (note you are required to pay a broads toll when using any park of the Broads. However if you wish to launch at this slip and go out to sea through Mutford lock, the £8 lock fee includes passage through Oulton Broad. If you get challenged explain you are using the lock).
SUITABILITY: Large trailer needs a car.
ACCESS: Non-tidal. **TYPE OF RAMP:** Ramp is well maintained and concrete. **UPPER AREA:** Concrete. **LOWER AREA:** Concrete.
DIRECTIONS: Follow signs to Oulton Broad. Slip is accessed through the pay and display carpark next to "Pets corner" - follow signs or ask a local for directions.
RAMP DESCRIPTION: Good slip for launching just about any sized trailer boat (although larger trailers will require skilled reversing). Very popular with sailers. Good for RIBs as you can go through Mutford lock into the North Sea (easier launching than Lake Lothing slip)
FACILITIES: Oulton Broad offers lots of facilities. Lavatories nearby. Slip is off a pay and display car park so plenty of car parking.
HAZARDS: This area is very popular with tourists, so watch out for drunken people who have no boating experience driving pleasure cruisers!

Bossom's Boatyard Slip, Oxford
Lat. 51.7639, Long. -1.2812.
SUITABILITY: Large trailer needs a car.
ACCESS: Non-tidal. **TYPE OF RAMP: UPPER AREA:** Unknown.
LOWER AREA: Unknown.
DIRECTIONS: On the right bank going downstream.
RAMP DESCRIPTION: Get permission to use the site.
FACILITIES: All boatyard facilities including slipway.
HAZARDS: ALL boats require a licence from the Environment Agency and 8kph speed limit.

2

2

Osney Mill Marina, Oxford
Osney Mill, Mill Street,, Oxford, Oxfordshire,
England OX2 0AN
Lat. 51.7495, Long. -1.2715.
01865 240480

Salter Bros Boatyard, Oxford
Lat. 51.7468, Long. -1.2699.
SUITABILITY: Large trailer needs a car.
ACCESS: Non-tidal. TYPE OF RAMP: UPPER AREA: Unknown.
LOWER AREA: Unknown.
DIRECTIONS: Salter Bros. boatyard at Folly Bridge. On the left bank
going downstream.
RAMP DESCRIPTION: Get permission to use the site. Slip inclined to be
obstructed by hire boats.
FACILITIES: Groceries and usual boatyard facilities.
HAZARDS: ALL boats require a licence from the Environment
Agency and 8kph speed limit.

Osney Marine Boatyard, Oxford
Lat. 51.7486, Long. -1.2699.
SUITABILITY: Large trailer needs a car.
ACCESS: Non-tidal. TYPE OF RAMP: Concrete UPPER AREA: Concrete.
LOWER AREA: Unknown.
DIRECTIONS: On the left bank going downstream. Osney Marine
boatyard just below Osney lock.
RAMP DESCRIPTION: Get permission to use the site. Slip sometimes
crowded with boats under repair.
HAZARDS: ALL boats require a licence from the Environment
Agency and 8kph speed limit.

Bossoms Boatyard, Oxford
Binsey Village, Oxford, Oxon, England OX2 0NL
Lat. 51.7639, Long. -1.2809.
01865 247780

Medley Beach, Oxford
Lat. 51.7639, Long. -1.2798.
SUITABILITY: Large trailer needs a car.
ACCESS: Non-tidal. TYPE OF RAMP: Sandy beach.
UPPER AREA: Unknown. LOWER AREA: Unknown.
DIRECTIONS: On the left bank going downstream. Above Medley Boat
Station. From Walton Well Road launch over sandy beach.
HAZARDS: ALL boats require a licence from the Environment
Agency and 8kph speed limit.

Oundle Marina, Peterborough
Barnwell Road, Oundle, Peterborough,
Cambridgeshire, England PE8 5PA
Lat. 52.4742, Long. -0.4734.
01832 272762

Fengate, Peterborough
Lat. 52.5657, Long. -0.2310.
CHARGES: None
SUITABILITY: Large trailer needs a car.
ACCESS: Non-tidal. TYPE OF RAMP: Concrete
UPPER AREA: Unknown. LOWER AREA: Unknown.
DIRECTIONS: From A 1139 southern ring road leave at intersection
for Fengate. Right at roundabout below, sign 'Eastern Industry'. Right
at mini roundabout, right at T junction, follow road down and take last
left turning.
RAMP DESCRIPTION: Good public slipway but there are reports of a lot
of break ins to the cars and trailers stolen from this site. It is a good idea
to remove your car and trailer after launching.
FACILITIES: Parking available close to the ramp and possible to park
overnight but not advisable. Gives access to River Nene. NRA licence
required.

Caribbean Cruisers Slip, Pinkhill
Lat. 51.7635, Long. -1.3581.
Caribbean Cruisers Ltd
SUITABILITY: Large trailer needs a car.
ACCESS: Non-tidal. TYPE OF RAMP: UPPER AREA: Unknown.
LOWER AREA: Unknown.
DIRECTIONS: Slip at Caribbean Cruisers Ltd.
RAMP DESCRIPTION: Get permission to use the site.
FACILITIES: All boatyard facilities.
HAZARDS: ALL boats require a licence from the Environment
Agency and 8kph speed limit.

Island Green, Radcot
Lat. 51.6935, Long. -1.5876.
SUITABILITY: Large trailer needs a car.
ACCESS: Non-tidal. TYPE OF RAMP: UPPER AREA: Unknown.
LOWER AREA: Unknown.
RAMP DESCRIPTION: Public slipway on the right bank going
downstream. Public green on island between the two bridges.
HAZARDS: ALL boats require a licence from the Environment
Agency and 8kph speed limit.

Redhill Marina slipway, Redhill
Lat. 52.8674, Long. -1.2694.
01509 672770
CHARGES: £6 minimum
SUITABILITY: Large trailer needs a car.
ACCESS: Non-tidal. TYPE OF RAMP: Concrete UPPER AREA: Concrete.
LOWER AREA: Concrete.
DIRECTIONS: Leave M1 at junction 24 - take A453 towards Nottingham
- turn left at Marina sign 3 miles up road. From Nottingham - take A453
towards M1 - turn left after power station (signposted to Kingston) - take
1st right (signposted to 'To the Church – no through road') - go under
main road and continue down long straight road. At end, turn right to
follow fence round into Marina. Ramp is through gate, approximately
200 yards on left hand side.
RAMP DESCRIPTION: May be occupied with marina boats.

FACILITIES: Parking and (crude) toilets.
HAZARDS: Only when the river is in flood - cruising is strongly discouraged (i.e. your insurance will be invalid) if you launch / cruise when the red traffic light is on at Redhill Lock.

Rutland Watersports, Rutland Water
Lat. 52.6627, Long. -0.6323.
Rutland Watersports 01780 460154

CHARGES: £9.00 per day or £14.00 per weekend.
SUITABILITY: Large trailer needs a car.
ACCESS: Non-tidal. **TYPE OF RAMP:** Concrete **UPPER AREA:** Concrete.
LOWER AREA: Shingle.
DIRECTIONS: Access from A606 Oakham to Stanford road. Turn left at Whitwell. The facilities are well signposted.
RAMP DESCRIPTION: On north shore of Rutland Water. Ramp is in good condition close to the sailing club. Pontoon near to the ramp.
FACILITIES: Ample facilities. Good parking and picnic area. Also restaurant on site. Large and active sailing club with sailing boats and canoes for hire. Good for children. 2,000 acres to explore and cheaper than Rutland SC on south shore. Very popular with windsurfers.
HAZARDS: No motor boats allowed.

Dobson's Boatyard, Shardlow
The Wharf, Shardlow, Derbyshire, England DE72 2GH
Lat. 52.8691, Long. -1.3440.
01332 792271

Rother Valley Country Park, Sheffield
Lat. 53.3384, Long. -1.3207.
0114 2471453

CHARGES: £7.00. There is a charge for "Engine Testing" for powerboats of £8.50. You will need to register as this gets you a card that allows your car into the park free of charge. This can be a useful facility. To register you will need insurance and two forms of ID plus £8.50 for the first session.
SUITABILITY: Small trailer can be pushed.
ACCESS: Non-tidal. **TYPE OF RAMP:** Concrete **UPPER AREA:** Concrete.
LOWER AREA: Concrete.
DIRECTIONS: Well signposted from about 4 miles away. Slip is part of watersports centre, adjacent to car park.
RAMP DESCRIPTION: Very easy and very safe.
FACILITIES: Café, toilets, changing rooms, showers, mooring pontoons, safety boats, parking, picnic tables, hire of buoyancy aids/kayaks/windsurfers/dinghies. Powerboats are not allowed on the lake while sailboats/dinghies/kayaks are about. There is a very useful facility for "Engine Testing" of powerboats if, like me, you live locally. You must arrive before 9.00a.m. and launch immediately at 9.00. There is a half hour session allowed which gives you time to adjust trim, balance and engine speeds with no speed limit on the lake. At 9.30a.m. you are required to recover your boat. In practice, if there is no-one else yet out on the lake or preparing to launch a yacht, then a blind eye may be turned to a further period. The staff are very friendly and helpful and, perhaps reassuringly for first-timers like myself, keep an eye on all the

lake from their control office. Any problems and they will recover you with one of their RIBs, and a wry smile. This is an excellent way of trying out a boat for the first time. The lake closes at the end of November and opens again at the beginning of March. All boating qualifications (Inland Waters) can be taken there at reasonable times and rates. This is a very safe place to start.
HAZARDS: Water ski area at southern end. Rocks spreading into the water adjacent to the small island. Hundreds of geese during migration which can leave the jetties very slippery (almost a broken hip one day!)

2

Calcutt Marina, Southam
Tomlow Road, Stockton, Southam, Warwickshire, England CV47 8HX
Lat. 52.2678, Long. -1.3178.
01926 813757

Napton Marina, Southam
Tomlow Road, Stockton, Southam, Warwickshire, England CV47 8HX
Lat. 52.2676, Long. -1.3178.
01926 813644

LH Jones and Son, St Ives
The Boathaven Low Road, St Ives, Cambridgeshire, United Kingdom PE27 5ET
Lat. 52.3169, Long. -0.0774.
01480 494040

St Neots Marina, St Neots
South Street, Eynesbury, St Neots, Cambs, England PE19 2BW
Lat. 52.2269, Long. -0.2694.
01480 472411

Crosshall Marine, St Neots
Crosshall Road, St Neots, Cambridgeshire, England PE19 7GE
Lat. 52.2332, Long. -0.2758.
01480 472763

Slipway, St. Neots
Lat. 52.2295, Long. -0.2726.

CHARGES: None
SUITABILITY: Large trailer needs a car.
ACCESS: Non-tidal. **TYPE OF RAMP: UPPER AREA:** Concrete.
LOWER AREA: Concrete.
DIRECTIONS: Would advise approaching from the A1 at Paxton (B1041). Follow 1041 for approx 1/4 mile then turn left into mill lane. Follow this road over the hump backed bridges and straight through the traffic lights. You should now be crossing the common. Carry on to the next traffic lights where you need to turn right into Tan Yard. Pass the car parks on both sides then turn left after approx 100yds. The slipway is now directly in front of you through the gate.

The Good Launch Guide

RAMP DESCRIPTION: Suitable for boats up to approx 20ft. Access through a car park which is not usually a problem. But local rowing club do like to try to claim this public slipway sometimes. Pay and display car park very nearby.
FACILITIES: Supermarket 2 min walk (you've just driven past it!!) nearest petrol is Cambridge Street. A few pubs in town. There is a pub on the river. Once you've launched turn left and there it is. Or carry on for a mile or so to the next lock and there is another. You pass a marina heading that way which does have a small shop. Opening hours seem to be random.

Russellcroft LLP, St. Neots
Rivermill Marina, School Lane, Eaton Socon, St. Neots, Cambs, England PE19 8GW
Lat. 52.2146, Long. -0.2837.
01480 473456

Richardsons Boat Yard, Stalham
Lat. 52.7669, Long. 1.5132.
Richardsons Cruisers 01692 581081

CHARGES: Yes
SUITABILITY: Large trailer needs a car.
ACCESS: Non-tidal. **TYPE OF RAMP:** Concrete
UPPER AREA: Unknown. **LOWER AREA:** Unknown.
DIRECTIONS: Richardson's Cruisers, Staithe Road, Stalham, Norfolk.
RAMP DESCRIPTION: Excellent slipway. Gives access to north Norfolk Broads - a licence needed. Always ring before using, they are not open at weekends during the winter.
FACILITIES: Good car and trailer parking facilities. This is a large cruiser hire operation. They also have a shop, café and showers and toilets.

Tallington Lakes, Stamford
Lat. 52.6707, Long. -0.3784.
Matt Marchant 01778 346573. Main office 01778 347000

CHARGES: Contact Tallington Lakes for full details.
SUITABILITY: Large trailer needs a car.
ACCESS: Non-tidal. **TYPE OF RAMP: UPPER AREA:** Unknown.
LOWER AREA: Unknown.
DIRECTIONS: Situated off the A16 between Stamford and Market Deeping.
RAMP DESCRIPTION: Operates April to October, 10am until dusk. Minimum insurance cover of £1,000,000 for all ski boats launched. A copy of your insurance certificate must be lodged before entering the water. All boat drivers must hold an SBDA Boat Driving Certificate.
FACILITIES: 160 acres of naturally spring fed, clean, clear water - ideal for watersports enthusiasts. Water-skiing on the finest lakes in the UK. Exclusive Jetskiing and sailing lakes, all with comprehensive facilities. Centrally heated toilets and showers. Convenient parking. Discount on day launching if hiring a static caravan from Tallington Lakes. Full range of refreshments from the Lakeside Bar and restaurant. Boat workshop facilities for repairs and servicing. On site engineer. Boat gas refills. Recognised service agent for Correct Craft Ski Nautique.

Lee Valley Marina, Stanstead Abbots
Lat. 51.7863, Long. 0.0047.
01920 870 499

CHARGES: £ 9.50 per day.
SUITABILITY: Large trailer needs a car.
ACCESS: Non-tidal. **TYPE OF RAMP: UPPER AREA:** Unknown.
LOWER AREA: Unknown.
DIRECTIONS: A414 St Margaret's High Street – South Street. On the upper reaches of the River Lea, Stanstead Abbotts Marina is a convenient base for cruising the rural stretches of the River Lea and Stort.
FACILITIES: Mains water supply, electric point (240v) Elsan toilet disposal, toilets and showers, battery charging, boat repair, facilities, diesel, boat sales, pump-out, inboard and outboard repairs and servicing. Nationwide boat transport up to 3 tonnes.

Slipway, Stratford St Mary
Lat. 51.9625, Long. 0.9733.

CHARGES: None
SUITABILITY: Portable Only.
ACCESS: Non-tidal. **TYPE OF RAMP:** Mud and grass. Watch out for the stinging nettles and you go through the gate. **UPPER AREA:** Mud.
LOWER AREA: Mud.
DIRECTIONS: Park on The Street to the West of the A12. There is a small parking bay for 3 or 4 cars, dont block the gates though. Walk through the gate, under the road bridge underpass of the A12 and through the other gate (about 20 yards in total) and the river is right there in your right as you enter the field.
RAMP DESCRIPTION: The river bank is sloped and easy to launch a canoe, kayak or dinghy.
FACILITIES: Pub nearby

Welford Boat Station, Stratford-Upon-Avon
Welford Boat Station, Binton Rd, Welford On Avon, Stratford-Upon-Avon, Warwickshire, England CV37 8PP
Lat. 52.1738, Long. -1.7930.
01789 750878

Sutton Staithe, Sutton
Lat. 52.7585, Long. 1.5286.
01692 581653

CHARGES: £10 for in and out
SUITABILITY: Large trailer needs a car.
ACCESS: Non-tidal. **TYPE OF RAMP:** Quite shallow fully enclosed concrete slipway. Ideal for Wilderness Beaver, may not be enough depth for large boat with a keel **UPPER AREA:** Shingle.
LOWER AREA: Concrete.
RAMP DESCRIPTION: A very good, fully enclosed gently sloping slipway, although approach involves a simple reverse 90 degree turn. Owned by Sutton Parish, there is a charge payable at boatyard alongside.
FACILITIES: Water alongside - small charge. Designated free parking for trailer with space for car available in public car park alongside. Although not secure it seems a safe area to leave car and trailer for a week.

L R Harris & Son, Syston
Old Junction Boatyard, Meadow Lane, Syston, Leics, England LE7 1NR
Lat. 52.7032, Long. -1.1013.
08456 123350

Old Junction Boatyard, Syston
Lat. 52.7028, Long. -1.1009.
Tel 0116 2692135

CHARGES: Depends on boat size
SUITABILITY: Large trailer needs a car.
ACCESS: Non-tidal. **TYPE OF RAMP:** Concrete slipway.
UPPER AREA: Concrete. **LOWER AREA:** Harbour.
DIRECTIONS: On the Grand Union Canal / River Soar Navigation in Leicestershire. L R Harris & Son, Old Junction Boatyard, Meadow Lane, Syston, Leicester, LE7 1NR.
FACILITIES: Chandlery shop. Both long term and temporary moorings are available. Slipway charges vary according to boat length, assisted launch is available, free parking to all who launch. Marina, diesel available.

Fazeley Mill Marina, Tamworth
Coleshill Rd, Fazeley, Tamworth, Staffordshire, England B78 3SE
Lat. 52.6100, Long. -1.7026.
01827 261138

Alvecote Marina, Tamworth
Robeys Lane, Alvecote, Tamworth, Staffordshire, England B78 1AS
Lat. 52.6357, Long. -1.6329.
01827 898652

Slipway, The Britannia Pub
Lat. 53.0604, Long. -0.8550.

CHARGES: £3.50 for launch and car parking. Pay the person behind the bar at The Britannia to obtain the key for the barrier. Please return key immediately once launched.
SUITABILITY: Small trailer can be pushed.
ACCESS: Non-tidal. **TYPE OF RAMP:** Gentle slope. Concrete non-tidal onto sandy river bed. **UPPER AREA:** Concrete. **LOWER AREA:** Sand.
DIRECTIONS: From Newark, take the A46 towards Nottingham for around three miles. Ignore the sign for the Newark Marina and take the next right. There is a sign with a boat on pointing in that direction. Follow the road around to the right until you arrive at the car park of The Britannia pub. The car park is free.
RAMP DESCRIPTION: The slip is concrete until it meets the waters edge. From there it is sandy. The key to the barrier is obtainable from the bar in the pub and costs £3.50 per launch/recovery (Car and trailer parking is free). There are small rocks on one side of the ramp and in the water that can make launch/recovery difficult in windy conditions. There is a small pontoon to the right about ten yards away. Between that and the slip there is an awkward metal construction that prevents you from 'leading' the boat around to the docking area by rope.

FACILITIES: Free car and trailer parking. Nice pub with lunchtime only food.
HAZARDS: Rocks alongside slip that could be easily moved if anyone cared enough. Water-skiing 100yards upstream. Speed limits elsewhere (as usual). Lots of anglers. A large but well-signposted weir about a mile upstream. Follow outer curves on river as the depth is very variable close to the inner bank.

2

Parish Staithe, Thurne
Lat. 52.6879, Long. 1.5520.

CHARGES: Donations to upkeep requested.
SUITABILITY: Small trailer can be pushed.
ACCESS: All of tidal range. **TYPE OF RAMP:** Concrete
UPPER AREA: Concrete. **LOWER AREA:** Concrete.
DIRECTIONS: Take the A149 from Great Yarmouth northwards. In the village Repps with Bastwick, look for signs to the left to Thurne. Follow the (narrow, twisting) lanes to the village. The Staithe is at the head of the dyke opposite the Lion pub.
RAMP DESCRIPTION: Parish staithe. Stated as suitable for boats up to 5 m and draught of about 0.5 m depending on tide (range here about 0.5 m).
FACILITIES: Pub with restaurant and showers. Public WC. Limited parking.
HAZARDS: Moored boats.

Slipway, Thurne
Lat. 52.6872, Long. 1.5534.

CHARGES: There in a box on the slipway where a contribution can be left.
SUITABILITY: Small trailer can be pushed.
ACCESS: All of tidal range. **TYPE OF RAMP:** Concrete
UPPER AREA: Concrete. **LOWER AREA:** Concrete.
DIRECTIONS: Opposite the pub in the village
RAMP DESCRIPTION: Small concrete slipway. Sign says max boat length 5 meters.
FACILITIES: Parking at the end on the staithe. Pub opposite.

Cowroast Marina, Tring
Cowroast, Tring, Herts, England HP23 5RE
Lat. 51.7834, Long. -0.6122.
01442 823222

Harefield Marina, Uxbridge
Moorhall Road, Harefield, Uxbridge, Middlesex, England UB9 6PD
Lat. 51.5840, Long. -0.4837.
01895 822036

Wallingford Marina, Wallingford
Lat. 51.5965, Long. -1.1236.
SUITABILITY: Large trailer needs a car.
ACCESS: Non-tidal. **TYPE OF RAMP: UPPER AREA:** Unknown.
LOWER AREA: Unknown.
DIRECTIONS: On the right bank going downstream.

RAMP DESCRIPTION: Public slipway. Wallingford Marina next to lane.
FACILITIES: Slip and boatyard facilities.
HAZARDS: ALL boats require a licence from the Environment Agency and 8kph speed limit.

Benson Waterfront, Wallingford
Benson, Wallingford, Oxon, England OX10 6SJ
Lat. 51.6200, Long. -1.1155.
01491 838304

Lee Valley Marina (Stnstd Abt), Ware
South Street, Stanstead Abbotts, Ware, Herts, England SG12 8AL
Lat. 51.7868, Long. 0.0056.
01920 870499

Car Park Slip, Wolvercote
Lat. 51.7811, Long. -1.2955.
SUITABILITY: Small trailer can be pushed.
ACCESS: Non-tidal. **TYPE OF RAMP: UPPER AREA:** Unknown.
LOWER AREA: Unknown.
RAMP DESCRIPTION: On the left bank going downstream. Over bank from car park into shallow backwater. Public toilets.
HAZARDS: ALL boats require a licence from the Environment Agency and 8kph speed limit.

Landamores, Wroxham
Lat. 52.7091, Long. 1.4122.
01603 782212

CHARGES: £6-£10
SUITABILITY: Large trailer needs a car.
ACCESS: Non-tidal. **TYPE OF RAMP:** Concrete **UPPER AREA:** Concrete.
LOWER AREA: Concrete.
DIRECTIONS: From centre of Wroxham(Hoveton) turn down side of Roys; Church Rd, 1st right down side of Norfolk Marine Chandlers; Marsh Rd, as road turns sharp left car park is in front of you.
RAMP DESCRIPTION: The slipway is available at any time, preferably in working hours as the site is manned then. At end of Dyke with very strict 4mph speed limit, leads into River Bure and Norfolk Broads.
FACILITIES: Car park when out of hours, very good chandlers at end of road, toilets, McDonalds, shops, phone 1/4mile. Car & trailer parking is available.
HAZARDS: Slip and car park locked so phone first. Broads licence required, 4mph limit.

Moore and Co, Wroxham
Lat. 52.7089, Long. 1.4079.
01603 783311

CHARGES: £12 in and £12 out.
SUITABILITY: Large trailer needs a car.
ACCESS: ¾ tidal. **TYPE OF RAMP:** Concrete **UPPER AREA:** Unknown.
LOWER AREA: Unknown.
DIRECTIONS: The boat yard is situated at the end of Staithway Road in the village of Wroxham.

RAMP DESCRIPTION: Must be booked ahead and no launching or recovery is possible on a Saturday as the yard is very busy with holiday changeovers.
FACILITIES: Parking for car and trailer. £12/week for car and £12/week for trailer. £6 for less than a week. Boating gas available and wash down facilities.

Wroxham Broad Slip, Wroxham
Lat. 52.6976, Long. 1.4139.

CHARGES: Parking charges.
SUITABILITY: Large trailer needs a car.
ACCESS: Non-tidal. **TYPE OF RAMP:** Hard shingle.
UPPER AREA: Shingle. **LOWER AREA:** Shingle.
DIRECTIONS: Norfolk Broads Yacht Club, The Avenue, Wroxham, Norfolk.
RAMP DESCRIPTION: Shingle slipway into the Broads. Bottom of the slipway is muddy which may cause problems for larger boats due to the now silted up margins in this part of the Broad. Water depth is only 18 inches, 20ft. out and the bottom is now soft mud. A 4-WD is necessary for anything larger than a dinghy. Land belongs to Norfolk Broads Yacht Club and road leads on into club pound. Slip is a public right of way. A nice spot to launch and recover. Norfolk Broads Yacht Club welcomes visiting sailors and has a nice bar and changing rooms with showers and WC. Wroxham Broad is a larger broad with good sailing and club racing.
FACILITIES: Parking charges- £5 per day pay and display. Overnight parking available.

3

South East England

Burnham on Crouch to Poole

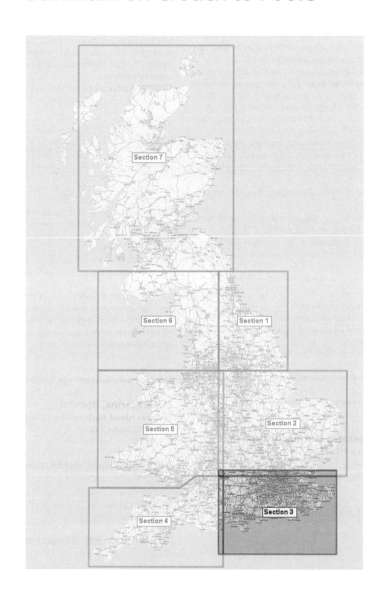

COASTAL SLIPWAYS
clockwise around the coast

Marina Slip, Burnham on Crouch
Lat. 51.6292, Long. 0.8025.
01621 782150

CHARGES: £10/day
SUITABILITY: Large trailer needs a car.
ACCESS: All of tidal range. **TYPE OF RAMP:** Wide concrete
UPPER AREA: Concrete. **LOWER AREA:** Mud.
DIRECTIONS: Drive in to Burnham on Crouch over the railway bridge. Immediately turn right (at Co-op) and follow road down to marina which is signposted. Ramp is in front of the main buildings.
RAMP DESCRIPTION: An easy comfortable launch on an excellent wide slipway. Open 24 hours. The bottom of the slipway can get muddy at very low tide but still usable. There is a restriction on launching speedboats but, ribs are exempt from the restriction. Check with the marina office before travelling if in doubt. Will need to pay Crouch Harbour Authority dues, can be paid in the marina office.
FACILITIES: Petrol, pub, good restaurant, toilets and changing rooms. Park close to slip or on raised car park at side of entrance drive. Slip water tap close by. Overnight berths available and a hoist for larger boats.

Burnham Yacht Harbour, Burnham-on-Crouch
Burnham Yacht Harbour Marina Ltd, Burnham-on-Crouch, Essex, England CM0 8BL
Lat. 51.6296, Long. 0.8029.
01621 782150, HM 01621 786832

Creeksea SC, Burnham-on-Crouch
Lat. 51.6281, Long. 0.7889.

CHARGES: For use by members only.
SUITABILITY: Small trailer can be pushed.
ACCESS: ½ tidal. **TYPE OF RAMP:** Rough concrete. **UPPER AREA:** Mud.
LOWER AREA: Mud.
DIRECTIONS: West of Burnham-on-Crouch, follow the sign to Creeksea.
RAMP DESCRIPTION: The slipway is for use by members only and the slipway can not be accessed from the public road. Membership details and fees are on the website www.creeksea.org.uk. Fees are very modest and the club welcomes new member enquiries.
FACILITIES: Parking and clubhouse.

Bridgemarsh Marine, Althorne
Bridgemarsh Lane, Althorne, Essex, England CM3 6DQ
Lat. 51.6453, Long. 0.7512.
01621 740414

Fambridge Yacht Haven, Chelmsford
Church Rd, North Fambridge, Chelmsford, Essex, England CM3 6LR
Lat. 51.6431, Long. 0.6725.
01621 740370

Slipway, South Woodham Ferrers
Lat. 51.6310, Long. 0.6129.
Waterski Club 07940 519450. Crouch Harbour 01621 783602

CHARGES: None
SUITABILITY: Large trailer needs a car.
ACCESS: ½ tidal. **TYPE OF RAMP:** Mud and rocks (bumpy).
UPPER AREA: Shingle. **LOWER AREA:** Mud.
DIRECTIONS: From South Woodham Ferrers, follow the directions to Marsh Farm and then carry on towards the river. Ramp is at the old river ford.
RAMP DESCRIPTION: There is a public slipway and one that belongs to the waterski club. The public one is bumpy and muddy and in a poor state of repair. It is also shallow in places and runs at an angle to the river bank. The Ski club has a wide concrete ramp with a good gradient. Available to members only.
FACILITIES: Public car park next to the ramp. Neighbouring waterski club has club house and storage facilities.

The Ford, Hullbridge
Lat. 51.6296, Long. 0.6136.
River Crouch Harbour Authority, 01621 783602 9.30-11.30.

CHARGES: None
SUITABILITY: Large trailer needs a car.
ACCESS: ¼ tidal. **TYPE OF RAMP:** Concrete onto shingle.
UPPER AREA: Concrete. **LOWER AREA:** Mud.
DIRECTIONS: Either by A127 or A12 head for Wickford (Essex) junction on A130. Follow signs for Battlesbridge, then onto Hullbridge. Hullbridge town is quite small, turn left at the mini roundabout and follow road - this will lead onto the slipway.
RAMP DESCRIPTION: The ramp is where the ford used to go into the river. It is narrow and has a long reverse down the narrow road leading onto the slipway.
FACILITIES: Anchor Pub overlooking ramp, with garden down to river bank. At high tide it is possible to moore up alongside the riverbank (wall) at the end of the pub garden. Ideal for a swift half and there is parking nearby. Also various boatyards and yacht clubs. The ramp is opposite the Woodham Ferres Waterski Club.
HAZARDS: Situated in the middle of a trot of moorings, 8 knots speed limit until you reach the ski area. Skiing only permitted if you're a member of Burnham-on-Crouch ski club.

Essex Marina, Rochford
Wallasea Island, Rochford, Essex, England SS4 2HF
Lat. 51.6217, Long. 0.7962.
01702 258531

Paglesham Hard, Paglesham
Lat. 51.5942, Long. 0.8107.
Paglesham Boatyard 01702 258885

CHARGES: £10.00 payable to Paglesham Boatyard.
SUITABILITY: Large trailer needs a car.
ACCESS: All of tidal range. **TYPE OF RAMP:** Wide concrete hard, gently sloping to water. **UPPER AREA:** Mud. **LOWER AREA:** Mud.

3

DIRECTIONS: Paglesham is a village a few miles from Rochford which is a small town to the north of Southend on Sea, Essex. On approaching Paglesham take the turning to 'East End', not 'Church End'. Continue to the end of the lane where there is a pub, the Plough and Sail, on the left. Take an unmade track to the left of the pub which leads down to the Paglesham Boatyard where the hard is.

RAMP DESCRIPTION: Good wide gentle sloping concrete ramp. Lower extremity of ramp tails off into mud at extreme low Spring tide but slip is usable by very large trailers at all other tide states. Boat yard has tractor and cranes for launching heavy boats. Jetskis can launch here.

FACILITIES: Boatyard with large car park. (Check with boatyard office in Portacabin to left of slip before launching). One toilet in small cubicle somewhere in boatyard. A café based in a caravan in the boatyard operates most weekends in the summer. Pub is Plough and Sail a few hundred yards up the lane.

East Beach, Shoeburyness
Lat. 51.5315, Long. 0.8028.

CHARGES: £10.30 power, £5.40 sailing.
SUITABILITY: Large trailer needs a car.
ACCESS: ½ tidal. **TYPE OF RAMP:** Concrete **UPPER AREA:** Sand.
LOWER AREA: Sand.
DIRECTIONS: East Beach is east of the railway station between the two MoD properties.
RAMP DESCRIPTION: Concrete ramp over sand. Plenty of car parking, café, toilets. Fresh water tap on the slipway. Warden on site during summer months to collect fees and check insurance. Rough in an onshore wind, popular with windsurfers. No Jetskis, go to Thorpe Bay Marine.
FACILITIES: Annual permits available, £101.50 power and £57.20 sailing.

Slipway, Ness Road
Lat. 51.5236, Long. 0.7762.

CHARGES: £121.00 per season ticket, £96.00 for SWC member, £15.00 day launch.
SUITABILITY: Large trailer needs a car.
ACCESS: All of tidal range. **TYPE OF RAMP:** Public access
UPPER AREA: Concrete. **LOWER AREA:** Shingle.
DIRECTIONS: Go along Southend seafront past Thorpebay Marine, you will come to Uncle Tom's Cabin; ramp is just past there on the right.
RAMP DESCRIPTION: Concrete ramp going into sand/shingle. 4 × 4 needed or car with long tow rope to pull out.
FACILITIES: Uncle Tom's Cabin 50yards away for light refreshments.

Thorpe Bay Marine, Southend-on-Sea
Lat. 51.5302, Long. 0.7450.
01702 588065

CHARGES: £10/day, £100/year.
SUITABILITY: Large trailer needs a car.
ACCESS: ¼ tidal. **TYPE OF RAMP:** Concrete **UPPER AREA:** Sand.
LOWER AREA: Sand.
DIRECTIONS: On the Seafront at Southend-on-Sea at the junction of Eastern Esplanade and Plas Newydd.

RAMP DESCRIPTION: Concrete ramp leads onto firm sand. Possible to launch from the beach 3 hours either side of high tide. Below this the sand is too shallow and sea is half a mile away. Jetskis and speed boats are welcome. Proof of insurance will be required. Can get busy on sunny weekends, but usually okay.
FACILITIES: Car park with public toilets and café nearby. Thorpe Bay Marine showroom and workshop half mile away. Next to family beach.
HAZARDS: 8 knot speed restriction within 200 metres of the shore.

Leigh Marina, Leigh
Lat. 51.5406, Long. 0.6421.
01702 479009

CHARGES: Launching fee for small craft is £4.00 each way. For larger craft requiring the assistance of the marina please contact Steve Frasle.
SUITABILITY: Small trailer can be pushed.
ACCESS: ¼ tidal. **TYPE OF RAMP: UPPER AREA:** Concrete.
LOWER AREA: Concrete.
DIRECTIONS: Follow directions to Leigh on Sea Train station. The Marina is 50 yards away from the station over the railway bridge and on the left.
RAMP DESCRIPTION: Large concrete slipway with an easy gradient to the water. Launching possible 2 hours either side of high water into a sheltered bay.
FACILITIES: There are washrooms and toilets in the yards, electricity and water can be provided to the slipway. Cranes and travel hoists are available for larger craft.
HAZARDS: Narrow channel into the marina, clearly marked with unlit markers.

Slipway, Two Tree Island
Lat. 51.5312, Long. 0.6261.
Foreshore office 01702 611889

CHARGES: £10.30 power, £5.40 sailing.
SUITABILITY: Large trailer needs a car.
ACCESS: ¾ tidal. **TYPE OF RAMP:** Concrete **UPPER AREA:** Concrete.
LOWER AREA: Mud.
DIRECTIONS: Follow A13 to Leigh-on-Sea. Go to Leigh Station. Follow road behind station for 1½ miles to slipway and car park.
RAMP DESCRIPTION: Warden on site during summer months to collect fees, must show valid insurance certificate. Slipway is prone to silting but it is used by the council boat and regularly cleaned. Slippery when wet. No Jetskis.
FACILITIES: Ample free parking and fresh water tap on site. Remote location. Lockers for rent, phone council. Annual permits available, £101.50 power and £57.20 sailing.
HAZARDS: Have to follow Ray Gutway (east to west running) except during high tide due to sandbanks.

Halcon Marine, Canvey Island
The Point, Canvey Island, Essex, England SS8 7TL
Lat. 51.5194, Long. 0.6219.
01268 511611

3

Slipway, Watt Tyler Country Park

Lat. 51.5458, Long. 0.5016.

44 (0) 1268 559833

CHARGES: £12.50 for a ski or £150 per years pass which includes a key to Country park gates and car park for slip way. This allows early mornings and late evenings when Country Park is closed.
SUITABILITY: Large trailer needs a car.
ACCESS: ¾ tidal. **TYPE OF RAMP:** Concrete ramp
UPPER AREA: Concrete. **LOWER AREA:** Concrete.
RAMP DESCRIPTION: Concrete ramp, tidal usable 2½ hours either side of high tide
FACILITIES: Part of a country park. Secure gated parking, hose to wash down. There is a café also available but it is a short walk.
HAZARDS: Mud banks at low tides.

Gallion's Point Marina, North Woolwich

Gate 14, Royal Docks, Royal Albert Basin, Woolwich Manor Way, North Woolwich, London, England E16 2QY

Lat. 51.5045, Long. 0.0755.

0207 476 7054

King George V Dock, London

Lat. 51.5040, Long. 0.0699.

020 7511 7000

CHARGES: £250 annual fee
SUITABILITY: Small trailer can be pushed.
ACCESS: Non-tidal. **TYPE OF RAMP:** Small crane into dock
UPPER AREA: Harbour. **LOWER AREA:** Harbour.
DIRECTIONS: Situated at the eastern end of George V Dock. Access the facility by turning east off Woolwich Manor Way and then take the first left. Follow the road underneath the main road and you will eventually reach the floating barge and car park.
RAMP DESCRIPTION: Small crane into a dedicated Jetski area. Waterskiing takes place at the other end of the dock.
FACILITIES: Floating barge has a bar and showers and changing facilities, car park. The club is open every day except Monday and Tuesday during the summer from 10am until dusk. From October to 31st March the club is closed Monday, Tuesday and Wednesday. Possible to hire Jetskis and tuition is available. Full membership is £450 for solo, £550 for two seater, £650 for three seater, and family membership is £750 per year. Launch membership is £250 plus £15 per launch for a solo, £300 plus £15 for a two seater and £375 plus £20 for a three seater.
HAZARDS: Stay within the buoyed area.

Bargehouse Causeway, London

Lat. 51.4996, Long. 0.0699.

PLA 020 7743 7900

CHARGES: None
SUITABILITY: Large trailer needs a car.
ACCESS: ¾ tidal. **TYPE OF RAMP:** Concrete. For trailered RIBs greater than 4.8m, suggest only usable at slack high tide. 4 × 4 highly desirable.
UPPER AREA: Concrete. **LOWER AREA:** Concrete.

DIRECTIONS: From the Junction of the A13 and the A406, follow the signs to the Woolwich Ferry. Barge House Road is about 400 metres after crossing the docks.
RAMP DESCRIPTION: The ramp is below the Thames Barrier so it has to thread its way over a flood defence before you get to the river. Some tricky turns to negotiate. Ramp starts off steep, and then shallows right out.
FACILITIES: Parking for car a trailer can be difficult. Gallions Point Marina is close (downstream). May be possible to park car / trailer there, or lock in (high tide +/- 5 hours) to stop overnight.
HAZARDS: Strong tidal currents.

Poplar Dock Marina, London

c/o Harbourmasters Office 46 Goodhart Place, London, London, England E14 8EG

Lat. 51.5055, Long. -0.0084.

020 7308 9930

Amsterdam Road, London

Lat. 51.4956, Long. -0.0062.

PLA 020 7743 7900

CHARGES: None
SUITABILITY: Large trailer needs a car.
ACCESS: ¼ tidal. **TYPE OF RAMP:** Concrete onto mud.
UPPER AREA: Shingle. **LOWER AREA:** Mud.
DIRECTIONS: On the east side of the Isle of Dogs, from Manchester Road turn onto Amsterdam Road past the shops and flats to the river.
RAMP DESCRIPTION: March 2008. Deep shingle at top of ramp. The top section of the ramp gets covered in shingle and general debris from the river. You will need a four wheel drive to pull a trailer up through the shingle or a shovel to do some clearing. If you have to recover at low tide DO NOT attempt to drive onto the mud below the ramp. It is very soft. From the ramp you can drive south along the shingle and find a firm path down to the river upstream of the ramp. For 4 wheel drive only and not for the faint hearted. Beware of numerous obstacles.
FACILITIES: There is good parking for car and trailer. There are warnings of wheel clamping in the area, but I have yet to see any activity.
HAZARDS: Below ramp is shallow shelving mud that may have shopping trolleys and other hazards. Big tidal range and fast currents when the tide is running.

Johnson Drawdock, London

Lat. 51.4863, Long. -0.0100.

PLA 020 7743 7900

CHARGES: None
SUITABILITY: Large trailer needs a car.
ACCESS: All of tidal range. **TYPE OF RAMP:** Concrete
UPPER AREA: Harbour. **LOWER AREA:** Mud.
DIRECTIONS: Ramp is located on the Southern tip of the Isle of Dogs, London.
RAMP DESCRIPTION: Long and narrow. The advantage of this ramp is that it has a full tidal range. The ramp is shared with the rowing club. The lower parts of the ramp get covered with a thin layer of silt and mud but not too bad due to the flow of the Thames. Do not attempt to beach your boat upstream of the ramp as there are several nasty boulders that will

3

damage your gel coat. Downstream of the ramp, i.e. opposite the Poplar Rowing club house should be okay. Probably the best access point for the lower part of the Thames.

FACILITIES: There are plenty of residents parking that is available at the weekend, but the site can get restricted especially in the summer.

HAZARDS: Strong currents in the river especially on the ebb tide. Best to launch and recover around slack tide. Usual shopping trolleys to be avoided.

Millwall Dock Slipway, London
Lat. 51.4939, Long. -0.0256.
PLA 020 7743 7900

CHARGES: None
SUITABILITY: Large trailer needs a car.
ACCESS: ½ tidal. **TYPE OF RAMP:** Wide concrete
UPPER AREA: Harbour. **LOWER AREA:** Mud.
DIRECTIONS: Ramp is on the west side of the Isle of Dogs. From the Limehouse Link, follow the signs for the Isle of Dogs. Follow the road that takes you along the river and the ramp is half mile south of the roundabout with the multi-traffic lights sculpture.
RAMP DESCRIPTION: A wide ramp with a shallow gradient. Tends to get clogged up with a lot of river debris making it unusable and very smelly in spite of regular cleaning by British Waterways. However when clear the ramp is fine and there are plans to put in a boom to stop debris getting onto the ramp. Used by the Docklands Sailing Centre tel: 020 7537 2626.
FACILITIES: Some parking nearby but often gets parked up.
HAZARDS: Debris in the river and traffic.

Limehouse Marina, Limehouse Marina
BWML, The Harbourmaster's Office, 46 Goodhart Place, Limehouse Marina, London, England E14 8EG
Lat. 51.5111, Long. -0.0354.
020 7308 9930

St Katharine Marina, London
50 St Katharine's Way, London, London, England E1W 1LA
Lat. 51.5071, Long. -0.0695.
020 7264 5312

Chelsea Harbour, London
Chelsea Harbour Ltd, C2-3 The Chambers, London, London, England SW10 0XF
Lat. 51.4753, Long. -0.1811.
0207 225 9100

Hammersmith Bridge, London
Lat. 51.4890, Long. -0.2284.
PLA 020 7743 7900

CHARGES: None
SUITABILITY: Small trailer can be pushed.

ACCESS: ¼ tidal. **TYPE OF RAMP:** Short concrete.
UPPER AREA: Shingle. **LOWER AREA:** Shingle.
DIRECTIONS: Adjacent to Queen's Wharf just downstream from Hammersmith Bridge on the north bank.
RAMP DESCRIPTION: Slipway is clogged up with debris and rubbish. Very smelly and there is a wooden anti flood barrier at the top of the ramp. Not recommended.
FACILITIES: No parking and difficult access.

Chiswick Mall, London
Lat. 51.4873, Long. -0.2477.

CHARGES: None
SUITABILITY: Small trailer can be pushed.
ACCESS: ¼ tidal. **TYPE OF RAMP:** Cobbled road ramp.
UPPER AREA: Concrete. **LOWER AREA:** Shingle.
DIRECTIONS: On the Chiswick Mall upstream of Hammersmith Bridge. Travelling west on the A4 turn left before the Fullers Brewery into Eyot Gardens. Narrow roads.
RAMP DESCRIPTION: Public access. Chiswick Mall floods often so don't leave your car on it. Can't use it below ½ tide because mud flat channel between ramp and Chiswick Eyot becomes exposed. Ramp leads onto shallow shingle bank, suitable for small boats only.
FACILITIES: Various pubs along River bank, nearest is ¼ mile.
HAZARDS: Strong currents. Try to launch and recover around slack tide. 8 knot speed limit.

Chiswick Church Drawdock, London
Lat. 51.4858, Long. -0.2497.
PLA 020 7743 7900

CHARGES: None
SUITABILITY: Small trailer can be pushed.
ACCESS: All of tidal range. **TYPE OF RAMP:** Narrow concrete.
UPPER AREA: Shingle. **LOWER AREA:** Shingle.
DIRECTIONS: Turn left at Chiswick roundabout immediately after the Fullers Brewery. Only a small turning and the approach roads are narrow.
RAMP DESCRIPTION: Straight and narrow with a good gradient.
FACILITIES: Very limited parking.
HAZARDS: 8 knots speed limit.

Chiswick Quay Marina, London
Marina Office Chiswick Quay, London, London, England W4 3UR
Lat. 51.4763, Long. -0.2713.
0208 994 8743

Kew Bridge Drawdock, London
Lat. 51.4881, Long. -0.2873.
PLA 020 7743 7900

CHARGES: None
SUITABILITY: Small trailer can be pushed.
ACCESS: ¼ tidal. **TYPE OF RAMP:** Hard shingle.
UPPER AREA: Shingle. **LOWER AREA:** Shingle.
DIRECTIONS: Just downstream of Kew Bridge on the north bank. Access the ramp from Strand on the Green.

RAMP DESCRIPTION: Ramp leads onto hard shingle that can be used at all states of the tide but the gradient is shallow at low tide. There is a lot of driftwood and rubbish on the ramp and the access from the road has a sharp hump and low cars may ground.
FACILITIES: Limited parking in street. Café and shops close by.
HAZARDS: 8 knots speed limit.

Brentford Dock Marina, Brentford
2 Justin Close Dock, Brentford, Middlesex, England TW8 8QE
Lat. 51.4818, Long. -0.3024.
0208 232 8941

Church Street, Isleworth, London
Lat. 51.4707, Long. -0.3213.

CHARGES: None
SUITABILITY: Large trailer needs a car.
ACCESS: ¾ tidal. **TYPE OF RAMP:** Wide cobbles onto shingle.
UPPER AREA: Shingle. **LOWER AREA:** Shingle.
DIRECTIONS: Ramp is by The London Apprentice opposite Isleworth Ait and sometimes blocked by 'pubbies'. Approach from Isleworth restricted to 7 foot width by posts. Easier approach from Sion House end.
RAMP DESCRIPTION: Wide firm ramp leading on to shingle at low water. Be careful taking car onto shingle as it is only a few inches deep with soft mud underneath. Cars often left parked illegally on the ramp which can prevent access. Otherwise a superb ramp.
FACILITIES: Very restricted parking, especially during the summer weekends when the pub is a very popular venue.
HAZARDS: 8 knots speed limit.

Isleworth Town Wharf, London
Lat. 51.4691, Long. -0.3223.
PLA 020 7743 7900

CHARGES: None
SUITABILITY: Small trailer can be pushed.
ACCESS: All of tidal range. **TYPE OF RAMP:** Very steep concrete.
UPPER AREA: Harbour. **LOWER AREA:** Shingle.
DIRECTIONS: Next to the Town Wharf pub in Swan Lane, Isleworth. Difficult access due to narrow roads.
RAMP DESCRIPTION: Very steep ramp, good width. Leads onto shingle at very low tide. Probably too steep to launch with a car.
FACILITIES: Very restricted parking due to the next door pub. It may be possible to tie on the wharf at the pub but access to the dock not good.
HAZARDS: 8 knots speed limit. Strong currents.

Richmond Slipway, London
Lat. 51.4579, Long. -0.3100.
PLA 020 7743 7900.

CHARGES: None
SUITABILITY: Large trailer needs a car.
ACCESS: All of tidal range. **TYPE OF RAMP:** Steep concrete.
UPPER AREA: Concrete. **LOWER AREA:** Concrete.
DIRECTIONS: Go down Park Road and follow the road around to the right. Ramp is on the left hand side at the end of the road.

RAMP DESCRIPTION: Good concrete ramp but quite steep, take care when launching.
FACILITIES: Parking for a couple of cars at the ramp. Mark Edwards in Richmond has boats for hire and will offer advice on where to launch, tel: 020 8948 8270. There are several other small ramps in the area.
HAZARDS: Strong cross currents in the narrow stream behind Corp Island, 8 knot speed limit.

St Margarets, Richmond, London
Lat. 51.4569, Long. -0.3075.
PLA 020 7743 7900.

CHARGES: None
SUITABILITY: Large trailer needs a car.
ACCESS: All of tidal range. **TYPE OF RAMP:** Shingle hard.
UPPER AREA: Shingle. **LOWER AREA:** Shingle.
DIRECTIONS: Just upstream of Richmond Bridge on the west side of the river.
RAMP DESCRIPTION: Rough concrete and shingle ramp leading into the river.
FACILITIES: Parking is difficult and restricted. Area around the ramp is liable to sudden flooding. Mark Edwards in Richmond has boats for hire and will offer advice on where to launch, tel: 020 8948 8270.
HAZARDS: 8 knots speed limit. Take extra care when the current is strong that you do not get swept under Richmond Bridge.

White Swan, Twickenham, London
Lat. 51.4468, Long. -0.3211.
Richmond Lock 020 8940 0634

CHARGES: None
SUITABILITY: Large trailer needs a car.
ACCESS: All of tidal range. **TYPE OF RAMP:** Concrete onto shingle.
UPPER AREA: Shingle. **LOWER AREA:** Shingle.
DIRECTIONS: Hard is on Riverside and the junction with Lebanon Park next to the White Swan pub.
RAMP DESCRIPTION: Concrete ramp onto hard shingle. The key for the hard is held at Richmond Lock 020 8940 0634 and Twickenham YC 020 8892 8487. There is also a small concrete ramp with a good gradient.
FACILITIES: White Swan Pub is next to the ramp. Parking is difficult and the road is liable to sudden flooding.
HAZARDS: 8 knot speed limit.

Riverside Draw Dock, Twickenham, London
Lat. 51.4467, Long. -0.3250.
PLA 020 7743 7900

CHARGES: None
SUITABILITY: Large trailer needs a car.
ACCESS: All of tidal range. **TYPE OF RAMP:** Concrete
UPPER AREA: Concrete. **LOWER AREA:** Mud.
DIRECTIONS: Turn into Church St from Richmond Road then left around the church.
RAMP DESCRIPTION: Public slipway open 24 hours. Draw dock with surface mud over firm ground suitable for car. Usable at any state of tide but water shallow at low water with outcrops of shopping trolleys.

3

Launching is also possible half a mile downstream opposite the Swan but road is narrow. It is half-tidal here. A barrier below Richmond holds the level up at low tide so that there is a two hour flood with a Neap range of 4½ feet at Neaps and 8½ft at Springs. The barrier can be sailed over at high water, at other times you must go through the lock.
FACILITIES: Park well away from dock, as water comes over road, and away from meters. All facilities at Twickenham. Public conveniences by Eel Pie Island footbridge.
HAZARDS: 8 knot speed limit.

Eel Pie Boatyard, Twickenham
Eel Pie Island, Twickenham, Middx, England TW1 3DY
Lat. 51.4453, Long. -0.3255.
020 8892 3626

Teddington Wharf, London
Lat. 51.4310, Long. -0.3256.
Concierge 020 8943 3501
CHARGES: None
SUITABILITY: Large trailer needs a car.
ACCESS: ¾ tidal. **TYPE OF RAMP:** Wide concrete.
UPPER AREA: Harbour. **LOWER AREA:** Mud.
DIRECTIONS: The ramp is inside Teddington Wharf development off Manor Road just downstream from Teddington Lock.
RAMP DESCRIPTION: Open 8am to 8pm or lighting up time. Get the key from the concierge tel: 020 8943 3501. The ramp is shared with the lifeboat service. Excellent wide concrete ramp with a good gradient.
FACILITIES: Excellent ramp, but no parking allowed. You must take car and trailer off the development after launching. Local parking is tricky.
HAZARDS: 8 knot speed limit.

Ferry Road, Teddington, London
Lat. 51.4299, Long. -0.3223.
The Boat Shop 020 8977 9978
CHARGES: None
SUITABILITY: Small trailer can be pushed.
ACCESS: ½ tidal. **TYPE OF RAMP:** Concrete **UPPER AREA:** Shingle.
LOWER AREA: Shingle.
DIRECTIONS: Follow Ferry Road to the river. Immediately downstream from Teddington Lock.
RAMP DESCRIPTION: Key to the ramp is kept in the Boat Shop. Good concrete ramp across a shingle hard. Access road is tricky, suitable for small trailers only.
FACILITIES: Parking is very difficult. Anglers' Pub next door and the Boat Shop chandlery.
HAZARDS: 4 knot speed limit.

Ham Landing, London
Lat. 51.4455, Long. -0.3185.
PLA 020 7743 7900
CHARGES: None
SUITABILITY: Portable Only.

ACCESS: Non-tidal. **TYPE OF RAMP:** Cobble **UPPER AREA:** Shingle.
LOWER AREA: Shingle.
DIRECTIONS: Follow Ham Street all the way to the river.
RAMP DESCRIPTION: Two ramps of uneven cobbles leading down into the river. Old ferry landing stage. There is no vehicle access to the ramps and the site is suitable for portable boats only.
FACILITIES: Large car park by the twin ramps. Plenty of space to picnic and Ham House is close by.
HAZARDS: Speed restriction in river.

River Lane Slip, Richmond, London
Lat. 51.4484, Long. -0.3057.
PLA 020 7743 7900
CHARGES: None
SUITABILITY: Small trailer can be pushed.
ACCESS: All of tidal range. **TYPE OF RAMP:** Firm shingle, will take car.
UPPER AREA: Shingle. **LOWER AREA:** Shingle.
DIRECTIONS: River Lane is a turning off Petersham Road on the elbow of a tight right hand bend most easily seen when coming from Kingston. Richmond Town is 1 mile away.
RAMP DESCRIPTION: Shingle ramp in good condition with no major potholes or ruts. Tends to get eroded by the river and roughed up. A popular spot, not particularly crowded. Richmond is half-tidal. A barrier below Richmond holds the level up at low tide so that there is a 2 hour flood with a Neap range of 4½ft and 8½ft at Springs. The barrier can be sailed over at high water, at other times you must go through the lock.
FACILITIES: Nice long access road. Can be narrow in places but nothing serious. At very high tides it floods up the road a short way so park up at the top of the lane once you've launched. The ramp is shingle at the bottom but it is a gentle slope with no obstructions. If you don't have a 4 × 4 you might want to consider a rope between tow vehicle and trailer. The area is busy with walkers and cyclists so take care if you use a rope and expect an audience. During the Great River Race in September the slipway is very very busy launching gig boats.
HAZARDS: Speed restriction on the river.

Water Lane, Richmond, London
Lat. 51.4588, Long. -0.3084.
PLA 020 7743 7900.
SUITABILITY: Small trailer can be pushed.
ACCESS: Non-tidal. **TYPE OF RAMP: UPPER AREA:** Unknown.
LOWER AREA: Unknown.
DIRECTIONS: Down Water Lane to the river. Next to the White Cross pub.
RAMP DESCRIPTION: Concrete draw dock with a drop off at the end. Boats may be blocking the slipway.
FACILITIES: Parking is very difficult and restricted especially on weekends. Area around the ramp is liable to sudden flooding. Mark Edwards in Richmond has boats for hire and will offer advice on where to launch, tel: 020 8948 8270. There are several other small ramps in the area.
HAZARDS: 8 knots speed limit.

Ship Lane, Barnes, London
Lat. 51.4711, Long. -0.2678.
PLA 020 7743 7900

CHARGES: None
SUITABILITY: Large trailer needs a car.
ACCESS: ¼ tidal. **TYPE OF RAMP:** Cobble onto shingle.
UPPER AREA: Shingle. **LOWER AREA:** Shingle.
DIRECTIONS: On the south side of Chiswick Bridge and downstream.
RAMP DESCRIPTION: Cobble ramp that leads onto a shallow shingle bank. A 4 × 4 vehicle with a low ratio gear box could launch/ recover almost anything at any state of the tide here. Launching a 4.8m RIB with a Ford Escort is no problem at quarter tide but lots of wheel spin pulling the trailer out. Recovering at low tide, best to keep the vehicle on the cobbles and used a winch to pull the trailer up to the car. Be careful using this slipway around Neap tides. Lack of current leads to a build-up of mud on the slipway so best used around Spring tides.
FACILITIES: Pub next door to the launch site. There is parking for boat and trailer in Ship Lane - provided it is not peak drinking time in the pub.
HAZARDS: 8 knots speed limit.

Putney Hard, London
Lat. 51.4696, Long. -0.2201.
Chas Newens Marine 020 8788 4587

CHARGES: None
SUITABILITY: Large trailer needs a car.
ACCESS: ¾ tidal. **TYPE OF RAMP:** Concrete **UPPER AREA:** Concrete.
LOWER AREA: Shingle.
DIRECTIONS: The launch site is just upstream from Putney bridge on the south bank. Very good access from road network.
RAMP DESCRIPTION: Two wide concrete strips along the river bank. Be careful taking car on to shingle as it is only a few inches deep with soft mud underneath. Easier, if dinghy can not be manhandled, to wait until tide comes up to embankment at about half tide. Not crowded except on regatta and Boat Race days. Wider slipway opposite the boat houses is best one to use when the tide is low. Slipway opposite Chas Newens extends to half tide and then onto shallow shingle.
FACILITIES: Busy area with lots of rowing club houses. Chas Newens Marine on-site with workshop and chandlery. Will provide an assisted launch for £5 between 9am and 6pm. Parking can get crowded in the summer but usually OK on a Sunday and there are no restrictions after 10.30am. Do not park on the slipways when high tide expected and don't be fooled if the rowers' cars are there. They will move whilst you're out on the water.
HAZARDS: Lots of traffic. The area is speed restricted to 8 knots. The many rowing boats in the area are easily swamped by boats travelling at speed.

Putney Bridge, London
Lat. 51.4665, Long. -0.2148.

CHARGES: None
SUITABILITY: Large trailer needs a car.
ACCESS: ¾ tidal. **TYPE OF RAMP:** Concrete **UPPER AREA:** Concrete.
LOWER AREA: Shingle.

DIRECTIONS: The launch site is just upstream from Putney bridge on the south bank.
RAMP DESCRIPTION: Large flat square London cobbles. Very good slipway with wooden piles on the river side of the ramp. It may also be possible to launch on the downstream side of Putney Bridge, up stream of the railway bridge - south bank of the river - over the shingle. Nice and shallow and you need a rope from tow hitch to trailer. Access down Brewhouse Street quite probably blocked by litter, flotsam & jetsam and there might be a step from off the tarmac road onto the shingle, depending on action of the current.
FACILITIES: Do not leave your trailer and car on the slip unless you want a parking ticket. Chas Newens Marine is nearby.
HAZARDS: Lots of traffic. The area is speed restricted to 8 knots. The many rowing boats in the area are easily swamped by boats travelling at speed.

Downstream Putney Bridge, Putney
Lat. 51.4655, Long. -0.2128.
SUITABILITY: Large trailer needs a car.
ACCESS: ¾ tidal. **TYPE OF RAMP:** Concrete **UPPER AREA:** Concrete.
LOWER AREA: Shingle.
DIRECTIONS: Just downstream of Putney bridge on the south bank.
RAMP DESCRIPTION: Concrete ramp on the river embankment
HAZARDS: 8 knot speed limit.

Battersea Church, London
Lat. 51.4763, Long. -0.1760.
PLA 020 7743 7900
SUITABILITY: Large trailer needs a car.
ACCESS: ¼ tidal. **TYPE OF RAMP:** Concrete **UPPER AREA:** Shingle.
LOWER AREA: Shingle.
DIRECTIONS: Slipway is upstream of Battersea Bridge on the south bank. Follow Battersea Church Street and the slipway is next to the church.
RAMP DESCRIPTION: Good concrete ramp onto hard standing forming a draw dock. Often a sill at the end of the ramp so take care when launching. Ramp is often blocked by parked cars.
FACILITIES: Street parking but limited. Cars are often parked on the ramp.
HAZARDS: 8 knot speed limit above Wandsworth Bridge. This part of the river tends to have less traffic than further downstream.

South Dock Marina, London
Rope Street, Plough Way, London, London, England SE16 7SZ
Lat. 51.4941, Long. -0.0346.
020 7252 2244

Plough Way Steps, Rotherhithe, London
Lat. 51.4929, Long. -0.0323.

CHARGES: None.
SUITABILITY: Portable Only.

ACCESS: All of tidal range. **TYPE OF RAMP:** Concrete steps.
UPPER AREA: Harbour. **LOWER AREA:** Shingle.
DIRECTIONS: Follow Plough Way all the way to the river where there is a car park. Steps lead down from the end of the car park.
RAMP DESCRIPTION: Concrete steps down to the foreshore. Some green slime on the lower steps and there is a metal hand rail to the side. Lead onto a shingle and sand shoreline which is covered at high tide. Suitable for kayaks and other portable craft.
FACILITIES: Car park.
HAZARDS: High speed ferries going up and down the Thames.

Greenwich Yacht Club, London
Lat. 51.4952, Long. 0.0179.
020 8858 7339 - Club secretary
CHARGES: £15 approximately, includes parking.
SUITABILITY: Large trailer needs a car.
ACCESS: ¾ tidal. **TYPE OF RAMP:** Concrete **UPPER AREA:** Shingle.
LOWER AREA: Mud.
DIRECTIONS: Go north on Peartree Way from Woolwich Road (A206) or from the A102 southeast of the Blackwall Tunnel. There is parking near the club entrance along Peartree Way. GYC visitors are cautioned to read and observe the posted parking restrictions that are routinely enforced by Greenwich Council.
RAMP DESCRIPTION: The ramp is inside the Greenwich Yacht Club which has a locked gate. Non members are allowed to use the ramp but please phone beforehand. The ramp may not be accessible if there are boat movements taking place. The ramp is concrete over the mud and the bottom half is very shallow. Best to launch close to high tide, however many do launch boats at low states of tide (and live to tell the tale).
FACILITIES: Boatyard facilities. Excellent pontoon at the club and petrol very close. Parking can be provided by arrangement with the club.
HAZARDS: Strong currents when the tide is running. The launch site is a short distance upstream from the Thames Barrier.

Erith Town Ramp, Erith
Lat. 51.4819, Long. 0.1807.
020 8313 0417
CHARGES: None
SUITABILITY: Small trailer can be pushed.
ACCESS: ¾ tidal. **TYPE OF RAMP:** Wooden planking set on wooden piers. **UPPER AREA:** Mud. **LOWER AREA:** Mud.
DIRECTIONS: Access directly off old High Street, part of Erith Town one-way system. Good parking and boat preparation area. Railings accessible to chain secure trailer.
RAMP DESCRIPTION: Gentle slope about 8 feet wide. Maximum trailer/boat width 7 feet. Drop-off at end means trailer launch of dinghy possible about three hours after low tide. Also with dinghy to 'Wanderer' type class, good size waders needed as water level is around thighs before boat floats off. Two-man operation in rough water especially when recovering boat. Well maintained and sanded each low water. Used by PLA to pick up and drop off Lightermen. Suggest bring in boat up to one hour after high tide after which the tide begins to race seaward. This effectively gives a maximum cruising period of four hours and 8hours if you miss this timetable!

FACILITIES: Parking 100 yards on road, garage and shopping centre 100 yards. Sheltered mooring up river alongside ramp in winds from southeast to southwest. Shops including 'Morrison' superstore within walking distance. Town centre and pubs also within walking distance.
HAZARDS: Only the submerged ramp itself, marked with scaffold-type poles. High mud banks immediately up-river ...easy to beach even small draught boats whilst 30 yards from shore. Moored Thames barges mid-water.

Allhallows Yacht Club, Allhallows
Lat. 51.4784, Long. 0.6388.
(0)1634 270788
CHARGES: - Day membership - on application - Family membership - £250 family (70p per day) - Joint membership - £210 Please email - info@ayc.uk.com
SUITABILITY: Large trailer needs a car.
ACCESS: ½ tidal. **TYPE OF RAMP:** The ramps are iroka.
UPPER AREA: Concrete. **LOWER AREA:** Mud.
DIRECTIONS: North Kent, Nr Rochester. Please see website for multimap link
RAMP DESCRIPTION: Our boat club has two slipways, east and west. There are electric winches or launch vehicles available, approximate width is 3 metres.
FACILITIES: Clubhouse Large entertainment hall Licensed lounge bar Kitchen open during the season for breakfasts and lunch Male and female changing rooms with hot showers Purpose built flat with in-house caretaker, which in turn offers another level of security Secure boat parking for all full members East and west launch ramps with electric winches Launch vehicle available Free parking Integral race tower Large patio area with BBQ facilities
HAZARDS: Please contact us through our website and our sectional captain will contact you with any navigational information that you require.

The Embankment Marina, Gravesend, Gravesend
Canal Basin Albion Road, Gravesend, Kent, England DA12 2RN
Lat. 51.4432, Long. 0.3825.
01474 535700

Hoo Marina, Nr Rochester
Vicarage Lane, Hoo, Nr Rochester, Kent, England ME3 9LE
Lat. 51.4109, Long. 0.5602.
01634 250311

Cuxton Marina, Rochester
Station Road, Cuxton, Rochester, Kent, England ME2 1AB
Lat. 51.3727, Long. 0.4610.
01634 721941

Port Medway Marina, Rochester
**Station Road, Cuxton, Rochester, Kent, England
ME2 1AB
Lat. 51.3724, Long. 0.4609.**
01634 720033

Elmhaven Marina, Rochester
**The Boathouse Road, Halling, Rochester, Kent,
England ME2 1AQ
Lat. 51.3661, Long. 0.4483.**
01634 240489

Allington Lock Slipway, Allington
Lat. 51.2951, Long. 0.5046.
01622 752864

CHARGES: Oct 08 charges are £5 in £5 out. Car parking currently free for cars with trailers
SUITABILITY: Large trailer needs a car.
ACCESS: Non-tidal. **TYPE OF RAMP:** 5 metre wide concrete, purpose built in September 2008. Tie up points and choice of a low or high level landing stage adjacent. Very good facility. **UPPER AREA:** Concrete.
LOWER AREA: Concrete.
DIRECTIONS: ME16 0LU M20 Junc 5 head A20 to Maidstone turn left into Castle Road and follow to very end turning left at Allington Castle gates. Slipway just along the river
RAMP DESCRIPTION: New in September 2008. Built by the Environment Agency. 5 metre wide slipway built to IWA slipway standards. Loads of car parking and plenty of room to turn and slip the boat. Toilets, showers, and excellent secure car parking for cars and trailers on site. Also electric hook-up and camping. Very friendly and helpful lock keepers. Malta Inn Pub right opposite - good pub with good food.
FACILITIES: Toilets, showers, power hook up, moorings, car parking for cars trailers and minibuses. Also camping on site. Very helpful staff
HAZARDS: Only when river is in flood. Phone ahead for advice from the lock keeper 01622 752864

Allington Marina, Maidstone
**Castle Road, Allington, Maidstone, Kent, England
ME16 0NH
Lat. 51.2923, Long. 0.5123.**
01622 752057

Foords Wharf Boatyard, Maidstone
**Foords Wharf, Allington, Maidstone, Kent,
England ME16 0BP
Lat. 51.2864, Long. 0.5085.**
01622 752918

Slipway, Maidstone
Lat. 51.2788, Long. 0.5152.

CHARGES: £7.50
SUITABILITY: Large trailer needs a car.

ACCESS: Non-tidal. **TYPE OF RAMP:** Concrete **UPPER AREA:** Concrete.
LOWER AREA: Concrete.
DIRECTIONS: Take St. Peter's Street from the town centre, go past Courts and Homebase, as the road turns to the left turn right under the railway bridge towards the Indoor Tennis Club. The slip is right in the town centre. There are bariers to go through these may be down.
RAMP DESCRIPTION: This tricky ramp is fairly narrow and short. Bushes either side are overgrown and the landing stage is in poor condition. Recommend you use Allington Lock slipway just around the corner instead. This is purpose built and was completed in Sep 2008
FACILITIES: Parking, toilets, restaurant, bar.
HAZARDS: Alington lock downstream and Teston lock upstream.

Medway Bridge Marina, Rochester
**Manor Lane, Rochester, Kent, England ME1 3HS
Lat. 51.3763, Long. 0.4823.**
01634 843576

Victory Moorings, Chatham
**Thunderbolt Pier, The Historic Dockyard,
Chatham, Kent, England ME4 4TZ
Lat. 51.3936, Long. 0.5271.**
07785 971797

Chatham Maritime Marina, Chatham
**The Loch Building, Leviathon Way, Chatham
Maritime, Chatham, Medway, England ME4 4LP
Lat. 51.4047, Long. 0.5321.**
01634 899200

Gillingham Pier, Gillingham
Lat. 51.3980, Long. 0.5553.

CHARGES: £10 to launch, pay harbourmaster. Or £60 per annum
SUITABILITY: Large trailer needs a car.
ACCESS: ¾ tidal. **TYPE OF RAMP:** Cobbles **UPPER AREA:** Concrete.
LOWER AREA: Concrete.
DIRECTIONS: From the barracks roundabout, continue for about half a mile heading east along the main road. Turn left at the traffic lights signposted Gillingham Pier. Follow road through industrial park 400 yards to pier.
RAMP DESCRIPTION: Good sized ramp. The channel has huge pilings. Third or fourth out has wooden sleepers projecting under water although piling has a large sign.

Gillingham Marina, Gillingham
**173 Pier Road, Gillingham, Kent., England
ME7 1UB
Lat. 51.3967, Long. 0.5602.**
01634 280022

Strand Slip, Gillingham
Lat. 51.3947, Long. 0.5601.

CHARGES: None
SUITABILITY: Small trailer can be pushed.

3

ACCESS: ¾ tidal. **TYPE OF RAMP:** Concrete **UPPER AREA:** Shingle.
LOWER AREA: Mud.

RAMP DESCRIPTION: The slip way will handle small trailers only and these need to be pushed by hand. Caution to be exercised in doing this as the slip is very narrow and slippery. In some places it is unkempt with large gaps in the concrete. In westerly or south westerly breezes, dinghy/non-power boaters have difficulty in returning to shore. Local clubs can usually assist with their safety boats. At high water there is a shingle beach with a promenade (grass and concrete) known as The Strand which can get crowded.

FACILITIES: Parking space is limited. Car park, toilets, café and fresh water 100 yards. At very low water the bottom consists of a shingle and mud mix, this is quite deep in places.

HAZARDS: Beware of beaching away from hard as there are many stakes. Jetskis should not be used in this area but are frequently seen at speed inshore. Look out for children if they are paddling at high water.

Public Slip, Queenborough
Lat. 51.4168, Long. 0.7407.
Harbour Controller 01795 662051

CHARGES: Yes, if collected.
SUITABILITY: Large trailer needs a car.
ACCESS: All of tidal range. **TYPE OF RAMP:** Concrete, drop to mud at bottom. **UPPER AREA:** Mud. **LOWER AREA:** Mud.
DIRECTIONS: Slipway is at the end of the High Street in the town of Queenborough.
RAMP DESCRIPTION: Slipway is accessible all states of the tide, except very low water as there is a drop off. Slip is long and narrow, with a bend in it, so will test your reversing skills to the limit! Near high water the slip runs level for 40 metres making launch and retrieving difficult. Can be crowded at weekends.
FACILITIES: Parking in small car park. Queenborough Yacht Club (01795 663955) welcomes visiting sailors. There is a pub at the top of the slipway, public toilets, a shop and a Yacht Chandlers. On the left of the slipway, (looking from the water) there is an all tidal landing pontoon, with fresh water available. No overnight mooring on the pontoon, but there is a trot boat service to and from the moorings during daylight hours. All info for the Trot boat and other services are posted on the pontoon.

Slipway, Barton's Point
Lat. 51.4367, Long. 0.7975.
SUITABILITY: Large trailer needs a car.
ACCESS: ½ tidal. **TYPE OF RAMP:** Concrete **UPPER AREA:** Shingle.
LOWER AREA: Shingle.
DIRECTIONS: This slipway is situated on the North Coast of Sheppey between Sheerness and Minster.
RAMP DESCRIPTION: Concrete ramp across a shingle beach. Exposed to north and east winds. Launching is possible 3 hours either side of high water. The slipway is steep, so 4WD is the best option.
FACILITIES: No moorings available, so only suitable for leisure day craft. There is a café called the White House, 100 metres away.

Slipway, Leysdown
Lat. 51.4000, Long. 0.9176.

CHARGES: £5 covers car parking, launch and recovery.
SUITABILITY: Large trailer needs a car.
ACCESS: ¾ tidal. **TYPE OF RAMP:** Hard shingle beach
UPPER AREA: Shingle. **LOWER AREA:** Shingle.
DIRECTIONS: After coming over the bridge onto the Isle of Sheppey turn right at the roundabout onto the B2231 sign posted to Leysdown. Just before entering Leysdown you will see a caravan park on the left, with a huge sign advertising the launch facilities.
RAMP DESCRIPTION: Popular with small motor boats but Jetskis are currently banned due to problems with the neighbouring holiday park. Definitely need 4 × 4 for large boat as the beach is shingle, we launched and recovered 19 foot Fletcher with no problems. If worst comes to worst the campsite has a tractor. Smaller cars have no problems launching small boats as the shingle is very compact.
FACILITIES: You have to drive through the campsite to get to the beach, so has all the usual camp site facilities.

Ferry Inn, Sheppey
Lat. 51.3549, Long. 0.8922.

CHARGES: None
SUITABILITY: Large trailer needs a car.
ACCESS: All of tidal range. **TYPE OF RAMP:** Hard shingle.
UPPER AREA: Mud. **LOWER AREA:** Mud.
DIRECTIONS: Follow the signs to the Harty Inn on the Isle of Sheppey. Signs are easily missed and last part of road is fairly rough with many potholes.
RAMP DESCRIPTION: Hard shingle next to a narrow concrete ramp that has almost completely fallen away at the top. Ramp is very shallow and you may have to go out a long way to get enough water. Really only useful for portable boats unless launching at high tide. Ramp is regularly used by local fishermen.
FACILITIES: Parking in at the local pub, the Harty Ferry Inn. Serves good food and welcomes yachtsman. Gets very busy in the summer. There are plans to put in a pontoon. Moorings are £5 per night and most Sundays there is a clay pigeon shoot. Big area for bird watchers.
HAZARDS: Lots of mud flats in the area.

Swale Marina, Conyer
Lat. 51.3468, Long. 0.8122.
01795 521562

CHARGES: £8/day
SUITABILITY: Large trailer needs a car.
ACCESS: ¼ tidal. **TYPE OF RAMP:** Concrete, mud at bottom.
UPPER AREA: Mud. **LOWER AREA:** Mud.
DIRECTIONS: Swale Marina, Conyer, Near Teynham, Kent.
RAMP DESCRIPTION: Slip is straight and wide with a good gradient. Check with the yard that the slipway will be clear before using.
FACILITIES: Plenty of parking at the yard. Slip water tap at top of slip. Ask the yard about leaving car or trailer for any length of time. Chandlery and boatyard facilities on site.

Swale Marina, Teynham
Conyer Wharf,, Teynham, Kent, England ME9 9HN
Lat. 51.3466, Long. 0.8136.
01795 521562

Harty Ferry, Faversham
Lat. 51.3463, Long. 0.8892.

CHARGES: Free
SUITABILITY: Small trailer can be pushed.
ACCESS: All of tidal range. **TYPE OF RAMP:** Concrete
UPPER AREA: Mud. **LOWER AREA:** Unknown.
DIRECTIONS: You can find Harty Ferry by going to Oare, west of Faversham, and then taking the road north down to the Swale, sign posted Harty Ferry. There is a small car park. Faversham is only 3 minutes from junction 6 of the M2; there is a mainline station with frequent trains from London, Rochester, Canterbury and the Kent coast.
RAMP DESCRIPTION: Not in particularly good condition. Landing by tender is possible on both shores at all but the lowest of tides. The Harty Ferry Road leading to the slipway is in a terrible condition and is only barely passable by a normal car. A 4 × 4 is recommended as a normal car is in serious danger of having its underside damaged by the 12 inch high ridge running down the centre of the road.
FACILITIES: Harty Ferry is a delightful spot on the Swale about 1mile northeast of Faversham. Harty Ferry is so named after the rope-drawn the ferry service which used to cross the Swale from the mainland to the Isle of Harty, the southwest part of the Isle of Sheppey, until 1946. Parking on south side. On the north shore it is but a short walk to the Ferry House Inn, whilst on the south shore a walk of about a mile, will take you into the village of Oare and one of three pubs.

The Slipway, Oare Creek
Lat. 51.3328, Long. 0.8863.
01795 538735

CHARGES: D.I.Y launch & recovery £10 Assisted one way £20
SUITABILITY: Large trailer needs a car.
ACCESS: ¼ tidal. **TYPE OF RAMP: UPPER AREA:** Harbour.
LOWER AREA: Mud.
FACILITIES: 4 × 4 vehicle or tractor available

Youngboats, Faversham
Oare Creek, Faversham, Kent, England ME13 7TX
Lat. 51.3308, Long. 0.8852.
01795 536176

Iron Wharf Boatyard, Faversham
Abbey Fields, Faversham, Kent, England ME13 7BY
Lat. 51.3237, Long. 0.9103.
01795 537122

Hampton Ramp, Herne Bay
Lat. 51.3698, Long. 1.0980.
01227 266719

CHARGES: None
SUITABILITY: Large trailer needs a car.
ACCESS: ½ tidal. **TYPE OF RAMP:** Concrete **UPPER AREA:** Concrete.
LOWER AREA: Mud.
DIRECTIONS: Ramp is just to the west of Herne Bay in the small bay by the play park.
RAMP DESCRIPTION: Concrete at top going to a wooden ramp leading onto soft sand. Do not attempt to launch unless the bottom of the slip is covered. Patrol boathouse at the ramp and wardens on site to ensure safe use.
FACILITIES: All usual seaside facilities including a boule pitch. Fish and chips, cafés and pubs, public toilets. Large free car park gets full in peak periods. Good coastguard station, very friendly. Jetski play area nearby.
HAZARDS: Speed limit of 8 knots in the harbour and within yellow buoys. Tide goes out a long way; forget launching a few hours after high tide.

Central slipway, Herne Bay
Lat. 51.3734, Long. 1.1257.
01227 266719

CHARGES: £10 to park car and trailer.
SUITABILITY: Large trailer needs a car.
ACCESS: ½ tidal. **TYPE OF RAMP:** Wide concrete ramp.
UPPER AREA: Harbour. **LOWER AREA:** Mud.
DIRECTIONS: Head for the sea front and go into the public car park. Go to the left and find car and trailer parking in marked bays.
RAMP DESCRIPTION: 2 ramps at the site. A wide ramp leads into the harbour. The second ramp goes north onto the seaward side of the breakwater. Ground below the ramps is soft mud. Only launch when there is water on the ramps. Also sea is very shallow here when tide is low. It is OK to launch 3 hours either side of high tide on the main ramp and 3.5 hours on the smaller ramp.
FACILITIES: All usual seaside facilities. Fish and chips, cafés and pubs. Manned throughout the summer to ensure safe usage. There is a fee to use the car park but not the ramp.
HAZARDS: Speed limit of 8 knots in the harbour and within yellow buoys.

Minnis Bay, Birchington
Lat. 51.3798, Long. 1.2851.
Foreshore Office 01843 577529

CHARGES: £20 one off fee.
SUITABILITY: Large trailer needs a car.
ACCESS: ¼ tidal. **TYPE OF RAMP:** Ramp onto beach
UPPER AREA: Sand. **LOWER AREA:** Sand.
DIRECTIONS: The ramp is just to the east of Birchington, off The Parade.
RAMP DESCRIPTION: Sailing and fishing boats only. To use slipways in the Margate area you must register with Thanet District Council and show proof of £2m insurance. A one off £20 fee gets you a key, boat sticker and car windscreen sticker. All the launch sites have locked barriers. Dangerous to use slip at high water when rough, especially in northerly wind - best to wait an hour. Can launch from beach at all states of tide. Never drive vehicle beyond groynes. Minnis Bay Sailing Club www.minnisbaysailingclub.co.uk uses slip and promenade extensively on Sundays during season.
FACILITIES: Café, car park, pub and toilets. Ramp is on a beach.

3

Beresford Gap, Birchington

Lat. 51.3819, Long. 1.3022.

Foreshore Office 01843 577529

CHARGES: £20 one off fee to Thanet District Council.
SUITABILITY: Large trailer needs a car.
ACCESS: ¼ tidal. **TYPE OF RAMP:** Ramp onto beach
UPPER AREA: Sand. **LOWER AREA:** Sand.
DIRECTIONS: At Birchington on Sea railway station, take the road immediately to the right (adjacent) to the station car park called Station Approach. Over a small bridge. Take the second right on to Beach Avenue. Straight across at the crossroads. Down a very steep slip.
RAMP DESCRIPTION: Very steep ramp for speed boats and waterskiing. To use slipways in the Margate area you must register with Thanet District Council and show proof of £2m insurance. A one off £20 fee gets you a key, boat sticker and car windscreen sticker. All the launch sites have locked barriers.
FACILITIES: There are a lot of rocks. The area is sometimes overtaken by smelly seaweed at - the Council are trying to deal with it, but it is absolutely overpowering. There are no facilities at the site
HAZARDS: A lot of rocks. Not really suitable area for water skiing.

Western Esplanade, Westgate

Lat. 51.3820, Long. 1.3291.

Foreshore Office 01843 577529

CHARGES: £20 one off fee.
SUITABILITY: Large trailer needs a car.
ACCESS: ¼ tidal. **TYPE OF RAMP:** Ramp onto beach
UPPER AREA: Sand. **LOWER AREA:** Sand.
DIRECTIONS: By the Western Esplanade at West Bay in Westgate on Sea.
RAMP DESCRIPTION: Sailing and fishing boats. To use slipways in the Margate area you must register with Thanet District Council and show proof of £2m insurance. A one off £20 fee gets you a key, boat sticker and car windscreen sticker. All the launch sites have locked barriers.
FACILITIES: Café and car park. Ramp is on a beach.

Westbrook, Margate

Lat. 51.3859, Long. 1.3607.

Foreshore Office 01843 577529

CHARGES: £20 one off fee to Thanet District Council
SUITABILITY: Large trailer needs a car.
ACCESS: ¼ tidal. **TYPE OF RAMP:** Ramp onto beach
UPPER AREA: Concrete. **LOWER AREA:** Sand.
DIRECTIONS: Past Westgate on Sea railway station on right. Turn right at crossroads on to Westgate Bay Avenue. Past tennis courts on left and turn left on to The Esplanade. Follow road and turn left opposite Barnes Avenue. Big free of charge car park by beach plus space to leave car/ trailer through barrier if car park full
RAMP DESCRIPTION: Speed boats and water skiing only at this ramp. Good concrete ramp, but if tide in, almost impossible to launch with waves breaking, as ramp is parallel to sea wall. Very very soft sand as tide going out (people sink let alone recovery vehicle!). There are a lot of rocks in this bay and launching at low tide is almost impossible even

with a 4 × 4 as the rocks go out a considerable way. Well marked out area for skiing in bay on information board at the top of the ramp. Not recommended at all due to launch conditions of soft sand/treacherous rocks. To use slipways in the Margate area you must register with Thanet District Council and show proof of £2m insurance. A one off £20 fee gets you a key, boat sticker and car windscreen sticker. All the launch sites have locked barriers.
FACILITIES: There is a café and toilets above the public bathing area, along the next part of the beach (about 1/4 mile walk). Boats are not allowed in this area beyond the ski groyne.
HAZARDS: Rocks, rocks, rocks everywhere - be very careful in this bay.

Margate Harbour, Margate

Lat. 51.3904, Long. 1.3810.

Foreshore Office 01843 577529

CHARGES: £20 one off fee.
SUITABILITY: Large trailer needs a car.
ACCESS: ½ tidal. **TYPE OF RAMP:** Concrete on cobbles.
UPPER AREA: Harbour. **LOWER AREA:** Sand.
DIRECTIONS: Margate is situated to the East of Herne Bay. northeast of Canterbury. Follow the A28 to Margate Beach.
RAMP DESCRIPTION: Slipway leads into a sheltered, sandy harbour that dries right out at low tide. You can take a trailer onto the sand, but watch out for soft spots. No Jetskis or speedboats allowed at the harbour slipway. Speed boats can launch at a second slipway around the back of the harbour to the east. To use slipways in the Margate area you must register with Thanet District Council and show proof of £2m insurance. A one off £20 fee gets you a key, boat sticker and car windscreen sticker. All the launch sites have locked barriers. Member of council present throughout summer weekends to check insurance and unlock barrier for visiting craft.
FACILITIES: Parking next to the slipway. However this will go under the proposed regeneration scheme and you will have to use car parks on The Rendezvous 50 metres down the road. Slip is adjacent to the Margate Yacht Club 01843 292602.

Jet Ski World, Palm Bay, Cliftonville, Margate

Lat. 51.3926, Long. 1.4100.

Jet Ski World on 01843 231703

CHARGES: Tractor launch for a £15 fee. RYA PWC Recognised Training Establishment.
SUITABILITY: Large trailer needs a car.
ACCESS: All of tidal range. **TYPE OF RAMP:** Concrete
UPPER AREA: Concrete. **LOWER AREA:** Sand.
DIRECTIONS: Jet Ski World,Cliftonville is to the east of Margate. The road access ramp is situated at the end of Palm Bay Avenue next door to the new Coastguard Station.
RAMP DESCRIPTION: Access controlled by the Jetski operation on-site. The upper ramp and car park area is made up of concrete/ tarmac with loads of free parking for Jetskiers. See our web site for details. www. jetskiworld.co.uk
FACILITIES: Café with full menu. Large car park, PWC wash off area, customer showers and toilets. No need to register for this site to

launch Jetskis. For a £15 fee they will launch and recover your craft with their tractor.

HAZARDS: Some rocks at low water but all easily visible.

Foreness Bay, Cliftonville, Margate
Lat. 51.3925, Long. 1.4291.
Foreshore Office 01843 577529

CHARGES: £20 one off fee.
SUITABILITY: Large trailer needs a car.
ACCESS: ½ tidal. **TYPE OF RAMP:** Concrete **UPPER AREA:** Sand.
LOWER AREA: Sand.
DIRECTIONS: Cliftonville is to the east of Margate.
RAMP DESCRIPTION: Slip is unsheltered, facing almost due north and difficult to launch/recover in a swell. Launching is not recommended below ½ tide due to shallow slope of beech and rocks at low water, but is still possible. Sand is good and hard so will take car, main obstacle is the soft sand which collects around the bottom of the concrete slip. To use slipways in the Margate area you must register with Thanet District Council and show proof of £2m insurance. A one off £20 fee gets you a key, boat sticker and car windscreen sticker. All the launch sites have locked barriers.
FACILITIES: Café nearby. Forness water-ski club meet here at weekends throughout the summer.
HAZARDS: No Jetskis.

Royal Harbour Marina, Ramsgate
Military Road, Ramsgate, Kent, England CT11 9LQ
Lat. 51.3312, Long. 1.4190.
01843 572100

Sandwichbay Sailing and Waterski club, Sanwichbay
Lat. 51.2634, Long. 1.3882.
SUITABILITY: Large trailer needs a car.
ACCESS: All of tidal range. **TYPE OF RAMP: UPPER AREA:** Concrete.
LOWER AREA: Sand.

Highway Marine, Sandwich
Pillory Gate Wharf, Strand Street, Sandwich, Kent, England CT13 9EU
Lat. 51.2767, Long. 1.3399.
01304 613925

Sandwich Quay, Sandwich
Lat. 51.2745, Long. 1.3462.
CHARGES: None
SUITABILITY: Large trailer needs a car.
ACCESS: ½ tidal. **TYPE OF RAMP:** Concrete **UPPER AREA:** Concrete.
LOWER AREA: Mud.
DIRECTIONS: Sandwich is situated half way between Deal and Ramsgate. The slipway is situated on the town quay on the south side of the river and downstream from the bridge.
RAMP DESCRIPTION: Steep muddy drop at the end so low tide can be a problem. Sign on the slipway says to launch two hours either side of

high tide. Ramp goes into the River Stour which has a 6 knot limit. It is approximately two miles to the sea.
FACILITIES: Car park - cost normally £1. Free trailer parking area.

Public Slipway, Dover
Lat. 51.1225, Long. 1.3162.
Harbourmaster 01304 240400

CHARGES: None
SUITABILITY: Large trailer needs a car.
ACCESS: All of tidal range. **TYPE OF RAMP:** Concrete on one side; cobbles on the other. **UPPER AREA:** Harbour. **LOWER AREA:** Harbour.
DIRECTIONS: Enter Dover via M20. Take first left after swing bridge onto Esplanade. Slipway is opposite the Royal Cinque Ports yacht club.
RAMP DESCRIPTION: Opposite Royal Cinque Ports Yacht Club (01304 206262), who are friendly to visiting yachtsmen. Slipway is narrow and large trailers will require skilful reversing. Sunday mornings and Wednesday afternoon are busy at the club with dingy racing. Popular with divers at the weekend.
FACILITIES: Public slipway with very limited free trailer parking above, and vehicle parking on adjacent roads at parking meters. Dover Marina in Commercial Quay has a 50 tonne hoist (01304 241663) and showers and toilets to berth holders. Day berths available.
HAZARDS: Dover Western Docks is a busy international port with ferries operating from the Eastern Dock, and passenger liners and the Seacat from the Western Dock. Permission to enter or leave must be obtained from Dover Port Control on channel 74.

Dover Marina, Dover
Dover Harbour Board, Harbour House, Dover, Kent, England CT17 9TF
Lat. 51.1203, Long. 1.3113.
01304 241663

Harbour Slip, Folkestone
Lat. 51.0802, Long. 1.1872.
Folkestone Yacht & Motor Boat Club 01303 251574

CHARGES: None
SUITABILITY: Large trailer needs a car.
ACCESS: ½ tidal. **TYPE OF RAMP:** Concrete **UPPER AREA:** Harbour.
LOWER AREA: Sand.
DIRECTIONS: Slipway is at Folkestone Harbour on The Stade.
RAMP DESCRIPTION: Slipway is at the Folkestone Yacht & Motor Boat Club (01303 251574) has its own slip on The Stade which gives access to the Outer Harbour.
FACILITIES: Parking charges- Pay and display. Space is limited at peak times. Lots of facilities in Folkestone.

Dymchurch, Kent
Lat. 51.0246, Long. 0.9963.
01303875125

CHARGES: The slipway is free, join Dymchurch Angling Club for use of tractors (fishing boats only)
SUITABILITY: Large trailer needs a car.

3

ACCESS: All of tidal range. **TYPE OF RAMP: UPPER AREA:** Concrete. **LOWER AREA:** Sand.
DIRECTIONS: Middle of Dymchurch village, Romney Marsh, Kent.
RAMP DESCRIPTION: Stone-concrete public slipway onto firm sand
FACILITIES: Dymchurch is a seaside holiday resort, with many shops and food outlets. Parking can be found directly opposite the slipway area, fees apply.
HAZARDS: When launching beware of mud between the sand bars

H J Phillips Boatbuilders, Rye
Rock Channel, Rye, East Sussex, England TN31 7HJ
Lat. 50.9499, Long. 0.7373.
01797 223234

Varne Boat Club, Greatstone
Lat. 50.9744, Long. 0.9655.
01797 364640
SUITABILITY: Large trailer needs a car.
ACCESS: All of tidal range. **TYPE OF RAMP: UPPER AREA:** Shingle.
LOWER AREA: Sand.
RAMP DESCRIPTION: Hard standing car park area with plenty of room for cars and trailers. Ramp is wooden sleeper type and slates down to sand beach (when tide is out)
FACILITIES: Member club, with showers, changing rooms, wash down facilities, kitchen, social area with bar 2 pool tables and balcony overlooking the English Channel

Harbour Slip, Rye
Lat. 50.9387, Long. 0.7644.
Rye Harbourmaster - 01797 225225
CHARGES: £13/day £137.35/year.
SUITABILITY: Large trailer needs a car.
ACCESS: ¾ tidal. **TYPE OF RAMP:** Concrete **UPPER AREA:** Harbour.
LOWER AREA: Mud.
DIRECTIONS: Head in to Rye town, then once in Rye, take the A259, and follow the signs to Rye Harbour. Follow the road to the end (about a mile). You will see a caravan site to the right, and a pub and RNLI station to the left. The slip is next to the RNLI station.
RAMP DESCRIPTION: Steep ramp, the bottom tends to be slippery. Tractor assist is available from Rye Harbour Marine telephone 01797 227667 - They are very helpful; current charges are £5 for launch and recovery. The RNLI have their station at the top of the ramp and have priority. The harbourmaster is opposite the slip and will expect you to visit and pay. There is a channel of about 1 kilometre which leads to the sea from the slip. Deeper water in the channel is on the right as you leave. The harbour dries for about 1½ hours either side of low water on Neaps. There can be very strong currents in the channel (6 knot) so beware. Jetskis are welcome provided they observe the speed limit and proceed out to sea and not upstream. Good advice from the Harbour Master available 01797 225225.
FACILITIES: Pub, café, toilets, parking available. It is best to park car and trailer in the nearby public car park. At high water Springs the river bank floods and cars are often caught out with expensive results. The sailing

club car park is for members only and that can flood too. Rye Harbour Sailing Club 01797 223136.
HAZARDS: There is a bar in the channel about 200 yards from the slip. Travelling near low water you should beware.

Cooden Beach, Normans Bay
Lat. 50.8303, Long. 0.4156.
01323 761500
CHARGES: None.
SUITABILITY: Small trailer can be pushed.
ACCESS: No Ramp. **TYPE OF RAMP:** No ramp, launching over a shingle beach. **UPPER AREA:** Shingle. **LOWER AREA:** Shingle.
DIRECTIONS: Head west from the Cooden Beach Hotel along Herbrand Walk towards Eastbourne. 1/2 mile along the road is a flag pole, the launch lane is approx 25 metres each side.
RAMP DESCRIPTION: This is a single beach area marked out for launching of PWCs. It is quite hard going pushing over the shingle, but free and great location. Normally people visit on Sundays, so plenty of help for launching.
FACILITIES: Ice cream van on sunny days. Toilets, bar, restaurant and hotel 1/2 mile away.
HAZARDS: Heavy rocks and soft sand at low tide and a small sand bar on long tides. PWCs can still be launched at low tide with some care.

Premier Marinas (Eastbourne) Ltd, Eastbourne
North Lockside Pacific Drive, Eastbourne, England BN23 5BJ
Lat. 50.7926, Long. 0.3268.
01323 470099

Eastbourne PW Association, Eastbourne
Lat. 50.7812, Long. 0.3153.
01323 509665 / 01323 507833
CHARGES: Launching only at weekends
SUITABILITY: Small trailer can be pushed.
ACCESS: No Ramp. **TYPE OF RAMP:** Shingle beach
UPPER AREA: Shingle. **LOWER AREA:** Shingle.
DIRECTIONS: Follow the Eastbourne seafront in an easterly direction. Look for the Sovereign Leisure Centre. Eastbourne Personal Watercraft Association is located behind the leisure centre on the promenade by the Skate Park just off the Sovereign Parade.
RAMP DESCRIPTION: Assisted launch using Bigfoot. Launching trolley, large diesel winch for recovery.
FACILITIES: Fresh water, electricity, changing room, parking, nearby toilets, skate park, indoor swimming pool, nearby adventure playground. Tesco superstore ¼ mile away. Annual membership is available, contact: Ron Tel.01323 507833 or Richard Tel.01323 509665.
HAZARDS: Proof of current insurance is required before launching. 4 knot speed limit inside 30 meter beach approach.

Piddinghoe Embankment, Newhaven
Lat. 50.8112, Long. 0.0323.
SUITABILITY: Small trailer can be pushed.
ACCESS: ¼ tidal. **TYPE OF RAMP:** Grass slope.
UPPER AREA: Unknown. **LOWER AREA:** Unknown.
DIRECTIONS: Heading north on A275, Piddinghoe is one mile from Newhaven. Turn right at signpost to Piddinghoe, then right signposted to church just past the Royal Oak.
RAMP DESCRIPTION: August 2003, slipway gated and no longer usable. Only suitable for light dinghies as they have to be manhandled down steep grassy slope with steep chalk and flint bank exposed at low tide. Recovery best at high water. Access to Lewes, 6 miles, and Barcombe Mills, 9 miles, the tidal limit. A narrow river, fast at Springs, not suitable for sailing but peaceful and pretty. If going down to Newhaven leave mast down to get under bridge.

Cantell & Son, Newhaven
The Old Shipyard, Robinson Road, Newhaven, East Sussex, England BN9 9BL
Lat. 50.7976, Long. 0.0461.
01273 514118

Peter Leonard Marine, Newhaven
Denton Island, Newhaven, East Sussex, England BN9 9BA
Lat. 50.7974, Long. 0.0496.
01273 515987

Simpson Marine, Newhaven
Lat. 50.7879, Long. 0.0523.
01273 612612
CHARGES: £20 for launch and recovery, £10 one-way.
SUITABILITY: Large trailer needs a car.
ACCESS: ¾ tidal. **TYPE OF RAMP:** Concrete **UPPER AREA:** Concrete.
LOWER AREA: Harbour.
DIRECTIONS: Take the second left after the swing bridge on the one-way system. When you start seeing boats on the left hand side, take the next left. The slipway is 150 yards on the right.
RAMP DESCRIPTION: Well used by chandlery / boat yard close by but staff are friendly. Muddy so best to launch / recover 3 hours either side of high water but possible up to 1hour either side of low water. Ramp is open 9am-5pm 7 days a week. No recovery after 5pm and you will be charged a £10 overnight fee to leave the boat in the water. You should check with the boat yard first. The slipway is only restricted on Spring tides where 2-3 hours either side of low tide must be allowed for. We can launch boats up to 23 ft or Newhaven Marina can be contacted for larger boats.
FACILITIES: Toilets in café, chandlery and dive shop close by. Free parking. Pontoon next to the slipway.
HAZARDS: The slipway leads straight into Newhaven Harbour where large ships and ferries operate.

Newhaven Marina, Newhaven
The Yacht Harbour, Newhaven, East Sussex, England BN9 9BY
Lat. 50.7863, Long. 0.0529.
01273 513881

Brighton Marina, Brighton
Premier Marinas (Brighton) LTD West Jetty Brighton Marina, Brighton, East Sussex, England BN2 5UP
Lat. 50.8099, Long. -0.0969.
01273 819919

Lady Bee Marina, Shoreham by Sea
Lat. 50.8303, Long. -0.2392.
Marina 01273 593801
CHARGES: £16.50 to launch recover and go through lock.
SUITABILITY: Large trailer needs a car.
ACCESS: Non-tidal. **TYPE OF RAMP:** Shallow concrete.
UPPER AREA: Harbour. **LOWER AREA:** Unknown.
DIRECTIONS: Lady Bee Marina, 138 - 140 Albion Street, Southwick, BN42 4EG. Turn off the Brighton Worthing road opposite Shoreham Harbour. Ramp is inside the marina lock gates next to the car park.
RAMP DESCRIPTION: Shallow concrete ramp into marina basin. Popular with RIBs and divers. Not suitable for trailer-sailors due to shallow angle. You can lock out on the hour and in on the half hour. Lock gates do not operate at low water. Tricky to manoeuvre large boats due to restricted room around the slip. Slipways drops off after 5 metres, take care to ensure the trailer wheels do not drop off the end. Also high lip at top of slipway may ground your trailer.
FACILITIES: Limited parking on site. Toilets and showers only available to those who have keys, and pub nearby.

Lady Bee Marina, Southwick
138-140 Albion Street, Southwick, West Sussex, England BN42 4EG
Lat. 50.8308, Long. -0.2382.
01273 593801

Surry Boat Yard, Shoreham-By-Sea
Brighton Rd, Shoreham-By-Sea, West Sussex, England BN43 6RN
Lat. 50.8323, Long. -0.2599.
01273 461491

Brighton Road Ramp, Shoreham by Sea
Lat. 50.8322, Long. -0.2687.
Sussex yacht club 01273 464868
CHARGES: Nominal £5.
SUITABILITY: Large trailer needs a car.
ACCESS: ¾ tidal. **TYPE OF RAMP:** Concrete **UPPER AREA:** Harbour.
LOWER AREA: Mud.

3

DIRECTIONS: On the Brighton Road, by Sussex Yacht Club. Next to the Parcel Force depot and opposite the petrol station.

RAMP DESCRIPTION: The Stow Gap slipway is in the boat/car park of Sussex Yacht Club and it is clearly marked as a public hard. You may have to dig around a bit to find the slipway. It is to seaward of the two town bridges but still about ¾ mile from harbour entrance. Sailing boats only.

FACILITIES: Club facilities are available to members of affiliated clubs.

Ropetackle Ramp, Shoreham by Sea

Lat. 50.8327, Long. -0.2805.

CHARGES: None

SUITABILITY: Large trailer needs a car.

ACCESS: ½ tidal. **TYPE OF RAMP:** Concrete in housing development

UPPER AREA: Concrete. **LOWER AREA:** Mud.

DIRECTIONS: Ramp is just upstream of the Norfolk Bridge on the east bank of the river.

RAMP DESCRIPTION: Upstream of Norfolk Bridge on the East bank and there is another bridge just upstream. This used to be a popular spot for small powered boats but since the site was redeveloped it doesn't seem to get much use. Wide concrete slip, running to mud. Only really usable for a couple of hours either side of high water. At July 07 parking and access for a 6m bowrider was near impossible, car park closed, residents cars all around ramp, access roads very narrow with parked cars. Parking 15-20min walk away over river. Shame-it would be a great ramp to use

FACILITIES: Petrol, parking and chandlery all nearby. No parking immediately by slipway though. Trailer parking at least 20min walk over river,

Emerald Quay, Shoreham by Sea

Lat. 50.8307, Long. -0.2669.

01273 440866

CHARGES: None

SUITABILITY: Large trailer needs a car.

ACCESS: ½ tidal. **TYPE OF RAMP:** Concrete **UPPER AREA:** Concrete.

LOWER AREA: Mud.

DIRECTIONS: Cross over Norfolk Bridge and follow the signs to Shoreham Beach. The ramp is off Riverside Road next to the Emerald Quay Housing Estate. Beware parking restrictions around the ramp (private property) Also, the main road is not signposted as NO Parking but is restricted despite the appearance of parking bays inside the double-yellow lines - as a result, it's a nice little earner for the council and frequently patrolled.

RAMP DESCRIPTION: To seaward of the two town bridges but still about ¾ mile from harbour entrance. Good new concrete slipway that has been rebuilt with the block of flats. The concrete part is fairly short & I recently saw someone trying to recover a boat at fairly low water in a lot of mud & a long way away from the bottom of the ramp.

FACILITIES: None

Riverside Marine, Shoreham Beach

The Boatyard, 41 Riverside Rd, Shoreham Beach, West Sussex, England BN43 5RB

Lat. 50.8299, Long. -0.2698.

01273 441165

Public Slip, Goring by Sea

Lat. 50.8058, Long. -0.4138.

Worthing council 01903 238977

CHARGES: None

SUITABILITY: Small trailer can be pushed.

ACCESS: All of tidal range. **TYPE OF RAMP:** Wooden ramp onto hard sand. **UPPER AREA:** Shingle. **LOWER AREA:** Sand.

DIRECTIONS: Ramp is by the car park at the end of Sea Field Avenue and Marine Crescent.

RAMP DESCRIPTION: Public with a steep gradient, a steep wooden ramp that ends just below high water on open beach of hard sand. No vehicles allowed on the ramp so boats have to be manhandled. A large PWC can be pushed up with two strong people; some users suggest more would be needed. Difficulty of launching at high water depends on sea state. It is only practical to use the slipway about three hours either side of high tide as rocks become exposed as the tide goes out. Jetskis are welcome.

FACILITIES: Parking at the top of the slip. Café nearby and toilets on the seafront. It does get VERY VERY busy with Jetskis in the summer, and the car park is only £1 a day.

HAZARDS: Keep to the buoyed channel and observe the speed limit close to shore. Patrol boats and beach wardens are on duty to ensure safe operations.

Public Slipway, Littlehampton

Lat. 50.8078, Long. -0.5439.

CHARGES: £8 harbour dues. Pay harbourmaster or can be paid at the 'Look and Sea' sited next to the slipway

SUITABILITY: Large trailer needs a car.

ACCESS: ¾ tidal. **TYPE OF RAMP:** Concrete then mud.

UPPER AREA: Concrete. **LOWER AREA:** Mud.

DIRECTIONS: Off high street in public car park. Next door to lifeboat station. Prior to launch PWC operators must visit the Harbour Office for a safety brief and submit a copy of RYA training other wise PWC users will be stopped by the river patrol. The speed limit of 6 knots is strongly monitored and there are CCTV cameras with linked to a radar monitoring system, so be warned.

RAMP DESCRIPTION: This is a brand new public ramp with lifeboat station at the top. Do not leave trailers or obstructions on the slipway. Avoid this slipway during the Littlehampton Regatta which in June unless you want to queue.

FACILITIES: Pub nearby. Car park next to slipway. Best to take trailer up to the Tesco car park and leave it there.

HAZARDS: Harbour entrance on a flooding tide can have 1.5 knots coming around the end as well as a cross tide which comes through the pier which makes it entertaining, not for the novice

Ship and Anchor Marina, Arundel

Ford, Arundel, West Sussex, England BN18 OBJ

Lat. 50.8265, Long. -0.5775.

01243 551262

Littlehampton Marina, Littlehampton
Ferry Road, Littlehampton, West Sussex, England BN17 5DS
Lat. 50.8105, Long. -0.5563.
01903 713553

Marina Slip, Littlehampton
Lat. 50.8101, Long. -0.5531.
01903 713553
CHARGES: Weekdays £24/day. Weekends and Bank Holidays £30.
SUITABILITY: Large trailer needs a car.
ACCESS: ¾ tidal. **TYPE OF RAMP:** Concrete **UPPER AREA:** Concrete.
LOWER AREA: Mud.
DIRECTIONS: From Littlehampton take the A259 toward Bognor. Cross the river on bridge road and take the next left, drive back to the road and turn left again.
RAMP DESCRIPTION: Slipping costs are inclusive with boat park agreements. Must provide a copy of current insurance certificate. Launch within marina operating hours only and up to 1 hour before low water and 2 hours after. Only marina staff may launch or recover craft, no other use is permitted. Please ensure all trailers are in good working order. No Jetskis.
FACILITIES: The marina has space for 110 wet moorings and 230 trailered craft. It also has large areas of hard-standing ground to allow winter storage or works to craft. Slipway launch is available seven days a week and included in the boat-park agreement. All the usual marina facilities are on site. Good wash down facilities.

Gloucester Road, Dorset
Lat. 50.7828, Long. -0.6658.
07973 839379
CHARGES: £7.50 RYA trained skis and boats. £15 untrained. £5 spear-fishers £20 dive ribs
SUITABILITY: Small trailer can be pushed.
ACCESS: All of tidal range. **TYPE OF RAMP:** Concrete onto sand with 3 metre depth of type 2 roadstone beneath. **UPPER AREA:** Shingle.
LOWER AREA: Sand.
DIRECTIONS: Look for access opposite Southcoast World Holiday Camp. Ramp is at Gloucester Road, Bognor Regis, West Sussex.
RAMP DESCRIPTION: Spiritual home of the Bognor Vegas Crew Jetskiers. Onsite training available by RYA instructor of the year 2007. Jetskiers are very welcome here, busy on summer weekends and hardcore only during winter. Please follow the rules posted. Two strikes and you are out. To access ramp go through the car park and across the Prom. Security/Lookout/launch assistance onsite April-September. Safety boat covers Littlehampton to Selsey Bill. Keep to the right at the bottom of the ramp as vehicles can get stuck in the clay to the left, assisted launching is available during the summer. Popular with skiers and divers. Shingle can restrict access during high winter tides, best ring first.
FACILITIES: Plenty of dedicated parking for cars £6 per day. Trailer parking free. Gets busy in the summer so get there early for a space. From April to September there is an onsite safety patrol and fresh water flushing point all year round. Good wreck diving nearby. Refreshments close by and family friendly bathing beach adjacent to launch area.

HAZARDS: None at high water. Rocks half mile west at low water.

East Beach, Selsey
Lat. 50.7341, Long. -0.7721.
CHARGES: None
SUITABILITY: Small trailer can be pushed.
ACCESS: ¼ tidal. **TYPE OF RAMP:** Wood **UPPER AREA:** Concrete.
LOWER AREA: Sand.
DIRECTIONS: Through the free car park at East Beach, Selsey.
RAMP DESCRIPTION: A bit steep. Firm sand at base of ramp. Tide goes out a long way.
FACILITIES: Pub up the road, - Lifeboat

West Sands Caravan Park, Selsey Bill
Lat. 50.7375, Long. -0.8143.
01784 253130 (Alan Rust)
CHARGES: £25 including launch and recovery and trailer parking.
SUITABILITY: Large trailer needs a car.
ACCESS: ¾ tidal. **TYPE OF RAMP:** Fully concrete ramp then onto shingle (at low tide) **UPPER AREA:** Concrete. **LOWER AREA:** Shingle.
DIRECTIONS: From Selsey Bill head for the Warner Sands Leisure and caravan park. Once on the site head for the Oasis leisure complex and the slipway is opposite.
RAMP DESCRIPTION: Steep ramp but the club operating it launch for you using a tractor (self launch NOT allowed). Maximum length of boat not to exceed 18feet with outboard OR 17ft 6ins with inboard due to ramp angle. FEES- Annual membership is £300 but includes boat storage if you wish. Casual membership is £25 per day including launch or £100 per week including launch. Ring before going to ensure launch facilities are available. Ask for Alan Rust or email HMAvison@lineone.net
FACILITIES: Parking for both car and trailer with pub and entertainment complex opposite. Campsite available locally and shops in Selsey Bill.
HAZARDS: Speed restriction of 8knots within 300 yards of the beach shown by yellow buoys.

Hill Field Road, Selsy
Lat. 50.7246, Long. -0.7969.
SUITABILITY: Small trailer can be pushed.
ACCESS: No Ramp. **TYPE OF RAMP:** Concrete **UPPER AREA:** Concrete.
LOWER AREA: Shingle.
RAMP DESCRIPTION: Concrete ramp through the breakwater onto the shingle beach. Ramp has a dog leg in it so only small boats can be launched here.

Slipway, Bracklesham Bay
Lat. 50.7608, Long. -0.8606.
CHARGES: No charge for launching. Car park charges for car only, trailer free.
SUITABILITY: Large trailer needs a car.
ACCESS: ¼ tidal. **TYPE OF RAMP:** Concrete onto beach.
UPPER AREA: Concrete. **LOWER AREA:** Sand.
DIRECTIONS: From Portsmouth follow A 27 to Chichester roundabout, turn right onto A286 for Witterings, follow main road till petrol garage

3

on right, then turn left at mini-roundabout B2198 and follow the road to Bracklesham. Car park and good slipway at the end of this road.

RAMP DESCRIPTION: Concrete ramp leading to hard sand beach. The ramp is public and can get busy in the hot weather; the car park can also be very busy in high season. Trailers can be left at top of ramp in trailer parking area. Best for large boats at 1-2 hours either side of tide. Speed restrictions 8 knots 300 metres from beach marked by yellow buoys. Chichester District Council operate a Safety Patrol Service from this location, they do not offer a launching service but the staff there will assist with launching/retrieval where difficulties are being experienced, this will be carried out without charge. February 2009 - the slipway is currently blocked by 'sea defences' – approximately 4 foot high gravel bank across the slip. It was not apparent if this is a temporary winter feature or permanent.

FACILITIES: Cafeteria, drinks, toilets, shops pubs, fuel about 300 yards. Fish and chips, camping sites, children's water toys at top of ramp. Steps leading to ramp are good viewing point of Solent and Isle of Wight on clear day. Watch for red flag as good indication of wind state, this area often wins on the clean beach guide and is very good for children of all ages.

HAZARDS: The ramp area is nearly always crowded with small children so BE VERY CAREFUL as ramp is only 10 feet wide and used for playing by the bucket and spade brigade.

Itchenor Hard, Itchenor
Lat. 50.8075, Long. -0.8674.

CHARGES: Yes
SUITABILITY: Large trailer needs a car.
ACCESS: All of tidal range. **TYPE OF RAMP:** Public hard
UPPER AREA: Shingle. **LOWER AREA:** Shingle.
DIRECTIONS: Head for Chichester and take the ring road and follow the signs for the Whitterings. On the road to the Witterings go past Chichester Marina and follow the signs for Itchenor. The ramp is at the end of the road.

RAMP DESCRIPTION: Wide expanse of hard shingle that is suitable for large boats and car. The gradient is shallow higher up so may be best to launch larger boats at low tide on a steeper gradient. There can be a swift cross current. Nearest clubs Itchenor Sailing Club. Site manager, Chichester Harbour Conservancy. The main access point for trailed craft using Chichester Harbour.

FACILITIES: Car parking limited at hard, but large pay and display car park nearby. Boat parking within car park. Clean toilets are beneath the Harbour Office and there is a water hose at the top of the hard.

HAZARDS: 8 knots speed limit. Water skiing prohibited and those caught waterskiing will be prosecuted.

Birdham Pool, Chichester
Birdham, Chichester, West Sussex, England
PO20 7BG
Lat. 50.8020, Long. -0.8322.
01243 512310

Chichester Marina, Chichester
Birdham, Chichester, West Sussex, England
PO20 7EJ
Lat. 50.8031, Long. -0.8197.
01243 512731

Chichester Marina, Chichester
Lat. 50.8044, Long. -0.8182.
Marina Office, 01243 512731

CHARGES: £16.50 inc. vat for launch and recovery.
SUITABILITY: Large trailer needs a car.
ACCESS: Non-tidal. **TYPE OF RAMP:** Concrete **UPPER AREA:** Concrete.
LOWER AREA: Harbour.
DIRECTIONS: From the Chichester By-pass (A27) follow the signs to Wittering (A286). Chichester Marina is situated within 2 miles on the right hand side.

RAMP DESCRIPTION: Launch into the sheltered marina basin, there is trailer storage if required. The marina is locked in and out but has free flow for up to four and a half hours dependent on tides. Pontoon is available for loading and unloading.

FACILITIES: The marina offers restaurant and bar facilities and has its own general store. Yachting needs are served by Peters - The One Stop Boat Shop. Fuel and slipway services with free parking. Also travel hoist, toilets, showers and launderette, winter boat storage, 24 hour security and Yacht club. Wash down and outboard flushing tank available.

HAZARDS: Two tide gauges (one in the lock and one on pile number six) indicate the depth of water in the channel, and a red flashing light, situated on the roof of the lock control, indicates when the depth has dropped to less than one metre. All mariners should ensure that they have enough depth for their draught for both the marina channel itself and the Chichester Harbour bar. If you are in any doubt or need assistance then contact the lock control on VHF Channel 80 or 37.

Slipway, Dell Quay
Lat. 50.8196, Long. -0.8160.

CHARGES: None
SUITABILITY: Large trailer needs a car.
ACCESS: ½ tidal. **TYPE OF RAMP:** Hard **UPPER AREA:** Shingle.
LOWER AREA: Mud.
DIRECTIONS: Dell Quay is signposted off the A286.
RAMP DESCRIPTION: Suitable for all trailer craft, subject to speed limit. No water-skiing. Launch site faces west. Nearest clubs Dell Quay Sailing Club. Predominantly used by Dell Quay Sailing Club and Apuldram Fishing and Boating Club. Only crowded at peak times - Sundays and Bank Holidays.

FACILITIES: Limited space for parking. Petrol 1½ miles in Stockbridge, provisions in Chichester 2 miles.

HAZARDS: 8 knots speed limit, water skiing prohibited.

Bosham Lane, Bosham
Lat. 50.8290, Long. -0.8555.
CHARGES: Harbour dues payable.

SUITABILITY: Small trailer can be pushed.
ACCESS: ½ tidal. **TYPE OF RAMP:** Slipway **UPPER AREA:** Shingle.
LOWER AREA: Mud.
DIRECTIONS: Bosham is signposted off the A260.
RAMP DESCRIPTION: Suitable for small craft only, subject to speed limit. No water-skiing. Seldom used and frequently blocked by cars.
FACILITIES: Free car parking but beware as Shore Road regularly floods at high tide. Boat parking in car park. Nearest clubs Bosham Sailing Club.
HAZARDS: 10 knots speed limit, water skiing prohibited.

Bosham Quay, Bosham
Lat. 50.8280, Long. -0.8614.

CHARGES: Harbour dues payable plus £6 for the day launch/recovery.
SUITABILITY: Small trailer can be pushed.
ACCESS: All of tidal range. **TYPE OF RAMP:** Public slipway
UPPER AREA: Concrete. **LOWER AREA:** Concrete.
DIRECTIONS: Bosham is signposted off the A259. The approach to the ramp is through a winding narrow road by the waters edge. The Quay Masters hut is at the top of the ramp.
RAMP DESCRIPTION: Suitable for small craft only, subject to speed limit. No water-skiing. Very busy with dinghy launching during summer weekends. The concrete ramp runs down about 70 metres and is covered at all but Spring lows when there is no water in the Bosham Channel anyway. To the side of the ramp is a deeper channel where the river flows in that can be used for tying up once launched. The ramp is very gradual and is concrete all the way into the water.
FACILITIES: Nearest clubs Bosham Sailing Club.
HAZARDS: 10 knots speed limit, water skiing prohibited. Nature reserve so be careful of wash

Slipway, Prinsted
Lat. 50.8400, Long. -0.9137.

CHARGES: No, but harbour dues payable.
SUITABILITY: Small trailer can be pushed.
ACCESS: ½ tidal. **TYPE OF RAMP:** Foreshore **UPPER AREA:** Shingle.
LOWER AREA: Shingle.
DIRECTIONS: Signs to Prinsted off A259.
RAMP DESCRIPTION: Suitable for small sailing boats. Launch site faces south.
FACILITIES: Car parking roadside, 6 cars. Boat parking in car park. Nearest clubs Prinsted Sea Scouts.
HAZARDS: Bye-Laws 10 knots speed limit, water skiing prohibited.

Thornham Marina, Emsworth
Thornham Lane, Prinsted, Emsworth, Hampshire, England PO10 8DD
Lat. 50.8362, Long. -0.9166.
01243 375335

Thorney Island SC Slip, West Thorney
Lat. 50.8169, Long. -0.9083.
Watersports Centre: 01243 388315

CHARGES: None. Permission must be obtained from either the Thorney Island Watersports Centre, 01243 388315, or a member of the Thorney Island Sailing Club, who must be present. Access is restricted, as the TIWSC is on military land.
SUITABILITY: Small trailer can be pushed.
ACCESS: All of tidal range. **TYPE OF RAMP:** Concrete.
UPPER AREA: Concrete. **LOWER AREA:** Concrete.
DIRECTIONS: Permission must be obtained from either the Thorney Island Watersports Centre, 01243 388315, or a member of the Thorney Island Sailing Club, who must be present when a guest is entering the site. Access is restricted, as the TIWSC is on military land.
RAMP DESCRIPTION: Two slipways, both restricted to TIWSC members, guests and pupils under instruction. 1. Short wide slipway, available between 1-2 hours either side of high water. Shallow at Neaps. This slipway can be used by shallow draft trailed yachts. 2. Long narrow ramp reducing in width at lower end. Keep on slipway: deep mud either side. Available most tides except low water Springs. This slipway is suitable for dinghies and other small craft.
FACILITIES: Car park 250 yards. Slip water tap on wall at top of slipway. Thorney Island SC nearby only open weekends. No storage for large trailers at the top of the slip. Access may be restricted if army training courses are using the slip.
HAZARDS: Mud

Emsworth Yacht Harbour, Emsworth
Thorney Road, Emsworth, Hampshire, England PO10 8BP
Lat. 50.8429, Long. -0.9301.
01243 377727

Emsworth Yacht Harbour, Emsworth
Lat. 50.8431, Long. -0.9305.
01243 377727

CHARGES: £10/day
SUITABILITY: Large trailer needs a car.
ACCESS: All of tidal range. **TYPE OF RAMP:** Concrete
UPPER AREA: Harbour. **LOWER AREA:** Harbour.
DIRECTIONS: Come off A27 onto A259 towards Emsworth. Just after passing through Emsworth turn right onto Thorney Road. Shortly after that, turn right into Tarquin and then keep right. The slip is at the end behind the buildings.
RAMP DESCRIPTION: Narrow ramp about 9′ and access to the slip is often difficult because of yachts at the base of the slip and boats on the crane at the top. Not much room in the water so large boats will need walking on and off the trailer using ropes, but plenty of pontoons to do so. Ramp can be used at all tides, but access to the yacht harbour is tidal. On the plus side, no tide and very well protected from wind. Access to the marina is 3 hours either side of high water.
FACILITIES: Yacht Harbour has parking and chandlery. There is a winch at the top of the slip. The key is available from the marina office. Office staff are friendly and helpful. Pubs, restaurant in Emsworth nearby.
HAZARDS: Bye-Laws 8 knots speed limit. Water skiing prohibited.

3

South Street, Emsworth

Lat. 50.8444, Long. -0.9374.

SUITABILITY: Small trailer can be pushed.

ACCESS: ½ tidal. **TYPE OF RAMP:** Concrete **UPPER AREA:** Shingle. **LOWER AREA:** Mud.

DIRECTIONS: Slipway is situated at the end of South Street off Esmworth High Street.

RAMP DESCRIPTION: Public slipway. It gets crowded with dinghy sailors at high tide, even in winter, and the sides of the slip are obstructed with launch trailers.

FACILITIES: Toilets and chandlery. Public parking is close by (40p for the first hour).

HAZARDS: Bye-Laws 8 knots speed limit, water skiing prohibited.

Langstone Bridge, Langstone

Lat. 50.8373, Long. -0.9803.

CHARGES: Launching permits from harbour office in Itchenor

SUITABILITY: Large trailer needs a car.

ACCESS: ½ tidal. **TYPE OF RAMP:** Public slipway

UPPER AREA: Concrete. **LOWER AREA:** Mud.

DIRECTIONS: Situated on the side of the road where the A3023 crosses over onto Hayling Island on the north shore next to the Ship Inn.

RAMP DESCRIPTION: The slipway has a difficult entrance off busy main road opposite Langstone Sailing Club. There are two slipways, a large one next to the bridge and a smaller one opposite the Ship Inn. Both have large expanses of shingle so portable boats can get in the water at least two hours either side of high tide. Gives access into a tidal creek. A long way from the open sea so not really suitable for power boats but great for rowing. The water is simply brilliant, open enough to get a good speed up without having to look round all the time, but sheltered enough not to worry about going in. The area is often congested and it may be better to use Northney slipway. Please do not use the Sailing Club slipway on the west side of the bridge. Upper ramp area is compacted gravel on mud. Lower ramp is gravel and rough stones and only suitable for tenders or small dinghies - both areas can be coated with mud particularly at Spring tides.

FACILITIES: Sailing club and petrol nearby. Langstone is a picture postcard village, with two pubs and the stump of a windmill looking out on the harbour towards Hayling Island. Oddly, it looks out on Chichester harbour, not Langstone. Car parks are often full with pub traffic and the slipway is can get blocked off with cars. Parking is limited to the roadside verge on access road. Parking is NOT allowed on the foreshore.

HAZARDS: Strong tidal flow. It is not advisable to allow children to launch small rubber or plastic boats. Please note this is a no planing area and owners of this type of boat should launch further down the estuary.

Northney Marina, Hayling Island

Northney Road, Hayling Island, Hampshire, England PO11 0NH

Lat. 50.8333, Long. -0.9676.

023 9246 6321

Marina Slip, Northney

Lat. 50.8321, Long. -0.9682.

Northney Marina 023 9246 6321

CHARGES: £20/day.

SUITABILITY: Large trailer needs a car.

ACCESS: All of tidal range. **TYPE OF RAMP:** Concrete

UPPER AREA: Harbour. **LOWER AREA:** Mud.

DIRECTIONS: From the A27, first left over the bridge to Northney. After 200 yards or so, go straight on to where the road goes sharp left. It will appear as if you are driving into the hotel. Sign posted Northney Marina.

RAMP DESCRIPTION: Big enough for a large trailer, but narrow. The bottom can get very muddy at low tide. The ramp is steep, may need four wheel drive. Can get busy. The slipway now has a pontoon next to it and the actual slipway concrete was replaced a couple of years ago 2007/8

FACILITIES: Good facilities at the marina. Showers toilets. Sport shop selling windsurf gear. Petrol nearby. Secure parking with payment of launching fee.

HAZARDS: 8 knot speed restriction in the harbour. Channels are well marked.

The Hayling Yacht, Hayling Island

Mill Rythe Lane, Hayling Island, Hampshire, England PO11 0QQ

Lat. 50.8053, Long. -0.9715.

02392 463592

Sparkes Yacht Harbour, Hayling Island

38 Wittering Road, Sandy Point, Hayling Island, Hants, England PO11 9SR

Lat. 50.7852, Long. -0.9418.

02392 463572

Seafront, Hayling

Lat. 50.7847, Long. -1.0003.

CHARGES: None

SUITABILITY: Portable Only.

ACCESS: All of tidal range. **TYPE OF RAMP:** Beach launching.

UPPER AREA: Sand. **LOWER AREA:** Sand.

DIRECTIONS: Signposted off Ferry Road.

RAMP DESCRIPTION: Suitable for: Portable, non-motorised craft only. Launch site faces south. Beachlands staff in summer. Probably the most significant windsurf site on the south coast.

FACILITIES: Car parking for 300 cars, no charge. Boat parking in car park. Toilets.

HAZARDS: Bye-Laws 10 knots speed limit within 500 yards of shore, windsurfing zone in force during summer.

Eastney Ferry Ramp, Hayling Island

Lat. 50.7962, Long. -1.0257.

CHARGES: Jetski: £14.50/day, £90/year. Boat: £8.40/day, £59.44/year.

SUITABILITY: Large trailer needs a car.

ACCESS: All of tidal range. **TYPE OF RAMP:** Car ferry ramp.

UPPER AREA: Harbour. **LOWER AREA:** Shingle.

3

DIRECTIONS: Situated on the south western tip of Hayling Island. Follow road onto western tip of Hayling Island next to Ferryboat Inn. 15-20 minutes from A3M but it can take a lot longer to get of the Island on busy weekends.

RAMP DESCRIPTION: Steep and wide concrete ramp into the harbour entrance, east side. This was an old ferry ramp, can be step off the end at low Spring tide, tide race at half tide can make launch and recovery difficult. Possible to launch off the beach to the seaward side with a 4 × 4 vehicle. Difficult for car at low water, ramp get covered in pebbles after storm and even 4 × 4 have trouble, take a tow rope. Can get crowded in the summer.

FACILITIES: Parking in The Ferry Boat car park and public car park. Both charge and get very busy. A recovery vehicle is available. Ask chandlers nearby. If you park in the Ferry Road you are likely to get a ticket. Harbour office and compound, public loos, shower (cold) attached to harbour office.

HAZARDS: Speed restriction in the harbour. Area is very popular with PWC and there can be a lot of traffic. When the tide is running the entrance to Langstone Harbour has a strong current and can get very rough.

Slipway, North Hayling Halt
Lat. 50.8210, Long. -0.9829.

CHARGES: None
SUITABILITY: Portable Only.
ACCESS: ¼ tidal. **TYPE OF RAMP:** Beach launching.
UPPER AREA: Unknown. **LOWER AREA:** Unknown.
DIRECTIONS: Off Langstone Road.
RAMP DESCRIPTION: Suitable for: Portable, non-motorised craft only. Launch site faces west. An important small scale windsurfing venue which can attract reasonably substantial use. Background of concern about windsurfers landing on RSPB Reserve, although this situation appears generally well managed.
FACILITIES: Free car parking 40 cars. Boat parking in car park.
HAZARDS: 10 knots speed limit, water skiing permitted only in designated area with permission from harbourmaster.

Brockhampton Quay (Broadmarsh Slipway), Brockhampton
Lat. 50.8436, Long. -1.0032.
HM 01705 463419

CHARGES: Harbour dues are payable to Langstone Harbour Board, but patrols are rare.
SUITABILITY: Large trailer needs a car.
ACCESS: ¾ tidal. **TYPE OF RAMP:** Smooth concrete
UPPER AREA: Concrete. **LOWER AREA:** Concrete.
DIRECTIONS: The ramp is in an industrial area and can be tricky to find. From the W on A27, take A3(M) and then the first slip road, signed B2177 Bedhampton. Go round the large roundabout (i.e. under the A3) and take the 4th exit. Cross the bridge over the A27 and go straight across the next roundabout. Keep going straight ahead down Harts Farm Lane and look for turning to R after about 1/3 mile. Lane leads to car park and slipway after about 500 yards.
RAMP DESCRIPTION: This slipway is officially called Broadmarsh Slipway, and is within the Broadmarsh conservation area. There is a

6ft high entry barrier to prevent occupation by travellers, so beware of dinghy masts. A very wide concrete ramp will take several trailers side by side. Moderate slope, slippery with mud near bottom, especially on falling tide. Bottom of ramp just covered at 3.0m of tide. The area immediately beyond the ramp is cluttered with obstacles at low water.
FACILITIES: Parking area may be congested in busy summer periods. Nice views to seaward, Tescos nearby, about a mile from A3(M). No mooring buoys or pontoons. The site is open to the public at all times, remote from housing and unsupervised, so overnight parking is inadvisable.
HAZARDS: Concrete blocks and other junk at low water levels off the end of the ramp. Langstone Harbour gives a long fetch to the south and south west, with consequent chop at the launch site in strong winds from those directions. 10 knot speed limit in the harbour.

Southsea Marina, Portsmouth
Fort Cumberland Road, Portsmouth, Hampshire, England PO4 9RJ
Lat. 50.7917, Long. -1.0338.
023 9282 2719

Langstone Harbour Entrance, Portsmouth
Lat. 50.7892, Long. -1.0290.

CHARGES: Free
SUITABILITY: Large trailer needs a car.
ACCESS: All of tidal range. **TYPE OF RAMP:** Concrete
UPPER AREA: Concrete. **LOWER AREA:** Concrete.
DIRECTIONS: Turn right into a lane before the Eastney Cruising Assoc. compound
RAMP DESCRIPTION: Public slipway, concrete ramp. No charge, free parking. Access all states of the tide except low water Springs, where the bottom of the ramp had a drop. Also after storms the concrete may be swept by loose gravel
FACILITIES: Free parking
HAZARDS: Fast tides at mid tide range

Eastney Beach, Eastney
Lat. 50.7922, Long. -1.0295.

CHARGES: Jetski: £10.00/day, £71.25/year. Boat: £8.40/day, £59.44/year. Fees payable to Langstone harbour board; their office is by the ferry pontoon on the Hayling side.
SUITABILITY: Large trailer needs a car.
ACCESS: All of tidal range. **TYPE OF RAMP:** Concrete
UPPER AREA: Shingle. **LOWER AREA:** Sand.
DIRECTIONS: From A3M follow on west to A27, take the next slip and turn left at roundabout, follow A2030 Eastern Road around the Harbour after which it becomes Velder Rd. At mini roundabout turn left on A288, at 2nd set of lights turn left into Bransbury Rd, follow road until road bears sharp right, turn left but take right hand fork along Fort Cumberland Road. Keep the Fort on your right. On your left you will see a marina. There is a small turning on the right that takes you through

3

the sand dunes to the launch. The turning is just before the Eastney Cruising club.

RAMP DESCRIPTION: Wide concrete ramp, busy in the summer, you may have to queue to launch and recover. At low tide the sand adjacent to the ramp is firm and it is possible to recover from the beach when the ramp is busy. This slip is shared with the Southsea Sea Angling Club who is only able to help those who are members of the club (due to insurance limitations). This slip is useable at almost all states if tide, but do not go off the end of the slip at very low Spring tides in anything other that a 4 wheel drive vehicle. Countless cars caught out here. Eastney Cruising Association runs the two adjacent slipways. The one that launches into the fast moving part of Langstone harbour (often referred to as THE RUN) adjacent to the public slipway, is private and for the use of ECA members only. The one that launches into the part of Langstone Harbour know as 'Eastney Lake' is run by the ECA and does have public access but is tidal and only really useable 1-2 hours either side of high tide. The slips in the main channel are very exposed to south or north winds. The slipway does get covered by shingle following winter storms, the local council are responsible for keeping it clear, but use a contractor who often fails to perform, as a result the slip has a 18-24" hump of shingle which is difficult to manoeuvre over as trailer wheels dig in badly.

FACILITIES: Good car parking. Does get busy. Usually there is a food stand. Langstone Marina 200 yards. Slipway is usually only manned at the weekend.

HAZARDS: Very strong currents in the harbour entrance when the tide is running. Popular with Jetskis, lots of high speed traffic. There is a speed limit of 10 knots in the harbour and there are restrictions on certain activities. There is access to Chichester Harbour under the Hayling road bridge for vessels of low air draught at certain states of the tide.

Seafront, Southsea
Lat. 50.7798, Long. -1.0701.

CHARGES: None
SUITABILITY: Portable Only.
ACCESS: All of tidal range. **TYPE OF RAMP:** Beach launching.
UPPER AREA: Unknown. **LOWER AREA:** Unknown.
DIRECTIONS: Well Signposted.
RAMP DESCRIPTION: Portable, non-motorised craft only. Launch site faces south. Lifeguards during summer season. Important windsurfing area, although I believe it is not as well used as Hayling or Stokes Bay.
FACILITIES: Car parking for 500 cars on seafront. Car park charges in some areas. Toilets.
HAZARDS: 10 knots within 1000 metres of shore, waterskiing prohibited within 1000 metres of shore except in designated areas. Windsurfing prohibited in Portsmouth Harbour approach and within shipping channels.

Camber Dock, Portsmouth
Lat. 50.7921, Long. -1.1080.
Ken Brown Boats (023) 9281 4246

CHARGES: £2.50 each way
SUITABILITY: Large trailer needs a car.
ACCESS: All of tidal range. **TYPE OF RAMP:** Concrete
UPPER AREA: Harbour. **LOWER AREA:** Harbour.

DIRECTIONS: From the M275 follow the signs to Camber Dock. Keep going to Camber Dock, veer right into Broad Street and finally you have to go right into a one way system that takes you to the ramp.
RAMP DESCRIPTION: Wide ramp with a barrier entry system. You will require £2.50 to operate the barrier. Recent construction has reduced the width of the ramp so that it will only take two cars at time and occasional fishing boats on the slip can reduce width to one boat. Still a good place to launch. Bottom of the slip does get slippery but four wheel drive cars do not seem to have much problem pulling boats up at low water. Jetskis are not allowed to launch from here.
FACILITIES: Wide ramp with parking nearby (£6.00 for the full day). You can park for several days. From the top of the ramp turn right and follow the one way system left and left again. This takes you into the main car park. The trailer park is towards the water opposite a large shed.
HAZARDS: All vessels must cross the Main Channel direct to Ballast Buoy and leave harbour through the Small Boat Channel. Vessels fitted with engines are to use them until exiting the Small Boat channel.

Portsea Common Hard, Portsmouth
Lat. 50.7982, Long. -1.1071.
SUITABILITY: Large trailer needs a car.
ACCESS: ¾ tidal. **TYPE OF RAMP:** Hard **UPPER AREA:** Unknown.
LOWER AREA: Mud.
DIRECTIONS: On the harbour front just to the north of the Portsmouth Harbour Railway station.
RAMP DESCRIPTION: Wide public hard gives shallow access into the harbour. Well used by locals.
HAZARDS: If you are intending to exit Portsmouth Harbour, you must obtain permission from Harbour Control on VHF Channel 11 before proceeding. All vessels are then to cross the Main Channel direct to Ballast Buoy and leave harbour through the Small Boat Channel. Vessels fitted with engines are to use them until exiting the Small Boat channel. Check in with Harbour Control on VHF Ch11 on your return.

Port Solent Marina, Portsmouth
South Lockside, Port Solent, Portsmouth, Hampshire, England PO6 4TJ
Lat. 50.8420, Long. -1.1015.
02392 210765

Port Solent, Portsmouth
Lat. 50.8460, Long. -1.1025.

CHARGES: None
SUITABILITY: Large trailer needs a car.
ACCESS: ¼ tidal. **TYPE OF RAMP:** Shallow cobbles.
UPPER AREA: Concrete. **LOWER AREA:** Concrete.
DIRECTIONS: By Car; from the West, motorway access is via the M27 at junction 12. From the East, take the Hilsea exit off the A27, and follow the signs to Port Solent. From the City, take the M275 and again, follow the signs to Port Solent. The ramp is to the north of Port Solent and not part of the marina. On entering the Port Solent traffic lights, perform a U-turn round the first roundabout, and the ramp is the left turn after Lock View road just before the traffic lights.

RAMP DESCRIPTION: The ramp is owned by Portsmouth City Council and is free to use. Being at the top end of the harbour, it can get rather choked with weed; the Council clear it three or four times a year.

FACILITIES: Limited parking on the grass by the side of the ramp (approximately two cars) or in Lock View Road (approximately six cars).

HAZARDS: Shallow water outside the main channel beware mud banks and underwater obstructions between the ramp and Port Solent at mid or low tide. The entrance to Port Solent lock can result in heavy traffic at times. Ten knot speed limit in Portsmouth Harbour, four knots above Portchester Castle. No waterskiing in the harbour.

Wicormarine Ltd, Portchester

Lat. 50.8404, Long. -1.1458.

01329 237112

CHARGES: Call office.

SUITABILITY: Large trailer needs a car.

ACCESS: ¼ tidal. **TYPE OF RAMP:** Concrete **UPPER AREA:** Concrete. **LOWER AREA:** Mud.

DIRECTIONS: Turn off M27 at Junction 11 towards Gosport and Fareham. Almost immediately bear left and then turn left at roundabout on A27 towards Portchester. At second roundabout, approximately 1 mile, turn right. This passes a pub on the left hand side - 300 yards the road turns sharp left, turn sharp right and follow this road for approximately ¼ mile past houses on left and fields on right. After new estate on left, turn left into road leading to Wicomarine. Wicomarine office is on the left of the slipway.

RAMP DESCRIPTION: Not a public slipway, Wicormarine is a working boatyard and during the busy launching and hauling-out periods in the spring and autumn, the slipway is in constant use and it is not suitable for DIY launching. However, during the sailing season, the slipway may be used for DIY launching and recovery but only with prior arrangement with the office. Cost for DIY launch and recovery is £50 inclusive. This includes use of the car park for one car and trailer for the day. Additional charges may apply for longer periods. Tidal swinging moorings available for short term periods.

FACILITIES: Chandlery, parking, toilets - no fuel. In winter car parking taken up by yachts being over wintered.

HAZARDS: Shallow water and mud.

Fareham Marine, Fareham

Lower Quay, Fareham, Hants, England PO16 0RA

Lat. 50.8475, Long. -1.1789.

01329 822445

Lower Quay, Fareham

Lat. 50.8463, Long. -1.1791.

CHARGES: None

SUITABILITY: Large trailer needs a car.

ACCESS: ¼ tidal. **TYPE OF RAMP:** Concrete ramp.

UPPER AREA: Concrete. **LOWER AREA:** Mud.

DIRECTIONS: Slipway is in Lower Quay Road.

RAMP DESCRIPTION: Roadway down onto a shingle foreshore. Well used and maintained facility. Only room for 1 launch/recovery at a time. Can get congested if several boats are waiting to launch/recover

FACILITIES: Parking for car and trailer is available in car park adjacent to slipway- charge (2004) is £1 per night for car, £1 per night trailer, payable at Fairweather Marine next to the car park.

Hardway Slip, Gosport

Lat. 50.8134, Long. -1.1341.

02392 723694

CHARGES: None

SUITABILITY: Large trailer needs a car.

ACCESS: ¾ tidal. **TYPE OF RAMP:** Concrete block sloping foreshore to mud. Hardway SC website relates to this area: http://www.hardwaysailingclub.co.uk/ **UPPER AREA:** Concrete.

LOWER AREA: Mud.

DIRECTIONS: Hardway is at the northern end of Gosport. The slipway is off Priory Road.The postcode of the nearby Hardway Chandlery (good) is PO2 4LF. The foreshore area is spacious and includes a smooth concrete scrubbing bay controlled by Hardway SC.

RAMP DESCRIPTION: Go through a small car park (3hr max) straight down onto a sloping concrete block foreshore, once part of a naval facility. Slope is moderate but the concrete blocks are uneven and a car may be needed for recovery. Bottom of slip dries to a gravel patch and slushy mud. Rise of approx 2.5m above chart datum is needed to launch from the gravel patch at foot of slip.

FACILITIES: Recent development in the area means that parking may be a problem, but there is a large free car park about 300 yards from ramp. Hardway SC is a very popular and busy sailing club which is friendly to visitors. They have a long pontoon which does not dry and may be used by visitors subject to permission - note that it has a security gate. A shorter public pontoon may be used for loading dinghies, but dries at its outer end at about 1.5m above chart datum.

HAZARDS: Very busy especially in harbour entrance - ferries, naval activity, police security patrols, much yachting. Keep well clear of naval craft and shore bases.

Royal Clarence Marina, Gosport

Royal Clarence Marina Weevil Lane, Gosport, Hampshire, England PO12 1AX

Lat. 50.8021, Long. -1.1250.

023 9252 3523

Coldharbour, Gosport

Lat. 50.7968, Long. -1.1210.

Gosport council 02392 545421

CHARGES: None

SUITABILITY: Small trailer can be pushed.

ACCESS: ½ tidal. **TYPE OF RAMP:** Concrete ramp.

UPPER AREA: Harbour. **LOWER AREA:** Mud.

DIRECTIONS: Slipway is off Harbour Road which is accessed via Mumby Road.

RAMP DESCRIPTION: There is a steep drop of 2 feet at the end of the ramp. The slip is awkward to access, being right on the edge of a roadway. It's also very narrow, only 8 feet wide.

FACILITIES: No parking available nearby. Moorings are available.

The Good Launch Guide

Gosport Marina, Gosport
Mumby Road, Gosport, Hampshire, England
PO12 1AH
Lat. 50.7962, Long. -1.1176.
023 9252 4811

Haslar Marina, Gosport
Lat. 50.7912, Long. -1.1221.
Haslar Marina 023 9260 1201

CHARGES: None
SUITABILITY: Large trailer needs a car.
ACCESS: ½ tidal. **TYPE OF RAMP:** Public hard **UPPER AREA:** Shingle.
LOWER AREA: Mud.
DIRECTIONS: Slipway is next to Haslar Marina by Seaway Marine.
RAMP DESCRIPTION: Shingle and mud hard. Dodgy below half tide but maybe possible with a 4 × 4. Also need to take into consideration the air draught below the bridge to get into the marina and out to sea. Only about 1.5 metres clearance at high tide.
FACILITIES: Parking for trailers for 48 hours only at the ramp. Cars must be moved elsewhere. Speak to the marina and it should be possible to use their car park if you take a day berth. Also you can then use their toilet and shower facilities.

Slipway, Alverstoke Creek
Lat. 50.7852, Long. -1.1396.

CHARGES: None
SUITABILITY: Small trailer can be pushed.
ACCESS: ¼ tidal. **TYPE OF RAMP:** Public slipway
UPPER AREA: Concrete. **LOWER AREA:** Mud.
DIRECTIONS: Proceed east along Stokes Bay turning left at mini roundabout. Take 3rd right into Little Anglesea Road and continue until the road veers left. The slipway is on your immediate right.
RAMP DESCRIPTION: Short concrete slipway used by general public and local Sea Scouts.
FACILITIES: Free parking in lay-by opposite
HAZARDS: 10kt speed limit.

Haslar Marina, Gosport
Haslar Road, Gosport, Hampshire, England
PO12 1NU
Lat. 50.7904, Long. -1.1213.
02392 601201

Stokes Bay Angling Club, Gosport
Lat. 50.7785, Long. -1.1504.

CHARGES: None
SUITABILITY: Large trailer needs a car.
ACCESS: All of tidal range. **TYPE OF RAMP:** Public slipway
UPPER AREA: Shingle. **LOWER AREA:** Sand.
DIRECTIONS: Off the roundabout at the junction of Stokes Bay Road and Fort Road. Adjacent to the inshore rescue station.
RAMP DESCRIPTION: A useful and well maintained local facility that gets a lot of use. Very good slipway over a shingle beach but can get covered with shingles after a storm. Need to have good launching technique if there is surf.
FACILITIES: Car parking for 80 cars and trailers can be left in the car park. Charge for parking.
HAZARDS: 10 knots within 1000 yards of shore, water-skiing prohibited within 1000 metres of shore except in designated areas, windsurfing prohibited in Portsmouth Harbour approach and within shipping channels.

Stokes Bay Central, Gosport
Lat. 50.7820, Long. -1.1546.
Stokes Bay SC 023 9258 1513

CHARGES: None
SUITABILITY: Small trailer can be pushed.
ACCESS: ¾ tidal. **TYPE OF RAMP:** Public slipway
UPPER AREA: Shingle. **LOWER AREA:** Sand.
DIRECTIONS: From M27 J11 (Fareham Central) to Gosport along A32. Continue 3 miles to two roundabouts. Go straight over the first one, keep in right-hand lane to the second. Take third exit off second roundabout to Alverstoke/Haslar etc. (Military Road). This long straight road brings you to a roundabout (Cocked Hat pub on left, Texaco Garage far right). Go straight over into Gomer Lane. Carry on down to next small roundabout and go straight across. You will now see the sea. Follow road along the promenade east. You will see Stokes Bay Sailing Club on the right next to a large car park.
RAMP DESCRIPTION: A useful and well maintained local facility. There is no vehicular access to the slipway. For launching with a vehicle use the adjacent Angling Club slipway.
FACILITIES: Car parking for 200 cars and trailers can be left in the car park. Charge for parking. Adjacent to Stokes Bay Sailing Club with extensive facilities for members.
HAZARDS: 10 knots within 1000 metres of shore, water-skiing prohibited within 1000 metres of shore except in designated areas, windsurfing prohibited in Portsmouth Harbour approach and within shipping channels.

No 2 Battery, Gosport
Lat. 50.7857, Long. -1.1687.

CHARGES: None to launch - just to park.
SUITABILITY: Portable Only.
ACCESS: No Ramp. **TYPE OF RAMP:** Public slipway
UPPER AREA: Shingle. **LOWER AREA:** Shingle.
DIRECTIONS: Situated at the west end of Stokes Bay Road. Signposted as No 2 Battery.
RAMP DESCRIPTION: This slipway is no longer maintained and is effectively unusable. Other than a small area at the very top adjoining the access road, the original concrete slip has been allowed to break up and sink into the shingle (This was a deliberate decision by the Council as there are two other public slips nearby). This area is now only suitable for light dinghies that can be pulled over the shingle. For launching small sailing dinghies use the slipway at Stokes Bay Central or Stokes Bay Angling Club. For launching powerboats or any boat requiring a vehicle to assist the launch use Stokes Bay Angling Club slip only. (Council rules prohibit the use of vehicles on the Central slip - and in any case the Angling Club slip is a better quality slipway)

FACILITIES: Large parking area and public conveniences at top of slip. There is a charge to use the car park. Caravan Park nearby.
HAZARDS: Exposed beach.

Elmore Angling Club, Lee on Solent
Lat. 50.7933, Long. -1.1952.
D Barnes 023 92 589258

CHARGES: None
SUITABILITY: Large trailer needs a car.
ACCESS: ¾ tidal. **TYPE OF RAMP:** Public slipway
UPPER AREA: Shingle. **LOWER AREA:** Sand.
DIRECTIONS: Located at the eastern end of the Lee on Solent seafront.
RAMP DESCRIPTION: A useful and well maintained local facility used by the Elmore Angling Club. At very low tide the sand is shallow and a large area dries out.
FACILITIES: Car parking for 50 cars and trailers can be left in the car park.
HAZARDS: 10 knots within 1000 yards of shore, water-skiing prohibited within 1000 metres of shore except in designated areas, windsurfing prohibited in Portsmouth Harbour approach and within shipping channels.

Lee Sailing Club, Lee on Solent
Lat. 50.7947, Long. -1.1969.
Club House 023 9255 6067

CHARGES: None
SUITABILITY: Large trailer needs a car.
ACCESS: All of tidal range. **TYPE OF RAMP:** Public slipway
UPPER AREA: Shingle. **LOWER AREA:** Sand.
DIRECTIONS: Located at the eastern end of the Lee on Solent seafront.
RAMP DESCRIPTION: Gets heavy use from the local sailing club. Check fixtures on their web site www.lossc.co.uk. World championship is sometimes staged here.
FACILITIES: Club house next to the slip has extensive facilities.
HAZARDS: 10 knots within 1000 yards of shore, water-skiing prohibited within 1000 metres of shore except in designated areas, windsurfing prohibited in Portsmouth Harbour approach and within shipping channels.

HMS Daedalus, Lee on Solent
Lat. 50.8071, Long. -1.2107.

CHARGES: None
SUITABILITY: Large trailer needs a car.
ACCESS: All of tidal range. **TYPE OF RAMP:** Concrete
UPPER AREA: Shingle. **LOWER AREA:** Sand.
DIRECTIONS: The ramp is located at the western end of Marine Parade West opposite the large hovercraft works.
RAMP DESCRIPTION: Very popular for Jetskis and speedboats, launching directly on to the Solent. Jetskiers and water skiers must have a permit to Jetski or water ski within Portsmouth harbour or within the Dockyard port of Portsmouth outside the harbour within 0.5 nautical miles of the line of mean low water Springs. Permit application available from QHM Portsmouth. New concrete slipway but can be a problem

launching in heavy waves, has a buoyed ski lane. Can get very congested on summer weekends. Shingle will be on ramp after a storm.
FACILITIES: Car parking for 40 cars and trailers can be left on shingle at top right of slipway.
HAZARDS: 10 knots within 1000 yards of shore, water-skiing prohibited within 1000 metres of shore except in designated areas, windsurfing prohibited in Portsmouth Harbour approach and within shipping channels.

Salterns Road, Lee on Solent
Lat. 50.8133, Long. -1.2236.

CHARGES: None
SUITABILITY: Large trailer needs a car.
ACCESS: ¾ tidal. **TYPE OF RAMP:** Public slipway
UPPER AREA: Shingle. **LOWER AREA:** Shingle.
DIRECTIONS: Access is via Salterns Road off Stubbington Lane.
RAMP DESCRIPTION: The Salterns Road slip is timber paved for approximately 20 feet, then ordinary shingle. High tides and strong winds will tend to pile shingle onto the ramp. The shingle makes launching large craft difficult. Well used by locals.
FACILITIES: Car parking for 60 cars. Boat parking in car park. Toilets.
HAZARDS: 10 knots within 1000 yards of shore, water-skiing prohibited within 1000 metres of shore except in designated areas, windsurfing prohibited in Portsmouth Harbour approach and within shipping channels.

Public Hard, Warsash
Lat. 50.8521, Long. -1.3067.
Harbour Office 01489 576387

CHARGES: Personal Watercraft/Jetskis: £15 annual permit or £6 daily (2007 charges). May 2008 £3.50 for a 15ft boat or £25.00 for a year.
SUITABILITY: Large trailer needs a car.
ACCESS: All of tidal range. **TYPE OF RAMP:** Firm gravel.
UPPER AREA: Shingle. **LOWER AREA:** Mud.
DIRECTIONS: Go west down the hill from roundabout in centre of Warsash village and follow one way signs.
RAMP DESCRIPTION: Firm gravel, OK to drive on except close to water at lowest Spring tide. Gentle slope into water so may need to push trailer into deeper water (long rope required to recover. Space to launch two or three boats simultaneously. Very convenient place to launch except at lowest Spring tide when there is some mud near water but launching light boats is possible even then. Much used in summer months. Can be rather deep seaweed collecting near top of ramp. Preferred launch site for Jetskis. I have used this slip, and there have been HGVs parked on it blocking the slip.
FACILITIES: Free parking and toilets in car park 100 yards along the lane (but trailers must use the marked trailer bays or you will get a parking ticket). Car park adjacent hard is short stay only (No trailers). Pub at top of hard. Small shops in village. Car park spaces may all fill up at times of peak use.
HAZARDS: Wall along the right hand (northern) side extends underwater and the end is marked by a large post. Busy yacht traffic in the river during the summer. A few raised areas of rock on the left hand side (southern).

3

Warsash Marina, Southampton

Shore Road, Warsash, Southampton, Hants,
England SO31 9FR
Lat. 50.8524, Long. -1.3068.
01489 583 813

Universal Marina, Southampton

John Wilment Marine Ltd, Universal Marina,
Crableck Lane, Sarisbury Green, Southampton,
Hampshire, England SO31 7ZN
Lat. 50.8745, Long. -1.3045.
01489 574272

The Hard, Lower Swanwick

Lat. 50.8806, Long. -1.2983.

CHARGES: Free
SUITABILITY: Large trailer needs a car.
ACCESS: All of tidal range. **TYPE OF RAMP:** Shingle
UPPER AREA: Shingle. **LOWER AREA:** Shingle.
DIRECTIONS: M27 Junction 8. Head South. At roundabout take first
Left. (ignore signs for the Hamble. 2 miles under a rail bridge, go past
Aladdin's Cave Chandlery and Moody's Boat Yard. Small road immediately
on right past traffic lights and hard is on the right 200 metres. Ignore the
hard sign near the rail bridge.
RAMP DESCRIPTION: Very shallow well maintained ramp. Keep within
the poles or you may drop off. Sheer drop off to the right hand side so
need to be a bit wary. Also VERY soft mud to the other side, stay on the
hard. Best a low tide
FACILITIES: Free car park. New parking restrictions for 2010. Trailer
parking. Nearby a chandlers, Moody's boatyard and Swanwick Marina.
Nearest fuel is at park gate or Tesco, both on the A27 The Ship and The
Spinnaker pubs are also within walking distance.
**HAZARDS: Speed restriction 6 knots until you are out of the
Hamble.**

Swanwick Marina, Southampton

Swanwick, Southampton, Hampshire, England
SO31 1ZL
Lat. 50.8822, Long. -1.2997.
01489 884081

R.K. Marine, Southampton

Hamble River Boatyard, Bridge Road, Swanwick,
Southampton, Hampshire, England SO31 7EB
Lat. 50.8846, Long. -1.2994.
01489 583585

Deacons Boatyard, Southampton

Bridge Rd, Bursledon, Southampton, Hampshire,
England SO31 8AZ
Lat. 50.8851, Long. -1.3024.
023 8040 2253

Lands End Road, Bursledon

Lat. 50.8805, Long. -1.3022.
SUITABILITY: Portable Only.
ACCESS: All of tidal range. **TYPE OF RAMP: UPPER AREA:** Mud.
LOWER AREA: Mud.
RAMP DESCRIPTION: Small ramp at the end of a single track road. No
parking available.

Mercury Boat Yard, Hamble

Lat. 50.8718, Long. -1.3130.
023 8045 5994

CHARGES: £9 each way including parking. (MDLMarinas.co.uk)
SUITABILITY: Large trailer needs a car.
ACCESS: ½ tidal. **TYPE OF RAMP:** Concrete **UPPER AREA:** Harbour.
LOWER AREA: Mud.
DIRECTIONS: Out of Hamble and along School Lane. Take signs for
Mercury Yacht Haven. To get to slip as you go through gates drive
between the two sheds directly in front of you then turn right and follow
round to the right at the top of the slip turn right and then you can back
in easily.
RAMP DESCRIPTION: Dries to mud at low water. Ledge at bottom of
ramp, with a drop on to the mud. Can be a problem to launch at very
high tide because the top area is flooded. Marina advised only using two
hrs either side of high tide, unless using a 4 × 4.
FACILITIES: Large chandlers in the marina, bar and food. Good parking
in large compound. Very friendly staff. There is a wash off hose at the
head of the ramp. Pontoon by the ramp for loading.
**HAZARDS: Speed restriction 6 knots until you are out of the
Hamble.**

Mercury Yacht Harbour, Southampton

Satchell Lane, Hamble, Southampton, Hampshire,
England SO31 4HQ
Lat. 50.8709, Long. -1.3109.
02380 455994

Port Hamble Marina, Southampton

Satchell Lane, Hamble, Southampton, Hampshire,
England SO31 4QD
Lat. 50.8614, Long. -1.3137.
023 8045 2741

Hamble Yacht Services, Hamble

Port Hamble, Satchell Lane, Hamble, Hampshire,
England SO31 4NN
Lat. 50.8609, Long. -1.3131.
02380 454111

Public Hard, Hamble

Lat. 50.8583, Long. -1.3129.

CHARGES: None
SUITABILITY: Large trailer needs a car.
ACCESS: All of tidal range. **TYPE OF RAMP:** Hard standing.
UPPER AREA: Shingle. **LOWER AREA:** Shingle.

3

DIRECTIONS: Drive down through the one way system to the river front. Access is narrow and steep but wide enough for a 6 metre RIB and Land Rover.
RAMP DESCRIPTION: Wide hard standing between the Royal Southern Yacht Club and the car park. The hard standing is well marked; a large post marks the extremity. You can also go off to the left (upstream side of the ramp) but it does get muddy if you go too far. There are potholes on the hard, check before reversing trailer into the water.
FACILITIES: Car park nearby. Charges apply. (Car park up the hill is now closed, so parking a trailer is all but impossible) Also public toilets and a pub next door. There is also a pontoon you can tie up to load and unload. 60 minutes waiting time and you are not supposed to leave your boat unattended.
HAZARDS: Pontoons and river traffic.

Hamble Point Marina, Southampton
School Lane, Hamble, Southampton, Hampshire, England SO31 4NB
Lat. 50.8517, Long. -1.3118.
02380 452464

Hamble Point, Hamble
Lat. 50.8498, Long. -1.3097.
(023) 80452464
CHARGES: £30/day (as of June 2008). This includes car parking for the duration, even if a couple of days
SUITABILITY: Large trailer needs a car.
ACCESS: All of tidal range. **TYPE OF RAMP:** Wide concrete.
UPPER AREA: Harbour. **LOWER AREA:** Mud.
DIRECTIONS: From Hamble, drive to the end of School Lane. Take care on this road with a trailer as bits are narrow.
RAMP DESCRIPTION: Very wide ramp. Even so, it can get busy with a lot of large sailing craft launching. Pontoon available for loading and unloading. Launch site is at the mouth of the Hamble so only a short stretch to the open sea.
FACILITIES: Tractor on site, available on application. Wash down facility, parking, toilets and showers, restaurant and pub. Lots of facilities in Hamble Village with petrol and pubs. Hamble Point also offers monthly and annual contracts. Phone for details.
HAZARDS: Strong tidal current, pontoons and traffic. River is speed restricted.

Netley Hard, Netley
Lat. 50.8749, Long. -1.3574.
Hound Parish Council 023 8045 3732
CHARGES: None
SUITABILITY: Small trailer can be pushed.
ACCESS: ¼ tidal. **TYPE OF RAMP:** Public hard **UPPER AREA:** Shingle.
LOWER AREA: Sand.
DIRECTIONS: Follow signs to Royal Victoria Country Park off A3025. Slipway is at the end of Beach Lane off Victoria Road.
RAMP DESCRIPTION: Suitable for small craft only. There is no hard road between Beach Lane and the ramp and trailer will have to be pulled across a shingle beach. There is another slipway along Victoria Road owned by the Civil Service SC.

FACILITIES: Car parking in Beach Lane. Local Italian restaurant and pub in Victoria Road.
HAZARDS: 6 knots speed limit north of Hythe Pier. Keep 130 metres from Fawley and Hamble jetties. Substantial traffic around docks and in centre of Southampton Water.

Weston Hard, Southampton
Lat. 50.8859, Long. -1.3730.
CHARGES: None
SUITABILITY: Large trailer needs a car.
ACCESS: ¾ tidal. **TYPE OF RAMP:** Public hard
UPPER AREA: Unknown. **LOWER AREA:** Unknown.
DIRECTIONS: At west end of Weston Shore seafront.
RAMP DESCRIPTION: Suitable for all trailer craft, subject to speed limit. Width 3 metres. Launch site faces southwest. Believed to receive limited local use.
FACILITIES: Car parking 50 cars. Toilets.
HAZARDS: 6 knots speed limit north of Hythe Pier. Keep 130 metres from Fawley and Hamble jetties. Substantial traffic around docks and in centre of Southampton Water.

Weston Point, Southampton
Lat. 50.8896, Long. -1.3829.
CHARGES: None
SUITABILITY: Large trailer needs a car.
ACCESS: ½ tidal. **TYPE OF RAMP:** Public Slipway
UPPER AREA: Unknown. **LOWER AREA:** Unknown.
DIRECTIONS: Near junction of Victoria Road and Swift Road, Woolston.
RAMP DESCRIPTION: Suitable for all trailer craft, subject to speed limit. Width 2 metres. Launch site faces west into River. Nearest clubs Southampton Sailing Club. Believed to be fairly well used, mostly by locals. Useful local facility, particularly for sailing club.
FACILITIES: Car parking space for 10 cars. Toilets.
HAZARDS: 6 knots speed limit north of Hythe Pier. Keep 130 metres from Fawley and Hamble jetties. Substantial traffic around Docks and in centre of Southampton Water.

Floating Bridge Hard, Southampton
Lat. 50.8995, Long. -1.3828.
CHARGES: None
SUITABILITY: Large trailer needs a car.
ACCESS: All of tidal range. **TYPE OF RAMP:** Public hard
UPPER AREA: Unknown. **LOWER AREA:** Unknown.
DIRECTIONS: East bank of Itchen, south of Itchen Bridge.
RAMP DESCRIPTION: Reasonably sheltered slipway but the access is steep and at an angle. Also much flotsam on slipway. Parking is adjacent to slipway, however, not a great area to leave a car.
FACILITIES: Car parking on roadside. Some boat parking on foreshore.
HAZARDS: 6 knots speed limit north of Hythe Pier. Keep 130 metres from Fawley and Hamble jetties. Substantial traffic around docks and in centre of Southampton Water.

3

Ferry Hard, Southampton
Lat. 50.9004, Long. -1.3823.

CHARGES: None
SUITABILITY: Large trailer needs a car.
ACCESS: All of tidal range. **TYPE OF RAMP:** Public hard
UPPER AREA: Unknown. **LOWER AREA:** Unknown.
DIRECTIONS: East bank of Itchen, north of Itchen Bridge. Access via Hazel Road.
RAMP DESCRIPTION: Suitable for all trailer craft, subject to speed limit. Width 3 metres. Launch site faces west into river. Nearest clubs Southampton Amateur Rowing Club. Believed to be fairly well used, mostly by locals.
FACILITIES: Car parking on roadside. Local car repair shops mean that slipway is often blocked with parked cars.
HAZARDS: 6 knots speed limit north of Hythe Pier. Keep 130 metres from Fawley and Hamble jetties. Substantial traffic around docks and in centre of Southampton Water.

Kemps Quay, Southampton
Quayside Road, Bitterne Manor, Southampton, Hampshire, England SO18 1BZ
Lat. 50.9160, Long. -1.3786.
02380 632323

G & L Marine, Southampton
35a Vespasian Rd, Southampton, Hampshire, England SO18 1AY
Lat. 50.9195, Long. -1.3820.
023 8022 9641

Woodmill Lane Hard, Southampton
Lat. 50.9354, Long. -1.3766.

CHARGES: None
SUITABILITY: Portable Only.
ACCESS: ¾ tidal. **TYPE OF RAMP:** Public hard **UPPER AREA:** Shingle.
LOWER AREA: Mud.
DIRECTIONS: Off Woodmill Lane. The ramp is on the west side of the river.
RAMP DESCRIPTION: Gets well used by locals.
FACILITIES: Very limited parking.

Dyer Bros (Marine) Ltd, Southampton
129-131, St. Deny's Rd Cobden Bridge, Southampton, Hampshire, UK SO17 2JY
Lat. 50.9243, Long. -1.3795.
023 8055 5406

Priory Hard, Southampton
Lat. 50.9203, Long. -1.3871.

CHARGES: None
SUITABILITY: Large trailer needs a car.
ACCESS: ½ tidal. **TYPE OF RAMP:** Public slipway
UPPER AREA: Harbour. **LOWER AREA:** Mud.
DIRECTIONS: Off Priory Road.

RAMP DESCRIPTION: This is quite a good slipway, wide, easy access and plenty of parking. It can be deceptive; at high water it appears to be about 40 feet wide, but the wide bit ends level with the quay wall on the right (looking from the land). The slip extends further in the middle of its width only, with a 9 foot wide concrete 'mini-slip' to just beyond the half-tide level, then very soft mud beyond. It should be OK to leave a car and trailer here for half a day with no problems - but not recommend overnight or after dark. And secure any loose gear - children play in this area.
FACILITIES: Car parking space for up to 10 cars. Boat parking within car park.
HAZARDS: 6 knots speed limit north of Hythe Pier. Keep 130 metres from Fawley and Hamble jetties. Substantial traffic around docks and in centre of Southampton Water.

Drivers Wharf, Southampton
Northam Rd, Southampton, Hampshire, England SO14 0PF
Lat. 50.9130, Long. -1.3858.
023 8023 3302

Old Mill Quay Hard, Southampton
Lat. 50.9130, Long. -1.3826.

CHARGES: None
SUITABILITY: Portable Only.
ACCESS: ½ tidal. **TYPE OF RAMP:** Public hard
UPPER AREA: Unknown. **LOWER AREA:** Unknown.
DIRECTIONS: Off Prince's Street.
RAMP DESCRIPTION: Suitable for portable craft only, subject to speed limit. Width 3 metres. Long narrow access and poor condition make this a virtually unusable facility for recreation. Possible area of redevelopment so may be moved or improved.
FACILITIES: No car parking, narrow access. Next to the Red Light district, security may be a problem.
HAZARDS: 6 knots speed limit north of Hythe Pier. Keep 130 metres from Fawley and Hamble jetties. Substantial traffic around docks and in centre of Southampton Water.

Saxon Wharf, Southampton
Lower York Street, Northam, Southampton, Hampshire, England SO14 2QG
Lat. 50.9122, Long. -1.3810.
023 8022 9461

Shamrock Quay, Southampton
William Street, Northam, Southampton, Hampshire, England SO14 5QL
Lat. 50.9102, Long. -1.3801.
023 8022 9461

Belvidere Hard, Southampton
Lat. 50.9076, Long. -1.3870.

CHARGES: None
SUITABILITY: Large trailer needs a car.

3

ACCESS: ½ tidal. **TYPE OF RAMP:** Public hard
UPPER AREA: Unknown. **LOWER AREA:** Mud.
DIRECTIONS: Off Belvidere Road / Millbank Street.
RAMP DESCRIPTION: This slip has suffered some neglect and even has a sunken dory at the end (only visible at low tide). Serviceable though as long as it is viewed at all states of tide prior to use.
FACILITIES: Parking is available in nearby industrial estate. Very close to Saints FC and will get blocked if a game is on. Check the club web site, www.saintsfc.co.uk for details
HAZARDS: 6 knots speed limit north of Hythe Pier. Keep 130 metres from Fawley and Hamble jetties. Observe 'Moving Prohibited Zone'. Substantial traffic around docks and in centre of Southampton Water.

Itchen Marine (Towage), Southampton
American Wharf, Elm Street, Southampton, Hampshire, England SO14 5JF
Lat. 50.9060, Long. -1.3878.
023 8063 1500

Crosshouse Hard, Southampton
Lat. 50.9004, Long. -1.3874.
Southampton Open Spaces 023 80833605

CHARGES: None
SUITABILITY: Large trailer needs a car.
ACCESS: All of tidal range. **TYPE OF RAMP:** Public hard
UPPER AREA: Unknown. **LOWER AREA:** Mud.
DIRECTIONS: Just to the north of Woolston toll bridge.
RAMP DESCRIPTION: Excellent wide launching facility. The best used of the public hards in Southampton, particularly by local clubs. Beware at low tide. Nasty metal rails at the bottom of the slipway.
FACILITIES: Plenty of parking in the area and toilets nearby. BUT it is close to the Southampton Football Stadium and gets parked up when there is a home match. Check the club web site, www.saintsfc.co.uk for details. Cars have been known to park across the slipway. Parking will cost you 70p.
HAZARDS: 6 knots speed limit north of Hythe Pier. Keep 130 metres from Fawley and Hamble jetties. Observe Moving Prohibited Zone. Substantial traffic around docks and in centre of Southampton Water.

Southampton's Ocean Village Marina, Southampton
2 Channel Way, Ocean Village, Southampton, Hampshire, England SO14 3TG
Lat. 50.8965, Long. -1.3891.
02380 229385

Town Quay, Southampton
Lat. 50.8956, Long. -1.4036.

CHARGES: None
SUITABILITY: Large trailer needs a car.
ACCESS: ¾ tidal. **TYPE OF RAMP:** Public slipway.
UPPER AREA: Unknown. **LOWER AREA:** Unknown.

DIRECTIONS: Adjacent to Town Quay Marina.
RAMP DESCRIPTION: Suitable for all trailer craft, subject to speed limit. Width 5 metres. Launch site faces west. Believed to receive very little use. A good slipway, but not promoted and access only through private car park. All land on which you get to this slipway is owned by port authority and has clamping signs.
FACILITIES: Next to a private car park for 400 cars. Car park charges Pay and Display. Boat parking within car park. But getting into car park would mean a 180 degree turn, navigating the main road or going around the one way system to be able to turn into the car park. Fuel at marina, shops, restaurants, chandler, toilets at Town Quay.
HAZARDS: 6 knots speed limit north of Hythe Pier. Keep 130 metres from Fawley and Hamble jetties. Observe 'Moving Prohibited Zone'. Substantial traffic around docks and in centre of Southampton Water.

Town Quay Marina, Southampton
Town Quay Marina, Town Quay, Southampton, Hampshire, England SO14 2AQ
Lat. 50.8955, Long. -1.4045.
02380 234397

3

Mayflower Park, Southampton
Lat. 50.8969, Long. -1.4084.

CHARGES: None
SUITABILITY: Small trailer can be pushed.
ACCESS: All of tidal range. **TYPE OF RAMP:** Public slipway
UPPER AREA: Harbour. **LOWER AREA:** Concrete.
DIRECTIONS: Within Mayflower Park on Southampton Sea Front.
RAMP DESCRIPTION: Suitable for small craft only, subject to speed limit. Difficult access and an awkward location. Not recommended, steep, narrow slipway with restricted access, sheer drop to one side, numerous obstacles, fishing lines and debris. This is the site of the pontoons used for the Southampton International boat show every year and there is no where to park in the warmer months, that's if you can get to the slip in the first place.
FACILITIES: Car parking for 50 cars. Boat parking within car park which is closed at night.
HAZARDS: Southampton's old pier just south of slipway, hidden obstructions. 6 knots speed limit north of Hythe Pier. Keep 130 metres from Fawley and Hamble jetties. Substantial traffic around docks and in centre of Southampton Water.

Eling Quay, Southampton
Lat. 50.9125, Long. -1.4794.
Marian Quantrell 023 8086 3138

CHARGES: None
SUITABILITY: Large trailer needs a car.
ACCESS: ½ tidal. **TYPE OF RAMP:** Concrete public slipway.
UPPER AREA: Shingle. **LOWER AREA:** Mud.
DIRECTIONS: Follow signs to Eling off A326 or A35, Site next to Anchor Inn.
RAMP DESCRIPTION: Suitable for all trailer craft, subject to speed limit. Access to the Redbridge Water-Ski Area (open April-October). Width 6 metres. Launch site faces south into creek. Believed to be used

mainly by locals. The nearest launch point to the Redbridge Water Ski Area.

FACILITIES: Car parking for 25 cars. Boat parking within car park. Nearest clubs, Eling Sailing Club. Site is next to the Anchor Pub and parking is a problem, especially in the summer. Eling Sailing Club is on the other side of the pub. Concrete wharf next to the slipway to tie up to while parking the car. No long term mooring.

HAZARDS: 6 knots speed limit north of Hythe Pier. Keep 130 metres from Fawley and Hamble jetties. Very busy area, where large commercial vessels have limited manoeuvrability. Water skiing area just outside of the slipway area.

Marchwood Sailing Club, Southampton
Lat. 50.9016, Long. -1.4425.

CHARGES: None
SUITABILITY: Small trailer can be pushed.
ACCESS: ¾ tidal. **TYPE OF RAMP:** Public hard
UPPER AREA: Unknown. **LOWER AREA:** Unknown.
DIRECTIONS: Off A326. In Marchwood take road signed 'Magazine Lane'.
RAMP DESCRIPTION: Suitable for small craft only, subject to speed limit. Width 3 metres. Nearest clubs, Marchwood Yacht Club have slipway adjacent to the site. Signs on Site ABP Notice re Water Ski Area. Believed to receive limited use by locals. A useful facility, but with poor road access.
FACILITIES: Car parking for 15 cars. Boat parking within car park.
HAZARDS: 6 knots speed limit north of Hythe Pier. Keep 130 metres from Fawley and Hamble jetties. Very busy area, where large commercial vessels have limited manoeuvrability.

Cracknore Hard, Southampton
Lat. 50.8967, Long. -1.4272.

CHARGES: None
SUITABILITY: Small trailer can be pushed.
ACCESS: ¾ tidal. **TYPE OF RAMP:** Public hard **UPPER AREA:** Shingle. **LOWER AREA:** Unknown.
DIRECTIONS: Signposted from Marchwood off A326.
RAMP DESCRIPTION: Wide slipway. The ship yard is now under development with good road access. There is also the British Powerboat Trust and Little Ships of Dunkirk display shed there, with boat restoration company on hand for wooden boat repair/restoration.
FACILITIES: Very limited parking on site. The ship yard is now under development with good road access. There is also the British Powerboat Trust and Little Ships of Dunkirk display shed there, with boat restoration company on hand for wooden boat repair/restoration.
HAZARDS: 6 knots speed limit north of Hythe Pier. Keep 130 metres from Fawley and Hamble jetties. Very busy area, where large commercial vessels have limited manoeuvrability.

Marina Slip, Hythe
Lat. 50.8741, Long. -1.3979.
023 8020 7073
CHARGES: Pay and display, £5/day for car and trailer.

SUITABILITY: Large trailer needs a car.
ACCESS: ¾ tidal. **TYPE OF RAMP:** Public slipway
UPPER AREA: Harbour. **LOWER AREA:** Sand.
DIRECTIONS: Off A326, signs to 'Marina'.
RAMP DESCRIPTION: Wide south facing slipway. A well appointed and maintained facility.
FACILITIES: Ample parking for car and trailer. Public toilets. Showers and laundry facilities for berth holders only. Cost of berth; less than 4 hours, £5.50; overnight £2.50 per metre. Petrol, diesel, boat hoist, chandlery and general store on site.
HAZARDS: 6 knots speed limit north of Hythe Pier. Keep 130 metres from Fawley and Hamble jetties. Very busy area, where large commercial vessels have limited manoeuvrability. Small craft should give clearance of 1000 metres ahead and 100 metres of each side of large vessels.

Hythe Marina Village, Southampton
Shamrock Way, Hythe, Southampton, Hampshire, England SO45 6DY
Lat. 50.8756, Long. -1.3998.
023 8020 7073

Slipway, Ashlett Creek
Lat. 50.8264, Long. -1.3398.

CHARGES: None
SUITABILITY: Large trailer needs a car.
ACCESS: ½ tidal. **TYPE OF RAMP:** Public hard
UPPER AREA: Unknown. **LOWER AREA:** Unknown.
DIRECTIONS: Signposted to Ashlett off A326.
RAMP DESCRIPTION: Launch site faces: East. A well maintained but fairly minor site. Navigation of the Ashlett channel is for the experienced.
FACILITIES: Car parking 30 spaces. Boat parking within car park. Toilets, pub.
HAZARDS: Keep 130 metres from Fawley and Hamble jetties. Busy shipping channel in Southampton Water.

Activities Centre, Calshot
Lat. 50.8201, Long. -1.3088.
023 8089 2077

CHARGES: Public - Daily fee, including car to 7m and trailer parking, use of toilets/showers, fresh water wash off, £14.50 per boat up to 6m length overall or per PW craft, £18.50 per boat over 6m LOA, one week pass £58.00 (under 6m), £74.00 (over 6m). Daily rate canoe, wind surfer inc. parking £6.00 (additional boards/canoes on same car £1.00 each.), one week pass £24.00.
SUITABILITY: Large trailer needs a car.
ACCESS: All of tidal range. **TYPE OF RAMP:** Wide concrete ramp.
UPPER AREA: Concrete. **LOWER AREA:** Shingle.
DIRECTIONS: From M27 Junction 2, take A326 signposted Hythe and Fawley. Calshot Activities Centre is well signposted. Post code for satnav SO45 1BR.
RAMP DESCRIPTION: Excellent all-tide access to the Solent. Plenty of space and never too crowded. Ramp is located at Calshot Activities Centre run by Hampshire CC. The slip is very wide, (originally built to bring flying boats up onto the land). Lower ramp is tarmac but has to be cleared

each Friday of shingle. New concrete slip has been built and extends the tidal range use of this massive slipway; try to keep to the left side as the RNLI share the slip. There is also a small slip for half tide use by narrower trailer sailers such as McGregors, located at the south end of the fishing quay facing the power station, access 80m on left as you enter main car park. This is concrete and well sheltered. Use of the third slip, north end of Sunderland hangar, not recommended for vehicles as too steep and uneven. Marine info pack available from reception 7 days a week.
FACILITIES: Calshot Activities Centre - toilets, showers, cafeteria, bar, parking. No pontoon to tie to, single handed recovery very difficult. Normally quiet, busy on school days.
HAZARDS: Main shipping channel up Southampton Water. Calshot Spit (dries at low water).

Calshot Spit Car Park, Calshot
Lat. 50.8137, Long. -1.3115.
CHARGES: Car and trailer parking charges apply March to November inclusive.
SUITABILITY: Small trailer can be pushed.
ACCESS: ¾ tidal. **TYPE OF RAMP:** Public slipway
UPPER AREA: Shingle. **LOWER AREA:** Shingle.
DIRECTIONS: Signposted from A326 and B3053 from Southampton.
RAMP DESCRIPTION: Width 8 metres. Launch site faces: southeast. Nearest clubs Calshot Sailing Club, Castle Sailing Club, and various Calshot Activities Centre clubs. One of the principal windsurfing sites in Hampshire. A bathing beach with good water quality. Not usable below two thirds tide as no water offshore for a long way! (This is why Jetskis and windsurfers are principal users).
FACILITIES: Car parking 450 spaces on spit in total in Pay and Display car park. Boat parking within car park.
HAZARDS: Keep 130 metres from Fawley and Hamble jetties. Very busy area, where large commercial vessels have limited manoeuvrability. Small craft should give clearance of 1000 metres ahead and 100 metres of each side of large vessels.

Egypt Point, Cowes
Lat. 50.7674, Long. -1.3125.
CHARGES: None
SUITABILITY: Large trailer needs a car.
ACCESS: ¾ tidal. **TYPE OF RAMP:** Concrete slip.
UPPER AREA: Concrete. **LOWER AREA:** Shingle.
DIRECTIONS: From Cowes, continue west along the Parade and Queens Road.
RAMP DESCRIPTION: Width / length 3m x 14m. Launch site faces north into Solent. Approx 1.5ft vertical drop to shingle at quarter tide, and odd flat area at bottom. Signs on site; Public slipway, No overnight parking.
FACILITIES: Car parking along Queens Road (no overnight parking). Toilets on Mornington Road and the Parade. Parking gets very busy in the summer and forget it during Cowes Week (normally first week in August).
HAZARDS: Speed limit 6 knots. Shipping hazards, Cowes Harbour (moorings, ferries). Beware cross tides and wash from ships.

Watch House Lane, Cowes
Lat. 50.7650, Long. -1.2981.
CHARGES: None
SUITABILITY: Small trailer can be pushed.
ACCESS: All of tidal range. **TYPE OF RAMP:** Public (concrete)
UPPER AREA: Harbour. **LOWER AREA:** Unknown.
DIRECTIONS: The Parade, Cowes. From Cowes High Street turn into Watch House Lane onto Parade.
RAMP DESCRIPTION: Suitable for launch and recovery of small dinghies and tenders. Width 5m. Launch site faces northeast. Signs on site; Danger vessels manoeuvring. Swimming is prohibited from jetties and landing stages into the navigation channels. Prosecution liable pursuant to CH bye laws 1992 by order Cowes Harbour Commissioners.
FACILITIES: Car parking on the Parade only. Car park charges, small cost to park in Parade car parking. No boat parking. Nearest clubs, Royal London Yacht Club and Island Sailing Club. Rings along slip to tie up craft. Public toilets on Parade.
HAZARDS: Speed limit 6 knots. Shipping hazards, Cowes Harbour (moorings, ferries). Beware cross tides and wash from ships.

Market Slip, Cowes
Lat. 50.7641, Long. -1.2981.
CHARGES: None
SUITABILITY: Small trailer can be pushed.
ACCESS: Unknown. **TYPE OF RAMP:** Public (Tarmac, concrete, shingle at low water). **UPPER AREA:** Concrete. **LOWER AREA:** Sand.
DIRECTIONS: High Street, Cowes (old Post Office Slip). On the High Street, adjacent to the Slam shop and Harbour Lights pub.
RAMP DESCRIPTION: Adjacent owners, "The Waterside" Pub (previously Harbour Lights). Width 5m. Launch site faces east. Tidal access OK to low tide, uneven surface at top, sill at end of concrete, drop to shingle varies and there is a drain cover towards the bottom of the slip which obstructs low trailers. Can be difficult to drive off beach at low tides). Signs on site - Public slipway strictly no parking. Keep clear at all times. An excess charge of £50 will be issued for non-compliance. Isle of Wight Council. Little use by visitors, access difficult. Often blocked by parked vehicles and access can be difficult off the High Street.
FACILITIES: Car parking approximately 280 metres away. Small cost to park in Parade car parking. No boat park. Bins present. Nearest clubs Cowes Corinthian Yacht Club and Island Sailing Club.
HAZARDS: Speed limit not more than 6 knots. Cowes Harbour (moorings, ferries).

Sun Slip, Cowes
Lat. 50.7634, Long. -1.2974.
CHARGES: None
SUITABILITY: Small trailer can be pushed.
ACCESS: All of tidal range. **TYPE OF RAMP:** Public (concrete).
UPPER AREA: Concrete. **LOWER AREA:** Shingle.
DIRECTIONS: On the High Street, adjacent to HSBC Midland Bank.
RAMP DESCRIPTION: Adjacent owners, HSBC Midland Bank. Width 4 metres. Concrete to nearly low water, then shingle. Launch site faces east. However access is difficult off the high street. Signs on site - Caution this slipway may be slippery. Not cleaned nearly enough by the council.

3

Little use by visitors, access difficult. Sometimes closed by locked gates (key from HSBC Bank) and often blocked by parked vehicles. CAUTION: Be careful of rubbish such as shopping trolleys dumped at the bottom of the slipway.

FACILITIES: Parking is approximately 280 metres away, small cost to park in Parade car parking. No boat parking. Nearest clubs - Cowes Corinthian Yacht Club and Island Sailing Club.

HAZARDS: Cowes Harbour (moorings, ferries). Speed limit not more than 6 knots (see Harbour Bye Laws).

Cowes Yacht Haven, Cowes
Vectis Yard, High Street, Cowes, Isle of Wight, England PO31 7BD
Lat. 50.7612, Long. -1.2963.
01983 299975

Spencer Thetis Wharf, Cowes
Lat. 50.7587, Long. -1.2939.
01279833426

CHARGES: None
SUITABILITY: Small trailer can be pushed.
ACCESS: ¾ tidal. **TYPE OF RAMP:** Public (concrete)
UPPER AREA: Concrete. **LOWER AREA:** Mud.
DIRECTIONS: Near to the Chain Ferry on Medina Road.
RAMP DESCRIPTION: Suitable for dinghies, tenders, other leisure craft. Adjacent owners - Shepherds Wharf. Width 3 metres. Launch site faces east. Drops over sill into deep water at low tide. Nearest clubs - Cowes Corinthian Yacht Club. Signs on site - No swimming. Good slip but restricted due to the long narrow access. UPDATE - Has reopened, building work still underway but is usable for trailers no larger than the width of a large car.
FACILITIES: Car parking Medina Road.
HAZARDS: Cowes Harbour (moorings, ferries). Speed limit not more than 6 knots.

UK Sailing Academy, West Cowes
Arctic Road, West Cowes, Isle Of Wight, England PO31 7PQ
Lat. 50.7529, Long. -1.2947.
01983 294941

Odessa Marine, Newport
Odessa Cottage, Little London, Newport, Isle Of Wight, England PO30 5BS
Lat. 50.7035, Long. -1.2916.
01983 524337

Seaclose, Newport
Lat. 50.7056, Long. -1.2891.

CHARGES: None
SUITABILITY: Small trailer can be pushed.
ACCESS: ½ tidal. **TYPE OF RAMP:** Public **UPPER AREA:** Harbour.
LOWER AREA: Mud.

DIRECTIONS: Situated along the east side of the quay in Newport, between the Bus Museum and Jubilee Stores.
RAMP DESCRIPTION: Suitable for launch and recovery of small leisure craft. Width 5 metres. Launch site faces west. No access at low water. Nearest clubs - Newport Rowing Club. Signs on site - Keep Clear. A good slip but needs to be better sign posted. Concrete and stone blocks down to 2 feet drop over sill onto low tide mud.
FACILITIES: Car parking on Quay. Rings on slip.
HAZARDS: Speed limit 6 knots.

Island Harbour, Newport
Mill Lane, Binfield, Newport, Isle of Wight, England PO30 2LA
Lat. 50.7251, Long. -1.2769.
01983 822999

The Folly Inn, Cowes
Lat. 50.7334, Long. -1.2815.

CHARGES: None
SUITABILITY: Large trailer needs a car.
ACCESS: All of tidal range. **TYPE OF RAMP:** Public concrete slip.
UPPER AREA: Shingle. **LOWER AREA:** Mud.
DIRECTIONS: Folly Slip, The Folly Inn, Folly Road, East Cowes. From the A3021 between East Cowes and Newport, take the turn towards the Folly Inn.
RAMP DESCRIPTION: Suitable for launch and recovery of tenders and dinghies. Shingle beach, concrete slip with concrete sill at the end. Width 3m. Launch site faces west. No slip at high water however some launching could be done from the beach. Slip visible at ¾ tide. The end, of the slip is marked by a bucket on a stake. Signs on site - Please do not obstruct this slipway with your car. Probably the most used and best slip in the river. This is the only dinghy launch point along either side of the river outside of Cowes or Newport. It is possible to launch almost all the time but Springs can be a problem. This is a good slip that can be used to launch a small cruiser. The Folly Inn is happy for people with Jetskis to use the slipway, and to park in the car park behind the pub and use its (very nice) shower facilities.
FACILITIES: No specific car parking however arrangements can be made with the Folly Inn. A dinghy park managed by The Medina Mariners Association is located on site. There is an annual fee. Scrubbing berth and dinghy park owned by The Medina Mariners Association. The Folly Inn has facilities including showers.
HAZARDS: Moorings and boat traffic.

East Cowes Marina, Isle of Wight
Brittania Way, East Cowes, Isle of Wight, Hampshire, England PO32 6UB
Lat. 50.7518, Long. -1.2906.
01983 293983

White Hart Slip, Cowes
Lat. 50.7578, Long. -1.2911.

CHARGES: None
SUITABILITY: Large trailer needs a car.

ACCESS: All of tidal range. **TYPE OF RAMP:** Public concrete slip.
UPPER AREA: Unknown. **LOWER AREA:** Unknown.
DIRECTIONS: Immediately South of Red Funnel Ferry Terminal, East Cowes.
RAMP DESCRIPTION: It is possible to launch a small cruiser with no problems. Adjacent owners - Red Funnel and Trinity House. Width 3m. Launch site faces northwest. Nearest clubs - East Cowes Sailing Club or any clubs over in Cowes. Signs on site - Public Slipway no parking at any time. Gets regular use. Used by Rowing Clubs to launch.
FACILITIES: Good slip parking with trailer is available along Clarence road just go south past the restricted parking area, 5 minutes walk. Rings on the side of the slip to tie up along.
HAZARDS: Speed limit not more than 6 knots. Particularly dangerous due to it being directly adjacent to the Red Funnel ferry terminal and fast ebb tide.

Medina Slipway, Cowes
Lat. 50.7614, Long. -1.2896.
CHARGES: None
SUITABILITY: Large trailer needs a car.
ACCESS: All of tidal range. **TYPE OF RAMP:** Public
UPPER AREA: Unknown. **LOWER AREA:** Unknown.
DIRECTIONS: Columbine Road, East Cowes. Just north of Westland Aerospace hangar and in front of the Barracks.
RAMP DESCRIPTION: Suitable for all small leisure craft (cobbled surface ending in 4 feet drop to beach). Adjacent owners - GKN Westland's Aerospace. Slipway is very steep, approximately 5m wide and extends down to the low water mark. Launch site faces northwest. Signs on site - Life Buoy 999 Safety Watch. If Life Belt is missing or damaged please contact Isle of Wight Council 823353 or Wightcare 821105 out of hours. This site gets little use. There are a number of means for access to the water in this area, including steps, landing platform and a slipway.
FACILITIES: Car parking along Esplanade, East Cowes. Mon - Sat 8am to 6pm limited to 2 hours. No return within 2 hours. Nearest clubs - West Cowes Clubs and East Cowes Sailing Club. Toilets, bins, benches, Green, Isle of Wight Council Life Buoy.
HAZARDS: Speed limit 6 knots. Shipping hazards, Cowes Harbour (moorings, ferries). Beware cross tides and wash from ships.

Wooton Bridge, Wooton
Lat. 50.7247, Long. -1.2259.
CHARGES: None.
SUITABILITY: Large trailer needs a car.
ACCESS: Unknown. **TYPE OF RAMP:** Wooden. **UPPER AREA:** Concrete.
LOWER AREA: Mud.
DIRECTIONS: Next door to the Sloop Inn, just to the right.
RAMP DESCRIPTION: Wooden ramp to Wooton Creek.
FACILITIES: Pub next door :)
HAZARDS: Small boats, car ferry.

Ryde Harbour, Ryde
Lat. 50.7322, Long. -1.1553.
CHARGES: No charges to launch see harbourmaster for berthing charges.

SUITABILITY: Large trailer needs a car.
ACCESS: ½ tidal. **TYPE OF RAMP:** Watch out for Hovercraft and High Speed Cat. **UPPER AREA:** Concrete. **LOWER AREA:** Concrete.
DIRECTIONS: Next to hovercraft slip.
RAMP DESCRIPTION: Forms part of a small harbour, a concrete slip usually clean with a pontoon berth nearby to tie up whilst parking a trailer, a large car park adjacent with charges. Only usable 2 hours before and after high tide.
FACILITIES: Town close by

Ryde Harbour, Ryde
The Esplanade, Ryde, Isle of Wight, England
PO33 1JA
Lat. 50.7317, Long. -1.1533.
01983 613879

St Helen's, Bembridge
Lat. 50.6984, Long. -1.0989.
CHARGES: None
SUITABILITY: Large trailer needs a car.
ACCESS: ¼ tidal. **TYPE OF RAMP:** Concrete then sand / gravel beach.
UPPER AREA: Concrete. **LOWER AREA:** Sand.
DIRECTIONS: B3330 to St Helens' from Ryde or Bembridge. Just at the eastern end of St Helen's Green the B3330 does a 90 degree turn. At this point there is a road called Duver Road. Follow this road for approximately ½ mile when you get to the bottom carry straight on into the car park. You will find the slip. in the car park.
RAMP DESCRIPTION: Concrete ramp quite steep. Then goes onto the beach which is sand / gravel. At high water you can launch from the concrete ramp. At low water there is not enough water to float a boat.
FACILITIES: Waterfront café. Parking is a bit limited in the summer.
HAZARDS: Entrance to Bembridge harbour. Dries at low water. Make sure you follow the markers out when the tide is in right out to the fort. Even in the channel, water can get very shallow.

Bembridge Harbour, Ryde
The Duver, St Helens, Ryde, Isle of Wight, England
PO33 1YB
Lat. 50.6936, Long. -1.1086.
01983 872828

Slipway, Bembridge
Lat. 50.6927, Long. -1.1048.
Harbourmaster 01983 872828, Ch M80
CHARGES: Pay Harbourmaster.
SUITABILITY: Large trailer needs a car.
ACCESS: ½ tidal. **TYPE OF RAMP:** Concrete **UPPER AREA:** Concrete.
LOWER AREA: Mud.
DIRECTIONS: Main ramp is on the South Side of the harbour on the Embankment.
RAMP DESCRIPTION: Large wide ramp. There are several other launch facilities in the harbour, all of them are controlled by the Bembridge Harbourmaster.

3

FACILITIES: Nearby marina has showers and toilets and there are all the usual facilities in the village of Bembridge, an overnight berth for a 5.5m RIB is approximately £8. Also worth investigating the Xoron floating B&B who were very friendly when I inquired about accommodation, telephone 01983 874596.

HAZARDS: The harbour almost dries out at low tide. The entrance is marked with buoys but there is not always a lot of water in the channel, especial further out to sea, be very careful at low tide, even inside the marked channel.

Yarmouth Harbour, Yarmouth

Harbour Commissioners Harbour Office The Quay, Yarmouth, Isle of Wight, England PO41 0NT
Lat. 50.7058, Long. -1.5029.
(0)1983 760321

Harbour Slip, Yarmouth

Lat. 50.7058, Long. -1.5013.
SUITABILITY: Large trailer needs a car.
ACCESS: All of tidal range. **TYPE OF RAMP:** Wide concrete.
UPPER AREA: Harbour. **LOWER AREA:** Harbour.
DIRECTIONS: Ramp is into the harbour near where the Lymington car ferry comes in.
RAMP DESCRIPTION: A good slip, nice and wide very good shelter. Only problem is at very low water there is a sill to watch out for.
FACILITIES: Yarmouth has all the facilities required. There is also a small boats berth nearby for which the harbourmaster will collect a fee. Parking is available in a car park 3 minutes walk but it is not cheap if you are going out for any length of time. Much better to cross the Yarmouth Bridge and then head up the hill turn right and park in the housing estate. I have left the car and trailer here for over a week with no problems. But it is a 10 minute walk.
HAZARDS: Yarmouth harbour gets busy in the summer and is speed restricted.

The Marsh Boatyard, Cowes

4 Marsh Rd, Cowes, Isle of Wight, England PO31 8JQ
Lat. 50.7563, Long. -1.3318.
01983 281200

Slipway, Lepe Country Park

Lat. 50.7842, Long. -1.3559.
John Maskrey (Manager) 01590 674656
CHARGES: None
SUITABILITY: Portable Only.
ACCESS: All of tidal range. **TYPE OF RAMP:** Beach Launching.
UPPER AREA: Unknown. **LOWER AREA:** Unknown.
DIRECTIONS: Signposted right off A326 in Holbury.
RAMP DESCRIPTION: Suitable for portable, non-motorised craft only. Launch site faces south. Jetskiing discouraged. Very popular with windsurfers. One of the principal windsurfing sites in Hampshire.
FACILITIES: Car parking, 600 spaces in pay and display car park. Boat parking within car park. Toilets, water hose, café.

Bucklers Hard Yacht Harbour, Beaulieu

Harbourmaster's Office, Buckler's Hard Yacht Harbour, Beaulieu, Hampshire, England SO42 7XB
Lat. 50.8004, Long. -1.4225.
01590 616200

Slipway, Bucklers Hard

Lat. 50.7997, Long. -1.4219.
01590 616200

CHARGES: £9 to launch or recover, plus £5 per day parking for a cruise. Go to the harbour master office first to pay - they will issue you with the gate key code to access the slip area.
SUITABILITY: Large trailer needs a car.
ACCESS: All of tidal range. **TYPE OF RAMP:** Concrete/gravel upper stretch. **UPPER AREA:** Concrete. **LOWER AREA:** Mud.
RAMP DESCRIPTION: Concrete ramp with a reasonable slope. Entrance to ramp is straight, although the tide can run across it at 2 knots max on a Spring tide. Recovering from the ramp can result in wheel spin on the gravel area at the top of the ramp, lower sections can also be very slippery at low tide - if you don't have a 4 × 4 take a good rope to keep pulling vehicle higher up the ramp if necessary. There is a 2 foot drop off at the bottom of the concrete section, which can catch out larger boats with trailers at low water Springs who don't fancy launching across the mud and need to float their boat over the trailer rather than winch it on. There is also a fast tide which can prove troublesome at Springs after high water +2 approx. Pontoon almost next to the ramp for loading if you need it. You will be charged £10 short stay fee to use pontoon if it more than loading and unloading.
FACILITIES: Very well served. Car and trailer park near the ramp. Showers and toilets available free. Hose down facilities near ramp. Chandlers and boat yard with boat hoist to 35 tonnes! To stay overnight at the marina is approx. £16 for a 20 foot boat, although trots are available at minimal cost. The nearby marina has fuel and there is a garage and pub very nearby. Pub is excellent but gets crowded in the summer.
HAZARDS: 5 knots speed restriction in the river. Approximately 4 miles to the Solent.

Haven Quay, Lymington

Mill Lane, Lymington, Hampshire, England SO41 9AZ
Lat. 50.7596, Long. -1.5368.

Town Quay, Lymington

Lat. 50.7590, Long. -1.5364.
Lymington Harbour Commissioners (01590 672014)
SUITABILITY: Large trailer needs a car.
ACCESS: All of tidal range. **TYPE OF RAMP: UPPER AREA:** Harbour.
LOWER AREA: Unknown.
RAMP DESCRIPTION: This slipway is only available for emergency use. There is no access at other times.

Berthon Lymington Marina, Lymington
The Shipyard, Bath Road, Lymington, Hampshire,
England SO41 3YL
Lat. 50.7575, Long. -1.5349.
01590 673312

Bath Road, Lymington
Lat. 50.7540, Long. -1.5288.
Lymington Harbour Commissioners (01590 672014)

CHARGES: Launch unassisted by vehicle £4 per day. Launch assisted by vehicle £10. Vehicle assisted launch for boats with engines of 100hp and over £15. For annual fees please contact the Harbour Office (harbouroffice@lymingtonharbour.co.uk. Tel: 01590 672014)
SUITABILITY: Large trailer needs a car.
ACCESS: ¾ tidal. **TYPE OF RAMP:** Wide concrete.
UPPER AREA: Concrete. **LOWER AREA:** Mud.
DIRECTIONS: Go through Lymington and head for the sailing club and Harbourmasters office.
RAMP DESCRIPTION: Suitable for all types of craft. Good wide and smooth concrete slipway with a fairly steep gradient. Very popular with all types of trailer craft and very congested at peak times. Pontoon next to the jetty for visiting yachts and useful for loading and unloading.
FACILITIES: Pay and display car park for cars and trailers but no overnight stay. Parking is very congested at summer weekends and larger boats would be advised to go to Calshot Activity Centre. Fuel from marina, toilets, chandlers, boat yards, pubs and shops.
HAZARDS: Bye-Laws 6 knot speed limit; Jetskiing, water skiing and windsurfing prohibited in harbour. Lymington-Yarmouth ferry has right of way in main channel.

Lymington Yacht Haven, Lymington
King's Saltern Road, Lymington, Hampshire,
England SO41 3QD
Lat. 50.7507, Long. -1.5277.
01590 677071

Slipway, Keyhaven
Lat. 50.7220, Long. -1.5656.
01590 645695 VHF 37

CHARGES: RIBs £15 per launch.
SUITABILITY: Large trailer needs a car.
ACCESS: ¾ tidal. **TYPE OF RAMP:** Gravel and 3.5m concrete.
UPPER AREA: Shingle. **LOWER AREA:** Shingle.
DIRECTIONS: From East (Lymington) A337 onto B3058 to Milford-on-Sea (direct) Village Green. Do not go down Lymore Lane, signposted Keyhaven, you will get stuck. From west (Christchurch) A337 onto B3058 to Milford-on-Sea village green. Common route thereafter from Milford-on-Sea following signposting to Keyhurst and/or Hurst Castle. At Keyhaven, straight on at War Memorial/Village Green (not left fork), round narrow right-hand bend, past pub The Gun (on right) and car park (on left) and left, after 200 metres into lane (often very busy, mind the children) leading to slipways, quay and river wardens office/lookout.
RAMP DESCRIPTION: Very busy in summer weekends, holidays and world sailing race starts. Best to use Calshot slipway. North slip for RIBS

and is closed October and November for oyster storage. South slip for sailing dinghies (faces east) but can be used including concrete slip but ONLY if not busy or as directed by river warden. No access at 2 hours before and after low water Springs. Tide stands approximately 2 hours after high water. Slips shared with other trailer-launchers and Keyhaven Yacht Club and Hurst Castle Sailing Club. There is only the one car park and no street parking May to October. Look out for children in the road, slips and river. The whole area is a 'Conservation Area' and a breeding area for sea birds.
FACILITIES: Boatyard, pub, parking 133 spaces inc. 4 disabled (pay and display £4.20 all day, March to October, max 20 hours, you pay for both car and trailer. No parking on quay or slipways, public toilets, fuel in Milford-on-Sea.
HAZARDS: Narrow winding river channel but follow densely moored boats to access Solent. Fishing trawlers and ferries (to Hurst Castle) also use river. Lots of sailing dinghies many under control of children. 4knts speed limit. Tide drops fast, don't push your luck, as the mud is very soft, smelly and particularly adhesive.

Mudeford Slipway, Christchurch
Lat. 50.7247, Long. -1.7420.

CHARGES: Summer only - £6.50 for hand launch and more for vehicle assisted launch.
SUITABILITY: Large trailer needs a car.
ACCESS: ¾ tidal. **TYPE OF RAMP:** Concrete onto shingle.
UPPER AREA: Concrete. **LOWER AREA:** Shingle.
DIRECTIONS: From main Christchurch / Lymington road head towards Mudeford. Look for turning signed Mudeford quay. Slip way at far end of car park, on harbour side.
RAMP DESCRIPTION: Wide enough for one trailer, has kink part way down. Bounded by steel rails. Shingle can have potholes - check before launching.
FACILITIES: Pay and display parking available - gets crowded in summer, £6.00 for 24 hours for a car. Toilets and pub adjacent. Trailers must be stored on the shingle to the right of the slipway.
HAZARDS: Can be shallow at low water. Watch for rocks by end of main quay - keep to harbour side of warning buoy. Harbour very shallow out of main channel. Caution - tidal run very fast on Spring ebb. Keep to buoyed channel - shifting sand banks make navigation tricky. 4 knot restriction in harbour and within 250 yards of beach. Channel is not buoyed during the winter months.

Christchurch Marine, Christchurch
c/o Rossiter Yachts, Bridge Street, Christchurch,
Dorset, England BH23 1DZ
Lat. 50.7334, Long. -1.7712.
01202 483250

River Stour, Christchurch
Lat. 50.7299, Long. -1.7796.
07802 652498

CHARGES: No ramp fee but it charge to park trailer and car.
SUITABILITY: Large trailer needs a car.

3

ACCESS: All of tidal range. **TYPE OF RAMP:** Cobbled stone.
UPPER AREA: Rock. **LOWER AREA:** Shingle.
DIRECTIONS: Follow signs to Wick ferry, slipway at end of public car park, slip directly into River Stour. Signposted as Public slipway.
RAMP DESCRIPTION: This slipway was repaired in 2005 so should be in good repair. However, there is still a significant drop-off at the end of the slipway and launch at low water is tricky due to this.
FACILITIES: Toilets within 300 metres often closed late evening by the Borough Council. Public car park on site or further parking 300m. Pay & display for car & trailer. Within 100 metres of slip there is a RYA approved Powerboat school, www.ashbypowerboatschool.co.uk.
HAZARDS: Moored boats 4 knot speed limit, no PWCs.

Slipway, Wick
Lat. 50.7289, Long. -1.7806.
CHARGES: None
SUITABILITY: Small trailer can be pushed.
ACCESS: ¾ tidal. **TYPE OF RAMP: UPPER AREA:** Shingle.
LOWER AREA: Shingle.
DIRECTIONS: From Christchurch town centre, head for Tuckton via Stour Road. Follow signs to Tuckton, and cross the bridge over the river Stour then turn left at the roundabout signposted Wick. Head along this road for approx 250yds, and the slipway is at the far end of the grassed area alongside the river.
RAMP DESCRIPTION: A small slipway ideal for small sailing craft, dinghies and canoes.
FACILITIES: Virtually none at the ramp, however car park and tea-rooms about 150yds upstream back along Wick Lane.
HAZARDS: Keep a look out for other moored boats close by the ramp

Salterns Marina, Poole
Lat. 50.7070, Long. -1.9481.
Marina Office 01202 709971
CHARGES: £31.50/day. £21 one way.
SUITABILITY: Large trailer needs a car.
ACCESS: ¼ tidal. **TYPE OF RAMP:** Steep concrete. Very little depth even at high tide, ok for Jetskis, water is shallow for quite away out. Very difficult for recovery at anything but high tide. Facilities good, hose available also. **UPPER AREA:** Harbour. **LOWER AREA:** Mud.
DIRECTIONS: 40 Salterns Way, Lilliput, Dorset. From Poole follow Sandbanks Road and turn right into Salterns Way.
RAMP DESCRIPTION: Steep concrete ramp only suitable for small craft. Very shallow sand gradient at bottom. Popular with Jetskis. One way launch £21.00 or £31.50 for the day. Also a boat hoist for larger craft. Up to 22 ′ £50 or £77 in and out one week; up to 27 ′ £61 or £88 in and out in one week. Add vat to all prices.
FACILITIES: 5 star marina facilities including showers and toilets, boatyard and chandlery. Parking available but limited, speak to the marina office.

Salterns Marina, Poole
40 Salterns Way, Lilliput, Poole, Dorset, England BH14 8JR
Lat. 50.7055, Long. -1.9505.
01202 709971

Parkstone Bay Marina, Poole
Turks Lane, Poole, Dorset, England BH14 8EW
Lat. 50.7117, Long. -1.9588.
01202 747857

Baiter Public Slip, Poole
Lat. 50.7112, Long. -1.9718.
CHARGES: £8.00 per day (£6.00 after 2:30pm) including car and trailer parking. Payment at machine accepting coins only.
SUITABILITY: Large trailer needs a car.
ACCESS: ¾ tidal. **TYPE OF RAMP:** Concrete **UPPER AREA:** Concrete.
LOWER AREA: Shingle.
DIRECTIONS: Slipway is in the large Car Park near Baiter Park on the Poole water front.
RAMP DESCRIPTION: Large wide ramp. Very shallow entry angle, which makes it easy to launch and recover. Trailer needs to be walked out a distance to adequate depth for boat/ski launching. That means that it is very difficult to get a cabin trailer sailer off its trailer without getting the brakes wet particularly when not at the top of the tide. A long warp will also be required to recover such a boat and trailer without getting salt water on the car. This is a very popular launching site, which in high season can become very busy. It is the recommended slipway for Jetskis and close to the designated Jetski area in Poole harbour.
FACILITIES: Large tarmac car park with area for trailers. Washing facilities available but take your own hose.
HAZARDS: 10 knot speed restriction in main channels, elsewhere 6 knots. 10 knot limit lifted during winter months (October - March). There are designated Jetski and water ski areas.

Poole Quay Boat Haven, Poole
Poole Town Quay, Poole, Dorset, England BH15 1HJ
Lat. 50.7129, Long. -1.9872.
01202 649488

C J Evans International, Poole
Dee Way Wharf, West Quay Road, Poole, Dorset, England BH15 1LJ
Lat. 50.7145, Long. -1.9931.
01202 680522

Shell Bay Boat Yard, Studland
Lat. 50.6779, Long. -1.9523.
Shell Bay Boat Yard Tel: 01929 450340

CHARGES: £4.5/day £27/week.
SUITABILITY: Large trailer needs a car.

ACCESS: ¾ tidal. **TYPE OF RAMP:** Both concrete.
UPPER AREA: Unknown. **LOWER AREA:** Unknown.
DIRECTIONS: Yard is just inside Poole Harbour entrance and shown on charts and maps as Bramblebush or Gravel Bay.
RAMP DESCRIPTION: There are NO casual launches from Shell Bay Boat Yard at Studland. You need to arrange a six month berth/launch. Booking is essential at all times. Contact Shell Bay Boat Yard before going. Self launch and recover: daily rate (weekly rate is x6); inflatable dinghies - no trailer (less than 5hp) £11.75, sailing dinghies (less than 5hp) £20, catamarans (less than 5hp) £30, sports boats up to 20ft (excluding harbour dues) £25. Weekly rates include overnight storage. Car parking (when available) £10, swinging moorings (when available) £8. Tractor launch or recovery (additional to slipway charge) each way £7.50.
FACILITIES: Parking space is for 50 cars. In winter full of boats. Nat Trust car park over road. Toilets and café adjoining. Slip water tap available. We may need to move your car to assist others, therefore please ensure your keys are deposited at reception each time your vehicle is left unattended. Obstructive vehicles will be towed away without notice and at the owners' expense. Cars and trailers may only remain on site at the discretion of the management. Slipways may not be used until all charges are paid and an invoice issued. Vehicles, boats and any other property are left at the owner's risk. Customers are responsible for any relevant insurances and should familiarise themselves with Poole Harbour Byelaws.

Studland Beach, Studland
Lat. 50.6511, Long. -1.9519.
01929 450259

CHARGES: £4/day car, £4.50 single hull, £10 double hull and boats less than 20hp.
SUITABILITY: Large trailer needs a car.
ACCESS: ¼ tidal. **TYPE OF RAMP:** Concrete onto firm sand.
UPPER AREA: Shingle. **LOWER AREA:** Sand.
DIRECTIONS: Near Corfe Castle. From Wareham take A351 south to Corfe Castle. At foot of castle turn left onto B3351 for Studland. At Studland follow signs to Knoll beach, National Trust car park and slip is on right hand side at bottom of hill. Approaching from the chain ferry you pass the Shell Beach Yard slip on the right and continue for a couple of miles till you see the entrance to the NTs Knoll beach.
RAMP DESCRIPTION: Motor boats are not allowed to launch here. Concrete sleepers are on a good slope but only to high tide line. Then gently shelving beach which can be soft on the ebb. Very popular beach area so pulling out with a rope is risky. Double high tides in Poole area helps.
FACILITIES: National Trust shop, café, loos, cold shower, parking - all about 250m from ramp. Bankes Arms 1 mile south near beach is highly recommended, but busy. Sheltered sea sailing, perfect family beach. Gets very crowded peak periods.
HAZARDS: Motor boats are not allowed to launch here. Visiting boats anchoring / mooring still allowed off beach. 5Knt speed limit beach side of yellow marker buoys. Watch out for cordoned swimmers area marked by yellow floats. Popular area for overnighters out of Poole. Redland rocks very close to beach are marked but not really a problem. Easterly winds can make

things lumpy. Check charts for reef between the ramp and shell bay offshore - well marked though

OceanBay Watersports, Swanage
Lat. 50.6164, Long. -1.9576.
07721 938949

CHARGES: Jetski & boats under 3m launch - £13/day boats over 3m - £17/day sailboards & small craft - £6/day canoes - £2/day. 4 × 4s available - £5 both ways
SUITABILITY: Small trailer can be pushed.
ACCESS: No Ramp. **TYPE OF RAMP: UPPER AREA:** Sand.
LOWER AREA: Sand.
DIRECTIONS: Ocean Bay Watersports, North Beach, Ulwell Road, Swanage, Dorset. BH19 1LH Located on the North Beach of Swanage where Ulwell Road meets Shore Road
RAMP DESCRIPTION: Private beach used for Jetski & boat launching & watersports hire

Slipway, Swanage
Lat. 50.6078, Long. -1.9477.
01929 423636

CHARGES: £25 to launch and park. £10 to launch only. Aug 2006: Launch only £10. Extra £5 to leave trailer in boat park. You have to leave car in adjoining public car park (limited spaces in high season peak hours) and it is £6 for all day (peak season)
SUITABILITY: Large trailer needs a car.
ACCESS: All of tidal range. **TYPE OF RAMP:** Large concrete slipway.
UPPER AREA: Harbour. **LOWER AREA:** Harbour.
DIRECTIONS: Head towards the lifeboat station at the southern end of Swanage and out towards Peveril Point. Slipway is just before you get to the lifeboat station.
RAMP DESCRIPTION: Very large steep ramp with some potholes.
FACILITIES: Pontoons on either side of the slip for loading and unloading. All the usual facilities in nearby Swanage. Pontoon sides demand a lot of fenders especially at low tide. Flushing tap. Very narrow lanes in yard and entrance / exit can be tight (was with 4 × 4 & 7m boat/ trailer). Mooring on buoys available from Dive Centre on the pier for c. £10 per day.

INLAND SLIPWAYS
alphabetical by place name

St Helens Warf, Abingdon
Lat. 51.6673, Long. -1.2823.

CHARGES: No charges
SUITABILITY: Small trailer can be pushed.
ACCESS: Non-tidal. **TYPE OF RAMP:** Cobble stones
UPPER AREA: Concrete. **LOWER AREA:** Mud.
DIRECTIONS: From the centre of Abingdon proceed behind the County Hall down East St.Helens Street. At the bottom of East St.Helens Street, carry on down past St.Helens Church and the slipway is straight ahead.
RAMP DESCRIPTION: Public slipway from the road. Fairly narrow and reasonably steep.

The Good Launch Guide

FACILITIES: Parking 200 yards in pay & display car park in West St.Helens Street. Pub with food 20 yards away on St.Helens Wharf. Abingdon Boat Centre 50 yards upstream with chandlery and fuel available.

HAZARDS: ALL boats require a licence from the Environment Agency and 8kph speed limit.

Abingdon Marina, Abingdon
South Quay, Abingdon, Oxfordshire, England OX14 5TW
Lat. 51.6589, Long. -1.2812.
01235 536147

Abingdon Marina, Abingdon
Lat. 51.6570, Long. -1.2837.
SUITABILITY: Large trailer needs a car.
ACCESS: Non-tidal. **TYPE OF RAMP:** Concrete **UPPER AREA:** Concrete.
LOWER AREA: Unknown.
DIRECTIONS: From the A34 Abingdon junction head toward Abingdon. Go straight over 2 roundabouts then turn right onto the B4017 toward Drayton. Straight over the roundabout then second left into Preston Rd. After road bends left turn right into Lambrick Way. Follow this road to slip. For parking return to Preston Rd and turn right to Wilsham Rd.
RAMP DESCRIPTION: Excellent wide concrete slipway.
FACILITIES: Excellent free slipway. Road access has height restriction of approx 7ft. This will be opened by the marina manager if he is on site. (Call for times). Parking is now available at the top of slip, no charge for launch or parking.
HAZARDS: ALL boats require a licence from the Environment Agency and 8kph speed limit.

Froud's Bridge Marina, Aldermarston
Froud's Lane, Aldermarston, Berkshire, England RG7 4LH
Lat. 51.3950, Long. -1.1518.
0118 971 4508

Farborough Road, Aldershot
Lat. 51.2630, Long. -0.7668.
01252 370073
CHARGES: Needs a BWB key to access the slipway and a valid license from the Basingstoke Canal Authority.
SUITABILITY: Large trailer needs a car.
ACCESS: Unknown. **TYPE OF RAMP: UPPER AREA:** Concrete.
LOWER AREA: Concrete.
RAMP DESCRIPTION: Concrete slipway with good access
FACILITIES: Parking available free

Old Ferry Landing, Aston
Lat. 51.5539, Long. -0.8677.
Environment Agency - Tel: 0118 953 5650
CHARGES: None - Car park is free.
SUITABILITY: Small trailer can be pushed.

ACCESS: Non-tidal. **TYPE OF RAMP:** Gravel hard.
UPPER AREA: Shingle. **LOWER AREA:** Unknown.
DIRECTIONS: At the end of Aston Ferry Lane, Aston, Berkshire. South side of the river. Note that there is also a slipway on the north bank of the river.
RAMP DESCRIPTION: Powered craft must be licensed by the Environment Agency - Tel: 0118 953 5650. It is quite steep at the top, but shallow at the river. Take a rope to avoid skidding your way up after recovering boat. Old ferry landing stage has space for two boats and is free, but may belong to the pub? Generally a good launch site.
FACILITIES: Park in lane.
HAZARDS: 8 kph (4 knots) speed limit on river.

Slipway, Barley Mow Bridge
Lat. 51.2779, Long. -0.8858.
01252 370073

CHARGES: Requires a BWB key to gain access and a valid license for Basingstoke Canal. 3-Day visitor license available
SUITABILITY: Large trailer needs a car.
ACCESS: Non-tidal. **TYPE OF RAMP:** Concrete **UPPER AREA:** Concrete.
LOWER AREA: Concrete.
RAMP DESCRIPTION: Concrete ramp, quite narrow with metal banked sides. Watch out for people on the towpath. As the canal is above the level of the surrounding land, there is a slope UP to the ramp.
FACILITIES: Pub across the road.

Hoseason's boatyard, Benson
Lat. 51.6189, Long. -1.1145.
SUITABILITY: Large trailer needs a car.
ACCESS: Non-tidal. **TYPE OF RAMP: UPPER AREA:** Unknown.
LOWER AREA: Unknown.
DIRECTIONS: On the left bank going downstream.
RAMP DESCRIPTION: Get permission to use the site. Two slips.
FACILITIES: All boatyard facilities.

Nitrojet Action Sports, Berinsfield
Lat. 51.6565, Long. -1.1653.
01865 341115

CHARGES: Morning launch £20.00. Full day launch £30.00. Annual membership £400.00
SUITABILITY: Small trailer can be pushed.
ACCESS: Non-tidal. **TYPE OF RAMP:** Concrete slipway, with sand beach area. **UPPER AREA:** Shingle. **LOWER AREA:** Unknown.
DIRECTIONS: Nitrojet is between Reading and Oxford on the A4074. It is also easily reached from the M4 via the A34/A415. From the roundabout on the A4074/A415, take the road sign posted to Berinsfield. Follow the road for approx 1/2 mile, the turning will be on your right hand side and there is a sign for Oxford waterski and wakeboard club
RAMP DESCRIPTION: The lake is open 7 days a week from 10am to all watercraft - both stand up and sit-downs. Closing times vary to season, please call for full details. Day launch is £30. Half day launch is available from 10am - 2pm and is £20. Annual membership is £400.
FACILITIES: Changing rooms, café and excellent stocked showroom, workshop for servicing and repair.

3

Bourne End Marina, Bourne End
Wharf Lane, Bourne End, Buckinghamshire, England SL8 5RR
Lat. 51.5768, Long. -0.7147.
01628 522813

Waterside Inn, Bray
Lat. 51.5090, Long. -0.7002.
SUITABILITY: Small trailer can be pushed.
ACCESS: Non-tidal. **TYPE OF RAMP:** Concrete blocks
UPPER AREA: Shingle. **LOWER AREA:** Unknown.
DIRECTIONS: Public gravel hard by Waterside Inn, Ferry Road. On the right bank going downstream.
RAMP DESCRIPTION: Definitely for small craft only, if you can get anywhere near the slip. Slip is shallow, concrete blocks and lots of debris build-up. Narrow access and even less turning space; watch out for bollards at top of slip. April 2006, a swan has built a nest right on the slipway and laid eggs in it, making it unusable without incurring the wrath of nature lovers, RSPCA, RSPB, and so on! It is against the law to move or disturb swans' nests. The eggs should hatch in mid-May, after which the nest will be abandoned and the slipway should be useable again.
FACILITIES: The Waterside Inn is a very upmarket restaurant run by one of the Roux Brothers, so the place is crawling with Rolls Royces. Limited parking.
HAZARDS: ALL boats require a licence from the Environment Agency and 8kph speed limit.

National Trust picnic spot, Buscot
Lat. 51.6839, Long. -1.6774.
SUITABILITY: Small trailer can be pushed.
ACCESS: Non-tidal. **TYPE OF RAMP:** Low bank.
UPPER AREA: Unknown. **LOWER AREA:** Unknown.
DIRECTIONS: On the right bank going downstream. National Trust picnic spot. Low bank.
RAMP DESCRIPTION: Public slipway.
HAZARDS: ALL boats require a licence from the Environment Agency and 8kph speed limit.

Red Lion Lawn, Castle Easton
Lat. 51.6608, Long. -1.7918.
SUITABILITY: Small trailer can be pushed.
ACCESS: Non-tidal. **TYPE OF RAMP: UPPER AREA:** Unknown.
LOWER AREA: Unknown.
DIRECTIONS: On the right bank going downstream. Lawn of Red Lion pub.
RAMP DESCRIPTION: Get permission to use the site from the pub.
HAZARDS: ALL boats require a licence from the Environment Agency and 8kph speed limit.

Bates Marina, Chertsey
W Bates & Son, Bridge Wharf, Chertsey, Surrey, England KT16 8LG
Lat. 51.3866, Long. -0.4863.
01932 562255

Penton Hook Marina, Chertsey
Staines Road, Chertsey, Surrey, England KT16 8PY
Lat. 51.4095, Long. -0.5040.
01932 568681

Fairmile Hospital Slip, Cholsey
Lat. 51.5651, Long. -1.1340.
SUITABILITY: Small trailer can be pushed.
ACCESS: Non-tidal. **TYPE OF RAMP: UPPER AREA:** Unknown.
LOWER AREA: Unknown.
DIRECTIONS: End of lane beside Fairmile Hospital grounds.
RAMP DESCRIPTION: Popular ramp. On the right bank going downstream.
HAZARDS: ALL boats require a licence from the Environment Agency and 8kph speed limit.

Harvester Pub, Cookham
Lat. 51.5621, Long. -0.7059.
SUITABILITY: Small trailer can be pushed.
ACCESS: Non-tidal. **TYPE OF RAMP:** Concrete **UPPER AREA:** Concrete.
LOWER AREA: Shingle.
DIRECTIONS: Public hard, concrete, at side of Harvester Pub by Cookham Bridge. On the right bank going downstream.
RAMP DESCRIPTION: Restricted access and you will need to reverse through the car park and a left 90degree bend to get the trailer into position for this slip. Pub patrons also like to park cars in this area making it even narrower. Concrete to gravel, useful landing stage alongside. 30cm drop at the end of the slipway.
FACILITIES: Parking space is limited. Pleasant area, and on return to launch slip you can sit outside by the river and have a drink in the pub.
HAZARDS: ALL boats require a licence from the Environment Agency and 8kph speed limit.

Thames Lane Ford, Cricklade
Lat. 51.6430, Long. -1.8517.
SUITABILITY: Small trailer can be pushed.
ACCESS: Non-tidal. **TYPE OF RAMP: UPPER AREA:** Unknown.
LOWER AREA: Unknown.
DIRECTIONS: On right bank when going downstream. Ford at farm at bottom of Thames Lane.
RAMP DESCRIPTION: Ask permission at farm.
HAZARDS: ALL boats require a licence from the Environment Agency and 8kph speed limit.

Devizes Wharf, Devizes
Lat. 51.3552, Long. -1.9985.
0380 721279
CHARGES: Yes - seasonal.
SUITABILITY: Large trailer needs a car.
ACCESS: Non-tidal. **TYPE OF RAMP:** Concrete
UPPER AREA: Unknown. **LOWER AREA:** Unknown.
DIRECTIONS: On Kennet Avon Canal close to the famous Devizes staircase of locks. Entering Devizes from the northwest (A342 / A361) at Wadworths Brewery turn left and after 150 yards turn left again signposted Wharf and Theatre. Slip water tap.

3

RAMP DESCRIPTION: Gradient is gentle.
FACILITIES: Overnight parking available. Parking space is for 100 + cars. Licence needed.

Devizes Marina, Devizes
Horton Avenue, Devizes, Wilts, England SN10 2RH
Lat. 51.3616, Long. -1.9664.
01380 725300

Ditton Reach Slip, Ditton Hill
Lat. 51.3912, Long. -0.3241.
SUITABILITY: Large trailer needs a car.
ACCESS: Unknown. **TYPE OF RAMP: UPPER AREA:** Unknown.
LOWER AREA: Unknown.
RAMP DESCRIPTION: Near City Arms.

Bell Weir Boats, Egham
Yard Mead, Egham, Surrey, UK TW20 0AA
Lat. 51.4405, Long. -0.5447.
01784 438 773

Hurst Park Public Slipway, Hampton Court
Lat. 51.4112, Long. -0.3586.
CHARGES: Parking free here. Car park opens during the hours of light.
SUITABILITY: Portable Only.
ACCESS: Non-tidal. **TYPE OF RAMP:** The concrete stops at the water level. **UPPER AREA:** Concrete. **LOWER AREA:** Concrete.
DIRECTIONS: At the top of Sadler's Ride, past the car park.
RAMP DESCRIPTION: It isn't really a ramp, but fine for SIBs, small RIBs and tenders.
FACILITIES: None
HAZARDS: Houseboats moored nearby. Watch your wake and keep under the 8kph speed limit.

Public Slipway, Henley
Lat. 51.5381, Long. -0.9003.
CHARGES: None
SUITABILITY: Small trailer can be pushed.
ACCESS: Non-tidal. **TYPE OF RAMP:** Concrete **UPPER AREA:** Concrete.
LOWER AREA: Shingle.
DIRECTIONS: At the bottom of New Street which is one way on a bend so you have to reverse onto the slip against the flow of traffic so you need a look-out and don't want to do it at peak times.
RAMP DESCRIPTION: Retrieval can be interesting when the ice cream van partially blocks the slipway, the queue doesn't want to move out the way and you have an audience waiting for you to mess it up. The slip is very shallow being nothing more than the gravel bed of the river. Long term parking is at the station although it is not allowed during Regatta week.
FACILITIES: Limited parking at the slipway.
HAZARDS: ALL boats require a licence from the Environment Agency and 8kph speed limit.

Hambleden Mill Marina, Henley-on-Thames
Mill End, Henley-on-Thames, Oxon, England RG9 3AY
Lat. 51.5600, Long. -0.8712.
01491 571316

Alf Parrott Moorings, Henley-on-Thames
15 Thames Side, Henley-on-Thames, Oxfordshire, England RG9 1BH
Lat. 51.5369, Long. -0.9013.
01491 572380

Hurley Farms Slip, Hurley
Lat. 51.5475, Long. -0.8267.
Caravan park 01628-823501

CHARGES: Requires "membership" of Hurley Riverside Park Picnic Grounds. £25 (£9 membership, two visits included). Thereafter, £8/visit. Includes car and trailer parking.
SUITABILITY: Large trailer needs a car.
ACCESS: Non-tidal. **TYPE OF RAMP:** Concrete
UPPER AREA: Unknown. **LOWER AREA:** Unknown.
DIRECTIONS: Access is from the A4130 (look for the signs for Hurley Farm caravan Site), and drive into the entrance to the main site. Stop there and ask for access at reception as there is a barrier on the slipway road.
RAMP DESCRIPTION: This is a caravan site downstream from Medmenham and upstream from Hurley. Slip is part of Hurley Riverside Park Picnic Grounds, a large (500m x 50m) grassy area. The slip is concrete, about 15 degrees and leads into the river from the south bank.
FACILITIES: You get a reasonably secure area for the car/trailer and the slip is more substantial than Aston with a lot of manoeuvring room ashore.
HAZARDS: ALL boats require a licence from the Environment Agency and 8kph speed limit.

Hurley Beach Slip, Hurley
Lat. 51.5506, Long. -0.8130.
Caravan park 01628-823501

CHARGES: Requires "membership" of Hurley Riverside Park Picnic Grounds. £25 (£9 membership, two visits included). Thereafter, £8/visit. Includes car and trailer parking.
SUITABILITY: Small trailer can be pushed.
ACCESS: Non-tidal. **TYPE OF RAMP:** Concrete
UPPER AREA: Unknown. **LOWER AREA:** Unknown.
DIRECTIONS: Situated near to the weir in the village of Hurley. Owned and run by the same people that run the Hurley Farms slip. Access is from the A4130 (look for the signs for Hurley Farm Caravan Site). You do not need to enter the caravan site to get to the slipway. Instead turn right at the gates of the site and head for the Riverside Car Park
RAMP DESCRIPTION: Very shallow gradient concrete ramp - easy launching and retrieval. Close to weir and subject to stronger flow and weir overspill right opposite plays havoc when trying to recover in strong

3

flow. Ramp has a deep drop-off about 6 feet into the river, beware if you have anything over about 15 feet to launch.

HAZARDS: ALL boats require a licence from the Environment Agency and 8kph speed limit.

Riverside Road, Kelmscot

Lat. 51.6866, Long. -1.6759.

SUITABILITY: Large trailer needs a car.

ACCESS: Non-tidal. **TYPE OF RAMP: UPPER AREA:** Unknown.

LOWER AREA: Unknown.

DIRECTIONS: On the left bank going downstream. Field at end of Riverside Road leading from village.

HAZARDS: ALL boats require a licence from the Environment Agency and 8kph speed limit.

Anglers Reach, Kingston, London

Lat. 51.3978, Long. -0.3105.

SUITABILITY: Large trailer needs a car.

ACCESS: ½ tidal. **TYPE OF RAMP:** Rough tarmac.

UPPER AREA: Concrete. **LOWER AREA:** Unknown.

DIRECTIONS: At the junction of Grove Road and Portsmouth Road, just south of Kingston-on-Thames.

RAMP DESCRIPTION: Rough tarmac in between sailing club facilities. Nasty drop from the road onto the ramp.

FACILITIES: Limited parking at the slipway.

HAZARDS: Speed restriction in river.

Ferry Lane, Laleham., Laleham

Lat. 51.4058, Long. -0.4925.

CHARGES: None

SUITABILITY: Small trailer can be pushed.

ACCESS: Non-tidal. **TYPE OF RAMP:** Concrete **UPPER AREA:** Concrete.

LOWER AREA: Concrete.

RAMP DESCRIPTION: Public ramp, suitable for dinghies and small boats. Reasonably user friendly. Overhanging willows need pruning!

FACILITIES: Parking opposite ramp.

Riverside Cafe, Lechlade

Lat. 51.6929, Long. -1.6933.

Mr Meek 01367 252229

CHARGES: £7/day

SUITABILITY: Large trailer needs a car.

ACCESS: Non-tidal. **TYPE OF RAMP:** Concrete

UPPER AREA: Unknown. **LOWER AREA:** Unknown.

DIRECTIONS: Turn South off A417 onto A361. Turn right into Marina before bridge.

RAMP DESCRIPTION: Good wide concrete slipway leading into the marina.

FACILITIES: Riverside café, boatyard, and chandlery. Plenty of parking. Cost approximately £7 + £1 car park per day.

HAZARDS: ALL boats require a licence from the Environment Agency and 8kph speed limit.

Riverside Lechlade Marina, Lechlade

Park End Wharf, Lechlade, Gloucestershire, England GL7 3AQ

Lat. 51.6931, Long. -1.6940.

01367 252229

Recreation Ground Car Park, Lechlade

Lat. 51.6911, Long. -1.6976.

SUITABILITY: Small trailer can be pushed.

ACCESS: Non-tidal. **TYPE OF RAMP: UPPER AREA:** Unknown.

LOWER AREA: Unknown.

DIRECTIONS: On the right bank going downstream. Car park at recreation ground flanks an arm of the river.

RAMP DESCRIPTION: Public slipway.

HAZARDS: ALL boats require a licence from the Environment Agency and 8kph speed limit.

Trowlock Island Slip, London

Lat. 51.4238, Long. -0.3092.

SUITABILITY: Small trailer can be pushed.

ACCESS: Non-tidal. **TYPE OF RAMP: UPPER AREA:** Unknown.

LOWER AREA: Unknown.

DIRECTIONS: Sited on left bank going downstream on River Thames. End of Trowlock Way, ex-ferry slip into 2ft water.

RAMP DESCRIPTION: Public slipway.

FACILITIES: Park in lane.

HAZARDS: ALL boats require a licence from the Environment Agency and 8kph speed limit.

Sunbury Public Slip, London

Lat. 51.4081, Long. -0.3997.

08708 506 506

CHARGES: None

SUITABILITY: Large trailer needs a car.

ACCESS: Non-tidal. **TYPE OF RAMP:** Concrete **UPPER AREA:** Shingle.

LOWER AREA: Concrete.

RAMP DESCRIPTION: Gradient is moderate. Up river from Sunbury Court, on Lower Hampton Road. Thames licences can be purchased at the nearest lock. DROP OFF AT THE BOTTOM OF RAMP. Can be difficult to launch due to vegetation. However vegetation has recently been cut back (Jan 2006)

FACILITIES: Free overnight parking. Parking space is for 6 cars. Security is reasonable for overnight stops. Toilet 200 metres away.

HAZARDS: ALL boats require a licence from the Environment Agency and 8kph speed limit.

Lee Valley Marina, London

Lat. 51.5730, Long. -0.0591.

Lee Valley Marina, 020 8806 1717

CHARGES: £20.50 each way or £32.50 both ways if paid in advance.

SUITABILITY: Large trailer needs a car.

ACCESS: Non-tidal. **TYPE OF RAMP:** Concrete

UPPER AREA: Unknown. **LOWER AREA:** Unknown.

DIRECTIONS: Lee Valley Marina, Spring Hill, Clapton, London E5 9BL.

3

RAMP DESCRIPTION: Call before using. Slip water tap close by. Electric locks downriver operated by key, available from marina (requires deposit). Navigation requires British Waterways licence, available at marina.
FACILITIES: Free parking. Crew can park at bottom of Spring Hill and walk over foot bridge. Car and trailer park in car park of Ice Centre, Lea Bridge Road (020 8533 3154). Petrol available nearby. Diesel on site, pub on site. Club room, shower and toilets, Calor gas, mains water supply, Elsan toilet disposal, battery charging, electricity points (240v) diesel, pump out, and towage. Repair and maintenance service for all types of craft in fully equipped modern workshop. Slipway maximum length 10.98 metres.

Kingston, London
Lat. 51.4204, Long. -0.3051.
08708 506 506

CHARGES: No charge for launching but a licence is required for motorised boats on the Thames. Contact the Environment Agency for more information
SUITABILITY: Large trailer needs a car.
ACCESS: Non-tidal. **TYPE OF RAMP:** Narrow concrete.
UPPER AREA: Concrete. **LOWER AREA:** Shingle.
DIRECTIONS: On Ham Road that runs along side the Thames just north of Kingston. Ramp is just to the north of Canbury Gardens.
RAMP DESCRIPTION: Small narrow ramp in picturesque surroundings. Lots of sailing clubs on this stretch of river.
FACILITIES: Limited parking nearby. Road liable to flooding. Good little slipway which unfortunately can get clogged up with flotsam. If you're prepared to get your hands dirty and arrive early it's a good slip with plenty of parking.
HAZARDS: Speed restriction in river.

Lee Valley Marina - Springfield, London
Spring Hill, London, England E5 9BL
Lat. 51.5723, Long. -0.0569.
0208 806 1717

Action Watersports, Lydd
Lat. 50.9351, Long. 0.9092.
01797 321885

CHARGES: Membership from £280 Non members from £29 per session
SUITABILITY: Small trailer can be pushed.
ACCESS: Non-tidal. **TYPE OF RAMP: UPPER AREA:** Unknown.
LOWER AREA: Unknown.
DIRECTIONS: Within easy reach of the M20. Just 15 minutes south of Ashford, Kent, Close to Camber, Hastings and Folkestone. Just follow the signs for Lydd Airport and the brown Watersports signs in Lydd. Lake 1, Dengemarsh Road. TN29 9JH
RAMP DESCRIPTION: Concrete easy to use ramp.
FACILITIES: A sheltered freshwater lake for Jetskis, water skiers and wake boarders. Owner riders welcome. PWC RYA Courses. Jetski Experience days. Lake side workshop offers service, repairs and tuning to all Jetskis and boats. Largest lakeside watersports shop in southeast. Genuine advice, internet prices. Changing rooms, toilets, hot & cold snacks

Taplow Investments, Maidenhead
Driftwood, Mill Lane, Taplow, Maidenhead, Berkshire, England SL6 0AA
Lat. 51.5273, Long. -0.7001.
01628 630249

Bray Marina, Maidenhead
Monkey Island Lane, Bray, Maidenhead, Berkshire, England SL6 2EB
Lat. 51.4987, Long. -0.6815.
01628 623654

Medway Wharf Marina, Maidstone
Bow Bridge, Wateringbury, Maidstone, Kent, England ME18 5ED
Lat. 51.2485, Long. 0.4211.
01622 813927

Pewsey Wharf, Marlborough
Lat. 51.3487, Long. -1.7745.
SUITABILITY: Large trailer needs a car.
ACCESS: Non-tidal. **TYPE OF RAMP:** Concrete
UPPER AREA: Unknown. **LOWER AREA:** Unknown.
DIRECTIONS: On A345 ½ mile north of Pewsey Station on east side of road bridge over canal.
RAMP DESCRIPTION: No sailing allowed on canal but you can take your mast for the tent. This is on the Kennet Avon Canal, licence needed. Gradient is gentle.
FACILITIES: Overnight parking available. Parking space is for 30 cars. Slip water tap.

Harleyford Estate & Marina, Marlow
Henley Road, Marlow, Bucks, England SL7 2DX
Lat. 51.5533, Long. -0.7989.
01628 471361

Temple Marina, Marlow
Temple Lane, Marlow, Buckinghamshire, England SL7 1SA
Lat. 51.5520, Long. -0.7889.
01628 823410

St Peter Street, Marlow
Lat. 51.5682, Long. -0.7721.
SUITABILITY: Large trailer needs a car.
ACCESS: Non-tidal. **TYPE OF RAMP:** Concrete **UPPER AREA:** Concrete.
LOWER AREA: Shingle.
DIRECTIONS: Small public slip at the end of St Peter Street which is a no-through road. In-between the two road bridges on the north bank.
RAMP DESCRIPTION: Slip is concrete block leading to riverbed gravel. The landing stages provided make launch / recovery a breeze.
FACILITIES: Very little, if any, space for turning. Nowhere to store the trailer although there is some 'Can't stay for more than 1 hour' parking available further up the road.
HAZARDS: ALL boats require a licence from the Environment Agency and 8kph speed limit.

Ferry Lane, Medmenham
Lat. 51.5469, Long. -0.8392.

CHARGES: No charges.
SUITABILITY: Large trailer needs a car.
ACCESS: Non-tidal. **TYPE OF RAMP: UPPER AREA:** Concrete.
LOWER AREA: Mud.
DIRECTIONS: Old ferry slip at bottom of Ferry Lane from Dog and Badger on A4155.
RAMP DESCRIPTION: Little room to turn a car and trailer, the trailer will have to be uncoupled and manhandled around. Popular with canoeists and small boats so parking can be a problem. Larger boats in danger of sinking into mud at end of ramp. Launched large 1.5 ton river launch on double axle trailer and 6 meter RIB ok with a good 4×4. Although mud at bottom of slip, it is solid and trailer did not sink. There is a steep drop at the top of the ramp which could ground out low clearance cars with heavy trailers.
FACILITIES: Some parking available at side of road. Trailers can be pushed into area at the side of the road and chained to a tree.
HAZARDS: ALL boats require a licence from the Environment Agency and 8kph speed limit. Licence can be purchased at nearest lock.

Slipway, Medmenham
Lat. 51.5543, Long. -0.8652.

CHARGES: No charge
SUITABILITY: Large trailer needs a car.
ACCESS: Non-tidal. **TYPE OF RAMP:** Track down to the river.
UPPER AREA: Concrete. **LOWER AREA:** Shingle.
DIRECTIONS: Directly opposite the village of Aston, upstream from the research centre in Medmenham.
RAMP DESCRIPTION: Shingle track leading into the river. Little room to turn a car and trailer, the trailer will have to be uncoupled and manhandled around.
FACILITIES: Limited parking on the verge by the ramp.
HAZARDS: ALL boats require a licence from the Environment Agency and 8kph speed limit.

Swan Hotel Slip, Pangbourne
Lat. 51.4866, Long. -1.0897.
Swan Hotel
SUITABILITY: Large trailer needs a car.
ACCESS: Non-tidal. **TYPE OF RAMP:** Concrete
UPPER AREA: Unknown. **LOWER AREA:** Unknown.
DIRECTIONS: On the right bank going downstream.
RAMP DESCRIPTION: Get permission to use the site. Slip at Swan Hotel car park - avoid busy times - and has a kerb at the edge, retrieval can be difficult without plenty of help. Ask at hotel.
FACILITIES: Pub is on south bank of Thames upstream of large weirs on A329.
HAZARDS: ALL boats require a licence from the Environment Agency and 8kph speed limit.

Potters Slipway, Potters Slipway
Lat. 51.2864, Long. -0.7212.

CHARGES: Ask in Potters before using and parking but never a problem.
SUITABILITY: Small trailer can be pushed.
ACCESS: Non-tidal. **TYPE OF RAMP: UPPER AREA:** Concrete.
LOWER AREA: Unknown.
DIRECTIONS: Within the carpark of the Potters Restaurant
RAMP DESCRIPTION: Concrete slip
FACILITIES: Restaurant and bar available right next to slipway

Pub slipway and pontoon, Pub slipway and pontoon
Lat. 51.3879, Long. -0.4529.
SUITABILITY: Large trailer needs a car.
ACCESS: Unknown. **TYPE OF RAMP: UPPER AREA:** Unknown.
LOWER AREA: Unknown.
RAMP DESCRIPTION: Small slip way in the car of the pub (there are two pubs here)

3

Bridge Slip, Pulborough
Lat. 50.9564, Long. -0.5121.
SUITABILITY: Small trailer can be pushed.
ACCESS: ½ tidal. **TYPE OF RAMP:** Concrete **UPPER AREA:** Unknown.
LOWER AREA: Unknown.
DIRECTIONS: Next to bridge in town centre opposite the Swan.
RAMP DESCRIPTION: Barricaded and unusable. Cannot access with vehicle. Very narrow river. Cannot easily turn boat around. Steep ramp with eye bolt at top. Narrow shallow stream below half tide. Current not strong here but gets stronger downstream. At Amberley, (7 miles), tide flows 4 hours and ebbs 8. Littlehampton 18.5 miles. Not much use for sailing but attractive scenery.
FACILITIES: Petrol parking and toilets and nearby pub.

Island Green, Radcot
Lat. 51.6935, Long. -1.5876.
SUITABILITY: Large trailer needs a car.
ACCESS: Non-tidal. **TYPE OF RAMP: UPPER AREA:** Unknown.
LOWER AREA: Unknown.
RAMP DESCRIPTION: Public slipway on the right bank going downstream. Public green on island between the two bridges.
HAZARDS: ALL boats require a licence from the Environment Agency and 8kph speed limit.

Reading Public Slip, Reading
Lat. 51.4668, Long. -0.9778.

CHARGES: None - Car park is free.
SUITABILITY: Small trailer can be pushed.
ACCESS: Non-tidal. **TYPE OF RAMP:** Concrete **UPPER AREA:** Concrete.
LOWER AREA: Unknown.
DIRECTIONS: Slip is at the end of Thames Side Promenade, off Richfield Avenue, by the Holiday Inn.
RAMP DESCRIPTION: Public slip at car park. Very narrow slip between walls. On south bank of Thames immediately upstream and adjacent to Caversham Bridge. The launching area is covered by swan droppings as

the public feed the swans on the river bank in spite of advice signs to the contrary, so this is a very unpleasant slipway. The steel plates at the end of the ramp are loose and may catch on outboard, trailer, or feet. Powered craft must be licensed by the Environment Agency - Tel: 0118 953 5650.

FACILITIES: Best fish and chips in the southeast 200 yards. Adjacent to Caversham Bridge.

HAZARDS: ALL boats require a licence from the Environment Agency and 8kph speed limit.

Thames & Kennet Marina, Reading
Caversham Lakes, Henley Road, Reading, Berkshire, England RG4 6LQ
Lat. 51.4660, Long. -0.9385.
0118 948 2911

Lagoona Park, Reading
Lat. 51.4176, Long. -1.0001.
0118 988 5959

CHARGES: Membership £330-380, day launches £20-30
SUITABILITY: Small trailer can be pushed.
ACCESS: Non-tidal. **TYPE OF RAMP:** Concrete **UPPER AREA:** Shingle.
LOWER AREA: Shingle.
DIRECTIONS: The lake is just off J 11 of the M4 at Reading. Follow the directions for Pingewood.
RAMP DESCRIPTION: Concrete slipway into man-made lake.
FACILITIES: Memberships; Runabouts £380 pa, solos £330pa. Day launches; Runabouts £30 (£25 after 4pm), solos £25 (£20 after 4pm). No charge for additional riders. Hire prices - from £25 per 30 minutes (includes buoyancy aid, wetsuit, helmet and tuition). Clubhouse housing a shop with wetsuits, parts and accessories, wet and dry carpeted area, satellite television, vending, showers and toilets. Also outside there is a seated decking area (overlooking the lake) with BBQ and hot food van. There is a large parking area and trailer park and slipway allowing easy access. We also have a workshop housing an experienced mechanic available for servicing of Jetskis. Yamaha PWC dealer with machines on-site to view.

Shepperton Marina, Shepperton
Felix Lane, Shepperton, Middlesex, England TW17 8NS
Lat. 51.3922, Long. -0.4281.
01932 260268

Railway Bridge, Staines
Lat. 51.4308, Long. -0.5108.
SUITABILITY: Portable Only.
ACCESS: Non-tidal. **TYPE OF RAMP:** Stone ramp. UNUSABLE except for maybe a canoe. **UPPER AREA:** Rock. **LOWER AREA:** Sand.
DIRECTIONS: Slipway is at the north west end of Laleham Road directly underneath the railway bridge.
RAMP DESCRIPTION: Small ramp underneath the railway bridge. The ramp has small steps in it so only really suitable for portable boats. Bollards have been fixed at the top placing it beyond use as a trailer slip.
FACILITIES: No Parking

HAZARDS: Unusable for anything on a trailer.

Bridge Slip, Staines
Lat. 51.4336, Long. -0.5167.
SUITABILITY: Portable Only.
ACCESS: Non-tidal. **TYPE OF RAMP: UPPER AREA:** Concrete.
LOWER AREA: Mud.
RAMP DESCRIPTION: NO LONGER A PUBLIC SLIP.
FACILITIES: NONE! This ramp has been taken over entirely by the sea scouts who have placed a BIG girder at the top to prevent public launching!
HAZARDS: ALL boats require a licence from the Environment Agency and 8kph speed limit.

Penton Hook Sailing Club Slips, Staines
Lat. 51.4100, Long. -0.5060.
CHARGES: £12 per day with parking
SUITABILITY: Large trailer needs a car.
ACCESS: Non-tidal. **TYPE OF RAMP:** Upper concrete, middle concrete, lower silt and mud. **UPPER AREA:** Concrete. **LOWER AREA:** Mud.
DIRECTIONS: On the right bank going downstream.
RAMP DESCRIPTION: Cost £11 to launch including secure parking for a day. Very uneven slip with old steel tram lines in place. Reasonable steep, with pontoons on both sides.
HAZARDS: ALL boats require a licence from the Environment Agency and 8kph speed limit.

Thames (Ditton) Marina, Surbiton
Portsmouth Road, Surbiton, Surrey, England KT6 5QD
Lat. 51.3923, Long. -0.3195.
020 8398 6159

The Swann Draw Dock, Thames Ditton
Lat. 51.3928, Long. -0.3312.
SUITABILITY: Large trailer needs a car.
ACCESS: Non-tidal. **TYPE OF RAMP:** Hard gravel. These is a drop off a little way in be careful as you could loose your trailer.
UPPER AREA: Shingle. **LOWER AREA:** Shingle.
DIRECTIONS: Just of the right hand side of the Swan pub as you go round a 90 degree bend. The ramp is accessed through the small and sloping car park. (very difficult in all but the most quiet periods)
RAMP DESCRIPTION: Hard gravel draw dock beside The Swan opposite the south tip of Thames Ditton Island. Gives access to reach between Hampton Court and Kingston. On the right bank going downstream.
FACILITIES: Parking space is in road. Park in road about ¼ mile north where road widens.
HAZARDS: ALL boats require a licence from the Environment Agency and 8kph speed limit.

Tonbridge, Tonbridge
Lat. 51.1965, Long. 0.2728.
01732 838858
CHARGES: None

SUITABILITY: Small trailer can be pushed.
ACCESS: Non-tidal. **TYPE OF RAMP: UPPER AREA:** Concrete.
LOWER AREA: Concrete.
DIRECTIONS: NRA Tonbridge District Office, Medway House, Powder Mill Lane, Leigh, Tonbridge, Kent TN11 9AS.
RAMP DESCRIPTION: Ramp not suitable for car launching into non-tidal, locked section of river. Ramp is free but buy licence for river from tourist information next to castle. Gate is removed to allow cars to slip way.
FACILITIES: Parking in public car park, toilets, very close to town centre.

Truss' Island, Truss' Island
Lat. 51.4189, Long. -0.5135.

CHARGES: None apart from river licence.
SUITABILITY: Small trailer can be pushed.
ACCESS: Non-tidal. **TYPE OF RAMP:** Concrete but CURVED! A strange slip as it curves as you go down. Can be tricky to launch. A front tow hitch is best. **UPPER AREA:** Concrete. **LOWER AREA:** Sand.
DIRECTIONS: On Chertsey Lane.
RAMP DESCRIPTION: This ramp has a nasty bend in it and a steel post that restricts the width to around 7 feet. It is possible to launch a boat up to 20 feet here (provided it will fit under the car park height restrictions) but reversing is tricky.
FACILITIES: Good parking for trailer and car. Also parking reserved for disabled drivers. There is a height restriction bar over the car park entrance set at 7 feet. Jetskis are NOT welcomed by British Waterways due to the speeds they do and the fact they cannot be licensed!
HAZARDS: Metal bar at the foot of the ramp prevents boats over 7 foot beam being launched. BEWARE it WILL tear the side out of your boat! Also if your draft is more than 18 inches FORGET IT you will hit bottom. Ideal slip for SMALL trailer cruisers up to about 20 feet. On returning to be hauled out WATCH THAT STEEL GIRDER! Have someone ready to fend you off on land!

Denham Marina, Uxbridge
100 Acres, Sanderson Road, Uxbridge, England UB8 1NB
Lat. 51.5518, Long. -0.4829.
01895 239811

Harefield Marina, Uxbridge
Moorhall Road, Harefield, Uxbridge, Middlesex, England UB9 6PD
Lat. 51.5840, Long. -0.4837.
01895 822036

Benson Waterfront, Wallingford
Benson, Wallingford, Oxon, England OX10 6SJ
Lat. 51.6200, Long. -1.1155.
01491 838304

Wallingford Marina, Wallingford
Lat. 51.5965, Long. -1.1236.
SUITABILITY: Large trailer needs a car.

ACCESS: Non-tidal. **TYPE OF RAMP: UPPER AREA:** Unknown.
LOWER AREA: Unknown.
DIRECTIONS: On the right bank going downstream.
RAMP DESCRIPTION: Public slipway. Wallingford Marina next to lane.
FACILITIES: Slip and boatyard facilities.
HAZARDS: ALL boats require a licence from the Environment Agency and 8kph speed limit.

Bridge Marine, Walton-on-Thames
Lat. 51.3870, Long. -0.4320.

CHARGES: £10 launch and recover. Tractor launch available.
SUITABILITY: Small trailer can be pushed.
ACCESS: Unknown. **TYPE OF RAMP:** Concrete **UPPER AREA:** Concrete.
LOWER AREA: Concrete.
RAMP DESCRIPTION: Bridge Marine includes a small chandlers, boat storage, service and repair facilities. The ramp is very user friendly and costs £10 to launch and recover.
FACILITIES: Parking for car and trailer included or park outside in the lane. Closes usually at 5pm.

Walton Lane, Walton-on-Thames
Lat. 51.3845, Long. -0.4327.
08708 506 506

CHARGES: None
SUITABILITY: Large trailer needs a car.
ACCESS: Non-tidal. **TYPE OF RAMP:** Concrete VERY slippy on lower sections. Covered in algae and hazardous at best. Would only recommend for dinghies/rowing boats/ portables. **UPPER AREA:** Concrete.
LOWER AREA: Concrete.
DIRECTIONS: In Walton Lane, south-west of Walton Bridge, Walton-on-Thames
RAMP DESCRIPTION: Ramp is at right-angle to Walton Lane. Very close to busy road. Be prepared to stop traffic whilst reversing on to the slip. VERY difficult when busy as no one will stop for you. Not suitable for boats longer than 20 feet as you wont get the swing to back round. SHARP DROP OFF INTO RIVER! Ramp does not extend far into the river BEWARE!
FACILITIES: 100 yards to car park (free) in Walton Lane. Fuel in Walton-on-Thames, half mile. Pubs downstream half mile. All non-tidal Thames launch ramps should include a note that ALL boats require a licence from the Environment Agency and 8kph speed limit.
HAZARDS: 8kph speed restriction. River can be busy as near two marinas.

Walton Marina, Walton-on-Thames
Walton Bridge, Walton-on-Thames, Surrey, England KT12 1QW
Lat. 51.3878, Long. -0.4275.
01932 226305

Ferry Lane Slip, Wargrave
Lat. 51.5027, Long. -0.8719.
SUITABILITY: Small trailer can be pushed.

3

ACCESS: Non-tidal. **TYPE OF RAMP:** Track into the river.
UPPER AREA: Unknown. **LOWER AREA:** Unknown.
DIRECTIONS: Roughish slope to water at end of Ferry Lane. Very narrow access road with a 90 degree bend in it.
RAMP DESCRIPTION: The council has put a bollard across the end (seldom raised) so it's only suitable for really small (dinghy) craft.
FACILITIES: Small pontoon next to the ramp area.
HAZARDS: ALL boats require a licence from the Environment Agency and 8kph speed limit.

Val Wyatt Marine - Willow Marina, Wargrave On Thames
Willow Marina Willow Lane, Wargrave On Thames, Berkshire, England RG10 8LH
Lat. 51.5102, Long. -0.8747.
0118 940 3211

Public Slip, Weybridge
Lat. 51.3806, Long. -0.4568.
CHARGES: FREE
SUITABILITY: Large trailer needs a car.
ACCESS: Non-tidal. **TYPE OF RAMP:** Concrete sharply curving! And beware concrete sides! It is a tricky reverse and high risk of scratching car. The lower section is concrete covered in a layer of dirt/mud just above waterline. This will cause a lot of problems for a NON 4 × 4 vehicle. **UPPER AREA:** Concrete. **LOWER AREA:** Mud.
DIRECTIONS: Public slip, access from A317. On the right bank going downstream.
RAMP DESCRIPTION: Public slipway. Not suitable for any boat longer than about 20 feet dues to the sharp bend in the ramp. Suitable for 4 × 4 ONLY! STEEP! On launch: consider detaching trailer and rope down. On recovery: consider walking trailer down separately (then reverse car.)
FACILITIES: NONE
HAZARDS: ALL boats require a licence from the Environment Agency and 8kph speed limit.

Eyot House Ltd, Weybridge
D'Oyly Carte Island, Weybridge, Surrey, England KT13 8LX
Lat. 51.3830, Long. -0.4546.
01932 848586

Toll Bridge slip, Whitchurch
Lat. 51.4874, Long. -1.0868.
SUITABILITY: Large trailer needs a car.
ACCESS: Non-tidal. **TYPE OF RAMP: UPPER AREA:** Unknown.
LOWER AREA: Unknown.
DIRECTIONS: Right beside northwest corner of Whitchurch Toll Bridge. On the left bank going downstream.
HAZARDS: ALL boats require a licence from the Environment Agency and 8kph speed limit.

Windsor Marina, Windsor
Lat. 51.4867, Long. -0.6603.
01753 853911

CHARGES: £15 per day, payable at the marina office
SUITABILITY: Large trailer needs a car.
ACCESS: Non-tidal. **TYPE OF RAMP:** Concrete **UPPER AREA:** Concrete.
LOWER AREA: Concrete.
DIRECTIONS: The ramp is based on the grounds of Windsor Marina (Maidenhead Road, Windsor, SL4 5TZ).
RAMP DESCRIPTION: This is a good ramp with a medium gradient, suitable for boat sizes up to 22´. Also, there is plenty of space to securely store your car & trailer after launching.
FACILITIES: 24 hour security. Shower and toilet facilities. Chandlery, car park, petrol, diesel and Calor gas. Engineering and repair services. Refuse and chemical toilet disposal and pump-out. Pubs are within walking distance of marina.

Racecourse Marina, Windsor
Maidenhead Road, Windsor, Berkshire, England SL4 5HT
Lat. 51.4880, Long. -0.6369.
01753 851501

Leisure Centre, Windsor
Lat. 51.4865, Long. -0.6231.
Windsor Leisure Centre 01753 850004

CHARGES: Car parking fee
SUITABILITY: Large trailer needs a car.
ACCESS: Non-tidal. **TYPE OF RAMP:** Concrete, slippery when wet.
UPPER AREA: Concrete. **LOWER AREA:** Concrete.
DIRECTIONS: Exit the M4 at J6 and follow sign to Windsor take first exit down to roundabout and first left. Follow signs to Leisure centre.
RAMP DESCRIPTION: Very good 30 degree public slip next to Windsor Leisure centre. On the right bank going downstream. There is a metal 'stop' bar at the bottom of the ramp to prevent trailers going over the drop off into the river. This happened recently! BEWARE back in SLOWLY!
FACILITIES: WATER POINT with mooring ring next to the slip ideal for filling boat tanks! This slipway is excellent. There is a free parking area for trailers but cars must park in the general car park, cost 50p for up to 3 hours, over 3 hours £5, disabled free of charge. Car park also has 2.2m height restriction bar. The parking meters will only allow you to buy tickets that day.
HAZARDS: ALL boats require a licence from the Environment Agency and 8kph speed limit. Jetskis are very much frowned on by BW as they are almost certain to break the 8MPH rule, also cannot be licensed.

Windsor Marina, Windsor
Maidenhead Road, Windsor, Berkshire, England SL4 5TZ
Lat. 51.4861, Long. -0.6617.
01753 853911

Pyrford Marina, Woking
Lock Lane, Pyrford, Woking, Surrey, England
GU22 8XL
Lat. 51.3237, Long. -0.4922.
01932 340739

Black Swan Sailing Club, Wokingham
Lat. 51.4466, Long. -0.8695.
0118 934 4424

CHARGES: £7 per half day, £12 per day or £30 per week (seven days)
SUITABILITY: Small trailer can be pushed.
ACCESS: Non-tidal. **TYPE OF RAMP:** Concrete ramp or beach launch or pontoon available **UPPER AREA:** Shingle. **LOWER AREA:** Shingle.
DIRECTIONS: It is in Dinton Pastures Country Park, near Wokingham Berkshire. From A329 (not the motorway) at Winnersh - between Woking ham and Reading) turn towards Twford at the Traffic Lights by Sainsbury in Winnersh B3030. Follow this road over the motorway and you will see signs to Black Swan Sailing Club/Hurst Golf Club - follow these signs until a left turn into Sandford lane - this is a narrow tree lined road – after about 400m metres you will see a sign on the left to Hurst Golf Club – this is the same entrance for the sailing club and the car park is 100m on your right after turning. Go to the end of the car park and follow the path to the sailing club (about 200m walk to register your presence and pay the steward on duty.
RAMP DESCRIPTION: There are two concrete ramps either side of a floating wooden pontoon. Monohull sailing dinghies only. There is a bridge over a stream to negotiate, big enough for a Wayfarer - all club boats have to go across this small bridge from boat park to launching - so many common types are known to be OK - may be problems with any boat with outrigger type bars. Boats up to Enterprise size can be lunched by a single person.
FACILITIES: Club house has changing facilities and toilets. Golf Club has bar and limited meals available at times. Pubs are about 5 minutes walk away and the Country Park has a Café about 15 minutes walk.

Twyford Bridge Marina, Yalding
Hampstead Lane, Yalding, Kent, England
ME18 6HG
Lat. 51.2213, Long. 0.4178.
01622 814378

Willowtree Marina, Yeading
West Quay Drive, Yeading, Middlesex, England
UB4 9TA
Lat. 51.5222, Long. -0.3837.
020 8841 6585

3

West Country

Poole to Bristol

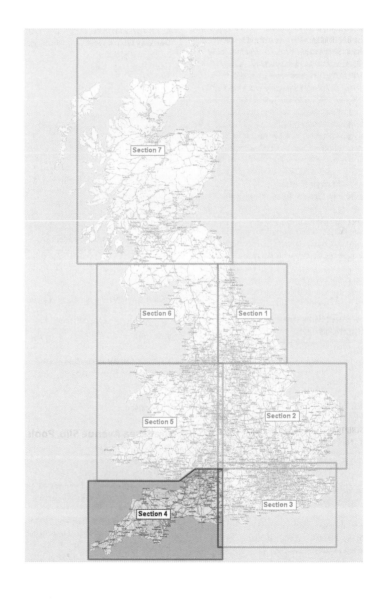

COASTAL SLIPWAYS
clockwise around the coast

Salterns Marina, Poole
Lat. 50.7070, Long. -1.9481.
Marina Office 01202 709971

CHARGES: £31.50/day. £21 one way.
SUITABILITY: Large trailer needs a car.
ACCESS: ¼ tidal. **TYPE OF RAMP:** Steep concrete. Very little depth even at high tide, ok for Jetskis, water is shallow for quite away out. Very difficult for recovery at anything but high tide. Facilities good, hose available also. **UPPER AREA:** Harbour. **LOWER AREA:** Mud.
DIRECTIONS: 40 Salterns Way, Lilliput, Dorset. From Poole follow Sandbanks Road and turn right into Salterns Way.
RAMP DESCRIPTION: Steep concrete ramp only suitable for small craft. Very shallow sand gradient at bottom. Popular with Jetskis. One way launch £21.00 or £31.50 for the day. Also a boat hoist for larger craft. Up to 22´ £50 or £77 in and out in one week; up to 27´ £61 or £88 in and out in one week. Add vat to all prices.
FACILITIES: 5 star marina facilities including showers and toilets, boatyard and chandlery. Parking available but limited, speak to the marina office.

Salterns Marina, Poole
40 Salterns Way, Lilliput, Poole, Dorset, England
BH14 8JR
Lat. 50.7055, Long. -1.9505.
01202 709971

Parkstone Bay Marina, Poole
Turks Lane, Poole, Dorset, England BH14 8EW
Lat. 50.7117, Long. -1.9588.
01202 747857

Baiter Public Slip, Poole
Lat. 50.7112, Long. -1.9718.

CHARGES: £8.00 per day (£6.00 after 2:30pm) including car and trailer parking. Payment at machine accepting coins only.
SUITABILITY: Large trailer needs a car.
ACCESS: ¾ tidal. **TYPE OF RAMP:** Concrete **UPPER AREA:** Concrete.
LOWER AREA: Shingle.
DIRECTIONS: Slipway is in the large Car Park near Baiter Park on the Poole water front.
RAMP DESCRIPTION: Large wide ramp. Very shallow entry angle, which makes it easy to launch and recover. Trailer needs to be walked out a distance to adequate depth for boat/ski launching. That means that it is very difficult to get a cabin trailer sailer off its trailer without getting the brakes wet particularly when not at the top of the tide. A long warp will also be required to recover such a boat and trailer without getting salt water on the car. This is a very popular launching site, which in high season can become very busy. It is the recommended slipway for Jetskis and close to the designated Jetski area in Poole harbour.
FACILITIES: Large tarmac car park with area for trailers. Washing facilities available but take your own hose.

HAZARDS: 10 knot speed restriction in main channels, elsewhere 6 knots. 10 knot limit lifted during winter months (October - March). There are designated Jetski and water ski areas.

Poole Quay Boat Haven, Poole
Poole Town Quay, Poole, Dorset, England
BH15 1HJ
Lat. 50.7129, Long. -1.9872.
01202 649488

C J Evans International, Poole
Dee Way Wharf, West Quay Road, Poole, Dorset, England BH15 1LJ
Lat. 50.7145, Long. -1.9931.
01202 680522

Cobbs Quay Marina, Poole
Lat. 50.7227, Long. -2.0066.
01202 674299

CHARGES: Annual pass £350. Day launch is £35.
SUITABILITY: Large trailer needs a car.
ACCESS: All of tidal range. **TYPE OF RAMP:** Concrete
UPPER AREA: Concrete. **LOWER AREA:** Harbour.
DIRECTIONS: Follow signs to Cobbs Quay Marina. Upon arrival at site please report to Dockmaster's office (clearly signed) for instructions.
RAMP DESCRIPTION: Wide and well surfaced but very busy.
FACILITIES: Marina, dry stacking, pub / club. 40 marine related tenants. Car and trailer parking, petrol, LPG and diesel.
HAZARDS: Lots of very shallow areas, but the channels are well marked.

Davis's Boatyard, Poole
Cobbs Quay, Hamworthy, Poole, Dorset, England
BH15 4EJ
Lat. 50.7224, Long. -2.0068.
01202 674349

Cobb's Quay Marina, Poole
Cobbs Quay, Hamworthy, Poole, Dorset, England
BH15 4EL
Lat. 50.7220, Long. -2.0036.
01202 674299

Branksea Avenue Slip, Poole
Lat. 50.7116, Long. -2.0174.

CHARGES: None
SUITABILITY: Small trailer can be pushed.
ACCESS: All of tidal range. **TYPE OF RAMP:** Shingle hard.
UPPER AREA: Shingle. **LOWER AREA:** Shingle.
DIRECTIONS: Via Coles Avenue, off A350.
RAMP DESCRIPTION: Ramp leads onto hard shingle which is quite shallow. Really only suitable for small boats. Popular with Jetskis.

4

There is a steel frame to prevent large vehicles getting onto the ramp. Approximately 2m wide and 2m high.
FACILITIES: Small, free car park alongside otherwise some distance to get away from yellow lines. Crowded weekends.

Lake Yard, Poole
Lake Drive, Hamworthy, Poole, Dorset, England BH15 4DT
Lat. 50.7127, Long. -2.0199.
01202 674534

Rockley Point, Poole
Lat. 50.7194, Long. -2.0395.
Rockley Boat Park 01202 665001.

CHARGES: £25/day plus £5 parking
SUITABILITY: Large trailer needs a car.
ACCESS: All of tidal range. **TYPE OF RAMP:** Concrete
UPPER AREA: Harbour. **LOWER AREA:** Sand.
DIRECTIONS: From Poole head towards the Rockley Park Caravan Site. Go all the way through the park and you will go down a steep hill. The boat park is on the right and Rockley Water Sports is on the left.
RAMP DESCRIPTION: Ramp is 30 feet wide and steep. Good for launching. It is shared with the sailing school and boat yard. Could get busy in the summer. See the boat park attendant before launching to pay fees.
FACILITIES: There is a small beach shop/café. Boats can be stored in the boat park overnight by prior arrangement. Weekend & weekly storage available, subject to availability. Yard & dry berth summer or annual spaces available. Toilets & showers located in boat yard, also pressure washer. The boat yard has a harbour launch service. All Jetskiers must be in possession of a Poole Harbour Permit and pay the £20 launch fee (Parking included). Slipway is 3 miles from the approved Jetski area and a 6 knot limit is in force throughout the year outside this area.
HAZARDS: Lots of very shallow areas, but the channels are well marked. Area is SSSI so 6 knot speed limit in force all year.

Redcliffe Farm, Wareham
Lat. 50.6799, Long. -2.0976.
Farm 01929 552225

CHARGES: £15/day, less if camping. £1for parking.
SUITABILITY: Large trailer needs a car.
ACCESS: All of tidal range. **TYPE OF RAMP:** Concrete onto soft mud at low water. **UPPER AREA:** Shingle. **LOWER AREA:** Mud.
DIRECTIONS: Back door route into Poole Harbour. Leaving Wareham town centre on A351 southward, turn left at Stoborough. After ¼ mile turn left again. Bear next left. Follow downhill to river. Redcliff SC adjacent has facilities but must get separate permission to use.
RAMP DESCRIPTION: The ramp has been extended and widened slightly and launching is at most states of the tide except low water Springs. Ramp was repaired winter of 2003/4. Don't use if you have to rope your trailer down slip as owner will not let you.
FACILITIES: Overnight parking available and there is ample space. Used mainly by owners of moored boats. Camping and caravan park adjacent. Farm does a B&B service. Very beautiful part of the river just downstream from Wareham.

HAZARDS: There is a 4 knot speed limit in the river and a 10 knot speed limit in Poole Harbour.

Ridge Wharf Yacht Centre, Wareham
Ridge, Wareham, Dorset, England BH20 5BG
Lat. 50.6837, Long. -2.0889.
01929 552650

Ridge Wharf Yacht Centre, Wareham
Lat. 50.6844, Long. -2.0891.
YC 01929 552650

CHARGES: £20/day £80/week includes parking.
SUITABILITY: Small trailer can be pushed.
ACCESS: ½ tidal. **TYPE OF RAMP:** Concrete- soft mud at low water.
UPPER AREA: Harbour. **LOWER AREA:** Mud.
DIRECTIONS: On River Frome leading to Poole Harbour. Take A351 south from Wareham. After 1km turn left into Nutcrack Lane. 1km to crossroads. Take left signposted Ridge / Redcliff. Take next right fork. Gateway to Y.C. a further 1km.
RAMP DESCRIPTION: Gradient is steep.
FACILITIES: Launch fee includes parking. Accommodation for boats on trailers on hard standing £20/week. Caravan park adjacent. Slip water tap. All the usual boatyard facilities. Fuel barge has diesel and petrol. Toilets and showers on site.
HAZARDS: 4 knot speed limit on the river.

Shell Bay Boat Yard, Studland
Lat. 50.6779, Long. -1.9523.
Shell Bay Boat Yard Tel: 01929 450340

CHARGES: £4.5/day £27/week.
SUITABILITY: Large trailer needs a car.
ACCESS: ¾ tidal. **TYPE OF RAMP:** Both concrete.
UPPER AREA: Unknown. **LOWER AREA:** Unknown.
DIRECTIONS: Yard is just inside Poole Harbour entrance and shown on charts and maps as Bramblebush or Gravel Bay.
RAMP DESCRIPTION: There are NO casual launches from Shell Bay Boat Yard at Studland. You need to arrange a six month berth/launch. Booking is essential at all times. Contact Shell Bay Boat Yard before going. Self launch and recover: daily rate (weekly rate is x6); inflatable dinghies - no trailer (less than 5hp) £11.75, sailing dinghies (less than 5hp) £20, catamarans (less than 5hp) £30, sports boats up to 20ft (excluding harbour dues) £25. Weekly rates include overnight storage. Car parking (when available) £10, swinging moorings (when available) £8. Tractor launch or recovery (additional to slipway charge) each way £7.50.
FACILITIES: Parking space is for 50 cars. In winter full of boats. Nat Trust car park over road. Toilets and café adjoining. Slip water tap available. We may need to move your car to assist others, therefore please ensure your keys are deposited at reception each time your vehicle is left unattended. Obstructive vehicles will be towed away without notice and at the owners' expense. Cars and trailers may only remain on site at the discretion of the management. Slipways may not be used until all charges are paid and an invoice issued. Vehicles, boats and any other property are left at the owner's risk. Customers are responsible for any relevant insurances and should familiarise themselves with Poole Harbour Byelaws.

Studland Beach, Studland
Lat. 50.6511, Long. -1.9519.

01929 450259

CHARGES: £4/day car, £4.50 single hull, £10 double hull and boats less than 20hp.

SUITABILITY: Large trailer needs a car.

ACCESS: ¼ tidal. **TYPE OF RAMP:** Concrete onto firm sand.

UPPER AREA: Shingle. **LOWER AREA:** Sand.

DIRECTIONS: Near Corfe Castle. From Wareham take A351 south to Corfe Castle. At foot of castle turn left onto B3351 for Studland. At Studland follow signs to Knoll beach, National Trust car park and slip is on right hand side at bottom of hill. Approaching from the chain ferry you pass the Shell Beach Yard slip on the right and continue for a couple of miles till you see the entrance to the NTs Knoll beach.

RAMP DESCRIPTION: Motor boats are not allowed to launch here. Concrete sleepers are on a good slope but only to high tide line. Then gently shelving beach which can be soft on the ebb. Very popular beach area so pulling out with a rope is risky. Double high tides in Poole area helps.

FACILITIES: National Trust shop, café, loos, cold shower, parking - all about 250m from ramp. Bankes Arms 1 mile south near beach is highly recommended, but busy. Sheltered sea sailing, perfect family beach. Gets very crowded peak periods.

HAZARDS: Motor boats are not allowed to launch here. Visiting boats anchoring / mooring still allowed off beach. 5Knt speed limit beach side of yellow marker buoys. Watch out for cordoned swimmers area marked by yellow floats. Popular area for overnighters out of Poole. Redland rocks very close to beach are marked but not really a problem. Easterly winds can make things lumpy. Check charts for reef between the ramp and shell bay offshore - well marked though

OceanBay Watersports, Swanage
Lat. 50.6164, Long. -1.9576.

07721 938949

CHARGES: Jetski & boats under 3m launch - £13/day boats over 3m - £17/day sailboards & small craft - £6/day canoes - £2/day. 4 × 4s available - £5 both ways

SUITABILITY: Small trailer can be pushed.

ACCESS: No Ramp. **TYPE OF RAMP: UPPER AREA:** Sand.

LOWER AREA: Sand.

DIRECTIONS: Ocean Bay Watersports, North Beach, Ulwell Road, Swanage, Dorset. BH19 1LH Located on the North Beach of Swanage where Ulwell Road meets Shore Road

RAMP DESCRIPTION: Private beach used for Jetski & boat launching & watersports hire

Slipway, Swanage
Lat. 50.6078, Long. -1.9477.

01929 423636

CHARGES: £25 to launch and park. £10 to launch only. Aug 2006: Launch only £10. Extra £5 to leave trailer in boat park. You have to leave car in adjoining public car park (limited spaces in high season peak hours) and it is £6 for all day (peak season)

SUITABILITY: Large trailer needs a car.

ACCESS: All of tidal range. **TYPE OF RAMP:** Large concrete slipway.

UPPER AREA: Harbour. **LOWER AREA:** Harbour.

DIRECTIONS: Head towards the lifeboat station at the southern end of Swanage and out towards Peveril Point. Slipway is just before you get to the lifeboat station.

RAMP DESCRIPTION: Very large steep ramp with some potholes.

FACILITIES: Pontoons on either side of the slip for loading and unloading. All the usual facilities in nearby Swanage. Pontoon sides demand a lot of fenders especially at low tide. Flushing tap. Very narrow lanes in yard and entrance / exit can be tight (was with 4 × 4 & 7m boat/trailer). Mooring on buoys available from Dive Centre on the pier for c. £10 per day.

Slipway, Kimmeridge Bay
Lat. 50.6093, Long. -2.1296.

01202 882336

CHARGES: £10 for boat and vehicle. Includes parking and toll for access via private road.

SUITABILITY: Large trailer needs a car.

ACCESS: ¾ tidal. **TYPE OF RAMP:** Concrete **UPPER AREA:** Rock.

LOWER AREA: Rock.

DIRECTIONS: Follow the road through Kimmeridge village, stop at the little hut and pay for access and launching. The slipway is in the southeast corner of the bay.

RAMP DESCRIPTION: The ramp is quite steep & tapers towards its lower end. There is a turning area at the top to enable you to reverse the trailer down. Note that there is a double low water which on Spring tides can make launching / recovery difficult at low water. Jetskis are NOT welcome.

FACILITIES: Diver's car park is gravel & grass with a toilet block. Please note there is no water flushing tap. After launching the boat, return the trailer to the diver's car park, do not leave it at the top of the slip. There is a compressor area just before the car park for divers to set up an air compressor.

HAZARDS: 5 knot speed limit in Kimmeridge Bay. Care must be taken of snorkellers and scuba divers swimming in the bay. Army firing range at Lulworth is close by & restrictions apply.

Beach Slip, Ringstead
Lat. 50.6309, Long. -2.3515.

CHARGES: Up to £6 including toll and parking.

SUITABILITY: Portable Only.

ACCESS: No Ramp. **TYPE OF RAMP:** Concrete **UPPER AREA:** Concrete.

LOWER AREA: Shingle.

DIRECTIONS: Between Osmington and Poxwell on the A353 east of Weymouth, turn south at the signposted road. If travelling from the East, the turn is a sharp hairpin bend. Just follow the signs south to the car park. Drive past the car park, stopping to ask at the shop to check it's OK to launch. Cars and trailers must be returned to the car park after being unloaded.

RAMP DESCRIPTION: Runs parallel to the shore onto a steep shingle beach. It is the only access to the beach for pedestrians, so should be used with consideration. Trailers cannot be taken to the water, so boats need to be carried.

4

FACILITIES: Parking, shop and snack bar, toilets. This is a private road so a toll/parking charge is payable.

HAZARDS: Shallow reef, which dries in places extends well to the east, charts should be consulted.

The Beachside Centre, The Beachside Centre

Lat. 50.6364, Long. -2.4209.

01305 833216

CHARGES: For the day Jetski launch and trailer parking £15. Dive boat launch fee £10. Small boat and sailing craft launch and trailer parking £7. Weekly Jetski / dive boat launch and trailer parking £60. Seasonal launch Jetski / dive boat unlimited launch and car/trailer parking £99.

SUITABILITY: Large trailer needs a car.

ACCESS: ¾ tidal. **TYPE OF RAMP:** Concrete with pier beside

UPPER AREA: Concrete. **LOWER AREA:** Sand.

DIRECTIONS: Bowleaze Cove is situated approximately 2 miles east of Weymouth town, and is approached via Bowleaze Coveway from Preston road (A353) at Overcombe. From Weymouth take the A353 towards Wareham. Bowleaze Coveway is a cul-de-sac running along the cliff top to Bowleaze Cove. Once you are there you cannot fail to find us! There are large grassed areas with ample, secure, parking adjoining a pleasant sand and pebble beach, slipway and pier.

RAMP DESCRIPTION: The Beachside Leisure Centre offers launch ramp services to annual members and occasional users. Membership charges together with the relevant insurance and other forms required to use these facilities to enable us to deal with you quickly on arrival, please remember to bring your documents along on the day for inspection.

FACILITIES: Shops parking and restaurants.

Weymouth Marina, Weymouth

Commercial Road, Weymouth, Dorset, England DT4 8NA

Lat. 50.6113, Long. -2.4576.

01305 767576

Public Slip, Weymouth

Lat. 50.6101, Long. -2.4571.

(01305) 206423

CHARGES: Pay at office.

SUITABILITY: Large trailer needs a car.

ACCESS: All of tidal range. **TYPE OF RAMP:** Concrete

UPPER AREA: Harbour. **LOWER AREA:** Harbour.

DIRECTIONS: On the A354 follow the signs to Portland until you see Radipole Lake on your left hand side. At the next roundabout turn left to cross over the lake on the large concrete bridge. At the next roundabout turn right and proceed along Commercial Road past the bus depot and several car parks. The slipway is located opposite the multi storey car park. Bridge between Dorchester and Weymouth has restricted headroom of 4.4 m. Visitors from west of Bridport towing a trailer are advised to travel via Dorchester and then follow the route shown from the north.

RAMP DESCRIPTION: Wide slipway. Small craft can use at all states of the tide. Larger vessels may require a higher tide. There is a 6 inch

upstand covered by water even at low water, it is easy to get your trailer hooked. A waiting pontoon was dredged to 2 metres over the winter of 1995/6. When slip is manned during summer months, pay the attendant. At other times pay at the Berthing Office at 13 Custom House Quay. Annual season tickets are available for vessel and trailer parking, however, the season tickets do not include the car parking concession. No Jetskies.

FACILITIES: Petrol nearby. Diesel in the Outer Harbour or from Raybar Tel 0860 912 401 or VHF Ch 6. LPG is proposed for the future. For a fee a trailer may be left at the slipway and includes space in the multi-storey car park. Opening hours for this car park are 8am - 7pm. Use of showers, laundry and toilet included in the fees at the Berthing Office on Custom House Quay, ten minutes walk. Public toilets are 5 minutes away near the Tourist Information Centre on the Esplanade, in Bond Street or adjacent to the Guildhall.

HAZARDS: Slipway is above the Town Bridge (min air draught circa 3.05 metres - 10 ft). In summer the bridge opens every 2 hours from 08.00 to 18.00 with an additional late opening according to the month. This late opening is April and September 19:30, May and August 20:30, June and July 20:00 and 21:30. Tel 01305 206423 for full details of bridge lifts and booking arrangements. The bridge lifts are free.

Blue Water Horizons, Weymouth

Lat. 50.5811, Long. -2.4701.

01305 782080

CHARGES: £15.00/per day plus £3.85 harbour dues. Phone Bluewater Horizons.

SUITABILITY: Large trailer needs a car.

ACCESS: All of tidal range. **TYPE OF RAMP:** Concrete

UPPER AREA: Harbour. **LOWER AREA:** Concrete.

DIRECTIONS: Ferrymans Way, off Portland road, Weymouth, DT4 9YU

RAMP DESCRIPTION: Assisted launches only. Phone Blue Water Horizons for rates. Bridge clearance high Springs is 2.4mtrs. Jetskiers can use this site - cost £15/day including parking. Two larger slipways available at adjacent yard on Portland Road, DT4 9JZ

FACILITIES: Blue Water Horizons offer a park and launch facility for people that need to use their time efficiently, but when they do want to go boating, they can access the boat quickly. They offer this service through having our own tractor and direct slip access to The Fleet. Blue Water Horizons will power wash and return your boat to the hard standing; maintain, winterise, antifoul and repair any incurred damage. Close Circuit TV Surveillance in their compound.

Weymouth and Portland Sailing Academy, Portland

Lat. 50.5698, Long. -2.4553.

01305 866000

CHARGES: About £18 including parking

SUITABILITY: Large trailer needs a car.

ACCESS: All of tidal range. **TYPE OF RAMP:** Concrete

UPPER AREA: Concrete. **LOWER AREA:** Concrete.

DIRECTIONS: Drive through Weymouth and Wyke Regis towards Portland. Towards the southern end of the causeway turn left at the new roundabout. This will take you through to the sailing academy.

RAMP DESCRIPTION: There are 3 ramps available. A shallow ramp is used by the dinghies, two wider and steeper ramps are used by larger craft. Tractor assistance is available.

FACILITIES: The Sailing Academy has food, plenty of parking, toilets and showers. There are also a few pontoons available for loading and unloading. Best to phone to make sure there is room for you as they have regattas and sailing competitions.

HAZARDS: A buoyed wreck, which beaks the surface at low tide is just off the two steep ramps.

Castletown Beach, Portland
Lat. 50.5686, Long. -2.4422.

01305 824044

CHARGES: The ramp is free, but parking can be expensive in the summer.

SUITABILITY: Large trailer needs a car.

ACCESS: ¾ tidal. **TYPE OF RAMP:** Concrete **UPPER AREA:** Concrete. **LOWER AREA:** Shingle.

DIRECTIONS: From Weymouth follow the signs to Portland through Wyke Regis and onto the road (A354) along Chesil beach. Once on Portland, take the second exit off the large roundabout that leads uphill and onto Portland. Next take the first left that leads down into Castletown. The slip is on your left approximately 300 metres past the mini-roundabout.

RAMP DESCRIPTION: The ramp is straight and approximately 10 feet wide, it has a grippy surface but you will need to kick a few stones clear before recovering your boat. At low tides the slip does not reach the sea but you can still launch / recover boats as the stony beach is quiet firm. The beach is often used by dive boats accessing the harbour and local dive sites. Divers should buy a permit to dive in the harbour, these permits also detail the areas in which you can and cannot dive and moor boats. No Jetskiers allowed here.

FACILITIES: Castletown is geared up for divers, there is a Dive shop, three hotel style B&Bs, a chandlery, air shop (Air, Nitrox and Trimix available) and several good pubs, they all serve food. Weymouth is only 20 minutes in the car and has pretty much everything a large town can offer.

HAZARDS: Some diving and boating restrictions apply around Portland Harbour, contact them for details. The southern most entrance to Portland harbour contains the wreck of the Hood; this extends from the bottom at 18 metres to within 2 metres of the surface. There is an electrical cable slung across this harbour entrance which is not very high.

Slipway, West Bay
Lat. 50.7103, Long. -2.7646.

Harbour Master 01308 423 222 or 01305 252356

CHARGES: All sizes £12.50 season tickets available. Overnight stays for launched vessels are available

SUITABILITY: Large trailer needs a car.

ACCESS: All of tidal range. **TYPE OF RAMP:** Concrete: Beware of slippery conditions at low water Springs - vehicle launch possible all states of the tide. Note: Winter storms can create a sandbar across the entrance to the harbour - almost dries at low water. Not

usable +/-1 hour around low water. Dredged for main season.

UPPER AREA: Concrete. **LOWER AREA:** Concrete.

DIRECTIONS: Follow signs to West Bay. From the old slipway as marked continue west over the river, left at the roundabout and along Quayside to the new 2005 slipway.

RAMP DESCRIPTION: Old slipway at the marker is now blocked off. Ample parking at new slipway for trailers, two boats can launch/ recover simultaneously with considerate driving. Launch all states of the tide - but beware of swell onto the slipway with any wind from the east. Charter boats have a designated area on the pontoons to work from leaving plenty of room for day boats to find a space with the recent installation of the latest pontoon in 2009 this has eased any congestion found in the past. Call harbourmaster on 01308 423 222 or VHF Ch. 11/16 for information.

FACILITIES: Pubs, shops, parking, toilets. Harbourmaster's office at The Mound, West Bay, which is above the slipway/trailer parking area and can be seen easily from the slipway. No fuel in the harbour, the nearest petrol station is 1.5 miles away in Bridport. The Angling centre provides diving air in West Bay. Two fishing tackle shops nearby. Three pubs in sight from the top of the slipway: The West Bay, The Bridport Arms and the George Hotel. Also various shop only a short walk away. The new pontoons offer a great place to tie up to load and unload also overnight stays can be arranged. Note that pontoons are removed for the winter, making load /unload more difficult.

HAZARDS: Swell comes into outer harbour with any east wind, and to a lesser extent in any southern wind, and launching and retrieving can be dangerous. Anyone staying alongside overnight is advised to be well fendered.

Slipway, Charmouth Beach
Lat. 50.7333, Long. -2.9018.

CHARGES: £3.60 for inflatable max 10 HP - collected by car park attendant - much cheaper than Lyme and easier parking too.

SUITABILITY: Large trailer needs a car.

ACCESS: No Ramp. **TYPE OF RAMP:** None, shingle upper beach and firm sand lower beach **UPPER AREA:** Shingle. **LOWER AREA:** Sand.

DIRECTIONS: Follow A35 to Charmouth then directions for beach - enter beach car park and drive off across shingle

RAMP DESCRIPTION: Launch across shingle on to firm sand

FACILITIES: Shops toilets and car park near by

HAZARDS: Some rocks off shore

Harbour Slipway, Lyme Regis
Lat. 50.7204, Long. -2.9386.

Harbour Master 01297 442137

CHARGES: £7-10/day

SUITABILITY: Large trailer needs a car.

ACCESS: ½ tidal. **TYPE OF RAMP:** Concrete **UPPER AREA:** Harbour. **LOWER AREA:** Sand.

DIRECTIONS: Ramp is at the west end of the harbour by the lifeboat station. The approach road is a one in four gradient so check your brakes and in some cases the gradient is even steeper due to subsidence.

RAMP DESCRIPTION: Large concrete ramp. Ramp extends to the half tide mark and then onto hard sand and it is possible to launch at all but the lowest states of the tide. Sand has a shallow gradient so may be

4

necessary to push trailer into deeper water. Cost is £7/day for 4-7 metre length boat, £10/day for boats over 7 metres. Popular spot with divers.

FACILITIES: Parking for trailers and some car parking nearby. However the car parking is a problem during weekends and it best to get there before 8am if you want to find a spot. Cafés and pubs in Lyme Regis. Air available at West Bay. Honda agent and training school.

Axe Yacht Club, Seaton
Lat. 50.7038, Long. -3.0606.

CHARGES: £10
SUITABILITY: Small trailer can be pushed.
ACCESS: ¼ tidal. **TYPE OF RAMP:** Beach, compressed pebbles.
UPPER AREA: Shingle. **LOWER AREA:** Mud.
RAMP DESCRIPTION: Small drying harbour behind shingle bank. Entrance tricky. Outboard essential. Leave from 2½-2 hours before high water and return no later than one hour after high water. Check the tide tables. Conditions dangerous in moderate to strong onshore winds. Local advice recommended.
FACILITIES: Parking nearby. Slip water tap.

Beer Beach, Seaton
Lat. 50.6964, Long. -3.0911.
SUITABILITY: Portable Only.
ACCESS: All of tidal range. **TYPE OF RAMP:** Steep pebble Beach
UPPER AREA: Shingle. **LOWER AREA:** Shingle.
DIRECTIONS: On the main street through the town head downhill. Fork left at the Anchor Inn.
RAMP DESCRIPTION: No ramp - launch over pebble beach - not friendly to anything larger than light dinghy.
FACILITIES: Town facilities close. Good anchorage in westerly/northerly winds, but very open to anything between northeast and south.

Mamhead Slip, Exmouth
Lat. 50.6163, Long. -3.4228.

CHARGES: None
SUITABILITY: Large trailer needs a car.
ACCESS: ¾ tidal. **TYPE OF RAMP:** Recently improved in concrete.
UPPER AREA: Concrete. **LOWER AREA:** Sand.
DIRECTIONS: Slipway is at Exmouth next to the old docks now Exmouth Quay right on the seafront at the mouth of the river Exe.
RAMP DESCRIPTION: Council slipway used by Exe Powerboat club. When tide is running hard, difficult to launch and recover, but a good window depending on size of boat. Slipway was extended in the winter of 2003 to give it a shallower gradient.
FACILITIES: Parking, pubs, shops all very close, petrol from garages on way in to Exmouth. Marine diesel available at docks.
HAZARDS: Sandbanks opposite and in river but well marked with buoys. If going up river do so on rising tide, still navigable at low water but unwary could be stuck on sandbank for a while.

Exmouth Marina, Exmouth
The Docks, Pierhead, Exmouth, Devon, England EX8 1DU
Lat. 50.6168, Long. -3.4233.
01395 269314

Recreation Ground, Exmouth
Lat. 50.6209, Long. -3.4222.

CHARGES: None
SUITABILITY: Large trailer needs a car.
ACCESS: ½ tidal. **TYPE OF RAMP:** Concrete **UPPER AREA:** Concrete.
LOWER AREA: Sand.
DIRECTIONS: From Exmouth Rail and Bus Station, turn right at the first roundabout, cross a pedestrian crossing, turn right at the next roundabout, past the rugby club and left down to the recreation ground keeping the sea to your right. The slip is at the end. Total distance from the station 400 metres.
RAMP DESCRIPTION: The entrance has a height restriction of 2.2 metres (sign reads 2 metres which was the height of the original bar suspended by chains). The slipway is extensively used for the launch and recovery of various wind sailers and kite surfers. Very user friendly ramp leads onto fairly hard sand. Best looked at at low water first to access the channel, kids often throw large boulders in to attempt to block the tide. The River Exe is very unforgiving especially during Spring tides. At peak Springs you can use the slipway up to 2 ½ hours either side of high water and this is safer than the alternative Mamhead Slip.
FACILITIES: Toilets are within 200 metres of the slipway. Exmouth town is 300 metres away with a large selection of pubs and clubs. Nearest petrol is approx ½ mile away. Good cheap long stay car-parking available for boats and trailers in the Station car-parks. Free trailer park next to slip while afloat. Road access excellent, but can get crowded with windsurfers at weekends.
HAZARDS: Occasional large boulders. Site is an historic rubbish tip so glass often rises to the top of the sand, in some form or other. There is also an L-shaped 200mts channel to navigate before reaching deeper water, then head for the lifeboat and you're clear.

W Trout & Son ltd, Exeter
W Trout & Son ltd Ferry Road Topsham, Exeter, Devon, England EX3 0JJ
Lat. 50.6817, Long. -3.4658.
01392 873044

Starcross slip, Dawlish Warren
Lat. 50.6293, Long. -3.4472.
Starcross YC 01626 890582
SUITABILITY: Large trailer needs a car.
ACCESS: ¾ tidal. **TYPE OF RAMP: UPPER AREA:** Unknown.
LOWER AREA: Unknown.
DIRECTIONS: Ramp is at Starcross near Dawlish Warren.
RAMP DESCRIPTION: Get advice from Starcross YC, Powderham Point. Launch from slipway except at low water Springs.
FACILITIES: Parking space is limited. Limited dinghy parking space.

Slipway, Cockwood
Lat. 50.6185, Long. -3.4482.

CHARGES: Free
SUITABILITY: Large trailer needs a car.

4

ACCESS: ¼ tidal. **TYPE OF RAMP:** Stone/concrete down to shingle/mud. **UPPER AREA:** Concrete. **LOWER AREA:** Shingle.
DIRECTIONS: At Cockwood half mile south of Starcross
RAMP DESCRIPTION: Small ramp at Cockwood Harbour. Launch possible 1 hour before and 2 hours after high water on Spring tides. Access to River Exe estuary via arch beneath railway with approx 1 metre clearance at high water Springs
FACILITIES: Adjacent free lay-by
HAZARDS: Railway arch with limited headroom

Quay Rd, Teignmouth
Lat. 50.5451, Long. -3.4996.

CHARGES: Free
SUITABILITY: Large trailer needs a car.
ACCESS: All of tidal range. **TYPE OF RAMP: UPPER AREA:** Mud.
LOWER AREA: Shingle.
RAMP DESCRIPTION: Loose surface slipway, careful for hidden concrete blocks
FACILITIES: None
HAZARDS: Concrete blocks under water level at high tide

Polly Steps, Teignmouth
Lat. 50.5462, Long. -3.5060.
Harbourmaster 01626 773165

CHARGES: Launching is free! But parking charge May-September is: Cars (day) £2.60 (2008) Trailer (day) £6.70 (2008) Out of season there is limited space as most of car park is taken over for boat lay-up.
SUITABILITY: Large trailer needs a car.
ACCESS: All of tidal range. **TYPE OF RAMP:** Concrete
UPPER AREA: Harbour. **LOWER AREA:** Rock.
DIRECTIONS: From Exeter follow the A379 to Teignmouth town centre. Drive through the docks signed 'Quays' and you will see the boat park.
RAMP DESCRIPTION: Great launch site which is free! Will take craft up to 8m, any longer will be a problem because of the right angle turn at the top of the slip. Can not be used at low water Springs. Slip is recently constructed at 10m width with a gentle slope. Beware of currents at mid tide.
FACILITIES: In season, ample parking for car and trailer. All the usual facilities in Teignmouth. Area for preparing your boat and getting into your wetsuit, then launch and park - still with trailer attached. Plenty of parking due to the site being through the docks and therefore full of boaters, not tourists. When you return there is another reserved area to strap down your boat. 1 unisex portaloo next to slipway.
HAZARDS: There is a 6 knot speed limit in the estuary and river. Further to that there is a 5 knot speed limit in within an area marked by yellow buoys off beaches. Look out for cross currents when launching.

Teign Corinthian YC Slip, Teignmouth
Lat. 50.5405, Long. -3.5500.
Teign Corinthian YC 01626 772734
SUITABILITY: Large trailer needs a car.
ACCESS: ¼ tidal. **TYPE OF RAMP: UPPER AREA:** Concrete.
LOWER AREA: Mud.

DIRECTIONS: Coombe Cellars is on the south bank of the River Teign between Newton Abbot and Shaldon.
RAMP DESCRIPTION: Launch from club slipway at Coombe Cellars. Get permission from Teign Corinthian YC 01626 772734 before using.
FACILITIES: Next door to the Coombe Cellars Inn. Get permission before using their car park.

Torquay Marina, Torquay
Torquay, Devon, England TQ2 5EQ
Lat. 50.4609, Long. -3.5259.
01803 200210

Harbour Slip, Torquay
Lat. 50.4577, Long. -3.5256.
01803 292429

CHARGES: Launching charges for Torbay harbours for 2009-2010 are at the web address above. In August 2009 it cost 13 GBP to launch a 4.4m boat and park a trailer.
SUITABILITY: Large trailer needs a car.
ACCESS: All of tidal range. **TYPE OF RAMP:** Concrete
UPPER AREA: Concrete. **LOWER AREA:** Concrete.
DIRECTIONS: Located in the Torquay outer harbour alongside Haldon Pier. Use the intercom at the barrier to Beacon Quay, at the end of Victoria Parade.
RAMP DESCRIPTION: Torquay has a new slipway opened in August 2006. Room for two to launch. (The two D-Day embarkation ramps formerly used as slipways remain nearby but have been put permanently beyond use. Note the Morse code built into the boardwalk above.) When approaching Beacon Quay by car to launch please drive up to the automatic barrier and press the intercom button on your right hand side and wait for a member of the Harbour Team to answer. You will then be directed to the harbour office before you launch. Personal Water Craft (Jetskis) must be registered with the Tor Bay Harbour Authority before being used within the Tor Bay Harbour Limits.
FACILITIES: Trailer parking at a fee. Dinghy parking available. Pay and display car park close by, but space unlikely to be available at busy times; other parking quite a distance away. Public toilets. Café and many shops nearby. Fuel and water by arrangement.

Slipway, Paignton
Lat. 50.4321, Long. -3.5572.
Harbourmaster 01803 557812

CHARGES: £6-10
SUITABILITY: Large trailer needs a car.
ACCESS: ¾ tidal. **TYPE OF RAMP:** Leads to firm sand.
UPPER AREA: Sand. **LOWER AREA:** Sand.
DIRECTIONS: Slipway leads into the harbour at Paignton.
RAMP DESCRIPTION: Good ramp in harbour, cost £6-7 depending on length. Dries for an hour and half around low water giving firm sandy bottom. You can drive a car across the sand in the harbour and launch at the harbour mouth at low water at your own risk. Jetskis are welcome and must be registered; £10 to launch and £7 if you have RYA training. Paignton SC 01803 525817.
FACILITIES: Trailer parking at no additional charge. Multi-storey car park near. Close to the centre of Paignton.

4

Oxen Cove, Brixham Harbour

Lat. 50.3994, Long. -3.5143.

Brixham YC; 01803 853332. Harbour office; 01803 853321

SUITABILITY: Large trailer needs a car.

ACCESS: ½ tidal. **TYPE OF RAMP:** Concrete **UPPER AREA:** Concrete.

LOWER AREA: Concrete.

DIRECTIONS: On the lower level of Freshwater Quarry in Oxen Cove right beneath the Yacht Club. Access is down a winding road that can be tricky in the summer with coaches on the road.

RAMP DESCRIPTION: Wide concrete ramp leading into the outer harbour. Can be tricky when the wind is in the north. Barrier at the top of the slipway.

FACILITIES: Very close to the Brixham Yacht Club.

The Strand, Brixham Harbour

Lat. 50.3963, Long. -3.5127.

01803 853321

SUITABILITY: Small trailer can be pushed.

ACCESS: ¼ tidal. **TYPE OF RAMP:** Substantial stone ramp.

UPPER AREA: Harbour. **LOWER AREA:** Harbour.

DIRECTIONS: Slipway is situated at the Inner Harbour on The Strand.

RAMP DESCRIPTION: Gets congested at times. Best to use at higher tides and only suitable for smaller boats.

FACILITIES: In the centre of town. Plenty of shops nearby but parking will be a problem, especially in the summer.

Brixham Marina, Brixham

Berry Head Road, Brixham, Devon, England TQ5 9BW

Lat. 50.3990, Long. -3.5064.

01803 882929

Breakwater Slipway, Brixham Harbour

Lat. 50.3995, Long. -3.5061.

01803 853321

CHARGES: £6 to launch, £4 for car park and £4 for trailer park.

SUITABILITY: Large trailer needs a car.

ACCESS: All of tidal range. **TYPE OF RAMP:** Steep concrete slipway.

UPPER AREA: Harbour. **LOWER AREA:** Unknown.

DIRECTIONS: Into centre of Brixham to Harbour area and leave town towards Berry Head up narrow road. Car park approximately ½ mile.

RAMP DESCRIPTION: All craft except PWCs. Road access is narrow. Main ramp is next to the breakwater inside the harbour and is usable any state of tide but best around high water. The lower part of the slipway is steep so may be a problem for heavier boats. Report to the harbourmaster's office before using the ramp. There is an additional ramp on the west side of the harbour that also has a car park. This is often locked due to a shortage of man power.

FACILITIES: Petrol parking toilets. Parking space is for 60 cars next to the slip. Dinghy park available. Brixham YC welcomes visitors 01803 853332. Wash down facilities are available and there is a loading pontoon.

HAZARDS: 5 knot speed restriction in the harbour.

Darthaven Marina, Dartmouth

Brixham Road, Kingswear, Dartmouth, Devon, England TQ6 0SG

Lat. 50.3508, Long. -3.5713.

01803 752242

Noss Marina, Dartmouth

Noss Marina Bridge Road Kingswear, Dartmouth, Devon, England TQ6 0EA

Lat. 50.3666, Long. -3.5772.

01803 839087

Dartside Quay, Galmpton

Lat. 50.3928, Long. -3.5762.

01803 845445

CHARGES: £10 per day including car parking.

SUITABILITY: Large trailer needs a car.

ACCESS: ½ tidal. **TYPE OF RAMP:** Concrete **UPPER AREA:** Concrete.

LOWER AREA: Mud.

DIRECTIONS: A3022 to Brixham turn left to Galmpton. Keep right to Galmpton and Waddeton. Follow signs through Galmpton village to Dartside Quay. Upon arrival please report to office.

RAMP DESCRIPTION: Easy to work.

FACILITIES: Chandlery, marine related tenants, toilets, car parking.

Dartside Quay, Brixham

Galmpton Creek, Galmpton, Brixham, Devon, England TQ5 0EH

Lat. 50.3930, Long. -3.5750.

01803 845445

Slipway, Stoke Gabriel

Lat. 50.4007, Long. -3.6231.

CHARGES: £1.80 to park all day. Launching free.

SUITABILITY: Small trailer can be pushed.

ACCESS: ¼ tidal. **TYPE OF RAMP:** Concrete **UPPER AREA:** Shingle.

LOWER AREA: Mud.

DIRECTIONS: Go through the village of Stoke Gabriel, bearing to your right before you reach the church.

RAMP DESCRIPTION: Shared with local yacht club which owns the wooden pontoon. Pontoon may not be used for mooring without Yacht Club permission. Access to the River Dart is probably only plus or minus 2 hours around high-tide.

FACILITIES: Parking, café at top of slip. Pubs, cafés and very pretty village within a short walk.

Steamer Quay Road, Totnes

Lat. 50.4246, Long. -3.6775.

CHARGES: Daily parking £5.40 and in addition leaving the boat trailer in the car park costs a further £5.40 obviously bringing the total charge to £10.80.

SUITABILITY: Large trailer needs a car.

ACCESS: ¾ tidal. **TYPE OF RAMP:** Concrete **UPPER AREA:** Concrete.

LOWER AREA: Concrete.

DIRECTIONS: Site is on Eastern bank of river adjacent to rowing club. ¼ mile downstream from bridge where Dart Steamers dock. At the end of Steamer Quay Road.
RAMP DESCRIPTION: Slip is adjacent to public car park. Parking for car and trailer available.
FACILITIES: Pub on opposite bank, shops and petrol in Totnes 5 minutes walk away. Chandlery in Totnes.

Blackness Marine, Blackness
Lat. 50.3891, Long. -3.6093.
01803 722654

CHARGES: All tariffs on our website, memberships available.
SUITABILITY: Large trailer needs a car.
ACCESS: All of tidal range. **TYPE OF RAMP:** Concrete, 7m wide suitable for use with onsite hoist. **UPPER AREA:** Concrete. **LOWER AREA:** Mud.
DIRECTIONS: Car Only: From Totnes: Follow signs for Dartmouth/Kingsbridge which will take you up the 'bypass'. At the top of the hill you will see a left turn signed Tuckenhay/Cornworthy Follow this road until you reach a cross roads at which you take the right hand turn down Bow Hill to Tuckenhay. Go over the bridge and proceed through Tuckenhay continue on this road passing a turning for Harbertonford, proceed up the hill taking the 2nd right turn. Follow this road passing turning for Cornworthy and proceed towards East Cornworthy/Dittisham, pass Whitestone Farm and we are the next left. Cars with Trailers/boats: From Dartmouth: Take the road out of the town gsoing up hill and past BP garage, go straight over at Roundabout and proceed until you pass Norton Park on your right - continue but take the next right at Henborough Post/Sportsmans Arms, you need to go immediately left avoiding Dittisham heading toward Tideford. Follow these lanes passing Gitcombe Holiday cottages and at the triangle junction bear right. Follow this to the cross roads and turn right again. Follow this road passing turning for Cornworthy and proceed down the hill towards E Cornworthy/Dittisham, pass Whitestone Farm and we are the next left.
RAMP DESCRIPTION: 1 in 8 gradient.
FACILITIES: Dry stack secure boat storage, slipway, launch and go memberships, lifting, toilets and parking.
HAZARDS: 6 knot speed limit in river.

Slipway, Dittisham
Lat. 50.3848, Long. -3.5965.

CHARGES: £5
SUITABILITY: Small trailer can be pushed.
ACCESS: All of tidal range. **TYPE OF RAMP:** Shingle to mud.
UPPER AREA: Shingle. **LOWER AREA:** Mud.
DIRECTIONS: Follow signs from village of Dittisham to the River.
RAMP DESCRIPTION: Gradient is gentle. Best sailing 2 hours +/- high water. It is possible to drive a car onto shingle to drop boat.
FACILITIES: Parking charges- £1/day £5/week. No overnight parking available. Parking space is for 50 cars. Extra parking free up the hill. Slip water tap available. Join Dittisham SC. (£5/week) and leave dinghy in the dinghy park alongside slipway. Very quiet and safe. Shower facilities are available.

Hole Farm Moorings, Dartmouth
Hole Farm, Dittisham, Dartmouth, Devon, England TQ6 0JG
Lat. 50.3633, Long. -3.5888.
01803 722340

Dart Marina Yacht Harbour, Dartmouth
Sandquay Road, Dartmouth, Devon, England TQ6 9PH
Lat. 50.3582, Long. -3.5772.
01803 837161

Ferry Slipway, Dartmouth
Lat. 50.3569, Long. -3.5764.
01803 832337

CHARGES: None
SUITABILITY: Large trailer needs a car.
ACCESS: All of tidal range. **TYPE OF RAMP:** Concrete slipway.
UPPER AREA: Concrete. **LOWER AREA:** Mud.
DIRECTIONS: From A38 (Exeter-Plymouth Road) take the A384 to Totnes. Turn onto the A381 and at Halwell take the A3122 following signs to the ferry.
RAMP DESCRIPTION: Shared with the ferry, the slip is accessible whilst the ferry is on the slip adjacent. Ramp is gets a lot of wash from passing craft. Good ramp, plenty of space. You should pay your harbour dues to a river officer or at the harbourmaster's office on the South Embankment.
FACILITIES: Limited parking on the road and a boat park opposite run by South Hams CC tel: 01803 861234. From May to September street parking is limited to 2 hours, outside this period it's free all day long. Use the park and ride at the top of the hill approximately 1½ miles away but you cannot park trailers there.
HAZARDS: 6 knot speed limit in river is strictly enforced. There is a lot of traffic on the river.

Southpool Creek, Kingsbridge
Lat. 50.2369, Long. -3.7458.

CHARGES: Harbour fees for Salcombe, see below.
SUITABILITY: Small trailer can be pushed.
ACCESS: ½ tidal. **TYPE OF RAMP:** Hard gravel onto sand.
UPPER AREA: Sand. **LOWER AREA:** Sand.
DIRECTIONS: Near East Portlemouth.
RAMP DESCRIPTION: Salcombe Harbour dues - you can now get a day-ticket for around £5.00 - £6.00, depending on size of craft. Charges may be paid at the harbourmaster's office at Whitestrand Salcombe, the sailing school at South Sands, or at the Batson Boat Park (when attendant present).
FACILITIES: Free parking. Overnight parking possible at Mill Bay. Parking space is limited. Security is good at Mill Bay. Boats can be kept on beach above high water mark in Mill Bay by prior arrangement with Miss Tyler 01548 842356.

Slipway, Frogmore
Lat. 50.2705, Long. -3.7200.
CHARGES: None

SUITABILITY: Large trailer needs a car.
ACCESS: ½ tidal. **TYPE OF RAMP:** Concrete **UPPER AREA:** Shingle.
LOWER AREA: Mud.
DIRECTIONS: Off A379 east of Kingsbridge. At Frogmore cross the bridge and slip is on the right.
RAMP DESCRIPTION: Public slipway. Concrete about 8 ′ wide with mud and shingle at the sides. Shallow slope with a steeper run off at the bottom. Accessible about ½ tide for small boats.
FACILITIES: Shop, pubs. Parking limited on narrow roads. Nearby boat yard may allow parking by prior arrangement. 01548 531257 / 07785972407.

The Quay, Kingsbridge
Lat. 50.2796, Long. -3.7754.
Harbourmaster 01548 843791

CHARGES: Harbour dues (and car park ticket) must be purchased.
SUITABILITY: Large trailer needs a car.
ACCESS: ¼ tidal. **TYPE OF RAMP:** Shallow concrete.
UPPER AREA: Concrete. **LOWER AREA:** Mud.
DIRECTIONS: The slipway is on the west side of the river off Ropewalk.
RAMP DESCRIPTION: Salcombe Harbour dues - you can now get a day-ticket for around £5.00 - £6.00, depending on size of craft. Charges may be paid at the harbourmaster's office at Whitestrand Salcombe, the sailing school at South Sands or at the Batson Boat Park (when attendant present). Not recommended at Neaps except for small dinghies. The end of the slipway is marked by a yellow pole. At this point there is a step down to soft mud.
FACILITIES: Parking charges- Pay and display. Overnight parking available by arrangement. Parking space is plentiful, but busy in summer. Security is minimal. Salcombe Harbour dues payable at Salcombe boat park down the coast. Kingsbridge harbour master does not issue permits. A large car boot on Sundays makes access impossible.
HAZARDS: 8 knots speed limit within the whole of the Salcombe Estuary, and all vessels should proceed at DEAD SLOW within Kingsbridge harbour (below 5 knots recommended). It is recommended that all boaters unfamiliar with the Kingsbridge harbour should observe the channel at low water as it is poorly marked and boats frequently run aground on the shallow banks. The channel is complex and marked by small red cans until the exit where the Salcombe Estuary marker poles start. Note that the creek at the end of the slipway is particularly shallow.

Batson Creek, Salcombe
Lat. 50.2419, Long. -3.7672.
01548 844010 Boat Park 0900-1800

CHARGES: £36/week for advance booking.
SUITABILITY: Large trailer needs a car.
ACCESS: All of tidal range. **TYPE OF RAMP:** Concrete
UPPER AREA: Concrete. **LOWER AREA:** Harbour.
DIRECTIONS: Follow directions to Salcombe but keep an eye out for the sign to the boat park on the way or else you'll end up threading your boat through narrow streets.
RAMP DESCRIPTION: Extremely easy to launch, nice and shallow angle with room for 3 people abreast all launching at the same time. Ramp charge gets you a parking space in which you can store car or trailer then pop what's left into the car park next door. No Jetskis. Harbour Office 01548 843791 (advance bookings advisable in summer). Salcombe estuary harbour dues must be purchased and are for a minimum of 1 month. Salcombe Harbour dues - you can now get a day-ticket for around £5.00 - £6.00, depending on size of craft. Charges may be paid at the Harbourmaster's Office at Whitestrand Salcombe (01548 843791), the sailing school at South Sands or at the Batson Boat Park (when attendant present).
FACILITIES: Lots of pubs, petrol barge on estuary, toilets close by, car park on site / short walk. You can book a space in advance for £36/week or turn up and pay £26/week. There is also a daily rate. Book ahead for summer months. Last week July and first week August go very early due to regattas.
HAZARDS: Follow dredged channel out at low tide. Famous Salcombe sand bar at harbour entrance keep to the west side. If in doubt ask the harbourmaster. Also large rocks just below water on east side of estuary. Follow someone out the first time and keep the speed down below the 8 knot limit as they are red hot with the radar guns.

South Sands, Salcombe
Lat. 50.2260, Long. -3.7840.

CHARGES: None
SUITABILITY: Large trailer needs a car.
ACCESS: All of tidal range. **TYPE OF RAMP:** Concrete
UPPER AREA: Concrete. **LOWER AREA:** Sand.
DIRECTIONS: Follow directions to Salcombe, Devon, then look for south sands beach on signposts.
RAMP DESCRIPTION: Short ramp that leads you out onto the flat beach where you can get to the sea at any time of day including low and high tides. Salcombe Harbour dues - you can now get a day-ticket for around £5.00 - £6.00, depending on size of craft.
FACILITIES: Tides Reach Hotel, watersports centre, RYA training centre.
HAZARDS: Rocks, but all marked with navigation poles

Lifeboat Slip Inner Hope, Hope Cove
Lat. 50.2435, Long. -3.8599.

CHARGES: £6.00 per day, £25.00 per week and £50.00 per year.
SUITABILITY: Large trailer needs a car.
ACCESS: All of tidal range. **TYPE OF RAMP:** Shallow concrete ramp onto firm sand. **UPPER AREA:** Shingle. **LOWER AREA:** Sand.
DIRECTIONS: From A38 (Exeter-Plymouth Road) take the A384 to Totnes then A381 to Marlborough via Kingsbridge. Turn right and follow the minor roads to Hope Cove. Site is the old lifeboat slip at Inner Cove.
RAMP DESCRIPTION: Open from 0800 - 1800. All craft are launched at the discretion of the harbourmaster. Harbourmaster on duty Easter to September. 6inch step at base of slip onto beach.
FACILITIES: Parking and toilets.
HAZARDS: There are rocks in the harbour entrance which are hazardous at low tide. When launching from the Inner Hope slipway, the Harbourmaster advises a safe line can be had by holding a course in line with the lie of the slipway. Having seen the rocks at low tide this advice is a little on the cautious side, however better safe than sorry. 5 knot speed restriction inshore of buoys. Waterskiing permitted offshore.

4

Beach slip, Sedgewell Cove
Lat. 50.2826, Long. -3.8915.

CHARGES: None
SUITABILITY: Large trailer needs a car.
ACCESS: No Ramp. **TYPE OF RAMP:** Concrete and soft sand.
UPPER AREA: Concrete. **LOWER AREA:** Sand.
DIRECTIONS: Off the main road to Bigbury on Sea
RAMP DESCRIPTION: Concrete leading on to sand.
HAZARDS: Many rocks to the right

Challaborough Bay, Bidbury-on-sea
Lat. 50.2887, Long. -3.8989.

CHARGES: £10 for launch and recovery
SUITABILITY: Large trailer needs a car.
ACCESS: All of tidal range. **TYPE OF RAMP:** Concrete on to sand
UPPER AREA: Concrete. **LOWER AREA:** Sand.
DIRECTIONS: Drive into the car park of the holiday park centre and ask at reception for a launch (cost about £10). The road to the bay is very narrow so take care.
RAMP DESCRIPTION: Assisted launch any time between 8.00am-5.00pm or you can launch yourself but beware the sand can be very soft. Narrow if you launch use 4 × 4 only as sand is soft. Boat must have shallow keel. Nearest wreck is the Persia which can be dived at all states of tide.
FACILITIES: Pub and food on site. Toilets, good sandy beach.
HAZARDS: Keep to starboard as rest of beach is for bathers (buoys mark the lane).

Bridgend, Newton Ferrers
Lat. 50.3143, Long. -4.0320.

CHARGES: Free, harbourmaster will charge if you want a mooring.
SUITABILITY: Large trailer needs a car.
ACCESS: ¼ tidal. **TYPE OF RAMP:** Launching on a Neap tide means you'll be wading out a long way. The surface is better than it looks. Best to wait for high tide if possible. **UPPER AREA:** Shingle.
LOWER AREA: Shingle.
DIRECTIONS: The road down is narrow. Towing a large boat down is a nightmare if you meet traffic and cannot reverse up a fairly steep road. We send a runner ahead to the next passing point to stop traffic coming up.
RAMP DESCRIPTION: Gravel, only mild slope but wide. Only useable 2-3 hours each side of high tide
FACILITIES: Parking may be difficult; the area is very short of residential parking. The quay is used as a car park. Builders often park vans on the slipway! Campsite back up the hill charges a small amount to leave your trailer there. Leave it on the Quay if there is a space.
HAZARDS: Dries out completely at low tide.

Village slipway, Newton Ferrers
Lat. 50.3134, Long. -4.0401.
01752 872533

CHARGES: None
SUITABILITY: Small trailer can be pushed.

ACCESS: ½ tidal. **TYPE OF RAMP:** Concrete **UPPER AREA:** Shingle.
LOWER AREA: Mud.
DIRECTIONS: Do not follow signs to harbour, but instead go down steep hill past post office at Newton Hill. Slipway is by the Dolphin pub.
RAMP DESCRIPTION: Ramp is only usable for half tides, i.e. 3 hours either side of high. It is mud the rest of the time. It is really only suitable for flat bottomed or slightly v shaped boats. Deeper hulled or sharp v boats cannot be launched from the ramp. No Jetskis and not suitable for powerboats due to extensive speed restrictions on the River Yealm.
FACILITIES: This slipway is really only suitable for residents and local holidaymakers due to single track access and lack of parking. Good for pottering about on the river.
HAZARDS: There is a 6 knot speed limit within the whole estuary (about 1½-2 miles from the ramp to the open sea where the limit ends). The speed limit is observed - the harbourmaster and harbour authority are all pretty keen.

Fort Bovisand Diving, Plymouth
Lat. 50.3371, Long. -4.1284.
01752 408021

CHARGES: None
SUITABILITY: Large trailer needs a car.
ACCESS: All of tidal range. **TYPE OF RAMP:** Concrete slipway.
UPPER AREA: Concrete. **LOWER AREA:** Sand.
DIRECTIONS: Follow A379 east towards Plymstock, then signs south to Bovisand Beach via Staddon Fort and continue along rough track to Bovisand Pier.
RAMP DESCRIPTION: OCTOBER 2003. SLIPWAY CLOSED UNTIL FURTHER NOTICE. Wide ramp that will take a large trailer, but it does have a 90 degree bend at the bottom so good reversing skills are required. Leads onto hard sand. No Jetskis.
FACILITIES: Parking, shower and toilet and accommodation. Also air fills available from the Diving Centre. See reception when you get there.
HAZARDS: Keep a very good look-out for surface marker buoys indicating divers in the water.

Mount Batten Slip, Plymouth
Lat. 50.3595, Long. -4.1267.
01752 404567 Mount Batten Centre

CHARGES: No charge for large slip.
SUITABILITY: Large trailer needs a car.
ACCESS: All of tidal range. **TYPE OF RAMP:** Wide concrete and stone slip. **UPPER AREA:** Sand. **LOWER AREA:** Mud.
DIRECTIONS: From the A38, follow signs to Plymouth city centre along A374, Embankment Road staying in right-hand lane. After 1mile follow signs for Kingsbridge (A379) across Laira Bridge. At first roundabout turn right to Plymouth, follow road to Hoe past McMullins Garage on left then going up hill, continue along road to Mount Batten. Site is south of Jetty.
RAMP DESCRIPTION: Available all states of tide. There are 3 slipways - 1 private, 2 public. The wide concrete slipway is free to use and accessible at all states of tide, except low water Springs. Congested when regattas are running. The slipway further to the west although smaller has a very large turning area at the top to allow greater manoeuvrability for car / trailer. Only suitable at the top half of the tide.

4

FACILITIES: Mount Batten Centre facilities are nearby with car park (£10/day), pontoon, bar, restaurant, showers and changing rooms. Chandlery nearby. The Mount Batten Centre is a 'not for profit' charity organisation and encourages affordable watersports for all. Full disabled access and disabled sailing / scuba diving capabilities but not responsible for the slipway.

HAZARDS: 8 knot speed limit with designated high speed areas.

Plymouth Yacht Haven, Plymouth
Lat. 50.3585, Long. -4.1255.

CHARGES: Yes
SUITABILITY: Large trailer needs a car.
ACCESS: ¾ tidal. **TYPE OF RAMP:** Concrete **UPPER AREA:** Concrete.
LOWER AREA: Rock.
DIRECTIONS: Western end of Plymouth Yacht Haven marina
RAMP DESCRIPTION: Concrete, nice gradient, step off at bottom
FACILITIES: Parking in Plymouth Yacht Haven car park or on road with trailer

Plymouth Yacht Haven, Plymouth
Shaw Way, Mount Batten, Plymouth, Devon,
England PL9 9XH
Lat. 50.3580, Long. -4.1222.
01752 404231

Slipway, Oreston
Lat. 50.3629, Long. -4.1102.

CHARGES: Boat park £50 per annum
SUITABILITY: Small trailer can be pushed.
ACCESS: ½ tidal. **TYPE OF RAMP:** Rough concrete
UPPER AREA: Concrete. **LOWER AREA:** Mud.
RAMP DESCRIPTION: Steep concrete with very tight turn at top of slipway, larger vessels not advisable and harbourmaster was talking about a 4HP restriction. Can be very busy at weekends and summer. Larger boats not advisable, small craft can use this slipway anytime except during low Spring tides. Warning there is a large step off the end of the slip. The lower part of the slip is very slippery.
FACILITIES: Tap for flushing/washing has been removed by PCC. Very limited car/trailer parking spaces, possible introduction of more restrictions May to September. No room for trailers in local streets, parking restrictions have been introduced. Nearest slip for larger vessels/Jetskis at Mountbatten. Locals Boat Park PCC £50 PA. Discussion of 4HP limit

HAZARDS: None for small boats however be careful at low Spring tide. Speed restrictions apply below Laira Bridge

Sutton Harbour Marina, Plymouth
The Jetty, Sutton Harbour, Plymouth, Devon,
England PL4 0DW
Lat. 50.3704, Long. -4.1330.
01752 204702

Queen Anne's Battery Marina, Plymouth
Lat. 50.3654, Long. -4.1316.
Queen Anne's Battery Marina 01752 671142

CHARGES: £12 including launch, recovery and car parking.
SUITABILITY: Large trailer needs a car.
ACCESS: ¾ tidal. **TYPE OF RAMP:** Concrete. **UPPER AREA:** Concrete.
LOWER AREA: Harbour.
DIRECTIONS: From A38 follow signs to Queen Anne's Battery Marina. Follow signs to Marina Office.
RAMP DESCRIPTION: Long, straight and easy.
FACILITIES: Restaurant, café, bar, shops, car parking, petrol, diesel, toilets / showers. Security is excellent.

Queen Anne's Battery Marina, Plymouth
Queen Anne's Battery, Plymouth, Devon, England
PL4 0LP
Lat. 50.3653, Long. -4.1306.
01752 671142

Elphinstone Boat Park, Plymouth
Lat. 50.3644, Long. -4.1343.
Landing officer 01752 304304

CHARGES: None
SUITABILITY: Large trailer needs a car.
ACCESS: All of tidal range. **TYPE OF RAMP:** Concrete
UPPER AREA: Sand. **LOWER AREA:** Mud.
DIRECTIONS: Just beneath the Barbican Centre by Madeira Road adjacent to the Mayflower Sailing Club.
RAMP DESCRIPTION: Very good well used concrete ramp next to the Plymouth Harbourmasters office. Jetskis are allowed to launch here.
FACILITIES: Car park and close to the old town centre. Congested when regattas are running and the car park maybe closed off, call 01752 304304 to check. Mayflower Sailing Club 01752 662526 has facilities for visiting yachtsmen.

Mayflower Marina, Plymouth
Richmond Walk, Plymouth, Devon, England
PL1 4LS
Lat. 50.3647, Long. -4.1672.
01752 556633

Near Mayflower Marina, Plymouth
Lat. 50.3648, Long. -4.1699.
Landing officer 01752 304304

CHARGES: None
SUITABILITY: Large trailer needs a car.
ACCESS: All of tidal range. **TYPE OF RAMP:** Concrete
UPPER AREA: Concrete. **LOWER AREA:** Rock.
DIRECTIONS: Proceed along Union Street towards Devonport, over roundabout beside Marine Projects, over Stonehouse Bridge and at next roundabout turn left down narrow road - Richmond Walk - past entrance to Mayflower Marina, past Ocean Quay flats, into car par, slip

4

immediately past car park. Approximately 200 metres after Mayflower Marina entrance.

RAMP DESCRIPTION: Relatively narrow with awkward corner at top - when pulling away from the slip with large trailer the one must back into car park to turn round. Slip used by canoeists. The sharp turn at the top of the slip restricts the combined length of car / trailer, especially during the summer months as people park at the top of the slip.

FACILITIES: Toilets at car park however more salubrious ones can be found at Mayflower Marina. Trailer parking at marina. All services available at Mayflower Marina. Cost for up to 6 metres £12.55/day.

HAZARDS: At low water nasty frayed wire hawser exposed approximately 10 metres into water.

River Tamar, Plymouth
Lat. 50.4051, Long. -4.2016.
Landing officer 01752 304304

CHARGES: None
SUITABILITY: Large trailer needs a car.
ACCESS: All of tidal range. **TYPE OF RAMP:** Stepped granite slipway.
UPPER AREA: Mud. **LOWER AREA:** Mud.
DIRECTIONS: Leave A38 at exit marked 'St Budeaux' (NOT the A3064). Follow Victoria Rd in southwest direction to Wolseley Rd. Turn left then immediate right across railway bridge. Follow separate part of Wolseley Rd in westerly direction until you reach two slips.
RAMP DESCRIPTION: The upstream (Royal Albert Bridge) slip is fully exposed only at low water Springs, showing a few feet of rubble and mud below it. Boats larger than 16´ on a trailer may have difficulty accessing the slipway due to the narrow entrance to the boat park.
FACILITIES: The downstream slip (the old Tamar ferry slip) has no parking of any sort but has full tidal access. The upstream one has a council boat park (no parking for cars), a refreshment kiosk with tables and a pub, and limited street parking for cars and has approximately half tidal access. Public toilets on Wolseley Road but no showers or petrol at either slip.
HAZARDS: 10 knot speed restriction in the harbour with designated high speed areas.

Weir Quay, Plymouth
Lat. 50.4607, Long. -4.2078.

CHARGES: None
SUITABILITY: Large trailer needs a car.
ACCESS: ¾ tidal. **TYPE OF RAMP:** Hard standing gravel with solid edges. **UPPER AREA:** Shingle. **LOWER AREA:** Mud.
DIRECTIONS: From Tavistock, follow the tourist signs for 'Morwellham Quay' after leaving the main road, turning left at the Harvest home pub, turn left at the next cross roads, sign posted Bere Alston. As you pass the village sign at the entrance to Bere Alston, take the next left (cross roads) follow this road, which takes a sharp right and then crosses straight over at another cross roads. Weir quay is about 3 miles further on down the lane. (15 minutes from Tavistock).
RAMP DESCRIPTION: The ramp is quite shallow at the top and bottom, but a good angle mid tide. It consists of a shingle beach which is held in place by lines of kerb stones laid on the beach. Very wide (enough for two trailers at once, it is an open site with easy access and reversing. Can be a bit slippery and muddy near the bottom - four wheel drives can

launch at all states of tides except very low water Springs. Tidal streams can get quite strong at times.
FACILITIES: Weir Quay Sailing Club opposite ramp. Weir Quay Boat Yard with small shop and fitter 100 metres away. Village of Bere Ferrers with 'Old Plough Inn' 5 minutes drive. There is free but limited off road parking nearby - it is a beautiful place. A haven for wildlife with avocets known to be seen on the opposite bank.
HAZARDS: Fast water ski area 10 minutes down stream, shallow, wide mud banks from ½ tide - channel well marked with moorings. 10 knot speed limit, military port of Plymouth 15 minutes south, Crooked Spaniard Pub on opposite bank ½ mile downstream - very difficult to pass!

Calstock Slipway, Plymouth
Lat. 50.4959, Long. -4.2077.

CHARGES: None
SUITABILITY: Large trailer needs a car.
ACCESS: All of tidal range. **TYPE OF RAMP:** Concrete
UPPER AREA: Harbour. **LOWER AREA:** Mud.
DIRECTIONS: Take the Calstock road to the centre of the village and the slipway is opposite the Tamar Inn.
RAMP DESCRIPTION: Finished November 2001 as part of the redevelopment of Calstock. It is a steep slipway that can be used at all states of the tide. Will require a car or suitable vehicle to tow up from the water, it is recommended that cars do not venture on to the slipway. Slipway is wide and will take large trailers, problems could arise with recovery at low tide. Calstock Pier is in use by the local ferry service and visiting Plymouth trip boats and is not a public mooring, pick-ups and drop-offs are tolerated but anyone mooring is politely asked to move on. There are buoys in the channel that do not dry out are available.
FACILITIES: Local village, parking, toilets, village shop and post office. Tamar Inn, phone box. Car park is 100 yards away, cars cannot be left on the top of the slipway as there is a public footpath across the top and the slipway is adjacent to the local bus stop.

Jubilee Green Slipway, Saltash
Lat. 50.4100, Long. -4.2067.

CHARGES: None.
SUITABILITY: Large trailer needs a car.
ACCESS: All of tidal range. **TYPE OF RAMP:** Concrete
UPPER AREA: Concrete. **LOWER AREA:** Concrete.
DIRECTIONS: North of the Tamar Bridge. Travel west over bridge following signs to Waterside. Entrance to the slipway is before you reach the free car park on your left
RAMP DESCRIPTION: Usable all times but strong current about half tide. Shallow ramp suitable for car. Gradient is gentle.
FACILITIES: Free car and trailer parking spaces, free overnight parking (12hrs maximum stay, 9 spaces). Parking space is ample in car park adjacent to the south of the slipway, opposite the pontoon. Further facilities in town ¼ mile. Nearest dinghy anchorage is St Germans River to the southwest which is exposed in southwest winds. Best shelter at Millbrook Lake (due south) or upstream beyond Weir Quay (4 miles north) all with safe mud. Pub at Cargreen west side, 2 miles north but very strong current at half-tide Springs makes stopping difficult.

4

HAZARDS: **10 knot speed restriction in the harbour with designated high speed areas.**

Ashtor Wharf, Plymouth
Lat. 50.4084, Long. -4.2059.

CHARGES: None
SUITABILITY: Small trailer can be pushed.
ACCESS: Unknown. **TYPE OF RAMP:** Concrete **UPPER AREA:** Concrete. **LOWER AREA:** Concrete.
DIRECTIONS: Travel west over the bridge following signs to Waterside. The slipway is situated directly beneath the Tamar bridge and access is next to the public conveniences.
RAMP DESCRIPTION: Ideal to explore River Tamar and Plymouth Sound. Saltash is across the river from Plymouth. Strong current about half tide. Shallow ramp suitable for car. Gradient is gentle.
FACILITIES: Free overnight parking. Parking space is ample in car park. Car park 400 yards north, adjacent its own slip. Fresh water top of slip other facilities in town ¼ mile. Nearest dinghy anchorage is St Germans River to the southwest which is exposed in southwest winds. Best shelter at Millbrook Lake (due south) or upstream beyond Weir Quay (4 miles north) all with safe mud. Pub at Cargreen west side, 2 miles north but very strong current at half-tide Springs makes stopping difficult.
HAZARDS: Access to Ashtor Wharf is restricted with a maximum width of 2.0 meters

Saltash Ferry Slip, Plymouth
Lat. 50.4081, Long. -4.2067.

CHARGES: None
SUITABILITY: Large trailer needs a car.
ACCESS: All of tidal range. **TYPE OF RAMP:** Concrete
UPPER AREA: Unknown. **LOWER AREA:** Unknown.
DIRECTIONS: South and west of Tamar Bridge, 300 yards downstream. Travel west over bridge following signs to Waterside.
RAMP DESCRIPTION: Ideal to explore River Tamar and Plymouth Sound. Saltash is across the river from Plymouth. Usable all times but strong current about half tide. Shallow ramp suitable for car. Gradient is gentle.
FACILITIES: Free overnight parking. Parking space is ample in car park. Car park 400 yards north, adjacent its own slip. Fresh water tops of slip other facilities in town ¼ mile. Nearest dinghy anchorage is St Germans River to the southwest which is exposed in southwest winds. Best shelter at Millbrook Lake (due south) or upstream beyond Weir Quay (4 miles north) all with safe mud. Pub at Cargreen west side, 2 miles north but very strong current at half-tide Springs makes stopping difficult.

Macey Street Promenade slipway, Torpoint
Lat. 50.3764, Long. -4.1947.

CHARGES: None.
SUITABILITY: Small trailer can be pushed.
ACCESS: ½ tidal. **TYPE OF RAMP:** Concrete **UPPER AREA:** Concrete.
LOWER AREA: Mud.

DIRECTIONS: Coming into Torpoint along the A374 turn left onto Fore Street, then left onto Quarry Street and then into King Street. You will have to reverse down King Street onto the slipway.
RAMP DESCRIPTION: Shallow ramp suitable for car. Gradient is gentle.
FACILITIES: Toilets are approximately 200m to the north on Antony Road, parking in the streets around the slipway is available, although would be limited at weekends and other peak times. No specified car & trailer spaces.
HAZARDS: 10 knot speed restriction in the harbour. Designated high speed areas. Torpoint Ferry crossing is just downstream of the slipway. Restricted access to the slipway maximum width of vehicle and trailer 2.8meters

Promenade Slipway, Torpoint
Lat. 50.3739, Long. -4.1947.

CHARGES: None
SUITABILITY: Small trailer can be pushed.
ACCESS: ½ tidal. **TYPE OF RAMP:** Concrete **UPPER AREA:** Concrete.
LOWER AREA: Mud.
DIRECTIONS: Public slipway off Ferry Street. Turn right off the A374, Anthony Road, before getting into the ferry lanes into Marine Drive. Promenade slipway is immediately on your left.
RAMP DESCRIPTION: Whilst the entrance at the top seems quite wide, only a small boat can be used because the upper slipway is very steep and where the upper slipway meets the lower slipway at 60 degrees, there is insufficient space to make the turn.
FACILITIES: Vehicles and trailers are not to be left on the slipway. No specified car & trailer spaces. Parking on the road is available, although would be limited at peak times. Town centre and shops 100m to the north.
HAZARDS: 10 knot speed restriction in the harbour. Designated high speed areas. Torpoint Ferry crossing is just downstream of the slipway.

Torpoint Slip, Plymouth
Lat. 50.3722, Long. -4.1954.
Torpoint Yacht Harbour 01752 813658

CHARGES: None
SUITABILITY: Large trailer needs a car.
ACCESS: ¾ tidal. **TYPE OF RAMP:** Concrete onto a firm beach.
UPPER AREA: Shingle. **LOWER AREA:** Shingle.
DIRECTIONS: Public slip off Marine Drive. Turn right off the A374. Anthony Road into Marine Drive. The two slipways are just to the northeast of the marina and are part of the marina.
RAMP DESCRIPTION: Good, wide ramp onto firm beach. Possible to launch at low tide by driving onto the beach. Shallow gradient makes it difficult to launch deep keel boats. Torpoint Mosquito Sailing Club runs a smaller adjacent slipway suitable for dinghies only. It is narrow and had difficult access. There is a tap and hose for flushing / washing the boats at the top of this long slipway next to the race start hut. It gets incredibly busy in the evenings, especially on Mondays and Thursdays when dinghy racing takes place.
FACILITIES: Slipway runs from the car park and trailers must not be left here. Must be taken outside the car park and parked on the road. Can be difficult to find a spot, especially at weekends. Day berths may

be available in the marina as are showers and toilets. Call marina office before using, weekdays are much less congested.
HAZARDS: 10 knot speed restriction in the harbour. Designated high speed areas.

Torpoint Yacht Harbour, Torpoint
Marine Drive, Torpoint, Cornwall, England PL11 2EH
Lat. 50.3719, Long. -4.1949.
01752 813658

Carbeile Wharf, Torpoint
Carbeile Wharf, Torpoint, Cornwall, UK PL11 2NW
Lat. 50.3724, Long. -4.2076.
01752 813201

Southdown Marina, Torpoint
Southdown Quay, Millbrook, Torpoint, Cornwall, England PL10 1HG
Lat. 50.3535, Long. -4.1973.
01752 816358

Voyager Yachts, Millbrook
Lat. 50.3526, Long. -4.1988.
Voyager Yachts 01752 823329
CHARGES: £10
SUITABILITY: Large trailer needs a car.
ACCESS: ½ tidal. **TYPE OF RAMP:** Concrete **UPPER AREA:** Harbour. **LOWER AREA:** Mud.
DIRECTIONS: Situated next to the marina in Southdown to the east of Millbrook. From Plymouth take the A374 via the Torpoint ferry, then take the B3247 to Millbrook. Alternatively take the A38 onto the B3247 and turn off to Millbrook.
RAMP DESCRIPTION: Best to phone ahead, unlikely to be any problem with smaller boats. At weekends there is a phone by the slipway. Please let the yard know you are using the ramp so they can send you a bill.
FACILITIES: Parking, toilets, fresh water, boat storage.
HAZARDS: 10 knot speed limit in harbour with designated high speed areas.

Harbour & Slipway, Portwinkle
Lat. 50.3612, Long. -4.3143.
01579363354
CHARGES: None.
SUITABILITY: Portable Only.
ACCESS: ¼ tidal. **TYPE OF RAMP:** Concrete and shingle beach **UPPER AREA:** Concrete. **LOWER AREA:** Shingle.
DIRECTIONS: Located to the west of Whitsand Bay. From Torpoint travel along the A374 and turn left at Crafthole and following signs to Portwinkle.
RAMP DESCRIPTION: Concrete bollards close the ramp usable only for portable boats that can be lifted over bollards. Ramp has 90 degree bend half way down and then 25yds of very soft shingle. Harbour destroyed by storm years ago just a small wall left.

FACILITIES: Public toilets about 250m away from the harbour opposite the two car parks. Caradon District Council's car park can accommodate cars and trailers out of holiday season.
HAZARDS: Large reef and rocks outside what is left of the harbour. Beware of reef break waves keep outside the stone marker on the seaward side do not approach in bad weather

Slipway, Downderry
Lat. 50.3607, Long. -4.3691.
CHARGES: Annual fee.
SUITABILITY: Large trailer needs a car.
ACCESS: No Ramp. **TYPE OF RAMP:** Concrete **UPPER AREA:** Concrete. **LOWER AREA:** Sand.
DIRECTIONS: Travel along the A387 towards Hessenford, turn onto the B3247 towards Seaton & Downderry. Travel through Seaton and follow the road into Downderry and turn right into Beach Hill. Slipway is at the bottom of Beach Hill.
RAMP DESCRIPTION: Access into Downderry is narrow in places. The slipway is situated at the bottom of Beach Hill. Slipway is now gated and requires a key. There's a narrow open access alongside the gate, too small for any trailer, but OK for kayaks. You can never launch directly off the slipway, and there is soft sand then shingle to cross before reaching firmer stuff lower down the beach. So you need a key and a 4 × 4 for anything on a trailer, even then it can be tricky, according to beach, sea and tide conditions. Warm summer days mean picking a safe route through sunbathers and children playing on the beach, and there are often kids in the water right where you launch, so please paddle clear before starting the engine.
FACILITIES: Shop and public toilets close by with pubs / restaurants and shop in the village of Downderry
HAZARDS: Rocks very close in to the shore with no navigational markers.

Slipway, Plaidy
Lat. 50.3591, Long. -4.4409.
CHARGES: None.
SUITABILITY: Small trailer can be pushed.
ACCESS: No Ramp. **TYPE OF RAMP:** Concrete **UPPER AREA:** Concrete. **LOWER AREA:** Sand.
DIRECTIONS: Travel along the A387 and turn off at Widgates onto the B3253. Plaidy is sign posted and you turn off before reaching Looe. Travel along Barbican Road, Bay view Road and Pladiy Lane.
HAZARDS: Rocks very close in to the shore. Very narrow access not suitable for large vehicles and boats.

The Mill Pool, Looe
Lat. 50.3578, Long. -4.4631.
01503 262839
CHARGES: £3.50 harbour fees
SUITABILITY: Large trailer needs a car.
ACCESS: ¼ tidal. **TYPE OF RAMP:** Concrete **UPPER AREA:** Concrete. **LOWER AREA:** Mud.
DIRECTIONS: At the Mill Pool Car park (largest in Looe) near to the Discovery Centre.

4

RAMP DESCRIPTION: The car park is large and busy in the holiday season pay and display is in operation and is policed. The ramp is usable 2 hours either side of high tide. Unless you have a boat light enough to carry. £3.50 Harbour fees payable to harbour master. The harbourmaster can be found in the office on East Looe Quay. Site is above a road bridge. Check air draught if you want to head out to sea. There is also slipway at Millpool Boatyard close by. Telephone 01503 262244.

FACILITIES: Public car park.

HAZARDS: Don't get the tide wrong or you'll be doing a miserable river dance. Stick to centre/left of channel.

Slipway, Looe Boats
Lat. 50.3575, Long. -4.4566.
01503262244

CHARGES: £2 each way on ramp £4.50 parking
SUITABILITY: Small trailer can be pushed.
ACCESS: ¼ tidal. **TYPE OF RAMP:** Concrete **UPPER AREA:** Concrete.
LOWER AREA: Sand.
DIRECTIONS: Head to the main Looe car park, then drive right to the Looe town end near chandlery. Ramp is in the small car park situated behind Looe Chandlery. Parking £4.50 per day per space used.
RAMP DESCRIPTION: Ramp only useable for 2 hrs either side of high tide. Unless you fancy walking out. Quite tight ramp with 90deg. turn at top. Entrance usually blocked by a digger that will be moved on request. Fairly steep solid till end in line with the wall. £2 in and £2 out charge payable at port cabin.
HAZARDS: Shallow until past bridge; keep to the centre/left.

Slipway, Hannefore, West Looe
Lat. 50.3448, Long. -4.4536.

CHARGES: None
SUITABILITY: Small trailer can be pushed.
ACCESS: ¼ tidal. **TYPE OF RAMP:** Concrete onto sand then rough rock
UPPER AREA: Concrete. **LOWER AREA:** Sand.
DIRECTIONS: Travel along the A387 to Looe and Polperro. When in Looe cross over the Harbour bridge and then turn left heading for Hannafore. The slipway is close to the Coastguard look out office at Hannefore point.
RAMP DESCRIPTION: Not really a slipway. 90 degree turn at top although not steep really a pedestrian walkway to the little bit of sand and public toilets a small boat could be pushed at very high tide only. A large rocky reef extends very shallow for 200 yards.
FACILITIES: Road parking available although it will busy at peak times. Public toilets next to the slipway. Café bar close by (open in the summer period).
HAZARDS: Looe Bay &Whitsand Bay

Slipway, Polperro Hard
Lat. 50.3313, Long. -4.5183.

SUITABILITY: Large trailer needs a car.
ACCESS: ¼ tidal. **TYPE OF RAMP:** Concrete **UPPER AREA:** Harbour.
LOWER AREA: Unknown.
RAMP DESCRIPTION: Slipway at top of harbour in village of Polperro.
FACILITIES: In centre of village.

Penmarlam Quay, Fowey
Lat. 50.3454, Long. -4.6293.
01726 832471/2

CHARGES: £9.00/day. Includes car and trailer parking.
SUITABILITY: Large trailer needs a car.
ACCESS: All of tidal range. **TYPE OF RAMP:** Concrete
UPPER AREA: Concrete. **LOWER AREA:** Concrete.
DIRECTIONS: From A390, At Taphouse turn off following signs for Looe/ Polperro/ Polruan. Thereafter, follow signs for Polruan/ Bodinnick Ferry. Boat park is situated just past the left turn to Polruan and is signposted with brown road signs.
RAMP DESCRIPTION: Newly refurbish concrete ramp run by the harbour authorities, wide enough for 2 cars to launch at once. Difficult to use at Spring low tide especially with a large heavy motor boat but no problem with a sailing boat say wayfarers size. You will need £9.00 in coins to get into the boat park, or buy token from campsite shop when open. From May to September the campsite office is manned and you can pay there. Weekly and annual passes also available.
FACILITIES: Parking and toilets. Camping for caravans and tents adjacent to boat park entrance. Boat storage available, winter and summer. 8.5 tonne boat hoist. Diesel at Toms Boatyard. The site has recently benefited from an upgrade to its electricity points - now card operated, an increase in fresh water connections and improved road access. Pressure washing for boats is available. Sandy beach adjacent to slipway. NEW FOR 2003, shore linked pontoon system. Slipway and access road are very steep, even sportsboats would need a substantial 4 × 4 to recover.

Slipways, Lerryn
Lat. 50.3840, Long. -4.6177.

CHARGES: None.
SUITABILITY: Large trailer needs a car.
ACCESS: ¼ tidal. **TYPE OF RAMP:** Concrete **UPPER AREA:** Concrete.
LOWER AREA: Mud.
DIRECTIONS: From Plymouth...Travel along the A390 towards Lostwithiel and turn left just before the town, following signs to Lerryn (3 miles). Cross the river into the main village & use the car park - free at the moment!
RAMP DESCRIPTION: The old, short slip is in the corner of the public car park. Access can be difficult, but OK for canoes. A new, longer slipway is located downstream of the car park, on the south bank of the River Lerryn.
FACILITIES: Public toilets near the car park, shop and local pub very close by.
HAZARDS: Stepping stones across the river are situated just downstream of the old slipway. Restricted depth in winding, unmarked channel - Local knowledge needed at low tides. Deep mud. Fluky winds off steep valley sides.

Public Slip, Lostwithiel
Lat. 50.4046, Long. -4.6696.

CHARGES: None
SUITABILITY: Large trailer needs a car.

ACCESS: ¼ tidal. **TYPE OF RAMP:** Rough concrete and stone.
UPPER AREA: Unknown. **LOWER AREA:** Unknown.
DIRECTIONS: Slip in centre of town.
RAMP DESCRIPTION: Gradient is moderately steep; railway bridge and overhead cable immediately below slip therefore need to lower mast.
FACILITIES: Free overnight parking. Parking space is for 15 cars. Busy car park on auction day.

Caffa Mill, Fowey
Lat. 50.3400, Long. -4.6332.
01726 832471/2

CHARGES: £1.40 harbour dues and 50p fee. £2.00 launch tickets available from machine.
SUITABILITY: Large trailer needs a car.
ACCESS: All of tidal range. **TYPE OF RAMP:** Concrete onto shingle.
UPPER AREA: Concrete. **LOWER AREA:** Shingle.
DIRECTIONS: Caffa Mill car and dinghy park. Directions are to follow signs from '4 Turnings' service station to Fowey Jetties and Bodinnick Car ferries. Caffa Mill car park and slip is next to and just past the ferry queue. This will avoid the very narrow streets of the town.
RAMP DESCRIPTION: Concrete slip onto shingle, good for all craft up to 25 feet. All states of tide although the slip is very steep and needs 4 wheel drive for larger craft. Access to site is via narrow roads and parking can be hard. A very worth while launch site with lots to do. Left side of slipway is longer and better suited to larger craft. Good diving is very close. Alternative ramp is Penmarlam Quay across the river.
FACILITIES: The main car park is above the town and is quite a walk back to slip but not so bad if you walk to the ferry steps and the boat meets you there. Toilets on site. Fuel is available from the garage on the way into town and diesel from Toms Boatyard.
HAZARDS: 6 knot speed limit in harbour.

Harbour Slip, Porthscatho
Lat. 50.1801, Long. -4.9739.
Harbourmaster 01872 580616

CHARGES: 20p per foot per day.
SUITABILITY: Small trailer can be pushed.
ACCESS: ¾ tidal. **TYPE OF RAMP:** Old steep cobble ramp.
UPPER AREA: Sand. **LOWER AREA:** Sand.
DIRECTIONS: Take to A3078 to Trewithian and follow the minor roads to Porthscatho.
RAMP DESCRIPTION: A 15 degree slipway that leads onto hard sand so it is possible to launch at all states of tide. Boats often left of slipway. It is possible to launch larger craft but the steepness and crowded nature make this difficult. A second slipway 50 yards to the north goes onto the beach. Take care, children playing on the beach. Harbour can get rough in an easterly.
FACILITIES: Large free car park on the way into Porthscatho about 5 minutes walk from slipway. Parking in the village can be difficult especially in the summer.

HAZARDS: Within the harbour there are numerous rock formations that are just below the surface at high to mid tide and are not visible from a small boat. There is a channel if you hug the harbour wall closely as you enter around the end so head (from the sea) directly for the end of the harbour wall. Keeping this to your left, turn sharply into the harbour and, keeping close to the wall, tie up to any rusty old ring you can find. Once stood on the harbour wall or higher up the bank it is possible to see the otherwise hidden rocks. (See photos by Bill Allerton 22/07/06)

Boat Yard Slip, Percuil
Lat. 50.1672, Long. -5.0008.
Percuil Boat Yard 01872 580564

CHARGES: £25-30 for assisted launch, otherwise donation to RNLI.
SUITABILITY: Large trailer needs a car.
ACCESS: ¾ tidal. **TYPE OF RAMP:** Uneven ramp onto shingle beach.
UPPER AREA: Shingle. **LOWER AREA:** Mud.
DIRECTIONS: Percuil is situated on the east side of the Pecuil River. Take to A3078 to Trewithian and follow the minor roads to Percuil.
RAMP DESCRIPTION: Slip is steep and narrow. Get permission to launch from boat yard on slipway. Always congested with dinghies and car parking difficult at peak times. Any craft can launch but there is a 5 knot speed limit in the river.
FACILITIES: Parking nearby, can be congested in summer. Water and usual facilities from yard, limited shopping in St Mawes. Good pub at Restronguet Point. Overnight mud in St Just.

Freshwater Boatyard, St Mawes , nr Truro
Freshwater Lane,, St Mawes , nr Truro, Cornwall, England TR2 5AR
Lat. 50.1609, Long. -5.0061.
01326 270443

Harbour Slip, St Mawes
Lat. 50.1578, Long. -5.0156.
Harbourmaster 01326 270553

CHARGES: £4-9, depending on length.
SUITABILITY: Large trailer needs a car.
ACCESS: ½ tidal. **TYPE OF RAMP:** Steep concrete ramp.
UPPER AREA: Shingle. **LOWER AREA:** Sand.
DIRECTIONS: The slipway is nestled in behind the harbour wall at St Mawes. The harbour is in the centre of town.
RAMP DESCRIPTION: Steep ramp in the corner of St Mawes harbour. Launch from the ramp 3 hours around high water or across the beach at all states of tide.
FACILITIES: Garage nearby, limited parking especially in the summer. Car park for trailers is 200 yards from the slipway. Very picturesque town, St Mawes Sailing Club 01326 270686 welcomes visitors and has showers and toilets.

4

Pasco's Boatyard, St Just-in-Roseland
Lat. 50.1819, Long. -5.0188.

Pascoe's Boatyard Jim Benney 01326 270269

CHARGES: £4.10/day

SUITABILITY: Large trailer needs a car.

ACCESS: All of tidal range. **TYPE OF RAMP:** Shallow concrete slipway.

UPPER AREA: Shingle. **LOWER AREA:** Mud.

DIRECTIONS: From Truro follow the A3078 towards St Mawes. Staying in St Just Lane, turn right onto a narrow road signposted St Just Church and Bar. The slipway is about 1 mile at St Just Creek, Pasco's Boatyard.

RAMP DESCRIPTION: Short ramp to beach suitable for cars, almost anytime but easiest near high water, gets muddy at low water so ask advice. Pay launching charge to Pascoe's boatyard. Can take boats up to 20 feet in length, longer by arrangement. PWCs prohibited. This site can get very busy in the summer. This location also suffers from strong southwest winds on occasion.

FACILITIES: Parking and toilets. Petrol and diesel in Mylor Harbour, 2 miles by sea. Shops in St Mawes (3 miles). Can be crowded weekends and Bank Holidays. Moorings available (£30 per week). Campsite at Tretham Mill (01872 580504).

HAZARDS: 5 knot restriction in Creek. Waterskiing is permitted in designated area.

Malpas Marine, Truro
Malpas Marine, Malpas, Truro, Cornwall, England TR1 1SQ

Lat. 50.2438, Long. -5.0275.

01872 271260

Truro Harbour Authority, Truro
Harbour Office Town Quay, Truro, Cornwall, England TR1 2HJ

Lat. 50.2621, Long. -5.0475.

01872 224231

Loe Beach, Feock
Lat. 50.2029, Long. -5.0480.

CHARGES: £6 for launch and recovery including parking.

SUITABILITY: Large trailer needs a car.

ACCESS: ½ tidal. **TYPE OF RAMP:** Concrete **UPPER AREA:** Shingle.

LOWER AREA: Sand.

DIRECTIONS: From Truro head towards Falmouth. Turn onto the B3289, following the sign posts to Feock. Just before you get to Feock turn right down a steep hill, sign posted to Loe Beach.

RAMP DESCRIPTION: Concrete ramp over a shingle beach and therefore often covered with a layer of shingle. If you need to launch with a car at low tide then you will need a 4 × 4 as you will have to reverse on to hard sand / shingle. Dinghies (wayfarer size) can easily be launched at all states of the tide by hand. Access to Loe beach is via a steep narrow lane. Jetskis are banned.

FACILITIES: Café, toilets and a water sports centre for sailing, windsurfing and kayaking lessons. You are right on the Carrick roads, so is ideal for when it is rough elsewhere, or for access up river to Truro. For beginners Loe Beach gives a really safe pool inside of the yacht moorings for learning to sail.

Public Slipway, Mylor
Lat. 50.1779, Long. -5.0548.

01326 372121

CHARGES: Free (marina £3).

SUITABILITY: Large trailer needs a car.

ACCESS: All of tidal range. **TYPE OF RAMP:** Shallow concrete slipway.

UPPER AREA: Harbour. **LOWER AREA:** Shingle.

DIRECTIONS: Follow A39 south from Truro 5 miles north Falmouth, past Devoran, left signposted Mylor Bridge, through Mylor Bridge follow south side of river to Mylor. Follow brown signs to Yacht Harbour. The slipway is just to the west of the marina.

RAMP DESCRIPTION: Excellent slipway recently built. Long and wide concrete slip with gentle gradient and a pontoon at the end of the slip. There is an additional slipway in the marina for which there is a £3 charge.

FACILITIES: Large parking area adjacent to the slip with a pay and display machine. Car park is locked in the evening. Mylor has an excellent chandlery only a few 100 yards away and there are public toilets. Marina has visitor moorings and a jet wash for cars and trailers. There is also the Ganges Restaurant which is highly recommended. Hose at top of slip for outboard / PWC flushing.

HAZARDS: 5 knot speed limit in Mylor Creek. Waterskiing is permitted in designated areas.

Mylor Yacht Harbour, Falmouth
Mylor, Falmouth, Cornwall, England TR11 5UF

Lat. 50.1771, Long. -5.0514.

01326 372121

Windsport Laser School, Mylor
Lat. 50.1770, Long. -5.0493.

01326 376191

SUITABILITY: Large trailer needs a car.

ACCESS: All of tidal range. **TYPE OF RAMP:** Concrete

UPPER AREA: Shingle. **LOWER AREA:** Shingle.

DIRECTIONS: Windsport International Laser School at Mylor Yacht Harbour near Mylor Bridge on Carrick Roads between Truro and Falmouth Cornwall.

RAMP DESCRIPTION: Safe launching was available at all states of the tide however, at low tide many large boulders are exposed and at high tide it may be difficult to access the dinghy park over the beach.

FACILITIES: Dinghy parking is available in a field about a quarter of a mile from the Laser School building, just off the beach and accessed via a reasonably steep ramp. The field is secured by a gate and padlock. Parking £17.00 per week. Cars are not normally allowed in the field (you could, at low tide, drive along the beach to deposit and retrieve boats from the park) but can be parked free, in the Mylor Yacht Harbour car park (normally about £5.00 per day) if you register with the Laser School. Parking in the yacht club car park could be expensive if you don't get a free pass from the school. It also gets quite busy at weekends.

HAZARDS: Boulders on the beach at low tide.

4

Flushing slipway, Falmouth

Lat. 50.1637, Long. -5.0702.

SUITABILITY: Large trailer needs a car.

ACCESS: ¼ tidal. **TYPE OF RAMP:** Cobble **UPPER AREA:** Harbour.
LOWER AREA: Unknown.

DIRECTIONS: Village of Flushing is opposite Falmouth. From Penryn, which is just north of Falmouth, follow the signs for Flushing.

RAMP DESCRIPTION: Ramp leads into small harbour that dries out at low tide.

FACILITIES: In the centre of quaint village of Flushing.

HAZARDS: 8 knot speed limit in inner harbour. Waterskiing permitted in designated areas in Falmouth Bay. PWCs prohibited.

Falmouth Marina, Falmouth

**North Parade, Falmouth, Cornwall, England
TR11 2TD**
Lat. 50.1637, Long. -5.0836.
01326 316620

Slipway, Falmouth Watersports Association

Lat. 50.1519, Long. -5.0634.
01326 312285

CHARGES: Launch/recovery is £10 per day. Trailer storage, if available, is £5 for 12 hours or £9 for 24. Once launched, it is advisable to moor up in the yacht haven across to the east of the harbour. This is gated and secure with toilets and showers and is run by the same company. Mooring fees apply. There is a petrol/diesel pontoon on the Yacht Haven with unleaded at £1.67 per litre!

SUITABILITY: Large trailer needs a car.

ACCESS: All of tidal range. **TYPE OF RAMP:** Full tidal range. Concrete upper and lower. Plenty of space to launch just about anything easily.

UPPER AREA: Concrete. **LOWER AREA:** Concrete.

DIRECTIONS: Entering Falmouth, follow the signs for the main DOCKS area. This will take you around the back of Falmouth town. Falmouth is composed of small streets and pedestrian areas which are inadvisable with a boat and trailer. Once at the dock entrance, take the road back towards town for approximately 1/3rd. mile. Go past mini roundabout and look for the entrance on your right after 100yds. If you see Trago Mills, you've gone past it. In front there is a dinghy storage compound and the gate is just prior to this. Once in, go straight forward to the Supervisors cabin which juts out from the end of the building on your left.

RAMP DESCRIPTION: Very large slip with a gentle slope. Wide enough to launch perhaps six or seven boats at once although it only has a small tie-up docking pontoon to the left hand side. The slip is concrete and the supervisors will help if required. In general, the supervisors were extremely helpful, cheerful and friendly

FACILITIES: There are toilets and some room for temporary storage of trailers. Parking trailers costs £5 up to 12 hours and £9 up to 24 hours. Trailer parking for more than 24 hours, if available, will be charged at £9 per day.

HAZARDS: The river Fal is tidal and can catch you out if you don't read the free set of tide tables given at the slip. If you want to go to Truro, the ferry times are a very good guide. There are times it doesn't go all the way so obviously avoid the same times. The river is buoyed for the deeper channel, but following the ferry all the way to Truro is an important navigational learning curve for spotting a decent course. Within Truro harbour you MUST follow the buoys correctly. A depth finder is invaluable in a tidal river such as this. Speed limits in the harbour and up the river. These are on a free sticker given when you launch and are 5, 8 & 10 knots respectively although there are waterskiing areas in the southern reaches of the river. Once clear of the harbour at Falmouth there are no speed limits. There is a chain-driven ferry half-way up the Fal. The King Harry Ferry. When it is moving, the front chains raise in the water. Cross only behind it or when it is at rest.

Port Pendennis Marina, Falmouth

**Challenger Quay, Falmouth, Cornwall, England
TR11 3YL**
Lat. 50.1515, Long. -5.0600.
01326 211211

Maen Porth Beach, Falmouth

Lat. 50.1261, Long. -5.0934.
Maen Porth Estate 01326 250605

SUITABILITY: Small trailer can be pushed.

ACCESS: All of tidal range. **TYPE OF RAMP:** Firm sandy beach.

UPPER AREA: Sand. **LOWER AREA:** Sand.

DIRECTIONS: On the beach at Maenporth.

RAMP DESCRIPTION: Firm sandy beach launch at all states of tide but 50 metre drag at low water. Unsuitable for car launch. Falmouth 2 miles.

FACILITIES: Parking space is limited. Car park, toilets, café, pub at head of beach.

Durgan Bay Ramp, Mawnan

Lat. 50.1038, Long. -5.1158.
National Trust 01326 250722

CHARGES: £5

SUITABILITY: Small trailer can be pushed.

ACCESS: ¾ tidal. **TYPE OF RAMP:** Concrete **UPPER AREA:** Sand.
LOWER AREA: Sand.

DIRECTIONS: Slipway is down between the cottages in the hamlet of Durgan.

RAMP DESCRIPTION: No boats over 16´ allowed to use the ramp, usable 4 hours either side high water. There may be a drop off at the end of the ramp. Not crowded. Slip is between two cottages and you may have to move dinghies to get through. Road is National Trust property. Pay due to warden in cottage. Durgan is a hamlet of five or six cottages, sheltered except from east.

FACILITIES: Parking space is limited. Parking at top of lane 400 yards. Fresh water at cottages, garage at Mawnan Smith (no petrol) and shops.

4

Helford Passage, Mawnan Smith

Lat. 50.1002, Long. -5.1286.

Nick Bailey 01326 250770

CHARGES: £7 by hand, £10 assisted launch.

SUITABILITY: Large trailer needs a car.

ACCESS: All of tidal range. **TYPE OF RAMP:** Concrete ramp onto sand.

UPPER AREA: Sand. **LOWER AREA:** Sand.

DIRECTIONS: From B3291 South of Falmouth take a left turn to Mawnan Smith. From village travel southwest 1.75 miles to Helford passage on north side of Helford river.

RAMP DESCRIPTION: Free to use if you are using local moorings. No cars are allowed onto the beach. If you can manhandle your boat the charge is £7. Larger boats will require an assisted launch with a local Landrover, cost £10. No Jetskis allowed. Beach can get crowded with high Spring tides.

FACILITIES: Very nice pub next to the slipway and the Shipwright Arms is across the river and has its own pontoon.

Gweek, Helston

Lat. 50.0951, Long. -5.2075.

01326 221657

CHARGES: Up to £16 for 18´ boat.

SUITABILITY: Large trailer needs a car.

ACCESS: ½ tidal. **TYPE OF RAMP:** Concrete **UPPER AREA:** Concrete.

LOWER AREA: Mud.

DIRECTIONS: From Falmouth on B3291. Gweek is East of Helston on the Helford River.

RAMP DESCRIPTION: Situated at the head of the Helford River. Access to river via a narrow channel - motoring recommended.

FACILITIES: Boat yard facilities. Showers, toilets, parking. Pub café and petrol in village. Boatyard also offers crane facilities.

HAZARDS: 6 knot speed limit on the Helford River.

Helford River Sailing Club, Helford

Lat. 50.0934, Long. -5.1360.

Helford River Sailing Club 01326 231460

CHARGES: Temporary membership: £35/week.

SUITABILITY: Large trailer needs a car.

ACCESS: ½ tidal. **TYPE OF RAMP:** Concrete to stones / mud.

UPPER AREA: Sand. **LOWER AREA:** Mud.

DIRECTIONS: Helford is to the East of Helston.

RAMP DESCRIPTION: Concrete ramp going across muddy sand. Pontoon at the ramp.

FACILITIES: Temporary membership gives use of club house with bar, restaurant, showers, laundry. You may not use the club car park, but there is public one close by. Shipwrights Arms in Helford (walking distance) and New Inn, Manaccan (10 minutes drive) recommended for food.

Slipway, Porthoustock Beach

Lat. 50.0555, Long. -5.0646.

CHARGES: None - Donation to beach maintenance fund via donation box on exit.

SUITABILITY: Large trailer needs a car.

ACCESS: All of tidal range. **TYPE OF RAMP:** Shingle and hard sand.

UPPER AREA: Rock. **LOWER AREA:** Shingle.

DIRECTIONS: From Helston Head towards St Keverne. Follow the road out of St Keverne down into Porthoustock signposted. Care is needed as the road is narrow. Just before you reach the beach the road is quite steep with a tight left hand bend at the bottom. Well worth the effort though!

RAMP DESCRIPTION: Big wide ramp regularly flattened by JCB, access at all states of tide. Local dive school, Dive Action, will assist with a tractor launch for beer money if needed.

FACILITIES: Petrol approximately 3 miles at the Zoar Garage other side of St Keverne. 2 local pubs in St Keverne. Toilets at top of beach, camping, accommodation plentiful.

HAZARDS: None but be careful of divers in the water when departing and returning to slip. Safe overnight mooring in the sheltered bay.

Harbour slipway, Mullion Cove

Lat. 50.0150, Long. -5.2582.

CHARGES: September 09 - £5 per boat plus £5 per person on board.

SUITABILITY: Large trailer needs a car.

ACCESS: ¾ tidal. **TYPE OF RAMP:** Concrete **UPPER AREA:** Harbour.

LOWER AREA: Shingle.

DIRECTIONS: Take the A3083 south from Helston. After 8 miles turn right at the village of Penhale. Follow road for a couple of miles to the coast.

RAMP DESCRIPTION: Excellent wide ramp with a good slope leading into the harbour.

FACILITIES: Slipway is in the centre of the small fishing village of Mullion Cove.

Slipway, Porthleven

Lat. 50.0853, Long. -5.3165.

01326 574270

CHARGES: Slip fee £12 (Summer 2005)

SUITABILITY: Large trailer needs a car.

ACCESS: ½ tidal. **TYPE OF RAMP:** Concrete **UPPER AREA:** Concrete.

LOWER AREA: Harbour.

DIRECTIONS: From Helston take the B3304 for 3 miles to Porthleven. Slipway is at the head of the harbour. Slipway is most inland section of harbour.

RAMP DESCRIPTION: Wide concrete slipway with a good gradient leading into a harbour. Available 2-3 hours either side of high water. Outside that time, a 4WD drive vehicle is required on the hard mud.

FACILITIES: Local shops and tackle/bait shop on quay.

HAZARDS: Heavy Atlantic swells can cause a problem so check forecasts.

Marazion Beach, Penzance

Lat. 50.1237, Long. -5.4764.

CHARGES: None

SUITABILITY: Small trailer can be pushed.

ACCESS: All of tidal range. **TYPE OF RAMP:** Concrete to hard sandy beach. **UPPER AREA:** Concrete. **LOWER AREA:** Sand.

4

DIRECTIONS: Ramp is adjacent to car park behind North St.
RAMP DESCRIPTION: Ramp drops onto hard sand of beach. Beach shelves gently and is quite shallow.
FACILITIES: All facilities available nearby in Marazion.

Harbour Slip, Penzance

Lat. 50.1198, Long. -5.5311.
Harbourmaster 01736 366113

CHARGES: £12.00, pay harbourmaster if around. Harbourmaster's office is the other side of the harbour.
SUITABILITY: Large trailer needs a car.
ACCESS: ½ tidal. **TYPE OF RAMP:** Concrete slipway.
UPPER AREA: Harbour. **LOWER AREA:** Mud.
DIRECTIONS: Follow A30 into town, going past the train station then turning left past the bus station. Site is 100 metres on the right by the sailing club in the corner of the car park.
RAMP DESCRIPTION: Wide concrete ramp that leads into the harbour. There is a dredged channel next to the harbour wall.
FACILITIES: The slipway is next to the car park which also caters for trailers. There is a tap and hose at the head of the slipway. Penzance has all the usual facilities and the Harbour Garage (01736 366406) caters for long term parking if you plan to go further afield e.g. the Scilly Islands. There are several good chandleries in Penzance.
HAZARDS: There is a 5 knot speed limit in the harbour. Waterskiing is allowed offshore. PWCs must observe the speed limit in the harbour.

Harbour slipway, Newlyn

Lat. 50.1016, Long. -5.5455.
SUITABILITY: Large trailer needs a car.
ACCESS: All of tidal range. **TYPE OF RAMP:** Concrete
UPPER AREA: Harbour. **LOWER AREA:** Harbour.
DIRECTIONS: The fishing port of Newlyn is 2 miles to the south west of Penzance. The slipway is tucked in behind the shed on the southern breakwater.
RAMP DESCRIPTION: Steep concrete ramp into the harbour. Gateway at the top of the slipway may require careful manoeuvring for larger boats.
FACILITIES: Busy fishing harbour.

Harbour slipway, Mousehole

Lat. 50.0822, Long. -5.5385.
SUITABILITY: Large trailer needs a car.
ACCESS: Unknown. **TYPE OF RAMP:** Concrete **UPPER AREA:** Harbour.
LOWER AREA: Harbour.
DIRECTIONS: The village of Mousehole is 3 miles south of Penzance. The slipway is at the southern end of the harbour.
RAMP DESCRIPTION: Wide concrete ramp. Often obstructed with boats and parked cars.
FACILITIES: Fishing village of Mousehole.
HAZARDS: Check the charts before leaving harbour. Lots of rocks near the entrance.

Harbour Slipway, Lamorna Cove

Lat. 50.0618, Long. -5.5639.

CHARGES: Now £10 per day
SUITABILITY: Large trailer needs a car.
ACCESS: ½ tidal. **TYPE OF RAMP:** Concrete **UPPER AREA:** Harbour.
LOWER AREA: Concrete.
DIRECTIONS: Lamorna Cove is 4 miles south of Penzance. The road down to the cove is very steep, very narrow and winding. It is one vehicle width and anyone meeting you pulling your trailer will have to back a long way up or down.
RAMP DESCRIPTION: Ramp has a sharp turn and may be difficult for larger boats. The ramp leads to a very small, not particularly well sheltered area inside the small harbour wall. In a force 2/3 wind, the waves were washing up the slip enough to make it difficult. The lady at the shop says that many divers launch there with large RIB boats. I think this would be useful for bouncing off the harbour wall. No fastening rings/cleats were visible. Not even a rusty one.
FACILITIES: Small harbour. Shop and café (very friendly and knowledgeable), good public toilets across the bay (75 yards). The café has now built an extension which blocks access to the area previously used to park trailers, which makes boat launching much more problematic.
HAZARDS: Lots of rocks in the small bay. Harbour relatively unsheltered from waves in an easterly.

St Marys, Isles of Scilly

Lat. 49.9150, Long. -6.3154.
CHARGES: Charges apply.
SUITABILITY: Large trailer needs a car.
ACCESS: ½ tidal. **TYPE OF RAMP:** Concrete onto sand.
UPPER AREA: Harbour. **LOWER AREA:** Sand.
DIRECTIONS: In the middle of Hugh Town harbour on the Island of St Mary's.
RAMP DESCRIPTION: Good condition concrete ramp onto the beach. Ideal for launch a sailing dinghy. Unless you are very adventurous you will want to bring any dinghy over on the Scillonian. Local cruising opportunities would make this a worthwhile venture. Otherwise it is 36 miles to Penzance.
FACILITIES: Slipway is in the centre of Hugh Town with all the usual facilities. No quayside petrol except in own cans from pump behind big building on quay. Expect to pay more for petrol than on the mainland as it has to be imported at extra cost. Petrol can be supplied in volume for very large ribs and powerboats at the quayside by arrangement.
HAZARDS: Shallow water and rocks can catch out the unwary. Also very heavy swell outside the protection of the islands.

Harbour slipway, Sennen Cove

Lat. 50.0778, Long. -5.7043.

CHARGES: None. But there may be a charge for the tractor if required.
SUITABILITY: Large trailer needs a car.
ACCESS: ½ tidal. **TYPE OF RAMP:** Concrete **UPPER AREA:** Harbour.
LOWER AREA: Sand.
DIRECTIONS: Sennen Cove is just to the north of Lands End. Take the A30 to Lands End and turn right 2 miles before Lands End to Sennen

4

The Good Launch Guide

Cove. The hill that winds down to the cove is VERY steep (approx. 1 in 4 or 5). Engage low gear (1st.) and descend carefully, especially with an unbraked trailer.

RAMP DESCRIPTION: Concrete ramp leading onto the sandy harbour. Beyond the black and white marker attached to the wall on the left, the ramp dips dramatically downwards onto the sand. I would approach it very carefully with a 4 × 4 and certainly not risk it with a front wheel drive car. There is a tractor parked between two adjacent buildings with a trailer attachment on the front so I guess this must be available although no-one was around at the time I went. The approach to the harbour slip is through a couple of tight chicane type bends of one vehicle width around various buildings and this is two-way traffic because of the car park above the slip.

FACILITIES: Village of Sennen Cove. Small harbour large pay & display car park at head of ramp. Inadvertently parked vehicles may make turning/reversing with a trailer difficult if busy.

HAZARDS: Notice on breakwater reads, 'Extreme danger, Keep off the breakwater at all times'. Currents and tidal races around the headlands.

Old Lifeboat slipway, St Ives
Lat. 50.2147, Long. -5.4793.
01736 795018

CHARGES: Approximately £10
SUITABILITY: Large trailer needs a car.
ACCESS: ¼ tidal. **TYPE OF RAMP:** Concrete ramp. **UPPER AREA:** Sand.
LOWER AREA: Sand.
DIRECTIONS: From A30 Take A3074 towards St Ives. Ignore signs for tourist parking and head to town centre and harbour. Ramp is half way along Wharf road (on right hand side) opposite Sloop Inn. Note one way system through St Ives that can prove challenging if pulling a larger trailer.
RAMP DESCRIPTION: Shallow ramp (at present it is completely covered by hard sand). Harbour beach sand is generally hard but check with harbourmaster as some soft spots have been known. Ramp must be kept clear at all times.
FACILITIES: Sloop Inn opposite ramp. Petrol ½ mile outside town. Toilets behind Sloop Inn. Parking close by, but to get to all parking there are a number of very narrow streets to negotiate.
HAZARDS: To left of ramp looking out to sea, various fishing boats moored in ropes that criss-cross harbour. 5 mph limit in harbour. No water skiing in harbour. No PWC in harbour.

Harbour Slip, Hayle
Lat. 50.1891, Long. -5.4235.

CHARGES: Yearly membership fee of £85.00 covers all launch fees.
SUITABILITY: Large trailer needs a car.
ACCESS: ¾ tidal. **TYPE OF RAMP:** Concrete **UPPER AREA:** Harbour.
LOWER AREA: Mud.
DIRECTIONS: From the High Street in Hayle look out for an old iron swing bridge. Cross over the bridge and the launch site is immediately on the left. As you enter Hayle harbour area you will see customs house (white building). Directly opposite this buiding is the designated slipway. Strictly members only but week membership available on request. Must hold insurance and display Datatage number on hull above waterline.

RAMP DESCRIPTION: This is one of the best slipways in the area and is can get busy. Fairly steep but wide enough to launch two craft at same time or other crafts such as fishing vessels or power boats. Shared with other clubs, sailing and canoe.
FACILITIES: Lots of parking. Garage within walking distance. There is also a sea side town with café; and shops nearby.
HAZARDS: Normal harbour restrictions and hazards like other water users, marker buoys and speed limit of 5 knots until out of mouth of estuary. Also at low tide there is a sand bar, tidal changes are quite rapid. Contact harbour officials for more information.

Harbour slipway, Portreath
Lat. 50.2612, Long. -5.2891.
SUITABILITY: Large trailer needs a car.
ACCESS: Unknown. **TYPE OF RAMP:** Concrete **UPPER AREA:** Harbour.
LOWER AREA: Harbour.
DIRECTIONS: Take the B3300 north from Redruth. Go 3 miles to Portreath. The slipway is at the head of the narrow harbour.
RAMP DESCRIPTION: Width of the boat that can use the ramp is restricted by the built up harbour walls on either side of the slipway.
FACILITIES: Slipway is in the centre of the town of Portreath.

Harbour Slip, Newquay
Lat. 50.4170, Long. -5.0870.
01637 872809

CHARGES: £2.50
SUITABILITY: Large trailer needs a car.
ACCESS: ¼ tidal. **TYPE OF RAMP:** Shallow granite slipway onto beach.
UPPER AREA: Concrete. **LOWER AREA:** Sand.
DIRECTIONS: Site is North East of town and access is via narrow and steep road. Access can be very congested in the summer.
RAMP DESCRIPTION: 4 wheel drive vehicles are recommended for launching over beach. Breaking waves can prevent launching. Safety equipment must be carried on board and a safety briefing from the harbourmaster is required.
FACILITIES: Boats cannot be left overnight. Petrol, toilets parking.
HAZARDS: 4 knot speed limit in the harbour. Waterskiing allowed 400 metres off beaches but PWCs are prohibited.

Harbour Slip, Padstow
Lat. 50.5412, Long. -4.9370.
Padstow Harbour 01841 532239

CHARGES: Harbour dues payable.
SUITABILITY: Large trailer needs a car.
ACCESS: ½ tidal. **TYPE OF RAMP:** Concrete ramp onto mud at low tide
UPPER AREA: Concrete. **LOWER AREA:** Mud.
DIRECTIONS: Ramp goes into the outer harbour and is behind the Harbour Office on the southern side of the harbour.
RAMP DESCRIPTION: Slipway into the harbour with high wall on either side. Needs skilful reversing and very wide boats may have a problem. Restricted by tide and the harbour dries out.
FACILITIES: Toilets and showers in the harbour office. Parking available.

HAZARDS: Overall speed limit of 40 knots in whole of Harbour Commissioner controlled estuary. 8 knot currents near Ferry Point, Doom bar takes lives most years! Polzeath is a surfing beach controlled by lifeguards so stay well away.

Padstow Harbour, Padstow

Padstow Harbour Commissioners, Harbour Office, Padstow, Cornwall, England PL28 8AQ
Lat. 50.5416, Long. -4.9384.
01841 532239

Rock Sailing Club Slip, Wadebridge

Lat. 50.5434, Long. -4.9202.
Rock SC: 01208 862431

CHARGES: Free to launch but harbour dues MUST be paid prior to launching. A ski number (licence) is required to use the ski area £36 pa or £25 for 2 weeks. Mooring available at approx £10 per day.
SUITABILITY: Large trailer needs a car.
ACCESS: ¾ tidal. **TYPE OF RAMP:** Slip onto firm sand, soft mud at end. **UPPER AREA:** Sand. **LOWER AREA:** Mud.
DIRECTIONS: Through Rock village, close to Mariners Motel.
RAMP DESCRIPTION: There are two launching areas; one at Rock Sailing Club and one at Ferry Point at the end of the road. The Sailing Club has facilities for members only - temporary membership is available except during August. At Ferry Point there are a total of three slipways. Best to launch at half tide when there is plenty of hard sand/stone beach space for turning and a gently sloping wide beach. Avoid launching in season when the sailing races are starting i.e. 1 hour before high water as you will be unable to find a space at the waters edge. Light dinghies can be launched and stored at Ferry Point 450 yards further to seaward adjacent to Quarry car park. Spring low tide exposes soft sticky mud - best avoided. Daily, weekly of annual rates for harbour due depend on boat size and power. Cheap rate is for boat up to 10 hp, more for power boats. Pay beachmaster at top of slip.
FACILITIES: Public toilets facilities are sited in Quarry car park near ferry point. Free car parking on the road but this will be full by 9.30am in July and August. Chargeable parking is available at Ferry Point. There is no parking on the beach except for trailers which will be completely immersed on Spring high tides. Fresh water at Rock Sailing Club. Nearest petrol is at Clock Garage some 1 mile up the road so fill up as you pass on the way in.
HAZARDS: Overall speed limit of 40 knots in whole of Harbour Commissioner controlled estuary. - 8 knot currents near Ferry Point, Doom bar takes lives most years! Polzeath is a surfing beach controlled by lifeguards so stay well away.

Slipway, Port Quin

Lat. 50.5890, Long. -4.8676.
01208 880586

CHARGES: Per day kayaks £2, all other £10. Per week, kayaks £10, all others £25
SUITABILITY: Large trailer needs a car.
ACCESS: ¼ tidal. **TYPE OF RAMP: UPPER AREA:** Harbour.
LOWER AREA: Rock.
DIRECTIONS: Port Quin, near Padstow, Cornwall

RAMP DESCRIPTION: Concrete slipway into harbour. Key to the slipway can be obtained from the food trailer if open.

Slipway, Port Gaverne

Lat. 50.5928, Long. -4.8229.
CHARGES: Pay at pub. £5 per launch or £15 per year.
SUITABILITY: Large trailer needs a car.
ACCESS: No Ramp. **TYPE OF RAMP: UPPER AREA:** Concrete.
LOWER AREA: Sand.
DIRECTIONS: NO JETSKIS - National Trust owned beach.
RAMP DESCRIPTION: Ramp onto shingle and sand beach. Few places to park. Steep access on roads from each direction. Soft sand.
FACILITIES: Few - a good pub.

Slipway, Boscastle

Lat. 50.6908, Long. -4.6962.
CHARGES: £5/day - see harbour master
SUITABILITY: Large trailer needs a car.
ACCESS: Unknown. **TYPE OF RAMP:** Concrete / stone onto harbour bed (rocky / stone / weed) **UPPER AREA:** Harbour. **LOWER AREA:** Shingle.
RAMP DESCRIPTION: Slipway either side of river. Slip on left hand side is old, slip on right hand side is better. Trailer and car parking in main village car park (gets really busy in summer). Sand bar across harbour mouth restricts launching to +/- 2hrs around high water.
FACILITIES: In village - fuel at top of village on Tintagel road
HAZARDS: Plenty

Slipway, Crackington Haven

Lat. 50.7409, Long. -4.6333.
SUITABILITY: Large trailer needs a car.
ACCESS: No Ramp. **TYPE OF RAMP: UPPER AREA:** Shingle.
LOWER AREA: Sand.
RAMP DESCRIPTION: Beach with access at either side of river. LHS access is best. RHS access is steep. Biggest problem is that this is a tourist beach with a large shingle ridge. Soft sand. Steep ridge. Not for the faint-hearted.

Harbour slipway, Bude

Lat. 50.8295, Long. -4.5525.
Kevin 07789 033573

CHARGES: £17 per week.
SUITABILITY: Large trailer needs a car.
ACCESS: Unknown. **TYPE OF RAMP: UPPER AREA:** Unknown.
LOWER AREA: Unknown.
RAMP DESCRIPTION: Slipway in the inshore lifeboat slipway. Before launching go and see Diane at local tourist office which is in main Bude Car park (by rowing boat lake) pay your £17.00 for one week and receive a key which removes the bollard blocking the slipway.
FACILITIES: Village of Bude
HAZARDS: Keep an eye on tides, low lying beach shallows out really quickly.

4

Harbour Slip, Appledore
Lat. 51.0549, Long. -4.1914.
Phil Hammond 01271 831439 or 07717 764676

CHARGES: None
SUITABILITY: Large trailer needs a car.
ACCESS: ¾ tidal. **TYPE OF RAMP:** Concrete **UPPER AREA:** Concrete.
LOWER AREA: Sand.
DIRECTIONS: Approach from A39 main Bideford bypass. At Bideford roundabout follow sign for Northam and then Appledore. All the way into Appledore, beyond the Quay. Large public car park and slip on right hand side.
RAMP DESCRIPTION: Sheltered and well maintained. Jetskis have come under a lot of pressure on this slip and signs have been put up saying "The use and launching of Jetskis in this area is banned." Not entirely true....... Jetskiers do use this slip but the local council have no way of enforcement, so you can imagine.....bedlam on the slip. The local Taw and Torridge Estuary Forum in partnership with Northern Devon Coastal and Countryside services do have a registration system but basically if you're going to launch a Jetski/PWC from Appledore you need to belong to the local Jetski club (insurance mandatory) and have your craft registered. Contact Phil Hammond 01271 831439 or 07717 764676 for club details.
FACILITIES: Slipway is part of car park with toilet facilities. Close to shops.

Slipway, Crow Point
Lat. 51.0763, Long. -4.1856.

CHARGES: £3.00 for car and trailer to park, no actual launch fees.
SUITABILITY: Large trailer needs a car.
ACCESS: No Ramp. **TYPE OF RAMP:** Sand beach. **UPPER AREA:** Sand.
LOWER AREA: Sand.
DIRECTIONS: From Braunton head towards Crow Point (signposted).
RAMP DESCRIPTION: Launch/recover at any time, 2 hours before/after high tide. Drive onto beach, unload, and then park your car/trailer in the car park.
FACILITIES: No facilities bring everything you need for a day on the water.
HAZARDS: Bideford bar can be a hazard, but makes for an enjoyable time on a Jetski!

Harbour Slip, Ilfracombe Harbour
Lat. 51.2097, Long. -4.1111.
Harbourmaster 01271 862108

CHARGES: £10 registration fee only.
SUITABILITY: Large trailer needs a car.
ACCESS: ½ tidal. **TYPE OF RAMP:** Concrete onto hard sand.
UPPER AREA: Harbour. **LOWER AREA:** Sand.
DIRECTIONS: Ramp goes into the harbour near to the lifeboat station.
RAMP DESCRIPTION: Concrete slipway onto hard sand. Launch and retrieve 2½ hours either side of high water. The slipway is also used by the lifeboat. Be prepared to clear the slipway in an emergency. Access gates are closed when tides are over 9.6 metres high. You must contact the harbourmaster before use. PWCs are allowed. Registration fee and proof of insurance. Speed limit inside harbour. Ilfracombe YC 01271 863969.
FACILITIES: Very busy resort in the summer months making parking for cars and trailers very difficult. Visitor's moorings, showers and toilets are available on payment of harbour dues.
HAZARDS: 4 knot speed restriction in harbour.

Slipway, Watermouth Cove
Lat. 51.2145, Long. -4.0695.
Harbourmaster 01271 865422

CHARGES: £4.50/day, £13/week.
SUITABILITY: Large trailer needs a car.
ACCESS: All of tidal range. **TYPE OF RAMP:** Concrete onto sand.
UPPER AREA: Concrete. **LOWER AREA:** Shingle.
DIRECTIONS: Watermouth Cove is to the east of Ilfracombe on the A361. Slipway is at the head of the cove.
RAMP DESCRIPTION: Concrete slipway onto hard surface. Launch and retrieve at any state of the tide. May have to go over gravel at very low water, quite few bumpy lumpy stony bits at low water, but solid everywhere. JCB on site to rescue stranded cars if necessary. Checked 15/09/09- Jetskis now not allowed.
FACILITIES: Plenty of parking for cars and trailers. Moorings available. From 2003 it should have toilets and showers and hot and cold drinks and chandlery. Local yacht club also offers facilities for visitors. Atermouth Yacht Club open Friday and Saturday evenings during summer, just Fridays in winter.
HAZARDS: Mouth of the cove has very strong currents at Spring tide. Check tides before leaving.

Porlock Weir, Minehead
Lat. 51.2198, Long. -3.6266.

SUITABILITY: Large trailer needs a car.
ACCESS: ¼ tidal. **TYPE OF RAMP:** Gravel and shingle.
UPPER AREA: Mud. **LOWER AREA:** Mud.
DIRECTIONS: Approach from east on A39 to Lynton. At Porlock, signs to Porlock Weir at west end of bay. Not advised to approach from west with trailer on A39, hills of 1 in 4.
RAMP DESCRIPTION: Basically a shingle hard which is quite muddy.
FACILITIES: Charges for parking. No sleeping in cars. Park within 100 metres of slip. Slip water tap.
HAZARDS: Sailing can be affected by high cliffs in the area.

Harbour Slip, Minehead
Lat. 51.2128, Long. -3.4746.
Harbourmaster 01643 702566

CHARGES: £2.50
SUITABILITY: Large trailer needs a car.
ACCESS: ½ tidal. **TYPE OF RAMP:** Steep concrete.
UPPER AREA: Harbour. **LOWER AREA:** Sand.
DIRECTIONS: Access from A39. At Minehead go towards the seafront turn West.
RAMP DESCRIPTION: A steep concrete slipway with a slight bend, onto sand. Launch and retrieve 2 hours either side of high water. Harbour dries at low water. It is possible to drive onto the soft sand and launch at lower tide. Best to ask local advice. Summer Sundays can be busy.

4

FACILITIES: Visitor's moorings available. Loading steps at end of quay. Ladders along quay wall. Freshwater available. Parking nearby.
HAZARDS: Sailing is affected by high cliffs.

Beach Slip, Blue Anchor
Lat. 51.1830, Long. -3.3881.

CHARGES: None
SUITABILITY: Small trailer can be pushed.
ACCESS: ¼ tidal. **TYPE OF RAMP:** Concrete onto sand.
UPPER AREA: Harbour. **LOWER AREA:** Sand.
DIRECTIONS: On the sea front at Blue Anchor to the east of the railway station. Blue Anchor is between Minehead and Watchet.
RAMP DESCRIPTION: A narrow cobblestone ramp that runs down the side of the sea wall takes you onto the beach. Take care of the rocky outcrops on the beach.
FACILITIES: Limited parking, toilets on seafront.

Harbour Slip, Watchet
Lat. 51.1831, Long. -3.3305.
Harbourmaster 01984 631264

CHARGES: £5
SUITABILITY: Large trailer needs a car.
ACCESS: ½ tidal. **TYPE OF RAMP:** Concrete **UPPER AREA:** Sand.
LOWER AREA: Mud.
DIRECTIONS: Access via A39 from Bridgewater. Follow signs to Watchet. Watchet slip is at end of Swain Street by museum.
RAMP DESCRIPTION: Two good slipways available, one leading into the marina and one on the inside of the western breakwater. No Jetskis allowed. It is possible to launch at all states of the tide but you won't be able to get out of the harbour due to the sill.
FACILITIES: Loading steps at end of west pier. Ladders along west pier wall. Car and trailer parking nearby in pay and display car park and marina car park.
HAZARDS: Harbour entrance can be dangerous in strong westerly winds.

Watchet Harbour Marina, Watchet
Harbour Road, Watchet, Somerset, England TA23 0AQ
Lat. 51.1827, Long. -3.3292.
01 984 631 264

Slipway, Combwich
Lat. 51.1737, Long. -3.0597.

CHARGES: Free
SUITABILITY: Small trailer can be pushed.
ACCESS: ¼ tidal. **TYPE OF RAMP: UPPER AREA:** Concrete.
LOWER AREA: Mud.
HAZARDS: Extreme high and low tides, many mud banks

Slipway, Burnham-on-Sea
Lat. 51.2345, Long. -3.0006.
Tourist office 01278 787852

CHARGES: £10 in 2002. £50 per year in 2009

SUITABILITY: Large trailer needs a car.
ACCESS: ¼ tidal. **TYPE OF RAMP:** Wooden slipway onto concrete.
UPPER AREA: Sand. **LOWER AREA:** Mud.
DIRECTIONS: Ramp is at the jetty at the southern end of the sea front by the lifeboat station. Tourist office is next door.
RAMP DESCRIPTION: Wooden slipway (15cwt weight limit) leading to concrete slip. Launch and retrieve 2 to 2 ½ hours either side of high water. Soft sand and mud either side of the slipway. It is wise not to drive onto the sand / mud. There are rocks at the end of the slip way and a very big drop. Tourist office issue launching permits. Normally someone is on the slip, gets very congested as the tide runs out.
FACILITIES: Parking nearby in the supermarket car park but along the front is better but gets full.
HAZARDS: Do your navigational homework if you are new to this venue. It is easy to get caught out here, especially on Spring tides coupled with northerly winds.

Uphill Boat Centre, Weston-super-Mare
Uphill Wharf, Weston-super-Mare, North Somerset, England BS23 4XR
Lat. 51.3194, Long. -2.9843.
01934 418617

Uphill Boat Centre, Uphill, Weston-super-Mare
Lat. 51.3213, Long. -2.9852.
01934 418617

CHARGES: Slip charges: Hauling out and relaunching on hydraulic travel hoist into yards, £3.30 per. ft. hull length, each operation, blocking up additional charge, all plus vat. Self launching and recovery allowed. Hauling out and relaunching, as above but from or onto transport and trailers, £3.90 per. ft. Owners use of slipway, unto 25 ft. length, £19.00, all inc. vat. Small craft and ski-boats in and out on one tide, £7.50, incl. parking for 1 car only, incl. vat. Special rates available for use of slipways and pontoons over weekends. Dry-out on slipway and scrubbing, 1 tide and 1 tide on pontoons, max. 30 ft. £18.00 inc. vat.
SUITABILITY: Large trailer needs a car.
ACCESS: ¼ tidal. **TYPE OF RAMP:** Concrete ramp for launching and recovery, also to dry out for scrub and repaint between tides. Pontoons alongside for use as required. Car parking available, toilets and shower block on site. Camping area for camper vans and tents.
UPPER AREA: Concrete. **LOWER AREA:** Mud.
DIRECTIONS: When approaching Weston-super-Mare, nr. Bristol, by the Motorway, turn off at the first signposted Junction and when approaching Weston-super-Mare look out for signposting to Uphill Beach and Sands, this will bring you by our yard. Look out for sign, Uphill Boat centre, on your left.
RAMP DESCRIPTION: A decent slipway giving access to the River Axe just off Weston Bay with access to tidal waters in the Bristol Channel.
FACILITIES: Pontoons and storage facilities in a yard area sited alongside a tidal river in a nature reserve. Enclosed lake area with pontoons for craft in use for short stay and weekending when laid up. Chandlery, engine repairs, welding and fabrication. See our web site www.uphillboatcentre.co.uk

4

HAZARDS: No known hazards, the River Axe is marked with navigational buoys.

Knightstone slip, Weston-super-Mare
Lat. 51.3515, Long. -2.9864.
Seafront Ranger 01934 621802

CHARGES: An annual permit scheme is now in operation. Both annual permits and day permits are available from the Tourist Information Centre on the sea front (proof of insurance required), contact 634543
SUITABILITY: Large trailer needs a car.
ACCESS: ¼ tidal. **TYPE OF RAMP:** Wide concrete. **UPPER AREA:** Sand.
LOWER AREA: Sand.
DIRECTIONS: Opposite Knightstone Island at the northern end of the bay.
RAMP DESCRIPTION: A large wide concrete slipway onto a hard surface. Launch and retrieve 2 hours either side of high water.
FACILITIES: Car parking in Pay and Display a few minutes walk from the slipway. Trailers can be left on the promenade next to the slipway. Island. Slipway is close to town centre.

Slipway, Clevedon
Lat. 51.4417, Long. -2.8552.
SUITABILITY: Small trailer can be pushed.
ACCESS: ½ tidal. **TYPE OF RAMP: UPPER AREA:** Unknown.
LOWER AREA: Unknown.
RAMP DESCRIPTION: The slipway is steep, narrow and has a nasty near 90 degree bend on it about one third the way down. If you are going to use it, smaller boats only. Launch and retrieve 2½ hours either side of high water.
FACILITIES: Parking is difficult, cars are not permitted on the promenade beach, and wardens are on patrol and have been known to call the police. Visitors can use the club facilities.

Portishead Quays Marina, Portishead
The Docks, Portishead, North Somerset, England BS20 7DE
Lat. 51.4914, Long. -2.7572.
01275 841941

Portishead Marina, Portishead
Lat. 51.4891, Long. -2.7599.
VHF 80 or 01275 841941
SUITABILITY: Large trailer needs a car.
ACCESS: All of tidal range. **TYPE OF RAMP:** Concrete
UPPER AREA: Concrete. **LOWER AREA:** Concrete.
DIRECTIONS: Portishead Quays Marina is conveniently located three miles from Junction 19 of the M5. Follow the signs to Portishead Marina. Will need to report to Marina control near the lock gates.
RAMP DESCRIPTION: The slipway is open 9am till 4pm Monday to Fridays (not bank holidays) with assisted launching with a tractor only on offer. Launch & recovery, locking fee, trailer storage and use of facilities - price per day £50.00
FACILITIES: 250 Sheltered and secure pontoon berths. 24 hour staffing. Better than 50% tidal access. Gasoil (red diesel - not for road use) and unleaded petrol available on the fuel pontoon. Toilets, showers, laundry and telephones are all available in the Control Building and in temporary facilities in the boatyard. Water and electricity (240 volts) is available on all pontoons. A full boatyard service is provided. Trained, qualified staff operates our 35T mobile hoist. Storage facilities are available in the boatyard. Chandlery, boat sales, boat and engine repair and rigging services are provided on site. Two cafés are also available. Car parking is available on site.

Marina Slip, Bristol
Lat. 51.4477, Long. -2.6093.
0117 9213198

CHARGES: Up to 3m £5.10 (min). Additional charge for longer boats, example 5m £8.50.
SUITABILITY: Large trailer needs a car.
ACCESS: Non-tidal. **TYPE OF RAMP:** Wide concrete, 1 in 6 gradient throughout, max depth 1.5m **UPPER AREA:** Harbour.
LOWER AREA: Harbour.
DIRECTIONS: Follow the signs for SS Great Britain in the Historic Ship Yard at Bristol. The marina is in Hanover Place off Cumberland Road.
RAMP DESCRIPTION: It is a very good slip with a good gradient into the Floating Harbour in Bristol. Launching fee includes launching, parking for car and trailer, river and harbour fees to Hanham Lock (about 8 miles upstream of Bristol) and locking fees giving access to the tidal River Avon and Bristol Channel. There is another slipway at the Underfall Yard near to the offices of the Harbourmaster. The charges are the same as for the Bristol Marina but the slipway is not as large and only really suitable for dinghies. You will need to produce your insurance certificate to the marina office or the harbourmaster or you will be charged approximately £7 a day in addition. To get to the Bristol Channel you will need to get through the lock which operates 3 hours before high tide. Last chance to get back is at high tide. Lockkeeper listens on Channel 14. Speed on River Avon - 9 knots and its 5 miles to the sea - Avonmouth Radio has CCTV cameras along the stretch.
FACILITIES: Marina with diesel at quay, petrol nearby. Also a chandlery. Pontoon next to the launch ramp (not the one on the left that belongs to the rowing club). A very well equipped site.
HAZARDS: Speed restrictions in the docks and in the River Avon.

Bristol Marina, Bristol
Hanover Place, Bristol, Bristol, England BS1 6UH
Lat. 51.4481, Long. -2.6107.
0117 921 3198

Sailing Club, Shirehampton
Lat. 51.4862, Long. -2.6771.

CHARGES: Launch fee payable.
SUITABILITY: Small trailer can be pushed.
ACCESS: ¼ tidal. **TYPE OF RAMP: UPPER AREA:** Unknown.
LOWER AREA: Unknown.
RAMP DESCRIPTION: Prior arrangement required. Small concrete / stone slipway. Spring tides only, launch and retrieve 1½ hours either side of high water.
FACILITIES: Cars and trailers kept in a secure compound.

INLAND SLIPWAYS
alphabetical by place name

Bath Marina, Bath
Brassmill Lane, Bath, Somerset, England BA1 3JT
Lat. 51.3896, Long. -2.4068.
01225 424301

Saltford Marina, Bristol
The Shallows, Saltford, Bristol, Avon, England BS31 3EZ
Lat. 51.3994, Long. -2.4486.
01225 872226

C Fletcher, Devizes
Foxhanger Wharf, Lower Fox Hangers, Rowde, Devizes, Wiltshire, England SN10 1SS
Lat. 51.3537, Long. -2.0501.
01380 828254

Devizes Marina, Devizes
Horton Avenue, Devizes, Wilts, England SN10 2RH
Lat. 51.3616, Long. -1.9664.
01380 725300

Devizes Wharf, Devizes
Lat. 51.3552, Long. -1.9985.
0380 721279

CHARGES: Yes - seasonal.
SUITABILITY: Large trailer needs a car.
ACCESS: Non-tidal. **TYPE OF RAMP:** Concrete
UPPER AREA: Unknown. **LOWER AREA:** Unknown.
DIRECTIONS: On Kennet Avon Canal close to the famous Devizes staircase of locks. Entering Devizes from the northwest (A342 / A361) at Wadworths Brewery turn left and after 150 yards turn left again signposted Wharf and Theatre. Slip water tap.
RAMP DESCRIPTION: Gradient is gentle.
FACILITIES: Overnight parking available. Parking space is for 100 + cars. Licence needed.

Jet Ski South West, Evercreech
Lat. 51.1518, Long. -2.5205.
Doug Ryall 01749 831234

CHARGES: £20 per day and £25 at weekends.
SUITABILITY: Small trailer can be pushed.
ACCESS: Non-tidal. **TYPE OF RAMP:** Concrete
UPPER AREA: Unknown. **LOWER AREA:** Unknown.
DIRECTIONS: 3 miles south of Shepton Mallet on the A371, opposite the Bath Showground.
RAMP DESCRIPTION: Access to 15 acre lake. You must show insurance.
FACILITIES: Open 7 days a week from 10am. Jetski hire includes wetsuit, helmet, life vest and tuition. Stand up and sit down craft available. Licensed clubhouse, showers and changing rooms. Annual membership available.

Watersports centre, Roadford Lake
Lat. 50.6964, Long. -4.2402.
01409 211507

CHARGES: See website for details
SUITABILITY: Small trailer can be pushed.
ACCESS: Non-tidal. **TYPE OF RAMP:** Concrete **UPPER AREA:** Concrete.
LOWER AREA: Mud.
DIRECTIONS: Situated between Okehampton and Launceston from the A30 Follow signs to Roadford Lake to the south west of the lake for to the Watersports centre
FACILITIES: Toilets and parking - tea-room on opposite side of the lake.

Watersports Centre, Siblyback Lake
Lat. 50.5104, Long. -4.4887.
Siblyback Watersports (01579) 346522

CHARGES: See website for details
SUITABILITY: Small trailer can be pushed.
ACCESS: Non-tidal. **TYPE OF RAMP:** Concrete **UPPER AREA:** Concrete.
LOWER AREA: Mud.
DIRECTIONS: From the A30 turn to St Cleer at Jamaica Inn and follow signs OR from A390 follow brown tourism signs.
FACILITIES: Toilets, tea-room, parking around the lake. Siblyback boasts one of the premier Watersports centres in the region with tuition in windsurfing, sailing and canoeing available. Rowing boats for hire and membership of our club on a day or season basis.

Watersports Centre, Stithians Lake
Lat. 50.1917, Long. -5.2093.
Watersports Centre 01209 860301
SUITABILITY: Small trailer can be pushed.
ACCESS: Non-tidal. **TYPE OF RAMP:** Concrete **UPPER AREA:** Concrete.
LOWER AREA: Mud.
DIRECTIONS: Follow brown tourism signs from A394 Falmouth - Helston or contact the centre.
FACILITIES: The Watersports Centre is located at the north end of the 274 acre lake (The Golden Lion Pub is nearby). Parking and toilets.

Hilperton Marina, Trowbridge
Hilperton Wharf, Hammond Way, Trowbridge, Wiltshire, England BA14 8RS
Lat. 51.3389, Long. -2.2046.
01225 765243

Watersports Centre, Upper Tamar Lake
Lat. 50.8793, Long. -4.4341.
Watersports Centre 01288 321712

CHARGES: See website for details
SUITABILITY: Small trailer can be pushed.
ACCESS: Non-tidal. **TYPE OF RAMP:** Concrete **UPPER AREA:** Concrete.
LOWER AREA: Mud.
DIRECTIONS: From A39 (Bude-Bideford) follow signs from the village of Kilkhampton.
FACILITIES: Parking, toilets and tea-room

4

Wales and West England

Newport to Liverpool

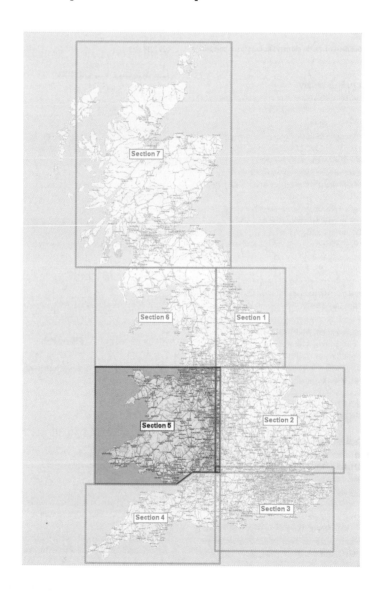

COASTAL SLIPWAYS
clockwise around the coast

Old Ferry Slipway, Severn Bridge
Lat. 51.5985, Long. -2.6323.

CHARGES: None
SUITABILITY: Large trailer needs a car.
ACCESS: All of tidal range. **TYPE OF RAMP: UPPER AREA:** Unknown.
LOWER AREA: Unknown.
DIRECTIONS: Under the south side of the old Severn Road Bridge. No longer usable.
RAMP DESCRIPTION: Was the old ferry slip. This slip is in disrepair - sections of the raised slip are missing - unusable.

Slipway, Beachley
Lat. 51.6138, Long. -2.6473.

CHARGES: None
SUITABILITY: Large trailer needs a car.
ACCESS: ¾ tidal. **TYPE OF RAMP:** Concrete and stone.
UPPER AREA: Shingle. **LOWER AREA:** Sand.
DIRECTIONS: Slipway is underneath the Severn Bridge. Take the road into Beachley and keep going until you reach the sea.
RAMP DESCRIPTION: Long shallow stone slipway leading across the foreshore.
FACILITIES: Car and trailer parking. Petrol nearby and pub.
HAZARDS: Caution: Do your navigational homework if you are new to this venue. This site is very dangerous, especially on Spring tides. There is a race of 8 to 10 knots. Good local knowledge is required. DO NOT ATTEMPT TO LAUNCH HERE IF YOU ARE A NOVICE OR OUT OF PRACTICE.

Uskmouth Sailing Club, Uskmouth
Lat. 51.5528, Long. -2.9675.
01633 271417

CHARGES: Must be member of club, see site for info
SUITABILITY: Large trailer needs a car.
ACCESS: ½ tidal. **TYPE OF RAMP: UPPER AREA:** Concrete.
LOWER AREA: Mud.
DIRECTIONS: Newport Uskmouth Sailing Club West Nash Road, Nash, Newport, Gwent, NP18 2BZ
RAMP DESCRIPTION: Concrete covered in thin mud from river us
FACILITIES: Club house, storage.

Channel View Slipway, Channel View Centre
Lat. 51.4621, Long. -3.1796.
02920378161

CHARGES: £6.90 for launch + £5 refunded deposit on return of day pass.
SUITABILITY: Large trailer needs a car.
ACCESS: Non-tidal. **TYPE OF RAMP:** Concrete with shallow gradient, getting steeper as you approach the water. **UPPER AREA:** Concrete.
LOWER AREA: Concrete.

DIRECTIONS: Head for Cardiff Bay of the M4, then head for Channel View centre. Sign posted.
RAMP DESCRIPTION: Purpose built concrete ramp, in good condition, owned by the leisure centre, where you get the day pass from. Non-tidal as is within the Cardiff Bay barrage.
FACILITIES: Toilets & showers available in the centre & limited amount of free parking for car & trailer.

Cardiff Marina, Grangetown
Ely Harbour Ferry Road, Grangetown, Cardiff, Wales CF11 0JL
Lat. 51.4478, Long. -3.1853.
029 2034 3459

Cardiff Bay YC, Cardiff
Lat. 51.4481, Long. -3.1748.
Office 029 2066 6627, Clubhouse 029 2022 6575

CHARGES: Club members only.
SUITABILITY: Large trailer needs a car.
ACCESS: Non-tidal. **TYPE OF RAMP:** Wide concrete.
UPPER AREA: Shingle. **LOWER AREA:** Unknown.
DIRECTIONS: Exit at Junction 33 on the M4 motorway follow the signs for the docks then exit the Slip Road at the junction for Penarth, turn left towards the ASDA supermarket then turn right at the next two roundabouts. Follow the road past the Red House pub and the Yacht Club is at the end of this road.
RAMP DESCRIPTION: Available for to club members only, temporary membership is not available. A very good recently constructed slipway that gives access to Cardiff Bay which is generally impounded by the Barrage, but is drained from time to time. For current information on the depth of water over the lock sills, call the lockmaster on 029 2070 0234 or call 'Barrage Control' on Ch 18. After exiting the lock coming into the bay, the clubhouse is visible directly ahead.
FACILITIES: Brand new clubhouse with extensive facilities. The visitors' pontoon is on the north bank of the River Ely.

Penarth Marina, Penarth
Crest Nicholson Marinas, Penarth Marina, Penarth, Vale of Glamorgan, Wales CF64 1TQ
Lat. 51.4447, Long. -3.1749.
02920 705021

Slipways, Penarth
Lat. 51.4347, Long. -3.1674.
01446 704754

CHARGES: £25 for annual permit.
SUITABILITY: Large trailer needs a car.
ACCESS: ½ tidal. **TYPE OF RAMP:** Concrete. **UPPER AREA:** Rock.
LOWER AREA: Sand.
DIRECTIONS: Slipways are on the Esplanade. Leave M4 at junction 33 taking the A4232 to Penarth and following signs through town to seafront.
RAMP DESCRIPTION: There are two slips. Northern is for large engines over 25hp and PWCs and southern for small engines and sailors. The keys

5

for the slips are different. The southern slipway is at the end of the beach next to the lifeboat station.

FACILITIES: Limited parking at the slipway where it is wider. Can leave car except at Spring tide, petrol, toilets. The Penarth Water Ski Club operates from the Northern Slipway, contact details: Warren Perry 07973 664073, or David Silver 029 2021 1193.

Hayes Road, Sully

Lat. 51.4033, Long. -3.2242.
01446 704754

CHARGES: Council controlled locked barrier now across slipway. Annual permit issued via the Vale of Glamorgan, must have RYA and insurance. Cost £25

SUITABILITY: Small trailer can be pushed.

ACCESS: ½ tidal. **TYPE OF RAMP:** Shallow concrete.

UPPER AREA: Shingle. **LOWER AREA:** Mud.

DIRECTIONS: Council slipway in Hayes Road. Leave M4 at junction 33 taking A4232 / A4050 south to Barry following signs to Barry Dock. At roundabout at link road take turning for Sully and then right at next roundabout. Site is behind municipal amenity waste site on the left. This launch site can be awkward to find for the first time. It is a long, narrow concrete ramp onto mud / rocks at low water.

RAMP DESCRIPTION: Access has a narrow 2.4m gateway. Site is not safe if the winds are over Force 4 from any southerly direction. The launch site is exposed to winds from the south. Also, great care must be exercised, as there are some dangerous areas around headlands. The sea conditions can also change very rapidly. PWCs are allowed here.

FACILITIES: Parking at the slipway. Access to both the ramp and parking facilities at this site are also restricted by a 2 metre height restriction

HAZARDS: Speed limit inshore and strong currents. Head west immediately after launch as there are rocks that stick up around Sully Island. There are also very, very strong tides in the Bristol Channel. It would be wise to use the tide when navigating this area, attempting to run against the tide will burn a large amount of fuel here, basically use it to your advantage, don't fight it.

Ray Harries Marine, Barry

Lat. 51.3930, Long. -3.2635.
01446 740924

CHARGES: Pay at boatyard

SUITABILITY: Large trailer needs a car.

ACCESS: ½ tidal. **TYPE OF RAMP:** Concrete with full hoist facilities.

UPPER AREA: Harbour. **LOWER AREA:** Mud.

DIRECTIONS: Junction 33 from the M4, follow signs for Barry Island then follow the signs for the RNLI pier head Barry Outer Harbour. The slip is next to the RNLI boat house.

RAMP DESCRIPTION: The slip is in the boat yard and has full hoist facilities.

FACILITIES: Yacht club, diesel, full boat yard facilities.

Watch Tower Bay, Barry

Lat. 51.3896, Long. -3.2956.

CHARGES: Residents of South Wales- £25/year for key. Non-South Wales residents - £40/year for key.

SUITABILITY: Large trailer needs a car.

ACCESS: ¾ tidal. **TYPE OF RAMP:** Slipway is in a very good state of repair having been refurbished in July 2007. Concrete slipway going onto a firm beach so you can launch at all states of tide. Access to the beach is for launching only. **UPPER AREA:** Concrete. **LOWER AREA:** Concrete.

DIRECTIONS: Leave M4 at junction 33 and take the A4232 / A4050 south to Barry following signs to The Knap.

RAMP DESCRIPTION: Under the management of South Wales Powerboat and Watersports Club. Slipway is for members use only, access is via a locked barrier. New members welcome, for details see our website. Short term visitors can apply for temporary membership, subject to availability. Please send us an e-mail with the proposed date and time of your visit. No PWCs allowed due to previous trouble - sorry.

FACILITIES: Access via a locked barrier. Free parking for members. Quiet beach. Large park next to slipway (ideal for the family). Toilets and showers close by (public). Shops and cafés close by.

HAZARDS: Strong currents inshore. Speed limit near beach.

Newton Beach, Newton

Lat. 51.4790, Long. -3.6759.

CHARGES: New full membership application: £240.00. Full membership renewal: £95.00

SUITABILITY: Large trailer needs a car.

ACCESS: ¾ tidal. **TYPE OF RAMP:** Concrete **UPPER AREA:** Sand. **LOWER AREA:** Sand.

DIRECTIONS: Drive through the old village of Newton towards the beach. Launch site in near the car park.

RAMP DESCRIPTION: The slip is run by Porthcawl Power Boat and Ski Club and is for members only.

FACILITIES: The clubhouse facilities include: Use of the changing rooms and showers, tea and coffee making facilities and free pool table. There is also an engine flushing tank.

HAZARDS: Rocks just off the end of the beach at low water.

Harbour Slip, Porthcawl

Lat. 51.4750, Long. -3.7009.
01656 782756

CHARGES: £3

SUITABILITY: Small trailer can be pushed.

ACCESS: ½ tidal. **TYPE OF RAMP:** Steep concrete ramp.

UPPER AREA: Unknown. **LOWER AREA:** Unknown.

DIRECTIONS: Harbour slipway in Porthcawl. Leave the M4 at junction 37 taking the A4229 and follow the signs to the seafront.

RAMP DESCRIPTION: This is a private slipway and day permits must be purchased in advance. You will need to show proof of insurance. Steep concrete ramp suitable for small powered craft. Access to the slipway has low overhead cables and priority must be given to the RNLI lifeboat. Site is exposed and there are very strong currents.

FACILITIES: Petrol, parking, toilets and boat storage.

HAZARDS: 3 knot speed restriction.

5

South Wales Jetski-club, Port Talbot
Lat. 51.5886, Long. -3.7826.
01443 206010 / 01656 669382

CHARGES: The cost of full membership for the 2005-2006 season is £220 (new members are required to pay a £50 joining fee). Members only.
SUITABILITY: Small trailer can be pushed.
ACCESS: Non-tidal. **TYPE OF RAMP:** Concrete **UPPER AREA:** Concrete.
LOWER AREA: Shingle.
DIRECTIONS: From the M4 take junction 40, head towards Port Talbot. Follow Abbey Road down to the traffic lights, turn right. Follow road to Texaco petrol station, turn left and go over level crossing to mini roundabout. Take the second exit and the club is 150 meters on right hand side in Llewellyn's Road.
RAMP DESCRIPTION: Ramp is for club members only. Easy ramp giving access to sheltered docks.
FACILITIES: Changing rooms, toilet. Pub and McDonalds are close by.

Afan Boats Club, Port Talbot
Lat. 51.5876, Long. -3.7975.
07751810305 Mobile. 01639 773505 home.

CHARGES: Yearly subscription £55.
SUITABILITY: Large trailer needs a car.
ACCESS: ¾ tidal. **TYPE OF RAMP:** Concrete **UPPER AREA:** Concrete.
LOWER AREA: Mud.
DIRECTIONS: M4 junction 40 and 41 aim for town centre turn left and right on roundabout pass Mc donalds turn left over bridge turn right follow road throue security gate 50 yard to slip
RAMP DESCRIPTION: Very wide sheltered slip suitable for car usable 4 hours either side high water. Permission from Port Talbot Small Boat Club at clubhouse. Access down a private road with numerous signs, BSC, BDB, Private.
FACILITIES: Lots of roadside parking next to slip, freshwater at clubhouse, shops in Port Talbot (½ mile).

Beach Slip, Port Talbot
Lat. 51.5880, Long. -3.8092.
SUITABILITY: Large trailer needs a car.
ACCESS: All of tidal range. **TYPE OF RAMP:** Concrete, then beach.
UPPER AREA: Sand. **LOWER AREA:** Sand.
DIRECTIONS: Leave M4 at junction 41 and follow signs.
RAMP DESCRIPTION: Wide concrete slips that leads onto gently sloping beach. Be prepared to launch and recover through surf. Usable any state of tide but with car only at high water. There is a dedicated Jetski area marked by yellow flags and large yellow writing on the sea wall. The beach on either side is busy with surfers.
FACILITIES: Car park 100 yards from slip between Aberafan Hotel and Afan Lido, charge in season.

Monkstone Marina, Port Talbot
Lat. 51.6292, Long. -3.8342.
01792 360082
SUITABILITY: Large trailer needs a car.

ACCESS: ½ tidal. **TYPE OF RAMP:** Concrete **UPPER AREA:** Harbour.
LOWER AREA: Sand.
DIRECTIONS: Marina in underneath the M4 on the west bank of the river. Leave the M4 at junction 42.
RAMP DESCRIPTION: Concrete ramp into the marina. There is a low tide barrier on the entrance.
FACILITIES: Boatyard and pub nearby.

Marina Slip, Swansea
Lat. 51.6169, Long. -3.9347.
01792 470310

CHARGES: £6.37 per metre
SUITABILITY: Large trailer needs a car.
ACCESS: Non-tidal. **TYPE OF RAMP:** Travel hoist.
UPPER AREA: Harbour. **LOWER AREA:** Harbour.
DIRECTIONS: Leave the M4 at junction 47 and take the A438 to Swansea, then A4067 and follow the signs to the marina.
RAMP DESCRIPTION: Marine travel hoist into the locked marina basin. Tidal access 8am to 2pm by prior arrangement only. Lock gates open 4 ½ hours either side of high tide.
FACILITIES: All the usual marina facilities. Petrol parking toilets and a very good chandlery.
HAZARDS: 4 knot speed limit.

Swansea Marina, Swansea
Lockside, Maritime Quarter, Swansea, Carmarthenshire, Wales SA1 1WG
Lat. 51.6158, Long. -3.9387.
01792 470310

Mumbles, Swansea
Lat. 51.5715, Long. -3.9862.
01792 360082

CHARGES: £5.50 to launch and park.
SUITABILITY: Large trailer needs a car.
ACCESS: All of tidal range. **TYPE OF RAMP:** One wide and one narrow concrete. **UPPER AREA:** Harbour. **LOWER AREA:** Sand.
DIRECTIONS: Take the road around Swansea Bay to the Mumbles. Launch site is opposite the Mumbles Yacht Club.
RAMP DESCRIPTION: There are 3 ramps in the immediate area. The first 'Village Lane' is opposite the Antelope pub, small and only accessible about an hour before high tide. Used in the main by the Mumbles Ski Club. At Knab Rock opposite the yacht club is the main ramp this is accessible for just about all states of the tide usually at least 3 hours either side - at full ebb you can still put a 4 × 4 over the sand to launch. Loads of places to tie off, as the ramp is at the end of the Mumbles moorings, you can tie off at any of the buoys, or when the tide is in there are tie off rings on the seawall running away to the east of the ramp. Approximately 200 metres east of the Knab Rock slipway is a long ramp. It can be difficult to reverse onto on a busy day as people seem to dump trailers everywhere. Knab Rock is a very good launch facility, but has no fuel or changing facilities. Local ice-cream parlour gets very busy, and means it is difficult to get into the car park as it is full of cars not involved with water sports. From 2005 the slip at the end of Knab Rock will be the

5

home of Mumbles Jetski Club and will have a barrier. All PWC users will have to be club members or purchase a day launch pass.

FACILITIES: Car parking £5.50 for a car and trailer. The car park does get busy on the summer weekends. Swansea is nearby. Petrol available. Boats over 15hp must be registered at a cost of £5.00. You may have to show insurance.

Beach Slip, Oxwich
Lat. 51.5569, Long. -4.1609.

CHARGES: £9.00for boat and car.
SUITABILITY: Large trailer needs a car.
ACCESS: ¼ tidal. **TYPE OF RAMP:** Concrete **UPPER AREA:** Sand.
LOWER AREA: Sand.
DIRECTIONS: Travel about 30 minutes out of Swansea on the South Gower Road the A4118, and you find the impressive entrance gates to Penrice estate, turn left here and you make the downhill run into Oxwich village. As you drive in the final mile you pass an expanse of sand dunes and marshland by Oxwich Bay which is rich in wild flowers and insects, including many rarities. There are even herds of mountain goats, used to keep the scrub at bay.
RAMP DESCRIPTION: A large slipway at the west end of the bay, allows recovery on full tide, when the tide is out the sand is flat and firm - driving down to the water is very easy.
FACILITIES: There is a very large car park at the end of the road, £9.00 for boat and car. Access to the car park is via an over head barrier 2mtrs high (6 ′6). There is also chained access to the right of this with no height restrictions. The car park closes at 21.00 and the chain is closed at the discretion of the car park attendant. This is usually weather dependent (17.00 if it's raining and 19.00 hr if it's fine). However some nights the chain stays open as long as the car park. Oxwich is popular with the weekend crowd who come down on a Friday and either stay at the water side Oxwich Bay Hotel, or any of the hundreds of small guest houses dotted around the Gower. They then use Oxwich as the base for a weekend of sailing or cruising the excellent Gower Peninsula. Facilities at the beach are fairly limited, a shop and toilet block, but miles of uncluttered waters is the reason people go there. The hotel serves good food, and provides reasonably secure parking overnight.

Beach, Port Eynon Bay
Lat. 51.5443, Long. -4.2103.
01792 360082

CHARGES: None
SUITABILITY: Small trailer can be pushed.
ACCESS: No Ramp. **TYPE OF RAMP:** Beach **UPPER AREA:** Sand.
LOWER AREA: Sand.
DIRECTIONS: Follow A4118 west from Swansea to south shore of Gower Peninsula.
RAMP DESCRIPTION: Concrete road onto the beach. 4 × 4 vehicles recommended. Can be used most states of tide. All boats should be registered with council, cost £3.
FACILITIES: Parking and toilets.
HAZARDS: 4 knot speed limit. All powered craft over 15hp must be registered.

Slipway, Loughor Slip
Lat. 51.6433, Long. -4.1046.
No number

CHARGES: Free
SUITABILITY: Portable Only.
ACCESS: ¼ tidal. **TYPE OF RAMP:** Narrow concrete beams only suitable for small craft or trailers. This is more or less launch from the side of the bank of the estuary from the car park. Not suitable for heavy boats.
UPPER AREA: Mud. **LOWER AREA:** Mud.
DIRECTIONS: From M4 leave onto the A483, then A484 and A4296 then B4295. Carry on to Pen-Clawdd until you reach Benson Street. From here there is an open carpark from which to launch your boat.
RAMP DESCRIPTION: Free tidal slip half hour either side of tide, only suitable for small trailer boats. On high tide can launch boat from bank and slip into water.
FACILITIES: Shops and pubs nearby.
HAZARDS: Stick to the main estuary as sand banks and strong currents are predominant. Ideas of the tidal state essential.

Loughor Boating Club, Loughor
Lat. 51.6643, Long. -4.0767.
01792 893147

CHARGES: £5 (may be rising).
SUITABILITY: Large trailer needs a car.
ACCESS: ¼ tidal. **TYPE OF RAMP:** Concrete **UPPER AREA:** Concrete.
LOWER AREA: Mud.
DIRECTIONS: Leave M4 at J47, follow A483 then A484 to Llanelli for five miles, do not cross the bridge. Loughor Boat Club is down the side of the estuary.
RAMP DESCRIPTION: Pretty good ramp with second ramp available (primarily for rescue boat). Can handle 25 to 30 foot boats by arrangement. Available about two hours before high water until about 3 hours after. Shifting sandbanks in Burry Inlet require careful navigation.
FACILITIES: Club house with bar and food. Showers / toilets when club open. Rescue station on site.

Harbour Slip, Burry Port
Lat. 51.6780, Long. -4.2444.
Millennium Park 01554 777744

CHARGES: Pay and Display car park.
SUITABILITY: Large trailer needs a car.
ACCESS: ½ tidal. **TYPE OF RAMP:** Concrete **UPPER AREA:** Unknown.
LOWER AREA: Unknown.
DIRECTIONS: Slipway is to the east of the harbour. Part of the new development. Turn off the M4 and junction 48 taking the A4138 to Llanelli and then A484 to Burry Port.
RAMP DESCRIPTION: This is a very tidal area and so pontoon access will be made available. Landscaping and some commercial development planned.
FACILITIES: There is a pay and display car park which is free until April 2002. Boatyard close by.
HAZARDS: 3 knot speed limit within harbour. Waterskiing permitted in Burry Inlet.

Slipway, Ferryside

Lat. 51.7691, Long. -4.3706.

01267 267366

CHARGES: £5 (refunded if you join club).
SUITABILITY: Large trailer needs a car.
ACCESS: ½ tidal. **TYPE OF RAMP:** Shallow concrete.
UPPER AREA: Unknown. **LOWER AREA:** Unknown.
DIRECTIONS: From Carmarthen follow A48 / A484 south, turn off at Llandyfaelog and follow the signs. Site is across the level crossing in centre of Ferryside.
RAMP DESCRIPTION: Shallow concrete slipway. You must call prior to using this site.
FACILITIES: Petrol, parking, toilets and boat storage.
HAZARDS: 5 knot speed limit in moorings. Waterskiing permitted in designated areas. Live firing range (no-go zone) in Carmarthen Bay, not usually active on weekends.

Slipway, Amroth

Lat. 51.7334, Long. -4.6520.

CHARGES: No
SUITABILITY: Large trailer needs a car.
ACCESS: ¼ tidal. **TYPE OF RAMP:** Concrete **UPPER AREA:** Concrete.
LOWER AREA: Sand.
DIRECTIONS: Slipway is on the main road through Amroth alongside beach. Amroth is about 5 miles north east along the coast from Tenby. Roads into Amroth all have steep gradients.
RAMP DESCRIPTION: Sharp turn at top. Access is free. There is a sign by the ramp asking boaters to report to the attendant, but the attendant is seldom on the site. Unfortunately bollards were installed preventing access by trailers in 2004. If you can lift your boat about 3ft (over bollards) you'll be OK
FACILITIES: Free parking adjacent. Toilets 300 yards.
HAZARDS: Pembrokeshire County Council byelaws apply to the area surrounding this launch site and include a speed restriction.

Coppet Hall Beach, Saundersfoot

Lat. 51.7157, Long. -4.6936.

SUITABILITY: Small trailer can be pushed.
ACCESS: No Ramp. **TYPE OF RAMP:** Beach **UPPER AREA:** Sand.
LOWER AREA: Sand.
DIRECTIONS: About ¾ mile east of Saundersfoot.
RAMP DESCRIPTION: Not suitable for car, manhandle dinghy over beach up to 300 yards depending on tide. Pay attendant for launching and parking. Shops and petrol in Saundersfoot ¾ mile. Heavy boats use Saundersfoot Harbour.
FACILITIES: Parking charges included in launch fee. Parking space is ample. Car park on beach with café.
HAZARDS: No motor powered boats to be launched from this site.

Harbour Slipway, Saundersfoot

Lat. 51.7098, Long. -4.6980.

Harbourmaster 01834 812094

CHARGES: £5 for launch and £2 for parking.
SUITABILITY: Large trailer needs a car.
ACCESS: ½ tidal. **TYPE OF RAMP:** Concrete **UPPER AREA:** Sand.
LOWER AREA: Sand.
DIRECTIONS: From Carmarthen follow A40 / A477 / A478 to Pentlepoir. Turn left into the B4316 to Saundersfoot.
RAMP DESCRIPTION: Concrete slipway onto hard sand. Available about 2 ½ hours around high water or at all states of tide over the sand for smaller craft. Certificate of insurance is required and the site gets very busy in the summer. Harbour dries at half tide to firm sandy bottom. It is also possible to launch small craft from the beach slipway, 200 metres from the harbour at low tide at no cost. The slipway is off the Strand next to the harbour car park, quite steep concrete onto soft sand. 4-wheel drive vehicles only recommended! The beach gets very busy during holiday periods.
FACILITIES: Petrol, parking, toilets. Showers in Saundersfoot SC 01834-812492 with temporary membership.
HAZARDS: 3 knot speed limit in harbour and within 250 m of shore. Waterskiing permitted in designated areas.

Harbour slipway, Tenby

Lat. 51.6727, Long. -4.6992.

Harbour Office 01834842717, mobile 07812 559482
SUITABILITY: Large trailer needs a car.
ACCESS: ½ tidal. **TYPE OF RAMP:** Concrete **UPPER AREA:** Harbour.
LOWER AREA: Sand.
DIRECTIONS: The slipway is in the harbour at Tenby just of the High Street and near to the Sailing Club. Access road is steep and narrow and the town gets congested in the summer months. Due to the inaccessibility of Tenby Harbour during the summer - there is a traffic ban preventing harbour access from 11am - 5pm every day in high summer.
RAMP DESCRIPTION: Long concrete ramp onto the hard sand within the harbour.
FACILITIES: Fuel available in town. Parking is limited.
HAZARDS: Pembrokeshire County Council byelaws apply to the area surrounding this launch site and include a speed restriction.

Slipway, Lydstep

Lat. 51.6501, Long. -4.7610.

Lydstep Beach Holiday Resort 01834 871871

CHARGES: Only available for residence of the camp site.
SUITABILITY: Large trailer needs a car.
ACCESS: Unknown. **TYPE OF RAMP:** Slipway **UPPER AREA:** Shingle.
LOWER AREA: Shingle.
DIRECTIONS: The access is via a private extremely well set up and run caravan site on the main Tenby road the A4139.
RAMP DESCRIPTION: This is a very sheltered cove, the next bay along from the highly popular and unfortunately overcrowded Tenby.
FACILITIES: The slipway is only available to those staying on the campsite. There is everything that goes with a very plush residential caravan site, including showers, toilets, and shops. Lots for the kids, and once you pay to get in you are entitled to use all the sites facilities. The cove has water at all states of the tide and is a very good place for water-

5

skiing, and is very quiet. The high cliffs on 3 sides also keep it sheltered from the wind. A few minutes off shore is the well known off shore Monastery island of Caldey, although landing is prohibited. Well worth a good day out in clean quite waters.

HAZARDS: The beach is well set out with the whole cove buoyed off, so that no powered craft are allowed into the swimming areas - with exception of through moorings lane. Pembrokeshire County Council byelaws apply to the area surrounding this launch site and include a speed restriction.

Slipway, Freshwater East

Lat. 51.6453, Long. -4.8613.

CHARGES: None, but restrictions on numbers of vehicles on beach in place and possibility of ban on PWCs for 2007.

SUITABILITY: Large trailer needs a car.

ACCESS: All of tidal range. **TYPE OF RAMP: UPPER AREA:** Concrete. **LOWER AREA:** Sand.

DIRECTIONS: Go past the car park from Freshwater East village, over the very narrow bridge and take first left with a One Way sign. Reach a T junction and turn left to go down to the beach. BEWARE - very soft sand. 4×4s only and even then at own risk. Author saw 4×4 tractor get stuck!

RAMP DESCRIPTION: Steep concrete running in to soft sand.

FACILITIES: According to the Good Beach Guide: Café/restaurant, local pub, shops, toilets, local village and holiday park.

HAZARDS: Try landing to west of slip and approaching it under tow along the beach rather than straight up from in front of slip where sand is most churned up. Pembrokeshire County Council byelaws apply to the area surrounding this launch site and include a speed restriction.

Stackpole Quay, Pembroke

Lat. 51.6238, Long. -4.9009.

01646 661359

SUITABILITY: Large trailer needs a car.

ACCESS: Unknown. **TYPE OF RAMP: UPPER AREA:** Harbour. **LOWER AREA:** Unknown.

DIRECTIONS: Stackpole Quay is near Stackpole about 5 miles south of Pembroke. Very small harbour, large enough for 2 or 3 boats at most.

RAMP DESCRIPTION: Restricted by a launch permit system. No day launching allowed.

FACILITIES: Very small harbour

HAZARDS: Pembrokeshire County Council byelaws apply to the area surrounding this launch site and include a speed restriction.

Slipway, West Angle

Lat. 51.6872, Long. -5.1100.

01646 696100

SUITABILITY: Large trailer needs a car.

ACCESS: All of tidal range. **TYPE OF RAMP:** Concrete but 12" drop at bottom on to beach which put author off from trying it. **UPPER AREA:** Concrete. **LOWER AREA:** Sand.

DIRECTIONS: Access from the car park at West Angle.

RAMP DESCRIPTION: Concrete and very steep. Locked post at top of slip - key available from café.

FACILITIES: Café.

HAZARDS: Dead Slow Minimum Wake in bay. A slow approach and departure is required as the bay is popular for swimming and can become shallow at low water. A port authority zoning scheme is in place throughout the waterway. Information is available from www.mhpa.co.uk and leisure user's guides are available in local TIC's

Old Point Slip, Angle

Lat. 51.6871, Long. -5.0786.

01646 696100

CHARGES: None

SUITABILITY: Large trailer needs a car.

ACCESS: ½ tidal. **TYPE OF RAMP:** Stone, natural slip, 3m wide. **UPPER AREA:** Shingle. **LOWER AREA:** Mud.

DIRECTIONS: From Angle follow signposted dirt track to Old Point House pub. Slip is opposite pub. Publican is very friendly.

RAMP DESCRIPTION: Gradient is gentle compacted hard core over foreshore. Not suitable for large vessels.

FACILITIES: Overnight parking available in camp site 300 yards back. Parking space is good. Daytime parking in field next to pub.

HAZARDS: Launches into mooring area. Dead Slow Minimum Wake restrictions in the bay. There is an activity zoning scheme and Port Authority Byelaws in place for the whole waterway. Details are available at www.mhpa.co.uk copies of the leisure guide are also available in the pub

Front Street, Pembroke Dock

Lat. 51.6952, Long. -4.9454.

01646 696100

SUITABILITY: Large trailer needs a car.

ACCESS: ¾ tidal. **TYPE OF RAMP:** Concrete **UPPER AREA:** Shingle. **LOWER AREA:** Mud.

DIRECTIONS: Follow the A477 onto Pembroke Dock turning into Criterion Way and then Front Street. Site is at the corner of Front Street and Commercial Road. The entrance by Jewsons yard is narrow and approaching from the other end at the next right turn may be easier.

RAMP DESCRIPTION: Shallow concrete slipway which tends to silt up at the bottom end. Access 5 hours either side of high water. There is also modern slipway with good access just to the east. Follow the Western Way and signs for the Marine Park. Look for the Chieftain Tank on display by Criterion Way which leads to the free car park and slip. Only usable at high water ±1hour.

FACILITIES: Petrol, small free car park, toilets and boat storage.

HAZARDS: Slow speed in the moorings. Waterskiing permitted in the designated areas. Site is used by the Pembroke Haven Motor Boat Club.

Hobbs Point, Pembroke Dock

Lat. 51.6996, Long. -4.9420.

01646 683661

CHARGES: Free

SUITABILITY: Large trailer needs a car.

5

ACCESS: ¾ tidal. **TYPE OF RAMP:** Concrete, 9.25m wide.
UPPER AREA: Concrete. **LOWER AREA:** Unknown.
DIRECTIONS: This is an old ferry slip. Follow the A477 to its logical conclusion on the south bank of the Haven.
RAMP DESCRIPTION: Large free slipway with a good gradient under the Cleddau Bridge. This slip falls off into deep water at the end. Be very careful below half tide.
FACILITIES: Small free public car park but no secure parking. Chandlery and toilets at the site. Pontoons are put out in the summer months.
HAZARDS: Launches into mooring area so a slow approach and departure are required. There is an activity zoning scheme and Port Authority byelaws in force for the whole waterway. Leisure user's guides are available in the chandlery or via www.mhpa.co.uk

East Llanion, Pembroke
Lat. 51.6988, Long. -4.9219.
01646 622013

CHARGES: None
SUITABILITY: Large trailer needs a car.
ACCESS: All of tidal range. **TYPE OF RAMP:** Wide concrete with different access points at low water **UPPER AREA:** Concrete.
LOWER AREA: Shingle.
DIRECTIONS: Travel West along the A477 from Carmarthen to Pembroke and you pass the turn off South onto the A478 . 90% of the traffic will head this way down to the tourist havens of Saundersfoot and Tenby. However by staying on the main road you come to Pembroke Dock and the River Cleddau. On the run into Pembroke Dock you come to a roundabout with a large ships anchor in the middle of it. Turn right here and then take the next right and follow the road through what seems like an industrial estate, you reach the excellent very long new slipway belonging to the boat club.
RAMP DESCRIPTION: Wide concrete ramp. A great site and easy to launch from at all states of tide. Large wide turning area at the top of the slip. Small fee for parking. The activity centre has priority launching at this site but there is very little conflict.
FACILITIES: A large free car park. At the launch site there is a sailing club, under development to provide chandlery and toilets. Fuel, shops, restaurants all available locally. This river is often a good water-ski location when every where else is too windy, the river is one of the deepest in Europe - and was the main route in to the oil refineries at Pembroke. This is a very deep water river, depths of 20 metres only a couple of metres from the bank. You can always find flat water here, but it has the disadvantage that it can be cold, and sometimes with a strong current. If you get tired of skiing then head down river and you reach Dale. Go for a pint at the excellent Griffin Inn.

HAZARDS: The watersports centre has priority at this launch site. No planing in the Cosheston River (to east of slip/car park) Slip launches into main waterski area so can become busy in good skiing conditions. Area is also used to teach beginners from the watersports centre. There is an activity zoning scheme and Port Authority byelaws in force for the whole waterway. User guides are available at the Activity Centre or via www.mhpa.co.uk. Although Jetski friendly aquabatics are not permitted in the area directly adjacent to the slip way a designated area for Jetski aquabatics exists downstream of this area

Lawrenny Yacht Station, Lawrenny
Lat. 51.7183, Long. -4.8795.
01646 651212

CHARGES: £8 for each day's use of the ramp.
SUITABILITY: Large trailer needs a car.
ACCESS: All of tidal range. **TYPE OF RAMP:** Concrete
UPPER AREA: Concrete. **LOWER AREA:** Shingle.
DIRECTIONS: From Lawrenny village follow coast road to the Yacht Station.
RAMP DESCRIPTION: Access is via a narrow village road. A very good ramp originally built to launch sea planes. A launch fee is payable at the hotel or at the workshop by the slip. Ramp is available only during opening hours – access through secure fenced area. Ramp is steep and lower section slippy at less than high tide. Chandlery will launch with tractor for £10 – and £10 for slipping. At times a very fast tidal flow ACROSS the ramp makes slipping exciting.
FACILITIES: Trailer parking in the field opposite the yacht station. Chandlery and boatyard and the Lawrenny Arms. Follow the River Cresswell up to the fine pub (accessible high water +/- 1 hr). Slip water tap available. Fuel is available and there is a small but well stock chandlery on site. Also a number of moorings are managed by the site owners with all associated services. A very pretty and attractive spot.
HAZARDS: Slipway launches into mooring areas (4knot speed limit through moorings). Slipway also launches directly into a Dead Slow Minimum Wake zone of the Milford Haven waterway. This speed restriction begins downstream of the entrance to the yacht station and is indicated by yellow buoys during the summer. There is also an activity zoning scheme and port authority byelaws in place.

Slipway, Landshipping
Lat. 51.7694, Long. -4.8842.
01646 696100

CHARGES: None
SUITABILITY: Small trailer can be pushed.
ACCESS: ½ tidal. **TYPE OF RAMP:** Compacted gravel onto mud.
UPPER AREA: Shingle. **LOWER AREA:** Mud.
DIRECTIONS: Follow A4075 from Pembroke. Turn left at Cross Hands pub. Follow signs to Landshipping - 4 miles. Landshipping Boat Association address on notice board.
RAMP DESCRIPTION: Narrow access road onto a gently gradient slipway. The slip is primarily constructed of compacted hardcore and dressed annually by the local Boat Owners Association.

5

FACILITIES: Limited parking which can flood at very high Springs. Pub nearby.

HAZARDS: Launches into the no planing zone of the Milford Haven waterway. The no planing restriction begins downstream of Lawrenny Yacht station (approx 4 miles downstream of Landshipping) and is indicated by yellow buoys in the summer months. There is also an activity zoning scheme and port authority byelaws in force throughout the waterway. Upper reaches should be navigated with care as there are numerous mud flats and a narrow channel at low water.

Blacktar, Haverfordwest

Lat. 51.7483, Long. -4.9002.
01646 696100

CHARGES: None
SUITABILITY: Large trailer needs a car.
ACCESS: All of tidal range. **TYPE OF RAMP:** Raised concrete. 2.4m wide. **UPPER AREA:** Shingle. **LOWER AREA:** Shingle.
DIRECTIONS: From A4076 3 miles south of Haverfordwest turn left at Johnston towards Llangwm. At Llangwm take 2nd hard left and follow narrow Lane ¾ mile round a sharp right hand bend and past Knapp Farm to the river.
RAMP DESCRIPTION: The slipway is 8´ (2.4m) wide and straight. The top 2/3rds are clean and clear of weed and at an angle of 4.5degrees. The bottom 1/3rd has some light weed, but the angle increases to 9.5degrees making usage at low tide only realistic for 4 wheel drive vehicles. There are two stout rings set into the slip on the lower end. The beach alongside the slip is hard shingle and smaller boats regularly launch off the beach, care should be taken when reversing trailers. Narrow access road. Salt marsh reclamation work is occurring directly south of the slipway and all care should be taken not to disturb this work with trailers and vehicles. Salt marsh reclamation work is occurring directly south of the slipway and all care should be taken not to disturb this work with trailers and vehicles.
FACILITIES: Parking space is limited to 12 cars. Extra parking space by arrangement at Knapp Farm. Slip water tap available.
HAZARDS: Launches directly into moorings and the Dead Slow Minimum Wake zone of the Milford Haven Waterway. The no planing restriction begin downstream of Lawrenny Yacht Station (approx 2 miles downstream of Blacktar) and is indicated by yellow buoy during the summer months. There is an activity zoning scheme and Port authority Byelaws are in force.

Rudders Boatyard, Burton

Lat. 51.7062, Long. -4.9173.
01646 600288

CHARGES: All launching is by Rudders Staffed Tractor £8+vat each way
SUITABILITY: Large trailer needs a car.
ACCESS: All of tidal range. **TYPE OF RAMP:** Natural firm beach
UPPER AREA: Harbour. **LOWER AREA:** Shingle.
DIRECTIONS: Over Cleddeau Bridge towards Milford Haven take first right. At T junction turn left. At Stable Inn Turn Right into Church Road then third right.

RAMP DESCRIPTION: Wide privately owned slipway that works well at any state of the tide. Launching only allowed via Rudders Tractor and staff. Entrance to Rudders is now via a full concrete & tarmac road. Access all of Milford Haven with its many waterside pubs & restaurants. No speed restrictions from here all the way to open sea 8 miles away. Islands of Skomer, Ramsey all accessible & good sandy beaches such as Watic are available within the Haven.
FACILITIES: Launching service, parking, toilets, showers, deepwater pontoon, moorings. Repairs & basic chandlery
HAZARDS: No tidal flow within the launching bay but can be up to 2 knots just outside so keep clear of upstream side of pontoon on an outgoing tide.

Neyland Yacht Haven, Neyland

Brunel Quay, Neyland, Pembrokeshire, Wales SA73 1PY
Lat. 51.7103, Long. -4.9421.
01646 601601

Neyland Yacht Club, Neyland

Lat. 51.7049, Long. -4.9485.
01646 696100

CHARGES: None
SUITABILITY: Large trailer needs a car.
ACCESS: All of tidal range. **TYPE OF RAMP:** Concrete
UPPER AREA: Concrete. **LOWER AREA:** Concrete.
DIRECTIONS: Take Neyland exit from roundabout on A477, follow road through town to car park on promenade next to Neyland Yatch Club.
RAMP DESCRIPTION: Large concrete ramp accessed by tarmac road from public car park. As ramp was originally constructed for flying boats, there is plenty of space at the top of the ramp to manoeuvre several cars and trailers. A good site giving access to the eastern part of the haven.
FACILITIES: Cars & trailers can be parked in the public car park free of charge. Neyland Yacht Club is for members only and their yard should not be used for access to the slipway. The slipway itself, however, open to the public. Neyland Marina is a mile away with café and chandlery. Parking by arrangement at the Yacht Haven in the summer for cars and trailers. Visitor berths available.
HAZARDS: The slipway launches is in close proximity to the Neyland moorings and during training and good days can become busy. Slow speeds are required on approach and departure from this slip. There are also some underwater obstructions running out from the shoreline directly east of the slip. The outermost obstruction is marked with a yellow special mark. Care should be taken inline with these. Car ferry comes into Pembroke Dock opposite twice a day. There is also a port authority zoning scheme. Leisure user guide with details are available from local chandleries, TICs and the yacht club or via www.mhpa.co.uk

Milford Marina, Milford

Lat. 51.7137, Long. -5.0421.
01646 696312 or 696313

CHARGES: None at present, £10 fee may be introduced.
SUITABILITY: Large trailer needs a car.

ACCESS: Non-tidal. **TYPE OF RAMP:** Concrete **UPPER AREA:** Harbour. **LOWER AREA:** Harbour.

DIRECTIONS: Follow the A4708 to Milford Haven town centre. Take Hamilton Terrace to the marina. Turn left before the station roundabout into the marina.

RAMP DESCRIPTION: Can launch at all states of tide into the marina basin from a wide and modern slipway. Get permission from the marina office. There is also a tidal ramp immediately to the east of the marina. Access to the waterway is controlled by lock gates. Times are available from the marina office or from pier head on VHF channel 14.

FACILITIES: Parking at Whittow Wharf or in the compound behind the marina office. Visitor's moorings are available. Many local facilities in the area including chandlery, food and shops.

HAZARDS: A port authority zoning scheme exists. Users guide are available in the marina office or via www.recreation.mhpa.co.uk

Milford Marina, Milford Haven
The Docks, Milford Haven, Pembrokeshire, Wales SA73 3AF
Lat. 51.7120, Long. -5.0424.
01646 696312

Public Slip, Gellyswick
Lat. 51.7097, Long. -5.0592.
01646 692799

CHARGES: None
SUITABILITY: Large trailer needs a car.
ACCESS: ¾ tidal. **TYPE OF RAMP:** Concrete, 6.3m wide.
UPPER AREA: Shingle. **LOWER AREA:** Sand.

DIRECTIONS: From Milford Town centre follow Victoria Road west. At the roundabout near the railway station take St Lawrence Hill to Hubberston. At Hubberston, the road becomes Dale Road. Turn left into Gellyswick Road and travel ½ a mile to the Gellyswick Bay.

RAMP DESCRIPTION: Long broad and gently sloping slipway, the slip is approx. 6.3m wide running straight down the beach, with an additional slip to the side running onto the sandy beach at the top. The angle is 6.8degrees there is a floating pontoon in the bay, useful to wait for locking times at Milford. Approx. Position 51º 42.4N 05 º 03.6W, depth about 1.5m at low water Springs. Good width. Close to the Pembrokeshire YC 01646 692799. Popular alternative to Dale with divers as provides good access to coastal dive sites.

FACILITIES: Public toilets on the road opposite the slipway. Pub shop and post office are nearby.

HAZARDS: Dead Slow Minimum Wake in the bay (indicated by yellow buoy). Use only the designated small boat passage through the jetties to the west of Gellyswick. Safe passage is between the orange jetty legs. There is an activity zoning scheme and Port Authority Byelaws in place for the whole waterway. Copies of the leisure user guide are available in the yacht club or via www.mhpa.co.uk

Dale Slip, Dale
Lat. 51.7067, Long. -5.1683.
01646 636362

CHARGES: There may be restrictions to access during peak times. Check Dale Yacht Club website for details
SUITABILITY: Large trailer needs a car.
ACCESS: All of tidal range. **TYPE OF RAMP:** Concrete. Pontoon nearby.
UPPER AREA: Shingle. **LOWER AREA:** Sand.

DIRECTIONS: From Haverfordwest, take the B4327 west following the signs for Dale.

RAMP DESCRIPTION: This is a concrete slipway approximately 5m wide, shallow angle and runs straight down the beach. There is a hammerhead pontoon for pick up and drop off alongside the slip which dries 1.2m at chart datum. This pontoon can/will be a little congested as it is well used. There is also a floating pontoon in the bay with 2m of water but vessels with a draught of 1.7m should take care at low water due to the effect of the swell. Not recommended for overnight if there is any swell coming into the bay. As Dale is a popular launch site it can become very congested during summer and access restrictions may be in place at times during the season. Reversing trailers can be difficult as there is limited room to manoeuvre in the single track road. Parking and trailer storage can be limited in busy periods. Trailers and vehicle should not be left at the top of the slip as this limits access even further

FACILITIES: A pretty little village with a very good Inn supplying good food. A nearby car park is available for changing. Toilets are available alongside the sea front. Dale YC 01646 636362 and West Wales Sailing and Windsurfing 01646 636456.

HAZARDS: A Dead Slow Minimum Wake area extends from slip way to outer areas of bay marked by yellow buoys. Slipway launches direct into mooring area. Boats should approach and depart the slip north of the moorings. The bay is also very busy and popular with visitors so swimmers are present most days throughout the summers. The bay is also used to teach novices a range of watersports so consideration and caution should be expressed when in the vicinity of other vessels. The entire bay becomes very shallow at low water so care should be taken to ensure that depth is monitored to avoid contact with the sea floor. A port authority zoning scheme exists and leisure user guides are available from the pub, café and watersports centre. Also see www.mhpa.co.uk

Martins Haven, Marloes
Lat. 51.7359, Long. -5.2451.
Pembrokeshire Watersports Centre 01348 874803
SUITABILITY: Small trailer can be pushed.
ACCESS: ¼ tidal. **TYPE OF RAMP:** Steep road onto beach.
UPPER AREA: Shingle. **LOWER AREA:** Sand.

DIRECTIONS: From Haverfordwest follow B4327 west towards Dale turning north onto minor road to Maroloes.

RAMP DESCRIPTION: Steep road onto shingle. Really only suitable for a tractor launch. Not advisable to take cars onto the beach.

FACILITIES: Parking in the National Trust car park. Road leads directly onto the beach. The jetty gets lots of use from divers and day tripper boats.

HAZARDS: 8 knot speed restriction in the bay. Site is adjacent Skomer Nature Marine Reserve where there are voluntary restrictions. Beware dangerous currents in Broad Sound.

5

Slipway, Little Haven
Lat. 51.7738, Long. -5.1084.
Pembrokeshire Watersports Centre 01348 874803

CHARGES: None
SUITABILITY: Large trailer needs a car.
ACCESS: No Ramp. **TYPE OF RAMP:** Concrete **UPPER AREA:** Shingle.
LOWER AREA: Sand.
DIRECTIONS: Pembrokeshire, South Wales, adjacent The Swan public house.
RAMP DESCRIPTION: The best way to approach the slip is from the south, as a northern route is very narrow and twisty. The slipway is shared with the local RIB lifeboat. In windy conditions with any swell recovery here should be avoided and is very difficult. Alternative sites such as Dale are available. Note the beach here can prove to be difficult. A four wheel drive vehicle is recommended. Long rope good safeguard.
FACILITIES: Petrol approximately 3 miles, pubs 50 yards away. Nearby parking and toilets and village shops.
HAZARDS: Some small rocks. Pembrokeshire County Council byelaws apply to the area surrounding this launch site and include an 8 knot speed restriction.

Slipway, Broad Haven
Lat. 51.7814, Long. -5.1033.
Pembrokeshire Watersports Centre 01348 874803

CHARGES: None
SUITABILITY: Large trailer needs a car.
ACCESS: All of tidal range. **TYPE OF RAMP:** Concrete slipway onto sand.
UPPER AREA: Shingle. **LOWER AREA:** Sand.
DIRECTIONS: Go west from Haverfordwest on the B4341 past Broadway and onto Broad Haven. Ramp is by the hotel.
RAMP DESCRIPTION: Launch over a gently sloping beach with some rocks. Jetskis are allowed to launch here.
FACILITIES: Large car park nearby. Good pub and popular beach. Also a good surfing shop in the village.
HAZARDS: Pembrokeshire County Council byelaws apply to the area surrounding this launch site and include an 8 knot speed restriction.

Slipway, Nolton Haven
Lat. 51.8243, Long. -5.1079.
Pembrokeshire Watersports Centre 01348 874803

CHARGES: None
SUITABILITY: Small trailer can be pushed.
ACCESS: ½ tidal. **TYPE OF RAMP:** Ramp onto beach.
UPPER AREA: Shingle. **LOWER AREA:** Sand.
DIRECTIONS: From Haverfordwest follow A487. Turn left followings signs to Nolton Haven 1mile after Simpsons Cross.
RAMP DESCRIPTION: Small ramp onto a shingle and sandy beach. You should seek permission from Mr Canton of Nolton Haven Farm before going onto the beach. It can be tricky to launch and recover at low Spring tides.
FACILITIES: Parking, toilets and telephone and pub. Nearest petrol is Haverfordwest (7 miles).

HAZARDS: Pembrokeshire County Council byelaws apply to the area surrounding this launch site and include an 8 knot speed restriction. Site is exposed to Westerlies.

Slipway, Solva
Lat. 51.8712, Long. -5.1977.
Harbourmaster 01437 721703

CHARGES: £5 per day, £15 per week.
SUITABILITY: Large trailer needs a car.
ACCESS: All of tidal range. **TYPE OF RAMP:** Concrete slipway.
UPPER AREA: Rock. **LOWER AREA:** Unknown.
DIRECTIONS: Solva is on the A487 close to Saint David's. To get to the Main Quay go through Solva towards Saint David's and as you begin the ascent on the St David's side turn left half way up the hill.
RAMP DESCRIPTION: Concrete slipway in good condition.
FACILITIES: Parking available, speak with the harbourmaster. Moorings available, speak to Mike William of the Solva Boat Owners Association 01437 721538. Beautiful village and a good stopping off point if cruising around the coast. Good pub in the village.
HAZARDS: Pembrokeshire County Council byelaws apply to the area surrounding this launch site and include a speed limit.

Slipway, Porthclais
Lat. 51.8701, Long. -5.2835.
Pembrokeshire Watersports Centre 01348 874803

CHARGES: £3/day - cash in box to (National Trust).
SUITABILITY: Large trailer needs a car.
ACCESS: ½ tidal. **TYPE OF RAMP:** Concrete leading on to tidal river bed. **UPPER AREA:** Concrete. **LOWER AREA:** Shingle.
DIRECTIONS: From the centre of St. David's in Dyfed (west Pembrokeshire in Wales) take a single track road to Porthclais. Porthclais is a small sheltered inlet where the river Clais enters the sea at the north west end of St Brides Bay.
RAMP DESCRIPTION: Large and fairly steep concrete ramp leads down to the narrow inlet. Inlet dries out at low tide.
FACILITIES: Limited parking (15 cars?) and boat storage. Toilets. Occasional ice cream van and/or National Trust owned small shop.
HAZARDS: When tide out, it is 1/3rd mile from ramp to small isolated fishing quay. Pembrokeshire County Council byelaws apply to the area surrounding this launch site and include a speed limit.

Whitesands Bay, St Davids
Lat. 51.8964, Long. -5.2959.
Pembrokeshire Watersports Centre 01348 874803

CHARGES: £1.50 car parking charge per day.
SUITABILITY: Small trailer can be pushed.
ACCESS: ¼ tidal. **TYPE OF RAMP:** Concrete **UPPER AREA:** Rock.
LOWER AREA: Sand.
DIRECTIONS: From St David's take Whitesands Bay road. Ramp at end of car park.
RAMP DESCRIPTION: Vehicle access onto the beach to launch boats. This can be a difficult site to launch from in a westerly wind.
FACILITIES: Beach shop, parking, toilets, and coastguard.

5

HAZARDS: Pembrokeshire County Council byelaws apply to the area surrounding this launch site and include a speed limit.

Slipway, Abereiddy

Lat. 51.9360, Long. -5.2060.

Pembrokeshire Watersports Centre 01348 874803

CHARGES: None

SUITABILITY: Small trailer can be pushed.

ACCESS: ¼ tidal. TYPE OF RAMP: Ramp onto beach

UPPER AREA: Shingle. LOWER AREA: Sand.

DIRECTIONS: Abereiddy is on the coast road north of the A487 to the west of Fishguard.

RAMP DESCRIPTION: Small beach access ramp. Suitable for small boats only. Popular with windsurfers.

FACILITIES: Large car park near the slip. Suffered severe storm damage March 2002 and may not be usable.

Slipway, Porthgain

Lat. 51.9485, Long. -5.1823.

Pembrokeshire Watersports Centre 01348 874803

CHARGES: None

SUITABILITY: Large trailer needs a car.

ACCESS: ¼ tidal. TYPE OF RAMP: Concrete UPPER AREA: Harbour.

LOWER AREA: Sand.

DIRECTIONS: From Fishguard follow A487 south to Croesgoch. Turn right onto minor road to Porthgain for 2 miles.

RAMP DESCRIPTION: Very good concrete slipway into the harbour. Concrete slipway into the harbour. Access 2 hours either side of high water.

FACILITIES: Beautiful village with good pubs and restaurants. Toilets and public telephone. Makes a very nice stop-off point if cruising around the coast.

HAZARDS: Strong tide outside harbour. Pembrokeshire County Council byelaws apply to the area surrounding this launch site and include a speed limit.

Slipway, Abercastle

Lat. 51.9596, Long. -5.1271.

Pembrokeshire Watersports Centre 01348 874803

CHARGES: None

SUITABILITY: Small trailer can be pushed.

ACCESS: ¼ tidal. TYPE OF RAMP: Ramp onto beach

UPPER AREA: Shingle. LOWER AREA: Sand.

DIRECTIONS: Abercastle is on the coast road north of the A487 to the west of Fishguard. The bay has a steep access road.

RAMP DESCRIPTION: Small beach access ramp. Suitable for small boats only.

FACILITIES: Parking available on the roadside. Lovely little stop-off point if cruising around the coast.

HAZARDS: Pembrokeshire County Council byelaws apply to the area surrounding this launch site and include a speed limit.

Goodwick Slipway, Fishguard

Lat. 52.0031, Long. -4.9921.

Pembrokeshire Watersports Centre 01348 874803

CHARGES: None

SUITABILITY: Large trailer needs a car.

ACCESS: ¼ tidal. TYPE OF RAMP: Concrete slipway.

UPPER AREA: Sand. LOWER AREA: Sand.

DIRECTIONS: The Goodwick slipway at the Fishguard ferry port. From Cardigan follow A487 south. Site is adjacent to car park and watersports centre on the seafront. Photo of secondary, slipway, positioned to the LEFT (25 yards) of main, slipway, mentioned.

RAMP DESCRIPTION: One of the best ramps in the area giving excellent access to the beach for launching at all states of the tide. Jetskis are allowed. Information board at the head of the slipway.

FACILITIES: Large free parking area. Toilets, public telephone and visitors centre.

HAZARDS: Speed restriction in harbour and stay clear of ferries entering and leaving the harbour.

Lower Town, Fishguard

Lat. 51.9957, Long. -4.9690.

Harbourmaster 07775 523846

CHARGES: £5

SUITABILITY: Small trailer can be pushed.

ACCESS: All of tidal range. TYPE OF RAMP: Ramp onto firm sand

UPPER AREA: Sand. LOWER AREA: Sand.

DIRECTIONS: From Fishguard take the A487 east. As you leave Fishguard you will cross over a river, immediately turn left and left again to get down to the slipway.

RAMP DESCRIPTION: Awkward access to this site and you must not leave trailers on the slipway, but go back to the car park. It is not easy to turn a trailer on the slipway.

FACILITIES: Boat moorings available. Fishguard Yacht Club nearby. Toilets and a short walk to the car park.

Pwllgwaelod, Dinas Head

Lat. 52.0218, Long. -4.9100.

Pembrokeshire Watersports Centre 01348 874803

CHARGES: None

SUITABILITY: Small trailer can be pushed.

ACCESS: All of tidal range. TYPE OF RAMP: Ramp onto firm beach

UPPER AREA: Sand. LOWER AREA: Sand.

DIRECTIONS: From Fishguard take the A487 east. Turn left at Dinas. You need to go down a very steep access road that gets busy in the summer. Small boats only.

RAMP DESCRIPTION: Concrete ramp onto the beach.

FACILITIES: Slipway is in a very picturesque village that gets very crowded in the summer. Local pub can get very crowded. Limited parking. Well worth a visit, but probably best to arrive by sea.

HAZARDS: Pembrokeshire County Council byelaws apply to the area surrounding this launch site and include a speed limit.

5

Cwm yr Eglwys, Dinas Head
Lat. 52.0241, Long. -4.8943.
Pembrokeshire Watersports Centre 01348 874803

CHARGES: None
SUITABILITY: Small trailer can be pushed.
ACCESS: ¼ tidal. **TYPE OF RAMP:** Ramp onto firm beach. Cars not allowed on beach. Leave trailers standing on end in gulley to side of slipway. No trailers to be left on beach. **UPPER AREA:** Sand.
LOWER AREA: Sand.
DIRECTIONS: From Fishguard take the A487 east. Go past Dinas and take the next left. You need to go down a very steep access road that gets busy in the summer. Small boats only.
RAMP DESCRIPTION: Concrete ramp onto the beach.
FACILITIES: Slipway is in a very picturesque village that gets very crowded in the summer. Limited parking - £1 a day - but trailers not allowed in car park. Well worth a visit, but probably best to arrive by sea. Bay is good anchorage except in northwest to east winds. Watch out for swimmers and pot buoys.
HAZARDS: Pembrokeshire County Council byelaws apply to the area surrounding this launch site and include a speed limit.

Parrog Beach Slip, Newport
Lat. 52.0215, Long. -4.8362.

CHARGES: None
SUITABILITY: Large trailer needs a car.
ACCESS: ½ tidal. **TYPE OF RAMP:** Ramp onto firm beach
UPPER AREA: Sand. **LOWER AREA:** Sand.
DIRECTIONS: Narrow access road to Parrog. Follow the road down to the sea where is ends up in a boat yard. Facility is run by the Newport Boat Club.
RAMP DESCRIPTION: Shallow harbour with sheltered anchorage. It is also possible to launch at Newport Sands, 400 metres to the east. Large popular beach that you can take a car onto. Big car park nearby. This bay gets rough in a westerly wind. At high tide the gradient on the sand can be shallow and it is sometimes better to launch at a lower tide into the river channel.
FACILITIES: Car park and toilets adjacent. Shops at Newport and Parrog. The beach at Parrog can get quite busy with people on the beach during the middle of the day. The public car park outside the yacht club can be full also.
HAZARDS: Newport Bay is exposed to westerly winds. Care is needed to negotiate the bar where the river meets the sea. Access to the sea possible two hours either side of high water. Pembrokeshire County Council byelaws apply to the area surrounding this launch site and include a speed limit.

Cardigan, St Dogmaels
Lat. 52.0889, Long. -4.6815.

CHARGES: None
SUITABILITY: Large trailer needs a car.
ACCESS: ¾ tidal. **TYPE OF RAMP:** Concrete slipway.
UPPER AREA: Mud. **LOWER AREA:** Mud.
DIRECTIONS: On the Teifi Estuary. From Cardigan follow the B4546 through St Dogmaels. Site is on the west bank of the Teifi Estuary.

RAMP DESCRIPTION: Good concrete ramp. At the end of the ramp there is mud over hardcore so it is possible to launch at low tide, but messy. The slipway is used by the lifeboat service; do not leave trailers on the slipway. There is another slipway in the centre of St Dogmaels. Go through the Jewsons car park and between the house and pumping station. Gives access to a reasonable shallow gradient slipway. It is also possible to launch over the sand at Poppit Sands at the mouth of the estuary on the west side. Slipway, by Jewsons.
FACILITIES: Limited parking on the roadside. Picnic area at the top of the ramp.
HAZARDS: Speed restrictions apply.

Bridge Slip, Cardigan
Lat. 52.0812, Long. -4.6618.
SUITABILITY: Large trailer needs a car.
ACCESS: All of tidal range. **TYPE OF RAMP:** Concrete
UPPER AREA: Mud. **LOWER AREA:** Mud.
DIRECTIONS: Ramp is just downstream of the lower road bridge next to the Somerfields car park.
RAMP DESCRIPTION: Good slipway but water here is very shallow at low tide.
FACILITIES: Next to the Somerfields car park and close to centre of town.

Teifi Boat Club, Cardigan
Lat. 52.1049, Long. -4.6835.
01239 613846. Club house number.
SUITABILITY: Large trailer needs a car.
ACCESS: All of tidal range. **TYPE OF RAMP:** Concrete
UPPER AREA: Sand. **LOWER AREA:** Shingle.
RAMP DESCRIPTION: There are two slip - one private for Boat Club; one public about 20 yards from the Boat Club. Both ramps dry at low tide, so when you launch depends entirely on the draught of your boat. Ramps are straight, not steep. Access to sea is limited by draught of your boat - channel is less than half a metre at low tide. The bar can be a problem with wind against incoming tide.
FACILITIES: Public and club parking. Club has toilets and usual facilities. No fuel. Caravan site nearby. Moorings may be available.
HAZARDS: Need to follow the channel on the way out - visual check at low tide is essential. Ramp dries - if you can launch, then there will be enough water to get out to sea.

Slipway, Llangranog
Lat. 52.1600, Long. -4.4751.
CHARGES: None
SUITABILITY: Large trailer needs a car.
ACCESS: ¼ tidal. **TYPE OF RAMP:** Ramp onto firm sand
UPPER AREA: Concrete. **LOWER AREA:** Sand.
DIRECTIONS: Take the A487 to Brynhoffnant and take the turning to Llangranog. Ramp is at the southern end of village.
RAMP DESCRIPTION: Thought to be property of Llangranog Angling Club - annual membership something like £20 pa. They provide a tractor & driver for launch & recovery. Various small boats are often blocking the slipway. Secretary is Mr Jones, phone number is 01239 654 435. Fairly steep ramp on to firm sand at southern end of village. A small boat (e.g.

5

5 metre RIB) could be launched almost any time, probably depending more on sea conditions than tide. Exposed to Westerlies. Steep narrow access.
FACILITIES: Car park 400 yards for car and trailer.

Harbour Slip, New Quay
Lat. 52.2158, Long. -4.3585.
Harbourmaster 01545 560368
CHARGES: £4.30-8.00/day
SUITABILITY: Large trailer needs a car.
ACCESS: ½ tidal. **TYPE OF RAMP:** Steep cobbles onto beach.
UPPER AREA: Sand. **LOWER AREA:** Sand.
DIRECTIONS: From Cardigan follow A487 north taking A486 west at Synod Inn. From Aberaeron follow A487 south taking B4342 west at Llanarth.
RAMP DESCRIPTION: Steep cobbled slipway onto sandy beach. Access is via steep one-way street. Access through the town is difficult with larger boats. Wilderness conservationists strong lobby here as dolphins are regularly seen nearby. No Jetskis allowed. Weekly and monthly rates available, phone harbourmaster.
FACILITIES: Petrol, parking, toilets, food.
HAZARDS: 3 knot speed limit in harbour, 5 knot in bay and 8 knot off beaches.

Harbour slipway, Aberaeron
Lat. 52.2427, Long. -4.2645.
Harbourmaster 01545 571645
SUITABILITY: Large trailer needs a car.
ACCESS: Unknown. **TYPE OF RAMP:** Concrete **UPPER AREA:** Harbour.
LOWER AREA: Unknown.
DIRECTIONS: The harbour is signposted on the south side of the village of Aberaeron and the slipway leads into the harbour.
RAMP DESCRIPTION: The concrete slipway drops you right into the harbour.
FACILITIES: Aberaeron is between Aberystwyth and New Quay and is a lovely little village with a number of good pubs. There are two good caravan sites within 2 miles of the harbour. The slipway is next to a large car park with public conveniences about 30yards away. Fishing is good and there are dolphins and seals within the area between Aberystwyth and Newquay.

Aberystwyth Marina, Aberystwyth
Y Lanfa - Aberystwyth Marina, Trefechan, Aberystwyth, Ceredigion, Wales SY23 1AS
Lat. 52.4091, Long. -4.0871.
01970 611422

Aberystwyth Marina, Aberystwyth
Lat. 52.4111, Long. -4.0864.
01970 611422
CHARGES: £6.50
SUITABILITY: Large trailer needs a car.
ACCESS: ½ tidal. **TYPE OF RAMP:** Steep concrete ramp.
UPPER AREA: Shingle. **LOWER AREA:** Shingle.

DIRECTIONS: From Cardigan follow A487 north to town centre and then signs to harbour.
RAMP DESCRIPTION: Good gradient concrete ramp leading onto firm shingle so can use at lower tides. No PWCs allowed. You will be expected to have insurance.
FACILITIES: Petrol, parking, toilets on site. Also day berths at the marina if available which includes use of showers.
HAZARDS: 5 knot speed limit in harbour, 8 knots within 200 metres of shore. Bar at harbour limits access to 3 hours before and 4 hours after high tide in calm conditions for up to 1m draught. Dangerous conditions in onshore winds.

Aberleri Boatyard, Ynyslas, Machynlleth
Lat. 52.5186, Long. -4.0406.
CHARGES: Unknown, but there is a modest charge
SUITABILITY: Large trailer needs a car.
ACCESS: Unknown. **TYPE OF RAMP: UPPER AREA:** Concrete.
LOWER AREA: Mud.
DIRECTIONS: Turn off right on the Machynlleth/Aberystwyth road just before Taliesin (signposted Ynyslas)
RAMP DESCRIPTION: Wide concrete, good access. At low tide the bottom of the ramp is mud. Very tidal.
FACILITIES: A toilet. Pub nearby on main road.
HAZARDS: Channel is marked by fisherman's buoys, but twisty and narrow and lots of sand. Only attempt on a rising tide. Bar across the Dyfi estuary.

Frongoch Boatyard, Aberdovey
Lat. 52.5562, Long. -3.9721.
01654 767177
SUITABILITY: Portable Only.
ACCESS: ¼ tidal. **TYPE OF RAMP:** Concrete, onto sand.
UPPER AREA: Mud. **LOWER AREA:** Sand.
DIRECTIONS: Smugglers Cove, 4 miles upstream of Aberdovey. A493 Machynlleth to Aberdovey. On left hand side about 3 miles after Pennal. Access to Dovey estuary.
RAMP DESCRIPTION: Gradient is moderate.
FACILITIES: Boatyard.
HAZARDS: Channel downstream is difficult to find but bottom is sand. High sand banks. High risk of grounding. Use OS map for channel, not chart.

Slipways, Aberdovey
Lat. 52.5432, Long. -4.0468.
01654 767626
CHARGES: £4.50-£10.50 per day for council slip.
SUITABILITY: Large trailer needs a car.
ACCESS: ½ tidal. **TYPE OF RAMP:** Slip onto firm sand.
UPPER AREA: Sand. **LOWER AREA:** Sand.
DIRECTIONS: Ramps are on the Aberdovey foreshore by the church and lifeboat station.
RAMP DESCRIPTION: Two slipways to choose from. One is public and the other belongs to the sailing club. To use the sailing club one, get

5

temporary membership. Council office is next to the council slipway. Ramps lead on to a firm beach which gets steeper towards channel as tide recedes, suitable for car 3 hours either side high water.
FACILITIES: Parking space is limited especially in the summer. Fresh water at sailing club, other facilities in Aberdovey, ½ mile. Dinghy park available for trailer if membership of sailing club taken up. Slip water tap close by.
HAZARDS: Watch bar at entrance to estuary. Crowded in summer.

Town Slip, Tywyn
Lat. 52.5825, Long. -4.0989.

CHARGES: £10 per day
SUITABILITY: Small trailer can be pushed.
ACCESS: ¾ tidal. **TYPE OF RAMP:** Concrete at top and sand at the bottom. **UPPER AREA:** Concrete. **LOWER AREA:** Sand.
DIRECTIONS: Slipway in on the seafront in the village of Tywyn off Marine Parade.
RAMP DESCRIPTION: The ramp is very steep, very hard driving back up with trailer. Small boats only unless you have a powerful towing vehicle.
FACILITIES: Public toilets are on site along with eating places. Petrol station about ¼ of a mile, free parking at the top off the ramp.

Fairbourne Beach, Fairbourne
Lat. 52.6929, Long. -4.0573.

CHARGES: None
SUITABILITY: Small trailer can be pushed.
ACCESS: ¼ tidal. **TYPE OF RAMP:** Concrete onto shingle and sand. **UPPER AREA:** Shingle. **LOWER AREA:** Sand.
DIRECTIONS: Follow the signs to Fairbourne. Cross the level crossing and head down to the sea. Turn left at the beach. Site is by the Fairbourne Sailing Club hut.
RAMP DESCRIPTION: Steeply shelving shingle at top going onto firm but flat sand. Even a 4 × 4 can easily get stuck on the shingle. Site is used by Fairbourne Sailing Club.
FACILITIES: Café and pubs in Fairbourne. Parking.
HAZARDS: Can be tricky launching in surf.

Penrhyn point Fairbourne, Fairbourne
Lat. 52.7125, Long. -4.0510.
01341 250929

SUITABILITY: Large trailer needs a car.
ACCESS: ¼ tidal. **TYPE OF RAMP:** Short concrete ramp
UPPER AREA: Shingle. **LOWER AREA:** Shingle.
DIRECTIONS: Follow the signs to Fairbourne. Cross the level crossing and head down to the sea. Turn right at the beach and follow the small railway to car park.
RAMP DESCRIPTION: Launch into the estuary so check tides beforehand. Launching is normally possible 3hrs either side of high water
FACILITIES: Café and pubs in Fairbourne. Parking.
HAZARDS: Deep water channel from slip is narrow check channel at low water. Sand banks within the Mauddach Estuary. Strong currents in the main channel

Harbour Slip, Barmouth
Lat. 52.7186, Long. -4.0519.
01341 280671

CHARGES: £4.50-£20.00
SUITABILITY: Large trailer needs a car.
ACCESS: ½ tidal. **TYPE OF RAMP:** Steep concrete. **UPPER AREA:** Sand.
LOWER AREA: Sand.
DIRECTIONS: Harbour Slipway, The Quay.
RAMP DESCRIPTION: Concrete ramp onto soft sand. PWCs must be registered. Ramp is into the harbour that dries out at low tide. Powerboats £10.50/day, £85/season, less than 5hp £4.50/day, £40/season, Jetskis £16/day, £110/season. Jetskis need to register (£20 inc. days launch) and show insurance. Quite strict in the harbour on speed, parking is quite difficult. Catch the tide right and you will have an excellent few hours. Good pub food across from the slipway too.
FACILITIES: Parking petrol and limited boat storage. Barmouth is a beautiful seaside town with all the usual facilities. Does get very busy in the summer.
HAZARDS: 5 knot speed limit in the harbour. There are lots of sand bars in the Mawddach Estuary and watch out for strong currents.

Shell Island Yacht Club, Llanbedr
Lat. 52.8249, Long. -4.1327.

CHARGES: None
SUITABILITY: Small trailer can be pushed.
ACCESS: ¼ tidal. **TYPE OF RAMP:** Concrete **UPPER AREA:** Sand.
LOWER AREA: Sand.
RAMP DESCRIPTION: Moderate gradient on the slipway. Access is restricted to high tide so check the tide times before setting out.
FACILITIES: Overnight parking available. Part of Shell facilities. Slip water tap available.

Harbour Slip, Porthmadog
Lat. 52.9237, Long. -4.1291.
01766 512927

CHARGES: £4-8/day
SUITABILITY: Large trailer needs a car.
ACCESS: ½ tidal. **TYPE OF RAMP:** Concrete ramp.
UPPER AREA: Shingle. **LOWER AREA:** Mud.
DIRECTIONS: Harbour office is just downstream of the road bridge opposite the steam railway station.
RAMP DESCRIPTION: Fairly steep at the top and take care as the slipway narrows as you go down. Usable about 2 hours either side of high water.
FACILITIES: Petrol, parking, toilets. Close to centre of town and trailers can be left behind the harbour office.
HAZARDS: 6 knot speed limit within harbour and 4 mph within 100 metres of shore in other areas. No craft allowed in designated bathing areas. Waterskiing permitted outside these limits.

5

Borth-y-Gest Ramp, Porthmadog
Lat. 52.9161, Long. -4.1349.
01766 512927

CHARGES: £4-8/day
SUITABILITY: Small trailer can be pushed.
ACCESS: ¼ tidal. **TYPE OF RAMP:** Concrete ramp. **UPPER AREA:** Sand.
LOWER AREA: Mud.
DIRECTIONS: From the north, take the A487 via Caernarfon, turning right after the park then taking the first left. From the south, cross embankment and turn left after the pelican crossing.
RAMP DESCRIPTION: Steep at top, shallow at bottom. No Jetskis allowed. Locked barrier controlled by the harbourmaster. Quite narrow and very difficult to launch even a 14 foot fishing boat due to a very sharp turn required at the top. No water during Neap tides, need at least 4.7 metre tides to launch. Using a four wheel drive vehicle is risky since parts of the muddy area is deep and high possibility of cutting tyres on the slate and rocks. For smaller boats that can be wheeled manually, there is another narrow ramp at right angles to the main ramp which has water for at least half of the Neap tides. Some sand/mud has to be crossed to reach this but this is quite firm. No vehicles should venture down the slipway, as it gets very muddy very quickly! Ideally this slipway should only be used at high water on Springs.
FACILITIES: Petrol, parking, toilets.
HAZARDS: 6 knot speed limit within harbour and 4 mph within 100 metres of shore in other areas. No craft allowed in designated bathing areas. Waterskiing permitted outside these limits. When the tide turns, a significant surge will occur on Springs - so much so that you will be able to hear it!

Black Rock Sands, Porthmadog
Lat. 52.9151, Long. -4.1899.
01766 512927

CHARGES: When a boat launches at any Gwynedd council slipway or beach, it must first be registered with the council, for this you need to bring a copy of your insurance certificate, a fee of £20 in person or £15 by post, daily launching at £12, or £130 for the season, the same will apply for PWC.
SUITABILITY: Large trailer needs a car.
ACCESS: No Ramp. **TYPE OF RAMP:** Hard sand will support heavy vehicle. **UPPER AREA:** Sand. **LOWER AREA:** Sand.
DIRECTIONS: Morfa Bychan, nr. Porthmadog, Gwynedd. From Porthmadog town centre, follow road signposted to Black Rock Sands.
RAMP DESCRIPTION: Gently sloping beach. Launching area designated (see signs at entrance) to separate boats from bathers. Note that in the summer season the access road is closed at 8.00 p.m. daily. The very gentle slope of the beach makes it ideal for children to bathe here but it is necessary to take the trailer, and sometimes the towing vehicle, well into the water at high tide in order to get sufficient depth to launch.
FACILITIES: Parking on beach (2 miles long). Toilets. Mobile caterers on beach in season. Several garages selling both petrol and diesel in Porthmadog (2 miles), none on beach.
HAZARDS: Speed restriction close inshore, limit marked by a line of buoys. Sandbanks in Glaslyn estuary, buoyed channel into Porthmadog harbour.

Slipway, Criccieth
Lat. 52.9179, Long. -4.2301.

CHARGES: Under the control of County Council - see Pwllheli for full details
SUITABILITY: Large trailer needs a car.
ACCESS: ½ tidal. **TYPE OF RAMP:** Concrete **UPPER AREA:** Concrete.
LOWER AREA: Shingle.
DIRECTIONS: Off the main A497 in Criccieth, near the lifeboat station.
RAMP DESCRIPTION: Public slipway, onto shingle and large stones at low water.
FACILITIES: Petrol in the village, parking, nearby.

Hafan Pwllheli, Pwllheli
Glan Don, Pwllheli, Gwynedd, Wales LL53 5YT
Lat. 52.8868, Long. -4.4063.
01758 701219

Harbour Slip, Pwllheli
Lat. 52.8827, Long. -4.4046.
01758 704081

CHARGES: 2006 charges are - Daily launch fee is £10.00 for powerboats and £12.00 for PWCs monthly launching permit is £90.00 for powerboats and £96.00 for PWCs. Seasons launch permit is £112.00 for powerboats and £134.00 for PWCs. These launch permits give access to all council slips in Gwynedd i.e. from Aberdovey round to Caernarfon with the exception of Morfa Nefyn which is still under the control of the local council as opposed to the County Council. All powerboats and PWCs need to be registered (which covers all of North Wales) and costs £12.00 for powerboats and £14.00 for PWCs for the season.
SUITABILITY: Large trailer needs a car.
ACCESS: All of tidal range. **TYPE OF RAMP:** Concrete
UPPER AREA: Concrete. **LOWER AREA:** Shingle.
DIRECTIONS: Don't go near new marina, but go into Pwllheli, turn left (opposite Chinese takeaway) turn left again at island. Follow road over causeway towards beach. Turn first left through council houses. Just before Boat Yard is Harbourmaster's office and best slip in Wales. Life Boat station is just a few metres further on.
RAMP DESCRIPTION: It is a public slip, managed by a very friendly harbourmaster. It runs into sheltered water (at all states of weather) usable for about 4/5 of tidal range.
FACILITIES: Toilets and showers next to harbourmaster's office. Ample parking. Petrol nearby.
HAZARDS: Moored boats in the opposite marina.

Abersoch Land and Sea, Abersoch
Lat. 52.8270, Long. -4.5064.
01758 713434

SUITABILITY: Large trailer needs a car.
ACCESS: All of tidal range. **TYPE OF RAMP: UPPER AREA:** Unknown.
LOWER AREA: Unknown.
DIRECTIONS: Abersoch Land and Sea is on your right hand side as you go into Abersoch.

5

RAMP DESCRIPTION: Contract launch only for park and ride customers. If you want to turn up and launch, speak to Vic Jones who runs the launching facility opposite Land and Sea.

FACILITIES: Land and Sea provides a full range of services that makes it an integral part of the Abersoch boating community. Boat park and launch services 7 days a week during daytime hours and up to eight tractors in service at any given time to ensure you don't have to wait for a lift. Pre-arrange pick-up times or call from the water when you are ready to come in. Also petrol and diesel fuelling facilities.

Abersoch Beach, Abersoch

Lat. 52.8210, Long. -4.5020.

Harbourmaster's office in Pwllheli (01758 704081)

CHARGES: 2006 charges are - Daily launch fee is £10.00 for powerboats and £12.00 for PWCs Monthly launching permit is £90.00 for powerboats and £96.00 for PWCs. Seasons launch permit is £112.00 for powerboats and £134.00 for PWCs. These launch permits give access to all council slips in Gwynedd i.e. from Aberdovey round to Caernarfon with the exception of Morfa Nefyn which is still under the control of the local council as opposed to the County Council. Anglesey also included. All powerboats and PWCs need to be registered (which covers all of North Wales) and costs £12.00 for powerboats and £14.00 for PWCs for the season. Car parking is £4.00 per day.

SUITABILITY: Small trailer can be pushed.

ACCESS: ¼ tidal. TYPE OF RAMP: Concrete. 4 × 4 needed at high water Neaps due to short distance from water to ramp.

UPPER AREA: Concrete. LOWER AREA: Sand.

DIRECTIONS: From Village Centre follow minor road signposted To the Beach as you pass car park and toilet area (on right) continue along to slipway.

RAMP DESCRIPTION: The slipway has a padlocked barrier that opens 9am-8pm and closes for one hour at very high Spring tide due to flooding. Very busy location in season, windsurfers, Jetskis. Payment is made to the Beach Patrol and charges for 2006 are £10.00 per day for powerboats and £12 per day for Jetskis. Alternatively, you can get a monthly launching permit for £90.00 for powerboats and £96.00 for Jetskis or a seasons launch permit for £112.00 for powerboats and £134.00 for Jetskis - available from the Harbourmaster's office in Pwllheli (01758 704081). There is a second slipway to the south at Machroes, also run by the council. Requires a 4 × 4 due to the soft sand.

FACILITIES: Nearest petrol in approximately 2 miles. Beach side café, pubs, shops in village approximately 1 mile. Toilets, car parking area 200 metres away. No parking of vehicles is allowed on the beach. Town centre close by.

HAZARDS: Keep lookout for moorings. The council signs at the slip provide details on the user zoning in the bay.

Rhiw, Abersoch

Lat. 52.8227, Long. -4.6052.

CHARGES: None

SUITABILITY: Large trailer needs a car.

ACCESS: All of tidal range. TYPE OF RAMP: Shingle

UPPER AREA: Shingle. LOWER AREA: Shingle.

DIRECTIONS: At the western end of Hell's Mouth (Porth Neigwl). Access is down a long steep track near to the National Trust property in Rhiw.

RAMP DESCRIPTION: There are a number of boats kept on the beach. Need a tractor to get to and from the beach. Each spring a local fisherman / JCB owner takes the JCB down and spends a couple of days moving shingle around and creating a small 'harbour' and launch slip, the other fishermen/boat users 'chip in' to pay for his few days work, this only lasts for the season as winter storms churn up the rock / shingle. There are old tractors at the top of the track and also on the beach for launching the boats. Speak to local fishermen about using this slip.

FACILITIES: Only suitable if leaving boat at this site for the season. There are about 6 boats kept there with room for more, there are also some old buildings which are used for storage. A planning application has been put in for a concrete slip at Hells Mouth although access is down a steep track probably half a mile long.

HAZARDS: Hell's Mouth does not get its name lightly, it is about 4 miles wide and faces southwest, it is a popular surfing beach (towards the eastern end) and during a storm it is spectacular.

Beach Slip, Aberdaron

Lat. 52.8031, Long. -4.7124.

01758 704081

CHARGES: £5/day, call for season ticket prices.

SUITABILITY: Large trailer needs a car.

ACCESS: No Ramp. TYPE OF RAMP: Concrete ramp to beach.

UPPER AREA: Concrete. LOWER AREA: Sand.

DIRECTIONS: From village carry on over hump back bridge turn left, the ramp and access to the beach is on your immediate right.

RAMP DESCRIPTION: Ramp leads directly onto sandy beach and only suitable for 4 × 4 although Bardsey Island Trust operate a launch/recover service during the season (£10.)

FACILITIES: Petrol some way out of village, several pubs, café, toilets and car park approximately 300 yards away, fee payable.

HAZARDS: Isolated rocks. NOTE Beach prone to quite a lot of swell and breaking waves. A slick launch and recovery is required.

Porth Colmon, Pen-y-graig

Lat. 52.8760, Long. -4.6847.

CHARGES: None

SUITABILITY: Large trailer needs a car.

ACCESS: ¼ tidal. TYPE OF RAMP: Rough concrete.

UPPER AREA: Concrete. LOWER AREA: Shingle.

DIRECTIONS: From Morfa Nefyn take a right turn off the B4417 in Llangwnnadl, signposted Porth Colmon (or Golmon), about 2 miles from B4417.

RAMP DESCRIPTION: Not an easy launch down a short, fairly steep ramp onto a shingle / rock beach. 4 × 4s are OK on the beach but definitely not cars - plenty of manpower needed. This site gives free access to the more remote northern coast of the Lleyn Peninsula, away from Abersoch. Excellent diving/fishing from Maen Mellt and Bardsey.

FACILITIES: None, parking is free but space is limited.

HAZARDS: Wreckage of an old steamer at low water together with foul smelling weed.

5

Porth Ysgadan, Tudweiloig
Lat. 52.9042, Long. -4.6502.

CHARGES: None
SUITABILITY: Large trailer needs a car.
ACCESS: ¼ tidal. **TYPE OF RAMP:** Rough concrete/stone
UPPER AREA: Concrete. **LOWER AREA:** Sand.
DIRECTIONS: From Morfa Nefyn take B4417 to Tudweiloig, shortly after Tudweiloig there is a right turn down to the coast. Porth Ysgadan is not signposted but at each sharp bend in the lane there will be a narrower road going towards the coast, take each narrower road until you reach a bumpy dirt/stone track leading down to Porth Ysgadan.
RAMP DESCRIPTION: One of only two 'free' launches on the north coast of the Lleyn Peninsula. Porth Ysgadan is a natural harbour. The ramp onto the beach is narrow, uneven and twisty with a 90 degree bend. The beach is hard sand at low water and cars are OK, at high water there are submerged rocks at the end of the ramp. Site is used by fishermen and divers, a tractor may be available. The track down to Porth Ysgadan has had a layer of road stone put down to fill the pot holes.
FACILITIES: None, parking is free.
HAZARDS: Submerged rocks at high water.

Harbour Slip, Morfa Neyfn
Lat. 52.9374, Long. -4.5576.
01758 704081

CHARGES: £4-10/day, call for season ticket prices.
SUITABILITY: Large trailer needs a car.
ACCESS: All of tidal range. **TYPE OF RAMP:** Ramp onto beach
UPPER AREA: Sand. **LOWER AREA:** Sand.
DIRECTIONS: Follow the road straight down to the sea.
RAMP DESCRIPTION: Short concrete ramp leads onto a firm beach. PWCs must be registered. Wardens on site in the summer.
FACILITIES: Park back up in the village. Very popular sheltered beach.

Harbour Slip, Trefor
Lat. 52.9985, Long. -4.4224.
01758 704081

CHARGES: £4-10/day, call for season ticket prices.
SUITABILITY: Large trailer needs a car.
ACCESS: All of tidal range. **TYPE OF RAMP:** Ramp into harbour
UPPER AREA: Sand. **LOWER AREA:** Sand.
DIRECTIONS: Follow signpost for Trefor, 1mile north of Llanaelhaearn, junction of A499 & B4417. Harbour is north of village and visible as you travel towards the coast.
RAMP DESCRIPTION: Short concrete ramp leads onto the beach. PWCs must be registered.
FACILITIES: Car park and often an ice cream van.

Dinas Dinlle, Llandwrog
Lat. 53.0861, Long. -4.3373.
01758 704081

CHARGES: £5, call for season ticket prices.
SUITABILITY: Large trailer needs a car.
ACCESS: No Ramp. **TYPE OF RAMP:** Concrete onto hard sand.
UPPER AREA: Sand. **LOWER AREA:** Sand.

DIRECTIONS: Ramp is to the west of Llandwrog on the road towards Caernafon Airport. Easy to find in the middle of the beach.
RAMP DESCRIPTION: Ramp takes you onto a firm sandy beach. The hammerhead groyne offers some protection. Can be rough in a westerly and not a particularly easy to use site. Beach has a very shallow gradient.
FACILITIES: Parking and café. Nearby caravan sites.

Ty Calch (Ronnies), Caernarfon
Lat. 53.1280, Long. -4.3102.
07917 859345

CHARGES: Boats are launched and recovered by tractor only, and trailer stored for £15.00 per launch. (£3 Discount available for regular users)
SUITABILITY: Large trailer needs a car.
ACCESS: All of tidal range. **TYPE OF RAMP:** Concrete
UPPER AREA: Shingle. **LOWER AREA:** Sand.
DIRECTIONS: Take the Caernarfon to Pwhelli road A487. Past Tescos, straight over roundabout, then first right and immediately right again which leads to Aber foreshore road. Past the Golf course and approx one mile on left is a white cottage, slipway is in front.
RAMP DESCRIPTION: Any sized boat can be launched due to tractor assist at any state of tide.
FACILITIES: Open 7 days a week 8.30am to 7pm Monday to Friday and 7am to 7pm weekends, and all holidays. Season runs 10th April - 25th October 2009. Phone prior outside of these dates. Toilet / Shower / changing facilities. Live Bait usually available. Local Marine engineers nearby.
HAZARDS: Sandbanks and Caernarfon Bar

Victoria Dock Slip, Caernarfon
Lat. 53.1430, Long. -4.2766.
01286 672118 Harbourmaster

CHARGES: None
SUITABILITY: Large trailer needs a car.
ACCESS: ½ tidal. **TYPE OF RAMP:** Fairly steep concrete ramp
UPPER AREA: Shingle. **LOWER AREA:** Shingle.
DIRECTIONS: Follow the signs in Caerarfon to the Harbour. Access is through Victoria Dock access road which gets congested in the summer.
RAMP DESCRIPTION: Stone ramp into the Straits, runs parallel to the stream. Often gets parked up and access can be blocked by inconsiderate car owners. Jetskiers are tolerated and carefully monitored.
FACILITIES: Limited parking. Close to centre of Caernarfon.
HAZARDS: 5 knot speed limit in populated areas. Caernarfon Harbour Trust will prosecute any flagrant breach of Port byelaws.

Dinas Boatyard, Caernarfon
Lat. 53.1807, Long. -4.2158.
01248 671642

CHARGES: Not known
SUITABILITY: Large trailer needs a car.
ACCESS: All of tidal range. **TYPE OF RAMP:** Concrete
UPPER AREA: Harbour. **LOWER AREA:** Unknown.
DIRECTIONS: Boatyard is situated on Beach Road to the south west of Y Felinheli, or Port Dinorwig.

5

RAMP DESCRIPTION: Large ex-military slipway.
FACILITIES: Secure parking and under cover boat storage.
HAZARDS: Strong current in the Menai Straits.

Port Dinorwic Marina, Yfelinneli
Yfelinneli, Gwynedd, Wales LL56 4JN
Lat. 53.1874, Long. -4.2082.
01248 671500

Port Dinorwic Yacht Harbour, Caernarfon
Lat. 53.1853, Long. -4.2111.
Port Dinorwic Yacht Harbour 01248 671500

CHARGES: £10/day
SUITABILITY: Large trailer needs a car.
ACCESS: ¾ tidal. **TYPE OF RAMP:** Ramp, muddy at low water.
UPPER AREA: Sand. **LOWER AREA:** Mud.
DIRECTIONS: Marina sign-posted from the main road. Near Y Felinheli.
RAMP DESCRIPTION: Ramp suitable for car, launch any time but muddy at low water. No Jetskiers allowed.
FACILITIES: Charges for car parking and use of ramp. Apply at marina office. All facilities in marina or shops in village.
HAZARDS: Tide runs hard and the water level can be rising with the tide flowing either east or west.

Slipway, Rhosneigr Beach
Lat. 53.2292, Long. -4.5229.
07974 851 423

CHARGES: £20
SUITABILITY: Large trailer needs a car.
ACCESS: Non-tidal. **TYPE OF RAMP:** Concrete. **UPPER AREA:** Concrete.
LOWER AREA: Sand.
DIRECTIONS: Into Rhosneigr village, turn left down Beach road to the end.
RAMP DESCRIPTION: Access to the beach down the slip way. The sand can be soft in parts. There is help available if difficulty arises. Boat launch services available.
FACILITIES: Rhosneigr Boat Services provide full launch and recovery services. All types of boats / Jetski

Rhoscolyn, Holyhead
Lat. 53.2449, Long. -4.5913.
Pier master 01248 712312

CHARGES: None
SUITABILITY: Small trailer can be pushed.
ACCESS: No Ramp. **TYPE OF RAMP:** Ramp onto beach
UPPER AREA: Sand. **LOWER AREA:** Sand.
DIRECTIONS: Follow the A5 across Anglesey, turn left at the lights at Valley, follow signs to Rhoscolyn.
RAMP DESCRIPTION: Suitable for small craft only as this site has a narrow and tortuous access road with lots of right angle bends.
FACILITIES: Limited parking.

Slipway, Trearddur Bay
Lat. 53.2797, Long. -4.6209.
Pier master 01248 712312

CHARGES: Council now charge £10 per launch and £18 for first registration or £60 monthly or £200 yearly. Applies to all craft with engine 15hp or more. Car park is £1.50 per day for car and trailer.
SUITABILITY: Large trailer needs a car.
ACCESS: All of tidal range. **TYPE OF RAMP:** Concrete
UPPER AREA: Concrete. **LOWER AREA:** Sand.
DIRECTIONS: Follow the A5 across Anglesey, turn left at the lights at Valley, follow to Trearddur Bay and then turn left at the petrol station for the beach. The ramp is opposite the Trearddur Bay Hotel with free parking approximately 100 yards further on.
RAMP DESCRIPTION: Warden is on site from 8.30 -5.30pm, charge is £10/day, insurance documents required and a one off registration fee of £18 which allows you to launch off any slipway on the island. On the other hand a tractor launch/recovery is available from the local petrol station at £10 per day. When the warden feels that the bay has enough watercraft on it there is a barrier now which can be locked. The ramp is onto a sandy beach and can be used at all states (if you have a 4 × 4). If launching here for the first time look out for rocks to the left and right, head for the moorings and then turn left keeping the pipe marker to your right until you are well past then turn right and out to the fishing. Slight bend to left (looking down the ramp).
FACILITIES: Car park, £1.50 per day for car plus trailer. Hotel (bars) at top of ramp. Shell garage 300 metres away.

Porth Dafarch, Trearddur Bay
Lat. 53.2877, Long. -4.6514.
Pier master 01248 712312

CHARGES: None
SUITABILITY: Portable Only.
ACCESS: No Ramp. **TYPE OF RAMP:** Ramp onto beach.
UPPER AREA: Sand. **LOWER AREA:** Sand.
DIRECTIONS: Follow the A5 across Anglesey, turn left at the lights at Valley, follow to Trearddur Bay. Ramp is just up the coast from Trearddur Bay.
RAMP DESCRIPTION: There are bollards fixed into place with padlocks on the top of this very short ramp, so any plan to launch would involve negotiation first. The bumpy ramp runs at right angles to the narrow vehicle access, so it would be nearly impossible to launch with a vehicle and there is currently a small step down at the beach end. Used extensively by canoeists.
FACILITIES: Limited parking.

Holyhead Marina, Holyhead
Newry Beach, Holyhead, Anglesey, Wales LL65 1YA
Lat. 53.3174, Long. -4.6444.
01407 764242

Holyhead Sailing Club, Holyhead
Lat. 53.3175, Long. -4.6432.
01407 762526

5

CHARGES: £10 for daily use
SUITABILITY: Large trailer needs a car.
ACCESS: ¾ tidal. **TYPE OF RAMP:** Slipway is locked by Club Bosun.
May be opened on request between 0900 and 1900 (or by arrangement)
UPPER AREA: Concrete. **LOWER AREA:** Mud.
DIRECTIONS: Take A55 to Holyhead, continue over tr. lts under
footbridge to Left turn onto promenade after 1m (approx). Continue over
road humps until HSC Clubhouse is seen to right - Holyhead Marina, with
apartment block, has same approach. Turn right & park at top of road to
Club to arrange use of slipway.
RAMP DESCRIPTION: Concrete slipway primarily for the launching of
Club members' inflatable. Also used by Holyhead Inshore lifeboat (so
must be left clear at all times).
FACILITIES: Showers, bar & restaurant in Clubhouse by arrangement.
Chandlery nearby: all usual stock including "Anglesey & adjoining
waters" pilot.
**HAZARDS: None in Holyhead harbour. TSS across harbour
entrance, Carmel head, Skerries & South Stack tide races within
5nm.**

Newry Beach, Holyhead
Lat. 53.3180, Long. -4.6392.
Holyhead SC 01407 762526

CHARGES: £10 for the use of the ramp by non-members.
SUITABILITY: Large trailer needs a car.
ACCESS: ½ tidal. **TYPE OF RAMP:** Concrete slipway.
UPPER AREA: Shingle. **LOWER AREA:** Shingle.
DIRECTIONS: Enter Anglesey via A55 Expressway (over Britannia
Bridge) and continue to end of Expressway in Holyhead. Continue past
ferry port (on right) and turn left along promenade past coastguard
station to Club entrance on right.
RAMP DESCRIPTION: Ramp is run by the Holyhead Sailing Club.
FACILITIES: Petrol and red diesel available from Holyhead Marina.
Temporary berthing & boat storage at Holyhead Marina. Ample parking
on road - restricted to club members near slipway.
**HAZARDS: Speed limit in harbour. Waterskiing permitted
offshore. This is a very busy ferry port.**

Sandy Beach Caravan Park, Holyhead
Lat. 53.3342, Long. -4.5710.
SUITABILITY: Large trailer needs a car.
ACCESS: All of tidal range. **TYPE OF RAMP:** Concrete / sand.
UPPER AREA: Concrete. **LOWER AREA:** Sand.
DIRECTIONS: A55 to Holyhead, at Valley lights, turn right, follow
road for about 3 miles and you will pass through a small village called
Llanfracraeth, head through the village, then take next left, follow road
until the church take that next left, next right, over the hill and you are
there.
RAMP DESCRIPTION: Access to the slipway is controlled by an electric
gate system and only caravan site residents have access cards.
FACILITIES: Parking available, may have to pay caravan site. No charge
for using the launch site.
**HAZARDS: Three small rock formations visible at low tide,
covered at high tide, possible danger to displacement hulls.**

Church Bay, Holyhead
Lat. 53.3735, Long. -4.5554.
Pier Master 01248 712312

CHARGES: None
SUITABILITY: Small trailer can be pushed.
ACCESS: ¼ tidal. **TYPE OF RAMP:** Concrete onto sand.
UPPER AREA: Concrete. **LOWER AREA:** Sand.
DIRECTIONS: A55 to Holyhead, at Valley lights, turn right, follow
road for about 3 miles and you will pass through a small village called
Llanfracraeth, head through the village, then take second left, follow
road down to the coast.
RAMP DESCRIPTION: Launching from a sandy beach. The surf can
cause problems on this launch site. Suitable for small boats only.
FACILITIES: Small beach and access is tricky.

Cemaes Bay Slip, Anglesey
Lat. 53.4149, Long. -4.4526.
Pier master 01248 712312

CHARGES: All sites in Anglesey are subject to £18 boat registration by
the local council and a launch fee of £10 per day.
SUITABILITY: Large trailer needs a car.
ACCESS: ½ tidal. **TYPE OF RAMP:** Concrete **UPPER AREA:** Sand.
LOWER AREA: Sand.
DIRECTIONS: From the A5052 on the north coast of Anglesey, take the
road down to the beach.
RAMP DESCRIPTION: Gradient is moderate.
FACILITIES: Free parking. Overnight parking available. Parking space is
limited. Security is reasonable.

Bull Bay, Amlwch
Lat. 53.4219, Long. -4.3702.
Pier master 01248 712312

CHARGES: All sites in Anglesey are subject to £18 boat registration by
the local council and a launch fee of £10 per day.
SUITABILITY: Large trailer needs a car.
ACCESS: ½ tidal. **TYPE OF RAMP:** Concrete ramp onto shingle beach.
UPPER AREA: Shingle. **LOWER AREA:** Shingle.
DIRECTIONS: On crossing the bridge to Anglesey take the 5025 for
approximately 17 miles through the town of Amlwch, Bull Bay is 1 mile
further on.
RAMP DESCRIPTION: Short concrete ramp about 20 feet leads on to
shingle beach suitable for cars. Shingle may be soft after a storm.
FACILITIES: Bull Bay Hotel, public toilets. Limited parking.
**HAZARDS: Rocks on each side and the middle of the bay covered
at high tide, 5mph speed limit inside bay.**

Slipway, Amlwch
Lat. 53.4154, Long. -4.3367.
Pier master 01248 712312

CHARGES: All sites in Anglesey are subject to £18 boat registration by
the local council and a launch fee of £10 per day.
SUITABILITY: Small trailer can be pushed.
ACCESS: ¼ tidal. **TYPE OF RAMP:** Concrete **UPPER AREA:** Mud.
LOWER AREA: Mud.

5

RAMP DESCRIPTION: Gradient is fairly steep, quite narrow slip. OK for a car and Wayfarer, could get congested at peak periods. Tarmac at top with small turning area. Slipway leads onto firm ground.

FACILITIES: Car park close by. Café, pub and he nearest tackle shop is at Benllech Bay and is limited in what it sells.

Porth Eilian, Llaneilian
Lat. 53.4114, Long. -4.2940.
Pier master 01248 712312

CHARGES: Council now charge £10 per launch and £20 for first registration or £60 monthly or £100 yearly. Applies to all craft with engine 10hp or more.

SUITABILITY: Large trailer needs a car.

ACCESS: ¼ tidal. **TYPE OF RAMP:** Concrete onto hard sand.

UPPER AREA: Sand. **LOWER AREA:** Shingle.

DIRECTIONS: Head for point Lynas lighthouse, Porth Eilian bay on left hand side of point.

RAMP DESCRIPTION: There is a bollard at the top of the ramp which is locked in position from April - October. The maximum length of boat that can use this ramp is approximately 21´ unless you have a tow bar on the front of your vehicle. The ramp is very steep but has recently been widened.

FACILITIES: Key holder system in place. Parking is at the top of a very steep and long hill. Small narrow beach. Toilets 200 yards up hill. Tea & ice cream caravan by slipway.

HAZARDS: There is a speed limit in the bay (8 knots). A notice board explains the exact location.

Traeth Ligwy, Moelfre
Lat. 53.3617, Long. -4.2654.
Vic Brassey 01248 410882

CHARGES: £10/day, £30/season.

SUITABILITY: Large trailer needs a car.

ACCESS: No Ramp. **TYPE OF RAMP:** Concrete **UPPER AREA:** Sand.
LOWER AREA: Sand.

DIRECTIONS: Follow the A5025 to Brynrefail and take the small road down to the coast. Launch site is close to the car park.

RAMP DESCRIPTION: Ramp takes you onto firm sand. Beach is fairly shallow so more suitable for shallow draught boats. Pay at the caravan in the car park or the shop.

FACILITIES: Car park nearby. Beautiful sandy beach popular with Jetskiers and bathers from the neighbouring caravan sites.

Traeth Bychan, Moelfre
Lat. 53.3407, Long. -4.2331.
01248 752320

CHARGES: Council now charge £10 per launch and £20 for first registration or £60 monthly or £100 yearly. Applies to all craft with engine 10hp or more. Insurance proof min £1M third party required for registration.

SUITABILITY: Large trailer needs a car.

ACCESS: ¼ tidal. **TYPE OF RAMP:** Concrete **UPPER AREA:** Shingle.
LOWER AREA: Sand.

DIRECTIONS: From Menai Bridge take the A 5025 toward Moelfre. Slipway is on the turning on right before you get to Moelfre. Signs for cafe and wet suit sale at top of lane. Down narrow lane single track much of way.

RAMP DESCRIPTION: Ramp goes onto hard sand so it is possible to launch and recover at low tide if you are prepared to take a vehicle onto the beach. Some areas of soft sand especially at harbour side of beach.

FACILITIES: Pay and display parking close by for car + trailers. Parking £1-50 daily. Very busy at weekends. Toilets. Café and beach shop.

HAZARDS: Speed restricted area 8knots marked by buoys. As beach and launch area is used by Red Wharf Sailing Club often small sailing craft in area racing weekends and summer.

Fryars Bay, Beaumaris
Lat. 53.2762, Long. -4.0845.
Pier master 01248 712312

CHARGES: None

SUITABILITY: Large trailer needs a car.

ACCESS: ½ tidal. **TYPE OF RAMP:** Concrete **UPPER AREA:** Sand.
LOWER AREA: Sand.

DIRECTIONS: Head past Beaumaris on the coast road and the slipway is by the factory buildings.

RAMP DESCRIPTION: June 2004, the slipway has a chain across with a sign saying 'Private Slipway, Please Do Not Use'. Slipway was originally built to launch seaplanes so very wide.

FACILITIES: Limited parking space.

Slipway, Beaumaris
Lat. 53.2624, Long. -4.0905.
Pier master 01248 712312

CHARGES: Council now charge £10 per launch and £18 for first registration or £60 monthly or £200 yearly. Applies to all craft with engine 15hp or more.

SUITABILITY: Large trailer needs a car.

ACCESS: All of tidal range. **TYPE OF RAMP:** Slipway onto mud and shingle. **UPPER AREA:** Shingle. **LOWER AREA:** Mud.

DIRECTIONS: By the Inshore Lifeboat Station in Beaumaris on the Island of Anglesey.

RAMP DESCRIPTION: This launch site is a slipway onto mud and shingle. Slipway extends to the low tide mark but the lower part does get covered in mud. Great care needs to be taken, as there is a channel at the end of the slip and it has a very steep drop into it, which would swallow trailers and their towing vehicles too.

FACILITIES: Parking charges- £3 per day parking. Overnight parking available at owner's risk. Parking space is good.

HAZARDS: Caution must be exercised at low water - follow the buoy marked channel as there are a large number of sandbanks. Also, be wary of strong currents and rough water between Puffin Island and the lighthouse.

Gallows Point, Beaumaris
Lat. 53.2544, Long. -4.1050.
01248 811413

CHARGES: £4 or £18 by tractor. £7.50 per week storage inc. slipway use.

SUITABILITY: Large trailer needs a car.
ACCESS: ½ tidal. **TYPE OF RAMP:** Concrete ramp.
UPPER AREA: Shingle. **LOWER AREA:** Shingle.
DIRECTIONS: Ramp is in the boat yard at Gallows Point to the south of Beaumaris.
RAMP DESCRIPTION: Accessible 3 hours either side of high water. There is also a small public slipway on the north side of Gallows Point.
FACILITIES: Ramp is owned by ABC Marine. Petrol, parking and toilets, workshop and repairs. Used boat sales. Shop on site.
HAZARDS: Also, be wary of strong currents and rough water between Puffin Island and the lighthouse.

Slipway, Menai Bridge
Lat. 53.2238, Long. -4.1614.
Pier master 01248 712312

CHARGES: All sites in Anglesey are subject to £18 boat registration by the local council and a launch fee of £10 per day.
SUITABILITY: Large trailer needs a car.
ACCESS: All of tidal range. **TYPE OF RAMP:** Concrete
UPPER AREA: Shingle. **LOWER AREA:** Shingle.
DIRECTIONS: Cross over the road bridge and the ramp is just to the north of the bridge.
RAMP DESCRIPTION: Access is difficult to this launch site, and the slipway is awkward one too. The slipway is straight into water (Menai Straits), near the suspension bridge and is accessible 24 hours a day. Beware of the step at the bottom of the slipway at very low water. Numerous fishing marks between Beaumaris and Caernarfon are accessible from this launch site.
FACILITIES: There is no charge for parking from here, but there are very limited parking spaces available - vehicles are parked on grass verges.
HAZARDS: Local council registration and charges. Be wary of the currents in the Swellies (between the bridges). Also, caution must be taken as there are numerous nasty currents and rough water which are dependent on the state of the tide and the wind strength and direction.

Britania Bridge, LLanfair PG
Lat. 53.2170, Long. -4.1892.
SUITABILITY: Large trailer needs a car.
ACCESS: Unknown. **TYPE OF RAMP: UPPER AREA:** Unknown.
LOWER AREA: Unknown.

Moel y Don, Menai Strait
Lat. 53.1863, Long. -4.2181.
SUITABILITY: Large trailer needs a car.
ACCESS: Unknown. **TYPE OF RAMP: UPPER AREA:** Unknown.
LOWER AREA: Unknown.

The Beacons, Conwy
Lat. 53.2946, Long. -3.8409.
01492 596253

CHARGES: 2009 charges are - Daily launch fee is £18.00 Seasonal launch permit is - <15HP £45.00 - 16-40HP £72.00 - 40HP+ & PWCs £99.00. These launch permits give access to all council slips in Conwy County Council. All powerboats & PWCs need to be registered (which covers all of North Wales) and costs £20.00 for the season - contact the Harbour Master to do this.
SUITABILITY: Large trailer needs a car.
ACCESS: ½ tidal. **TYPE OF RAMP:** Steep concrete slipway.
UPPER AREA: Concrete. **LOWER AREA:** Shingle.
DIRECTIONS: Follow signs for marina after town on A55, take a left just before marina.
RAMP DESCRIPTION: Ramp goes onto a steep shingle beach that is too steep to use below ½ tide. Run by the council. You will need to have your boat registered with any of the North Wales Councils to be able to launch here. At Spring tides, the current past the slip can be very strong, so care needs to be taken. The slip becomes very busy in the summer months. However it does give access to some very good days afloat even when the wind has a good bit if chop on the water. You can venture up the Conwy River where you will always find some flat water for skiing or sight seeing. If using a 2 wheel drive car, it is best to access this slip between 1 ½hrs before and 1 ½ hrs after high water. Check the tides on Boatlaunch before you go.
FACILITIES: Parking. Petrol and toilets at the marina.
HAZARDS: 10mph speed limit inshore. Water-skiing allowed outside the harbour.

Conwy Marina, Conwy
Crest Nicholson Marinas Ltd Morfa, Conwy, Gwynedd, Wales LL32 8EP
Lat. 53.2917, Long. -3.8406.
01492 593000

Deganwy Quays Marina, Deganwy
Deganwy Quay, Deganwy, Conwy, Wales LL31 9DJ
Lat. 53.2930, Long. -3.8288.
01492 576888

Public Slips, Rhos-on-Sea
Lat. 53.3067, Long. -3.7388.
01492 596253

CHARGES: Sailing boats are free.
SUITABILITY: Large trailer needs a car.
ACCESS: ¾ tidal. **TYPE OF RAMP:** Concrete **UPPER AREA:** Concrete.
LOWER AREA: Concrete.
DIRECTIONS: The ramp is just to the south of the offshore breakwater opposite the Aberhod Old Hall Hotel.
RAMP DESCRIPTION: Ramp extends down to three quarters of tidal range. Warden is on site in the summer. From 2007, this slipway is for the use of sailing boats (and other non powered craft) only. Power boats must use the Victoria slipway by the pier and PWCs are to use the Eirias slipway 300m east of the pier.
FACILITIES: Parking at the slipway. Petrol toilets and café nearby.
HAZARDS: Watch out for isolated rocks.

5

Victoria Pier Slipway, Colwyn Bay

Lat. 53.2968, Long. -3.7232.

01492 596253

CHARGES: 2009 charges are - Daily launch fee is £18.00 Seasonal launch permit is - <15HP £45.00 - 16-40HP £72.00 - 40HP+ £99.00. These launch permits give access to all council slips in Conwy County Council. All powerboats need to be registered (which covers all of North Wales) and costs £20.00 for the season - contact the harbourmaster to do this.
SUITABILITY: Large trailer needs a car.
ACCESS: ¼ tidal. **TYPE OF RAMP:** Long and wide concrete ramp.
UPPER AREA: Concrete. **LOWER AREA:** Sand.
DIRECTIONS: On the seafront just to the east of the pier.
RAMP DESCRIPTION: Firm sand allows launching at all states of tide with a 4 × 4.(beware of a band of soft sand between the 1st and 3rd hazard buoys when launching - even with a 4 × 4) Warden on site in the summer. All powerboats need to be registered (which covers all of North Wales). This is the former PWC slipway that has now been designated for power boat use. The PWCs are now based 300m to the east.
FACILITIES: Parking at the slipway. There is a kiosk at the site selling teas, coffees, ice creams and snacks.

Eirias Slipway, Colwyn Bay

Lat. 53.2952, Long. -3.7151.

01492 596253

CHARGES: 2009 charges - Daily launch fee is £18.00 Seasonal launch permit is <15HP £45.00 16-40HP £72.00 40HP+ & PWCs £99.00 Colwyn Jetski members £40.00. These launch permits give access to all council slips in Conwy County Council. All powerboats & PWCs need to be registered (which covers all of North Wales) and costs £20.00 for the season - contact the harbourmaster to do this.
SUITABILITY: Large trailer needs a car.
ACCESS: ¼ tidal. **TYPE OF RAMP:** Concrete ramp onto sandy beach.
UPPER AREA: Concrete. **LOWER AREA:** Sand.
DIRECTIONS: On the sea front at Colwyn Bay, oppersite the entrance to Eirias Park
RAMP DESCRIPTION: New slipway that opened in 2007 for the launching of PWCs. On Sundays and Bank Holidays the use of this slipway is restricted to members of Colwyn Jetski Club
FACILITIES: Kiosk selling drinks and snack. Toilets nearby.

Rhyl Yacht Club, Rhyl

Lat. 53.3116, Long. -3.5105.

CHARGES: Yes
SUITABILITY: Large trailer needs a car.
ACCESS: ¼ tidal. **TYPE OF RAMP:** Concrete slipway.
UPPER AREA: Harbour. **LOWER AREA:** Mud.
DIRECTIONS: From Chester follow A55 west turning onto A525 to Rhyl. In town centre turn left onto A548. Site is on the south side of the bridge.
RAMP DESCRIPTION: Available 2 hours either side of high water by prior arrangement. Rhyl waterski club also have a ramp in the area and ski on Marine Lake.
FACILITIES: Parking toilets and boat storage.
HAZARDS: 5mph speed restriction in the harbour. Waterskiing permitted outside the harbour.

Barkby Beach, Prestatyn

Lat. 53.3451, Long. -3.4007.

01745 355456

CHARGES: £5 to launch and £3 to park car and trailer per day.
SUITABILITY: Large trailer needs a car.
ACCESS: ½ tidal. **TYPE OF RAMP:** Concrete ramp.
UPPER AREA: Concrete. **LOWER AREA:** Sand.
DIRECTIONS: Follow the minor road north from the costal road (A548). Site is adjacent to the Sands Hotel.
RAMP DESCRIPTION: SLIPWAY CLOSED TO PUBLIC AT PRESENT
FACILITIES: Parking and boat storage. Bathing beach adjacent to the ramp and Site of Special Scientific Interest. Please obverse speed limits close to shore.

Deeside Waterski Club, Connahs Quay

Lat. 53.2209, Long. -3.0522.

01244 545579, 01244 536002, 01244 821728

CHARGES: Daily fee or annual membership of Deeside water Ski Club.
SUITABILITY: Large trailer needs a car.
ACCESS: ½ tidal. **TYPE OF RAMP:** Concrete **UPPER AREA:** Mud.
LOWER AREA: Sand.
DIRECTIONS: Leave the A494 at the Queensferry junction. Follow the B5129 towards Flint. Pass through Q'ferry, Shotton and Connah's Quay. Turn right in to Dock Road, sign posted Dock Road Ind Est. Continue until you get to the wharf, at the far end of the wharf go through the yellow barrier into the car park. The clubhouse in on the right by the barrier.
RAMP DESCRIPTION: The ramp is operated by Deeside water ski club. It is accessible approximately 2-3 hours either side high water, by prior arrangement with Deeside Water ski club. Applications for membership are currently welcomed.
FACILITIES: Free parking, clubhouse with licensed bar, changing rooms, toilets, hot showers. Tractor available for launching. 2003 club house extended. The area is industrial so please don't expect picturesque scenery.
HAZARDS: The immediate area around the ramp is free of obstructions. There are other obstructions in the river but these are mostly marked.

Banks Road, Heswall

Lat. 53.3247, Long. -3.1226.

SUITABILITY: Large trailer needs a car.
ACCESS: ¼ tidal. **TYPE OF RAMP:** Ramp then mud
UPPER AREA: Mud. **LOWER AREA:** Mud.
DIRECTIONS: The ramp is at the end of Banks Road.
RAMP DESCRIPTION: Gentle gradient. Muddy and limited by tide but a sheltered access point to the Dee estuary. Very gradual ramp suitable for car if tide is well up.
FACILITIES: Car park 100 yards. Fresh water in toilet block in car park. Petrol 2 miles on Chester Road. Food a quarter of a mile. Slip water tap close by. Boatyard nearby.

Boatyard Slipway, Heswall

Lat. 53.3252, Long. -3.1234.

Enquire at boatyard: Hughie or John.

5

CHARGES: £10 per year for unlimited number of launches.
SUITABILITY: Large trailer needs a car.
ACCESS: All of tidal range. **TYPE OF RAMP:** Concrete
UPPER AREA: Sand. **LOWER AREA:** Mud.
DIRECTIONS: The ramp is at the end of Banks Road. 100m from existing slip but with concrete right into the channel.
RAMP DESCRIPTION: New ramp, laid December 2002 on site of a historic slip. 100m from existing slip but with concrete right into the channel. Further improvements being made. Launch fee currently £10 per year unlimited launches by joining Dee Boatowners Association. Half-tide access to the River Dee.
FACILITIES: Public car park, boatyard, restaurant. Moorings. Dee Boatowners Association charges £10 for yearly membership.
HAZARDS: Channels in the mud banks should be navigated with care. Do not attempt to walk across mud banks nearby as they are too soft.

Slipway, West Kirby
Lat. 53.3642, Long. -3.1807.
CHARGES: £10 but no one from the council ever charges.
SUITABILITY: Large trailer needs a car.
ACCESS: ¼ tidal. **TYPE OF RAMP:** Concrete **UPPER AREA:** Concrete.
LOWER AREA: Mud.
DIRECTIONS: South end of West Kirby promenade next to sailing club.
RAMP DESCRIPTION: Outside West Kirby Sailing Club but council owned. Can only be used 1-2 hours either side of high water. Slipway leads onto a wide expanse of shallow shelving sand.
FACILITIES: Petrol, pub, and toilets within 500 metres. Promenade is liable to flooding.
HAZARDS: Shallow water (1metre) for considerable distance on small tides. Keep away from breakwaters and coastal rock structures.

Meols Slipway, Wallasey
Lat. 53.4076, Long. -3.1534.
SUITABILITY: Large trailer needs a car.
ACCESS: ¼ tidal. **TYPE OF RAMP:** Concrete **UPPER AREA:** Concrete.
LOWER AREA: Sand.
DIRECTIONS: Meols is to the west of Wallasey. The slipway is know locally as Dove Point and is next to the Coast Guard station at the eastern end of Meols Parade.
RAMP DESCRIPTION: Only accessible 2 hours each side of high tide - concrete onto sand. Fairly steep, coastguard on duty during the summer - local permit required as per New Brighton.
FACILITIES: Trailer parking, toilets but no shops, picnic area. Can be difficult to turn trailer in busy periods.
HAZARDS: Keep away from breakwaters and coastal rock structures.

New Brighton, Wirral
Lat. 53.4392, Long. -3.0364.
0151 630 0466
CHARGES: Council permit charges: Annual - any powered craft £110. Annual - club member £50. Day permit - any powered craft £16.
SUITABILITY: Small trailer can be pushed.

ACCESS: Unknown. **TYPE OF RAMP:** Concrete slipway providing access onto hard sand beach. **UPPER AREA:** Concrete. **LOWER AREA:** Sand.
DIRECTIONS: Join the M53 from Chester or Liverpool and follow it until you reach junction 1 for Wallasey. Leave the motorway and turn left onto the A554. Continue until you reach the Promenade before turning right and passing straight across both roundabouts. Pass the marine lake, fort and lighthouse on your left. You will come to a small car park on the left with a red building with "Pier" written on it, the south slipway is immediately after this.
RAMP DESCRIPTION: Good access available at almost all states of tide except high water Spring tides. Concrete slipway provides access onto hard sand. Take car onto hard sand - keep close to rocks after leaving concrete as sand becomes softer away from here. Local council permit is required and can be obtained from Safe Water Training.
FACILITIES: Tractor launch and recovery service from Safe Water Training for £15. Free parking. Lifeguard service (seasonal).
HAZARDS: Coastal defence groyne constructions marked by posts but cover on tides greater than 8.3m

Slipway, Frodsham Watersports
Lat. 53.3010, Long. -2.7066.
01928733187
CHARGES: £25 day launch Mon, Tue, Thur, Fri, Sat
SUITABILITY: Large trailer needs a car.
ACCESS: Non-tidal. **TYPE OF RAMP: UPPER AREA:** Concrete.
LOWER AREA: Concrete.
DIRECTIONS: located 2 minutes of junction 12 of the m56 based right on the river weaver.
FACILITIES: RYA safe water training school, ski school, changing rooms. Under development observation area and shower rooms to be completed towards end of this season.

Fiddlers Ferry Yacht Haven, Warrington
Ferry Boat Yard, Penketh, Warrington, Cheshire, England WA5 2UJ
Lat. 53.3732, Long. -2.6613.
01925 727519

Liverpool Marina, Sefton Street
Harbour Marina Plc, Coburg Wharf, Sefton Street, Merseyside, England L3 4BP
Lat. 53.3908, Long. -2.9850.
0151 707 6777

Albert Dock, Liverpool
Unit 7M, Atlantic Pavilion Albert Dock, Liverpool, England L3 4AE
Lat. 53.3998, Long. -2.9908.
0151 709 6558

Liverpool Sailing Club, Liverpool
Lat. 53.3363, Long. -2.8829.
CHARGES: Current membership fees see website www. liverpoolsailingclub.org

5

SUITABILITY: Large trailer needs a car.
ACCESS: ¼ tidal. **TYPE OF RAMP:** Concrete **UPPER AREA:** Concrete.
LOWER AREA: Concrete.
DIRECTIONS: Club is situated at the end of the John Lennon airport runways. Approach from Speke Boulevard turning into Banks Lane at traffic lights near Speke Retail Park. Access road through Mersey Coastal Park. Members issued with keys to barrier.
RAMP DESCRIPTION: Only access slipway on the north bank of the Mersey Estuary. Members only but membership is open. There are also moorings available to members. Very long slipway with gentle gradient. 2 Hours either side of tide depending on boat type. Power Boat members welcome. Brand new clubhouse.
FACILITIES: State of the art sailing clubhouse. Boat park and moorings available.
HAZARDS: Upper estuary drying at low tides. Rocks off Garston. Tide can be up to 6 knots across slip on Springs.

Crosby Marine Lake, waterloo, merseyside
Lat. 53.4705, Long. -3.0297.
SUITABILITY: Small trailer can be pushed.
ACCESS: Non-tidal. **TYPE OF RAMP: UPPER AREA:** Concrete.
LOWER AREA: Concrete.
RAMP DESCRIPTION: Gentle concrete slope with jetty
FACILITIES: Now reopened with new facilities. Please check before visiting!!!

INLAND SLIPWAYS
alphabetical by place name

ABC Leisure Group, Alvechurch Marina, Alvechurch
Scarfield Wharf, Alvechurch, Worcestershire, England B48 7SQ
Lat. 52.3469, Long. -1.9724.
0121 445 1133

Glanllyn C&C Park, Bala
Lat. 52.8749, Long. -3.6478.
(0)1678 540227

CHARGES: £7 per day for one car and boat.
SUITABILITY: Small trailer can be pushed.
ACCESS: Non-tidal. **TYPE OF RAMP:** Gently sloping shingle beach.
UPPER AREA: Shingle. **LOWER AREA:** Shingle.
DIRECTIONS: Slip owned by Glanllyn camp site. On the northwest shore of Lake Bala off the A494 Bala to Dolgellau road, 3 miles SW of Bala.
RAMP DESCRIPTION: There is a large launching area for sailing, windsurfing, canoeing and fishing. There is a shallow, secluded launch area where children can splash around and play with supervision. Boats can be stored on the beach. Bala Lake can only be used by non-powered craft with the exception of sailing club rescue boats and the lake warden's boat

FACILITIES: Touring caravan, motor home and camping park - Wales Tourist Board 4 Star Site. Glanllyn Campsite is on the southwest corner of Lake Bala. The excellent facilities include free hot-all-day showers, laundry, dishwashing area, camp shop and plenty of electric hook-ups for caravans, motor homes and tents. Glanllyn Caravan Park opens mid March.

Bala Sailing Club, Bala
Lat. 52.9010, Long. -3.5969.

CHARGES: Day members welcome £10
SUITABILITY: Large trailer needs a car.
ACCESS: Unknown. **TYPE OF RAMP: UPPER AREA:** Unknown.
LOWER AREA: Unknown.
RAMP DESCRIPTION: Concrete slipway suitable for dinghies and keelboats.
FACILITIES: Clubhouse opens at weekends, hot showers and a bar!

Slipway, Bala Lake
Lat. 52.9060, Long. -3.6075.

CHARGES: £3.50 to launch + £2 to park
SUITABILITY: Small trailer can be pushed.
ACCESS: Non-tidal. **TYPE OF RAMP:** Block paving
UPPER AREA: Concrete. **LOWER AREA:** Concrete.
DIRECTIONS: A few hundred yards south of Bala village on the North West shore of lake Bala. Site run by Snowdonia National Park.
RAMP DESCRIPTION: Gentle easy to use ramp. Short jetty adjacent.
FACILITIES: Toilets, shower, parking, café, safety boat on patrol
HAZARDS: Gentle lake bed slope so you need to be well out before rudder and centre board can go down.

Lyons Boatyard, Birmingham
Canalside, Limekiln Lane, Warstock, Birmingham, England B14 4SP
Lat. 52.4140, Long. -1.8770.
0121 544 1795

Cambrian Cruisers, Brecon
Ty Newydd, Pencelli, Brecon, Powys, Wales LD3 7Lj
Lat. 51.9484, Long. -3.3917.
01874 665315

Sandy lane, Chester
Lat. 53.1903, Long. -2.8698.

CHARGES: Up to £10 if warden on-site, mostly weekends.
SUITABILITY: Large trailer needs a car.
ACCESS: Non-tidal. **TYPE OF RAMP:** 2 ramps both concrete - left one slightly deeper. **UPPER AREA:** Concrete. **LOWER AREA:** Concrete.
DIRECTIONS: The Slipway is in Sandy Lane, go past Sainsbury's (on the ring road - Whitchurch direction), turn right at bottom of road. Slipway is about 1-2 miles alongside the Dee after the Yacht Club.
RAMP DESCRIPTION: Two ramps, the left one has a slightly better drop if you have a larger boat. There is a small trailer parking area. No Jetskiers allowed. 6mph speed limit on river.

5

FACILITIES: Toilets and park with kids pool. Also there is a floating platform to moor your boat with a ramp to the bank, so you can load up and/or park the car.
HAZARDS: Kids swimming are the only obstacle. You need to obtain a river licence from local authority before arriving.

Droitwich Boat Centre, Droitwich
Hanbury Whay, Hanbury Rd, Droitwich, Worcs, England WR9 7DU
Lat. 52.2647, Long. -2.1178.
01905 771018

Portland Basin Marina, Dukinfield
Lower Alma St, Dukinfield, Cheshire, England SK16 4SQ
Lat. 53.4814, Long. -2.0994.
0161 330 3133

Blackwater Meadow Marina, Ellesmere
Birch Rd, Ellesmere, Shropshire, England SY12 9DD
Lat. 52.9025, Long. -2.8898.
01691 624391

Evesham Marina, Evesham
Kings Road, Evesham, Worcs, England WR11 3XZ
Lat. 52.0963, Long. -1.9350.
01386 768500

Sankey Marine, Evesham
Worcester Road, Evesham, Worcs, England WR11 4TA
Lat. 52.1076, Long. -1.9561.
01386 442338

Victoria Basin, Gloucester
Harbour house, West Quay, The Docks, Gloucester, Gloucestershire, England GL1 2LG
Lat. 51.8622, Long. -2.2538.
01452 318000

Coombeswood Canal Trust, Halesowen
Hawne Basin Hereward Rise, Halesowen B62 8AW
Lat. 52.4577, Long. -2.0396.
0121 550 1355

Furness Vale Marina, High Peak
The Moorings, Station Rd, Furness Vale, High Peak, Derbyshire, England SK23 7QA
Lat. 53.3494, Long. -1.9875.
01663 742971

New Mills Marina, High Peak
Hibbert Street, New Mills, High Peak, Derbyshire, England SK22 3JJ
Lat. 53.3602, Long. -2.0055.
01663 741310

Lower Lode Inn, Lower Lode
Lat. 51.9835, Long. -2.1781.
01684 293224

CHARGES: £7.50 payable at the Inn. Also need river licence from the Lock.
SUITABILITY: Large trailer needs a car.
ACCESS: Non-tidal. **TYPE OF RAMP:** Concrete **UPPER AREA:** Mud. **LOWER AREA:** Mud.
DIRECTIONS: M5 to Tewkesbury. From Tewkesbury head North on the A38 toward Upton upon Severn. After ½ mile turn left onto the A438. After 2 miles turn left, signposted Forthampton. After ½ mile follow road round to left then straight on for 1½ miles.
RAMP DESCRIPTION: Straight and narrow with a gentle slope. Can get muddy at the bottom of the ramp.
FACILITIES: Slip way is in the grounds of the Lower Lode Inn. Plenty of parking. Avoid the Saturday that falls closest to mid-summer. This is the day of the Tewkesbury Regatta.

Lymm Marina, Lymm
Warrington Lane, Lymm, Cheshire, England WA13 0SW
Lat. 53.3807, Long. -2.4409.
01925 752945

Macclesfield Canal Centre & Freedom Boats, Macclesfield
Boating Marina, Brook St, Macclesfield, Cheshire, England SK11 7AW
Lat. 53.2571, Long. -2.1173.
01625 420042

Manley Mere, Manley
Lat. 53.2445, Long. -2.7721.

CHARGES: Dinghy £12.50
SUITABILITY: Small trailer can be pushed.
ACCESS: Non-tidal. **TYPE OF RAMP:** Earth, tarmac upper section **UPPER AREA:** Unknown. **LOWER AREA:** Unknown.
RAMP DESCRIPTION: Mud ramp with steep banks either side. Shallow and on a 90° corner to make launching sailboats with an on shore breeze quite tricky. No jetty. Be prepared to get wet.
FACILITIES: Good facilities. Parking tight and very busy with other lake users.
HAZARDS: Shallow near edges, jetty's unsuitable for dinghies

5

Venetian Marina Village, Nantwich
Cholmondeston, Nantwich, Cheshire, England
CW5 6DD
Lat. 53.1148, Long. -2.5474.
01270 528251

Midway Boats Limited, Nantwich
Wardle, Nantwich, Cheshire, England CW5 6BE
Lat. 53.1112, Long. -2.5842.
01270 528482

Nantwich Canal Centre, Nantwich
Basin End, Chester Road, Nantwich, England
CW5 8LB
Lat. 53.0711, Long. -2.5388.
01270 625122

Northwich Marina, Northwich
Chester Way, Northwich, Cheshire, England
CW9 5JJ
Lat. 53.2578, Long. -2.5146.
01606 44475

Kingfisher Marine, Pershore
Defford Rd, Pershore, Worcestershire, England
WR10 3BX
Lat. 52.1042, Long. -2.0960.
01386 553804

Goytre Wharf, Pontypool
Lat. 51.7517, Long. -2.9967.

CHARGES: £1 honesty box. Free to National British Waterways licence holders. (Feb 2009) See above comments
SUITABILITY: Large trailer needs a car.
ACCESS: Non-tidal. **TYPE OF RAMP: UPPER AREA:** Unknown.
LOWER AREA: Unknown.
DIRECTIONS: Follow the A40 from Monmouth to Abergavenny. At the roundabout at the end of the dual carriageway take the first left towards Pontypool on the A4042. After 3 miles (when leaving Llanover) turn right. After 1 mile turn left. After 200 yards the slip is on the left. The turning after Llanover is easy to miss. If you do, take the next right then next left. Hopefully you won't meet anything as it is narrow.
RAMP DESCRIPTION: Good slipway although the surface is loose and this might be a problem with front wheel drive. (Feb 2009) Marina owners are not keen on "outsiders" using slip - only for berth holders. British Waterways no longer own the site.
FACILITIES: Plenty of parking. Access is through a gate using a British Waterways key, which also gives access to the excellent toilet and shower block. There is also a slip run by Red Line Boats adjacent.

Preston Brook Marina, Runcorn
Marina House, Preston Brook Marina, Runcorn,
Cheshire, England WA7 3AF
Lat. 53.3262, Long. -2.6549.
01928 719081

Trafford Watersports Centre, Sale
Lat. 53.4287, Long. -2.2933.
0160 962 0118 ex3

CHARGES: For engine tests £15, Jetski launch £25 peak, £15 off peak.
SUITABILITY: Small trailer can be pushed.
ACCESS: Non-tidal. **TYPE OF RAMP: UPPER AREA:** Concrete.
LOWER AREA: Concrete.
DIRECTIONS: Jct 6 off M60 Manchester Ring Road
FACILITIES: Parking, changing rooms, toilets, restaurant, café, bar.
HAZARDS: Uneven wind especially on westerly due to M60 overpass

Slipway, Shrewsbury
Lat. 52.7104, Long. -2.7567.
01743 242555
SUITABILITY: Large trailer needs a car.
ACCESS: Non-tidal. **TYPE OF RAMP: UPPER AREA:** Concrete.
LOWER AREA: Concrete.
DIRECTIONS: Aim for Frankwell in Shrewsbury by Welsh Bridge - behind new council building near the pay and display car park.
RAMP DESCRIPTION: Concrete
HAZARDS: Can be very fast flowing when river Severn in spate.

Otherton Boat Haven, Stafford
Penkridge, Stafford, England ST19 5NX
Lat. 52.7121, Long. -2.1096.
01785 712515

Stourport Marina, Stourport on Severn
Sandy Lane, Stourport on Severn, Worcestershire,
England DY13 9QF
Lat. 52.3291, Long. -2.2715.
01299 827082

Severn Valley Boat Centre, Stourport on Severn
The Boat Shop, Mart Lane, Stourport on Severn,
Worcestershire, England DY13 9ER
Lat. 52.3377, Long. -2.2788.
01299 871165

Bredon Marina, Tewkesbury
Riverside, Dock Lane, Bredon, Tewkesbury,
Gloucestershire, England GL20 7LG
Lat. 52.0339, Long. -2.1158.
01684 773166

5

Tewkesbury Marina, Tewkesbury
Bredon Road, Tewkesbury, Gloucestershire,
England GL20 5BY
Lat. 52.0010, Long. -2.1521.
01684 293737

Whixall Marine (Shropshire), Whitchurch
BWML -Whixall Marina Alders Lane Whixall,
Whitchurch, Shropshire, England SY13 2QS
Lat. 52.9019, Long. -2.7512.
01948 880 420

Winsford Flash, Winsford
Lat. 53.1904, Long. -2.5170.

CHARGES: Free
SUITABILITY: Small trailer can be pushed.
ACCESS: Non-tidal. **TYPE OF RAMP:** Concrete **UPPER AREA:** Concrete.
LOWER AREA: Mud.
DIRECTIONS: Take the A54 to Winsford there is a carpark and a wooden hut just as you get to a roundabout. Go in to the car park and the slip is in front of you.
RAMP DESCRIPTION: Concrete slip into murky water. Be careful as slip drops approx 1 foot 8-9 feet out. Parts of the lake are only 1 foot deep and keep away from south of river. There is lots of silt you can get stuck on. Follow river north for good scenery. Go slow or the fishermen will catapult bait at you.
HAZARDS: There are some rocks close in. Lake only 1 foot deep in places.

Calf Heath Marina, Wolverhampton
Kings Road, Calf Heath, Wolverhampton, Staffs,
England WV10 7DU
Lat. 52.6754, Long. -2.0992.
01902 790570

Strensham Mill Moorings, Worcester
The Mill, Mill Lane Strensham, Worcester,
Worcestershire, England WR8 9LB
Lat. 52.0539, Long. -2.1257.
01684 274244

Upton Marina, Worcester
Upton Upon Severn, Worcester, Worcs, England
WR8 0PB
Lat. 52.0649, Long. -2.2143.
01684 594287

Upton Marina, Worcester
Lat. 52.0645, Long. -2.2137.
01684 593111

CHARGES: Trailer £10.00 Portable £5.00.
SUITABILITY: Large trailer needs a car.

ACCESS: Non-tidal. **TYPE OF RAMP:** Concrete **UPPER AREA:** Concrete.
LOWER AREA: Concrete.
DIRECTIONS: M5 junction 8 - M50 junction 1, A38 north (Malvern), after half a mile left at crossroads with A4104 (Signposted to Upton-on-Severn), the marina is a quarter of a mile on the left, before the bridge over the river.
RAMP DESCRIPTION: Marina ramp, easy to use.
FACILITIES: Full marina facilities, food, shop, diesel, hoisting, water, showers, servicing, chandlery. Loads of facilities at the site, good cruising in the River Severn. River is safe but in times of heavy rain it floods and can rise 18 feet or more. Parking cost £5/day.

Kempsey, Worcester
Lat. 52.1414, Long. -2.2234.
0870 056 3533

CHARGES: £10
SUITABILITY: Large trailer needs a car.
ACCESS: Non-tidal. **TYPE OF RAMP:** Concrete **UPPER AREA:** Concrete.
LOWER AREA: Mud.
DIRECTIONS: Enter caravan site / boatyard through gates. Turn right then slipway is on the right.
RAMP DESCRIPTION: The ramp is part of the boatyard and caravan site. If no one is about go to the bungalow to pay. Long straight shallow sloping ramp. Pleasant cruising on River Severn. Locks at Worcester and Tewkesbury but unhindered in-between.
FACILITIES: Caravan site, boatyard, shops nearby. Plenty of parking. Public moorings at Upton-upon-Severn, good pubs and toilets.
HAZARDS: 6mph speed limit on the river. River licence required from British Waterways (£2.40 per day), but no one at slip will ask for one!

Chirk Marina, Wrexham
Whitehurst, Chirk, Wrexham, Clwyd, Wales
LL14 5AD
Lat. 52.9489, Long. -3.0656.
01691 773930

5

6 North West England and South Scotland

Lytham to Girvan

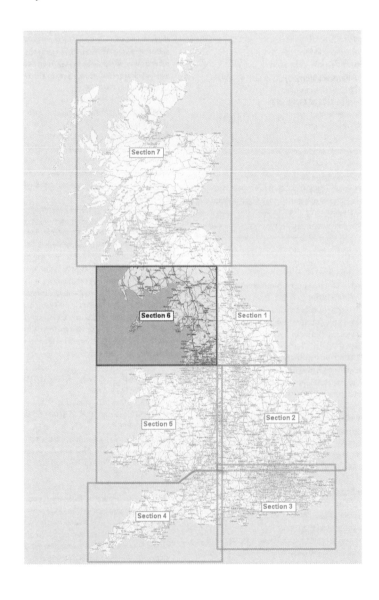

Section 7

Section 6

Section 1

Section 5

Section 2

Section 4

Section 3

COASTAL SLIPWAYS

CLOCKWISE AROUND THE COAST

Preston Marina, Preston

Navigation Way, Riversway Docklands, Preston, Lancashire, England PR2 2YP
Lat. 53.7607, Long. -2.7431.
01772 733595

Freckleton Boatyard, Freckleton Preston

Lat. 53.7488, Long. -2.8598.
01772 631661

CHARGES: £10 to launch. Boat storage and moorings available
SUITABILITY: Large trailer needs a car.
ACCESS: Unknown. **TYPE OF RAMP: UPPER AREA:** Concrete.
LOWER AREA: Unknown.
RAMP DESCRIPTION: Concrete

Star Gate, Blackpool

Lat. 53.7734, Long. -3.0545.

CHARGES: £80 for annual membership
SUITABILITY: Small trailer can be pushed.
ACCESS: No Ramp. **TYPE OF RAMP:** Over beach **UPPER AREA:** Sand.
LOWER AREA: Sand.
DIRECTIONS: At the southern end of the Promenade, directly opposite Squires Gate Lane, Blackpool where the sand dunes start. The slip situated between the premises of the Blackpool Boat Angling Club and the Blackpool Light Craft Club. Map Ref. (OS Sheet 102 Preston and Blackpool) SD 306 313.
RAMP DESCRIPTION: Be very careful launching from the beach (which is necessary most of the time). Every year 4 wheel drive vehicles are stuck in the sand and covered by the tide. Local clubs use tractors to launch and even they get stuck occasionally. Last heard, they won't pull non members out if they get stuck as someone tried suing them after they failed once.
FACILITIES: There is ample parking on the large Pay and Display car park by the slip. The slipway is adjacent to BLCC Watersports with club house and changing facilities. Must have annual membership @£80 which includes the tractor launch and recovery and use of the changing rooms and showers. For membership details call Bryan on 07733 315 352 or call into the Club House Beach Bar 01253 344096 on Tuesdays 9-11 pm Fridays 9-11 pm or Sundays 12-4 pm or email info@blackpool-watersports.co.uk

Princess Way, Blackpool

Lat. 53.8642, Long. -3.0492.
01253 825829
SUITABILITY: Large trailer needs a car.
ACCESS: All of tidal range. **TYPE OF RAMP:** Concrete
UPPER AREA: Shingle. **LOWER AREA:** Sand.
DIRECTIONS: At the northern end of Blackpool, a quarter mile past the Norbreck Castle Hotel, turn left across the tram tracks onto Princess Way. The slip is immediately on your left as the road curves away to the right

and is situated outside the headquarters of the Fylde Boat Angling Club whose members launch and retrieve here.
RAMP DESCRIPTION: Map Ref. (OS Sheet 102 Preston and Blackpool) SD 311 414. The slipway is wide but steep but gives good access to the beach. However, launching and retrieval a couple of hours either side of high tide can be awkward in anything but a flat calm sea.
FACILITIES: There is ample car parking nearby.
HAZARDS: At high water when the tide is up against the sea wall, this slip can be dangerous owing to the rough conditions caused by the waves or swell rebounding off the sea wall. In these conditions it would be advisable to anchor off and wait for the tide to drop sufficiently, to allow you to land on the beach and not up against the sea wall. The same applies to the many other slipways dotted along the sea front between Blackpool and Anchorsholme. Boats have been lost in the past, when trying to land on these slips.

Bull Nose, Blackpool

Lat. 53.8723, Long. -3.0479.
SUITABILITY: Large trailer needs a car.
ACCESS: All of tidal range. **TYPE OF RAMP: UPPER AREA:** Shingle.
LOWER AREA: Mud.
DIRECTIONS: Just over a quarter of a mile north of the Fylde Boat Angling Club slipway, still on Princess Way and directly opposite Anchorsholme Lane.
RAMP DESCRIPTION: This slip is less steep than that at the Fylde Boat Angling Club but does suffer from the same problems. Map Ref. (OS Sheet 102 Preston and Blackpool) SD 312 423.
FACILITIES: There is ample car parking nearby.
HAZARDS: At high water when the tide is up against the sea wall, this slip can be dangerous owing to the rough conditions caused by the waves or swell rebounding off the sea wall. In these conditions it would be advisable to anchor off and wait for the tide to drop sufficiently, to allow you to land on the beach and not up against the sea wall. The same applies to the many other slipways dotted along the sea front between Blackpool and Anchorsholme. Boats have been lost in the past, when trying to land on these slips.

The Royal Slipway, Cleveleys

Lat. 53.8804, Long. -3.0481.
SUITABILITY: Large trailer needs a car.
ACCESS: All of tidal range. **TYPE OF RAMP: UPPER AREA:** Shingle.
LOWER AREA: Mud.
DIRECTIONS: A mile north of the 'Bull Nose' just past Victoria Road and Cleveleys Town Centre is The Royal Hotel, directly opposite is the slipway used by the Wyre Boat Angling Club. Map Ref. (OS Sheet 102 Preston and Blackpool) SD 312 432.
RAMP DESCRIPTION: The slip leads down to a sand and shingle beach which can sometimes be steep and loose at the top, making launch or retrieval with anything other than a tractor, all but impossible. Numerous unfortunate people have discovered this over the years, when they have bogged down their cars on a flooding tide. This slip can however be used at all states of the tide, as there is always a section of dry beach to land on, even on high water Springs.

6

Fleetwood Haven Marina, Fleetwood
The Dock Office, Wyre Dock, Fleetwood, Lancs,
England FY7 6PP
Lat. 53.9158, Long. -3.0154.
01253 879062

Stanah Slip, Thornton
Lat. 53.8801, Long. -2.9827.

CHARGES: Free and free parking
SUITABILITY: Large trailer needs a car.
ACCESS: ¼ tidal. **TYPE OF RAMP:** Concrete **UPPER AREA:** Mud.
LOWER AREA: Mud.
DIRECTIONS: Stanah is off the B5412 at Thornton. Follow signpost To the River.
RAMP DESCRIPTION: A very steep slipway into a small, narrow and severely winding creek into the main river (River Wyre). Useable for only perhaps an hour and a half either side of high water. The secret here is to launch and navigate the channel whilst the water is down in the creek and the banks are still just visible. In this way you can see the route out because the obvious exit at high water is not necessarily the correct one and there are plenty of banks to catch you out! Keep to the outside edge of all the twists and turns (the insides of the bends are shallow). When returning let the water drop a little so that you can see the correct entrance. Useable in most weather condition.
FACILITIES: Parking space is ample. Busy at holiday weekends. Car park 50 yards. Fresh water, petrol, food in village ½ mile.
HAZARDS: Restrictions in place for Jetskis, can go no further up-river than the Shard Bridge and are restricted from entering the Port of Fleetwood controlled area where it meets the sea and the Lune Deep. Requires local knowledge - speak to the local boat owners-we don't bite! Very strong tides. If you get stuck because you miss the entrance you will probably be there for 9 hours so it is as well to carry an anchor to secure your boat.

Slipway, Knott End On Sea
Lat. 53.9284, Long. -2.9980.

CHARGES: £8 daily charge.
SUITABILITY: Large trailer needs a car.
ACCESS: ¾ tidal. **TYPE OF RAMP:** Concrete, lower section cobbled.
UPPER AREA: Concrete. **LOWER AREA:** Mud.
DIRECTIONS: Leave M6 junction 34 take A588 south turn onto B5270 to Preesall and Knott End On Sea. Follow B5377 into Knott End. That road leads directly to the concrete slip into the Wyre estuary at rear of Bourne Arms public house.
RAMP DESCRIPTION: Charges £8 per day (pay ferry man) or £50 plus vat per year. Slope is easy for a conventional car. Slipway is cleaned by ferry staff when operational but can still have a layer of muddy silt on lower area. Ramp is usable throughout the tide on Neap tides but water leaves the end of the ramp at low water Springs (if low water height below 2.4m). Water on ramp can be rough as water floods in over the concrete skeer to seaward side. Maybe a good idea to try launching over the side of the slipway in these conditions.
FACILITIES: Café and toilets at top of slip, large free public car park to rear of café.

HAZARDS: At low water sand spit straight off ramp end can be avoided by turning upriver to first red buoy. Be aware that this buoy is moored to a large concrete block which is a real hazard in itself at low water and could take your gearbox off! Passenger ferry uses upriver side of ramp and there are large container ships in the channel. Very strong tidal currents. Many drying banks outside the buoyed channel.

Glasson Sailing Club slip, Glasson
Lat. 53.9997, Long. -2.8512.
Membership sec 01772 451818, clubhouse 01524 751089

SUITABILITY: Large trailer needs a car.
ACCESS: ¼ tidal. **TYPE OF RAMP:** Concrete **UPPER AREA:** Harbour.
LOWER AREA: Mud.
DIRECTIONS: At Glasson dock proceed along West Quay and through industrial site to club.
RAMP DESCRIPTION: This slipway is for the use of Glasson Sailing Club members only. Owing to insurance restrictions only club members and those taking part in an organized event at the club may launch.
FACILITIES: There is a large apron at the side of the slip to facilitate rigging prior to launch and recovery. There is a combined sloping and horizontal jetty to the east of the slipway. This is suitable for the temporary drying out of keelboats, and loading and unloading.

Glasson Basin Yacht, Lancaster
Glasson Dock, Lancaster, Lancashire, England
LA2 0AW
Lat. 53.9959, Long. -2.8448.
01524 751491

Glasson Dock, Glasson
Lat. 53.9960, Long. -2.8442.
01524 751491

CHARGES: For the use of berth holders only.
SUITABILITY: Large trailer needs a car.
ACCESS: Non-tidal. **TYPE OF RAMP:** Concrete **UPPER AREA:** Concrete.
LOWER AREA: Concrete.
DIRECTIONS: Glasson Dock Marina is near Glasson dock sailing club near Lancaster Lancs.
RAMP DESCRIPTION: The slipway is in the canal basin. The sea lock is at the north end and it is manned by waterways staff. Locking down is one hour before high water.
FACILITIES: Diesel, parking, toilet/showers laying up facilities. The marina also has a travel hoist for larger boats.

RNLI Box, Morecambe
Lat. 54.0767, Long. -2.8604.
Tourist info 01524 582808

CHARGES: None
SUITABILITY: Large trailer needs a car.
ACCESS: ½ tidal. **TYPE OF RAMP:** Tarmac, gentle slope.
UPPER AREA: Concrete. **LOWER AREA:** Sand.
DIRECTIONS: About 100 yards south west of the slipway opposite the Town Hall - next to the RNLI box.

6

RAMP DESCRIPTION: This slipway along-side of the RNLI box this is a far better slip for the car user than the one at the Town Hall to the northeast, with a more gentle gradient. The water here is easily accessible some 3 hours before high tide.

FACILITIES: Car parking is £3.50 for 4 hours and busy in summer. Permit is required for parking at top of slip. Crowded in holiday periods. All facilities in town and at public toilets on promenade.

HAZARDS: Keep your speed down close to shore and do not cause a wake near the fishing boats. There is a move to try and get Jetskis banned.

Town Slip, Morecambe
Lat. 54.0777, Long. -2.8568.
Tourist info 01524 582808

CHARGES: None
SUITABILITY: Large trailer needs a car.
ACCESS: ½ tidal. **TYPE OF RAMP:** Tarmac, gentle slope.
UPPER AREA: Concrete. **LOWER AREA:** Sand.
DIRECTIONS: Opposite Town Hall - Morecambe Yacht Club have a large race control box there, you can't miss it.
RAMP DESCRIPTION: Morecambe Bay YC (100 yards) also operates from here. Choice of 2 slips fanning out from top, one into tideway - other more sheltered. Gradient is steep. Remove car from Promenade - park on road - access +/-2 hours on high water. Slipway gets a little steep when the tide is out.
FACILITIES: Free parking. Parking space is busy in summer. Permit is theoretically required for parking at top of slip. Crowded in holiday periods. All facilities in town and at public toilets on promenade.

Promenade slipway, Arnside
Lat. 54.2038, Long. -2.8370.

CHARGES: Free
SUITABILITY: Large trailer needs a car.
ACCESS: ½ tidal. **TYPE OF RAMP:** Concrete onto mud and sand.
UPPER AREA: Unknown. **LOWER AREA:** Unknown.
DIRECTIONS: Site is adjacent to Crossfields Boatyard at seaward end of promenade.
RAMP DESCRIPTION: Slipway leads down to beach at seaward end of promenade. Launch possible at all states of tide.
FACILITIES: Parking charges- Free roadside. Parking space is limited in daytime.
HAZARDS: Beware of strong tidal bore sweeping up River Kent.

Roa Island Boating Club, Barrow-in-Furness
Lat. 54.0764, Long. -3.1748.
Roa Island Boating Club

CHARGES: £25.00 for non RYA affiliated
SUITABILITY: Large trailer needs a car.
ACCESS: ½ tidal. **TYPE OF RAMP:** Concrete **UPPER AREA:** Concrete.
LOWER AREA: Shingle.
DIRECTIONS: Rampside, Roa Island.
RAMP DESCRIPTION: Get permission to use the site from Roa Island Yacht Club. Ramp suitable for car, usable about 3 hours either side low

water. Fairly steep at top but gentle further down. Concrete to about half tide then hard mud/shingle to low water.
FACILITIES: Parking at top of ramp within club grounds, toilets in clubhouse, and showers in clubhouse. Winch available for larger boats i.e. 6 tonnes+. Tractor available. Quad bike for smaller craft. Garage 3 miles.

Earnse Point, Barrow-in-Furness
Lat. 54.1191, Long. -3.2714.
SUITABILITY: Small trailer can be pushed.
ACCESS: All of tidal range. **TYPE OF RAMP:** Ramp onto hard sand
UPPER AREA: Concrete. **LOWER AREA:** Sand.
DIRECTIONS: From the M6 follow the A590 to Barrow-in-Furness. Once at Barrow head for Walney Island. On Walney Island turn right and the slipway is at the north of the Island on the west coast.
RAMP DESCRIPTION: Not suitable for car, launch off ramp to hard sand at all states of tide into Irish Sea. At low water you would have a quarter mile walk with the trailer.
FACILITIES: Car park 50 yards. Crowded on Bank Holidays. Shops quarter mile, garage 2 miles.

Ferry Pitching, Barrow-in-Furness
Lat. 54.1086, Long. -3.2466.
CHARGES: Free
SUITABILITY: Large trailer needs a car.
ACCESS: All of tidal range. **TYPE OF RAMP:** Concrete / Cobblestone.
UPPER AREA: Concrete. **LOWER AREA:** Concrete.
DIRECTIONS: From the M6 follow the A590 to Barrow-in-Furness. Once at Barrow head for Walney Island. Once you have crossed the bridge to Walney, take right turn at the Lights. The slipway is 200 metres on your right, opposite a pub called THE FERRY.
RAMP DESCRIPTION: Fairly steep, slippery on one side, 30 metres long. All craft must observe the 8 knot speed limit
FACILITIES: Parking on road (free). The Ferry Pub opposite serves food daily open all day. Toilets near traffic lights.
HAZARDS: If heading south down Walney Channel, depth of water only 2m, watch for obstructions when passing under bridge. Follow channel buoy system out to Morecambe Bay. At high water passage is with relative ease.

Millom Pier, Haverigg
Lat. 54.1963, Long. -3.2874.
SUITABILITY: Small trailer can be pushed.
ACCESS: Unknown. **TYPE OF RAMP:** Crude concrete
UPPER AREA: Unknown. **LOWER AREA:** Unknown.
DIRECTIONS: From Millom, follow the signs to Haverigg. The slipway is near Millom Pier
RAMP DESCRIPTION: The slip way is very crude but it is possible to launch a 2 seater Jetski using a small car.
FACILITIES: Parking available.

Car Park, Silecroft
Lat. 54.2185, Long. -3.3509.
CHARGES: None

6

SUITABILITY: Large trailer needs a car.
ACCESS: No Ramp. **TYPE OF RAMP:** Shingle beach onto sand.
UPPER AREA: Shingle. **LOWER AREA:** Sand.
DIRECTIONS: Through Silecroft village in southwest Cumbria.
RAMP DESCRIPTION: Boats up to 18´ are launched using tractors.
South Cumbria Sea Sports Association keeps 2 tractors at the beach for
its members use. The South Cumbria Sea Sports Association will assist
if you have trouble retrieving your boat. It should be noted the shingle
(near the bottom) is extremely soft at times and not suitable for cars or 4
wheel drive vehicles. You need a tractor to launch safely.
FACILITIES: Toilets, parking and nearby caravan site. Pub in the village.
**HAZARDS: Boats are launched and recovered from the sand.
Boats can only be launched and recovered when the tide is
on the shingle in calm conditions. The tide is on the shingle
approximately 2 1/2 hours either side of high tide. The shingle
can become soft after gales.**

Port St. Mary, Isle of Man
Lat. 54.0734, Long. -4.7369.

CHARGES: None
SUITABILITY: Large trailer needs a car.
ACCESS: All of tidal range. **TYPE OF RAMP:** Solid concrete
UPPER AREA: Concrete. **LOWER AREA:** Harbour.
DIRECTIONS: Port St. Mary is a southern town in the South of the Isle
of Man. The ramp can be found in the south harbour, opposite the Isle
of Man Yacht Club.
RAMP DESCRIPTION: Quite wide, nice and straight, shared with the
Isle of Man Yacht Club. Next the lifeboat slip in (foreground in picture)
with the new slipway behind. The slip is wide enough for two to launch
at the same time but it is normal for only one to launch at a time. At
low tide it is best to seek local knowledge as rocks present a problem.
Lifeboat slip is good for small ribs and PWCs but you must clear the slip
quickly. Take care at low water Springs.
FACILITIES: Parking, toilets, close to Yacht Club, shops and public
houses.

Ramsey Harbour, Isle of Man
Lat. 54.3228, Long. -4.3816.

SUITABILITY: Large trailer needs a car.
ACCESS: ¾ tidal. **TYPE OF RAMP:** Concrete **UPPER AREA:** Harbour.
LOWER AREA: Mud.
DIRECTIONS: The ramp is at the end of the famous swing bridge in the
middle of Ramsey Harbour.
RAMP DESCRIPTION: Steep and narrow.
FACILITIES: Toilets.

Slipway, Ravenglass
Lat. 54.3528, Long. -3.4109.

SUITABILITY: Large trailer needs a car.
ACCESS: ¼ tidal. **TYPE OF RAMP:** Concrete **UPPER AREA:** Sand.
LOWER AREA: Sand.
RAMP DESCRIPTION: Village Street ends in ramp into sheltered water.
Launch near high water, harbour almost dries at low water. Good sailing
in estuary.
FACILITIES: Parking nearby. Shops and petrol.

Harbour Slip, Whitehaven
Lat. 54.5485, Long. -3.5954.
Harbourmaster, Neil Foskett, 01946 694672

CHARGES: £10/day
SUITABILITY: Large trailer needs a car.
ACCESS: Non-tidal. **TYPE OF RAMP:** Concrete **UPPER AREA:** Harbour.
LOWER AREA: Sand.
DIRECTIONS: Ramp is situated at the southern end of the harbour in
the Custom House Dock. Close to the tourist office in Market Place, tel
01946 695678.
RAMP DESCRIPTION: Excellent wide slipway that gives access to the
harbour that is enclosed by a sea lock. You will need to speak to the
lockmaster before launching if you want to proceed to sea. You will not
be allowed to use the harbour lock facilities unless the boat has a vhf
radio on board.
FACILITIES: Secure parking for car and trailer. Close to the centre of
town. Marina with visitor pontoons, fuel, showers and all the usual
marina facilities.

Whitehaven Marina, Whitehaven
**Pears House, 1 Duke Street, Whitehaven, Cumbria,
England CA28 7HW**
Lat. 54.5500, Long. -3.5888.
01946 692435

Marina Slip, Maryport
Lat. 54.7150, Long. -3.5053.
01900 814431

CHARGES: £10 at marina.
SUITABILITY: Large trailer needs a car.
ACCESS: ½ tidal. **TYPE OF RAMP:** Concrete **UPPER AREA:** Harbour.
LOWER AREA: Mud.
DIRECTIONS: Follow Stenhouse Street over the bridge and left at T
junction onto Irish Street and then right into Marine Road. One slipway
into marina and one at the head of Stenhouse Dock.
RAMP DESCRIPTION: There are 2 slipways. The public slipway is at
the head of Stenhouse Dock and leads into the river. Shared with the
lifeboat, do not leave trailers or cars on the slip. Good wide concrete
slipway. The marina slipway leads into an enclosed basin. Lock operates
3 hours around high water. Water level in basin is shallow when the
tide is out.
FACILITIES: Boat repair facility, slipway and chandlery. Secure parking if
using the marina slipway. Public parking at public slipway.

Maryport Marina, Maryport
**Maryport Harbour & Marina, Marina Road,
Maryport, Cumbria, England CA15 8AY**
Lat. 54.7152, Long. -3.5068.
01900 814431

Slipway, Silloth
Lat. 54.8701, Long. -3.3936.
Lifeboat Station - 016973 61019, 07802 940671

CHARGES: Free

6

SUITABILITY: Large trailer needs a car.
ACCESS: ½ tidal. **TYPE OF RAMP:** Concrete **UPPER AREA:** Concrete.
LOWER AREA: Rock.
DIRECTIONS: Once in the town of Silloth, head towards the town centre and the Golf Hotel. Make along Lawn Terrace towards the seafront and the RNLI Lifeboat Station. The slipway is situated in front of the Lifeboat Station.
RAMP DESCRIPTION: The ramp was newly constructed in 1995 and is fairly steep. The local RNLI Lifeboat Station is situated at the top of the slipway and has priority of use but this is not a problem. Small boats / Jetskis can be launched / recovered by car. Bigger craft require 4 × 4 or tractor due to the gradient. The bottom of the slipway has a granite hardcore base which allows access to the sea at all states of the tide.
FACILITIES: Launch site is approx 500 metres from town centre. All facilities and amenities i.e. petrol, pubs, toilets, parking, shops are all nearby. Parking is free. There are quite a few caravan/camping sites locally.
HAZARDS: Sandbanks in the area - especially at low water.

Kippford Slipway, Dalbeattie
Lat. 54.8768, Long. -3.8142.
CHARGES: £5 per day and £20 per week - Sailing club requires weekly membership (£20)
SUITABILITY: Large trailer needs a car.
ACCESS: ¾ tidal. **TYPE OF RAMP:** Concrete **UPPER AREA:** Shingle.
LOWER AREA: Mud.
DIRECTIONS: Drive into Kippford near Dalbeattie (no thru road) - go past the Sailing Club Facilities and its steep slipway - carry on past the the Anchor Pub, and the newly opened Public Slipway (opened 2003) is on the right opposite the Chandelry. The two slips are about 500 - 600 metres apart.
RAMP DESCRIPTION: Wide concrete ramp. Cost is £5 per day and £20 per week - payable to the chandlery right at the top of the slip. Access is good. Launching at mid tide needs a little care as the tidal flow in & out of the estuary (tidal range in the Solway Firth is 8.5 metres Springs) can be quite fast - approx 3 to 4 knots. Bottom of concrete slip is exposed approx 2 hours before & after Spring low water, although muddy pebbles is still workable. The muddy estuary tends to make the slip just that - somewhat slipper & dirty with 1" to 2" of mud at low water.
FACILITIES: Pub, toilets - Petrol in Dalbeatie (5 miles). Chandlery opposite the slipway. There is space above high water to park trailers. Car parking can be tricky as the road into Kipford is a dead end and limited spaces, particularly at weekends.
HAZARDS: Solway Firth is very tidal (8mtrs plus in Spring tides). Jetskiers must keep speed down amongst the moorings.

Balcary Bay, Auchencairn
Lat. 54.8269, Long. -3.8353.
CHARGES: None
SUITABILITY: Large trailer needs a car.
ACCESS: No Ramp. **TYPE OF RAMP:** Shingle beach.
UPPER AREA: Shingle. **LOWER AREA:** Mud.
DIRECTIONS: A 711 into Auchencairn village. In the village, take the Shore Road about two miles to Balcary Hotel. Immediately past the hotel, there is a car park, and the road terminates on the shingle beach.

RAMP DESCRIPTION: Shingle beach - 4 × 4 advised. Can launch about 90 minutes either side of high water.
FACILITIES: Hotel immediately adjacent, car park within 100 yards.
HAZARDS: Solway tides are fast, and the bay is extremely shallow and tidal. Take care that you can get back to the launch site before the tide gets too far out - maximum about 90 minutes after high water.

Sailing Club, Kirkcudbright
Lat. 54.8362, Long. -4.0626.
Mark Nixon 01557 870 333
CHARGES: £10/week temporary membership.
SUITABILITY: Large trailer needs a car.
ACCESS: ¼ tidal. **TYPE OF RAMP:** Stone and concrete.
UPPER AREA: Mud. **LOWER AREA:** Mud.
DIRECTIONS: Ramp is on the bend in the river, downstream of the road bridge. Very close to the school.
RAMP DESCRIPTION: Good wide slipway, recently improved leading onto very soft mud at anything over 1 hour either side of high water. There is also a rough stone ramp in Kirkcudbright, call harbourmaster on 01557 331135 for further advice.
FACILITIES: Use of club house with showers and toilets. Food and petrol in Kirkcudbright.

Baity Timber Yard Slip, Kirkcudbright
Lat. 54.8317, Long. -4.0690.
Baity Timber Yard 01557 330051
CHARGES: Yes
SUITABILITY: Large trailer needs a car.
ACCESS: ½ tidal. **TYPE OF RAMP: UPPER AREA:** Unknown.
LOWER AREA: Unknown.
DIRECTIONS: On B727 out of Kirkcudbright take rough track to left one mile after junction A755. This is a timber yard run by the Baity family. There are several houses each occupied by members of the family.
RAMP DESCRIPTION: Steep, wide ramp that drops into deep water. Speak to Mr Baity, first house on left of track leading to timber yard. Small charge. Gives access to River Dee and Solway Firth. Keep a line on trailer or it will launch itself.
FACILITIES: Food and petrol in Kirkcudbright (3 miles). Parking and fresh water on the premises. Slip water tap close by.

Holiday Park, Brighouse
Lat. 54.7818, Long. -4.1310.
(01557) 870267
CHARGES: £7.50/day Mon-Fri, £10.00/day Sat/Sun.
SUITABILITY: Large trailer needs a car.
ACCESS: All of tidal range. **TYPE OF RAMP:** Concrete
UPPER AREA: Concrete. **LOWER AREA:** Concrete.
DIRECTIONS: Go to the camp site itself and drive through the whole site and you will get the slipway.
RAMP DESCRIPTION: The ramp is quite long and not of a steep gradient. This may have implications with the launch of a big boat in that the trailer may need to be submerged in the water to get the boat off.

6

Getting a large boat back in may require a tow rope attached to the car to avoid the car entering the water.

FACILITIES: Parking. Caravan park nearby.

HAZARDS: Some rocks either side but only a minor hazard.

Public Slipway, Garlieston

Lat. 54.7877, Long. -4.3657.

Harbourmaster 01988 600 295

SUITABILITY: Large trailer needs a car.

ACCESS: ¾ tidal. **TYPE OF RAMP:** Concrete **UPPER AREA:** Harbour. **LOWER AREA:** Shingle.

DIRECTIONS: At Harbour in Garlieston village, 13 miles south of Newton Stewart, Wigtownshire on the A746(B7004).

RAMP DESCRIPTION: 2 Car width from road to water with eyes let into concrete. Ramp ends in small river which feeds the harbour. Useable from half tide.

FACILITIES: Limited free parking, caravan club site 250 metres, public toilets, two pubs, post office, general store, telephone.

HAZARDS: Mud bank with moorings opposite slip 15m. Mud bank dries at 2 hours either side of high water.

Harbour slipway, Isle of Whithorn

Lat. 54.6986, Long. -4.3631.

CHARGES: £1 for the new slipway.

SUITABILITY: Large trailer needs a car.

ACCESS: All of tidal range. **TYPE OF RAMP:** Concrete **UPPER AREA:** Harbour. **LOWER AREA:** Sand.

DIRECTIONS: On the A75 from Stranraer to Castle Douglas turn south on to the A714 at Newton Stewart. Follow the road 18 miles to Whithorn and take the B7004 to Whithorn Isle.

RAMP DESCRIPTION: Concrete slipway leading onto firm sand in the harbour available for half the tidal range. New concrete slipway is available all of the tidal range just outside the harbour. Cost £1.

FACILITIES: Village store, nice pub and tea room. Parking nearby and summer lifeboat station.

Harbour Slipway, Port William

Lat. 54.7611, Long. -4.5858.

SUITABILITY: Large trailer needs a car.

ACCESS: ½ tidal. **TYPE OF RAMP:** Stone **UPPER AREA:** Harbour. **LOWER AREA:** Sand.

DIRECTIONS: Port William is a small village on the A747 on the east shore of Luce Bay. Slipway is in the harbour.

RAMP DESCRIPTION: Slightly curved, possible to recover 25 footer, but launching might be trickier. The slipway most people use is at the north side of the harbour just inside the breakwater. It is a short fairly steep concrete slip leading to sand and gravel. It is usable for perhaps 2/3 of the tide, though care is needed if retrieving on a flooding tide as every year cars get stuck. There is a third slip onto a small beach about 200m north of the harbour. This is usable all states of the tide, but it faces the prevailing wind and is unsheltered. Again very great care on a rising tide. At least two cars have been awash in the last 5 years.

FACILITIES: Friendly local fishermen, old style Formica pub.

HAZARDS: Bombing range and fierce tides round Mull of Galloway.

Stairhaven, Glenluce

Lat. 54.8467, Long. -4.7934.

CHARGES: This is a private slipway on private land. Boats may only be launched or landed with the permission of the landowner. Do not use this slipway without permission. If permission is granted then vehicles/trailers must not be parked on the property and are to be removed to the public car park.

SUITABILITY: Large trailer needs a car.

ACCESS: All of tidal range. **TYPE OF RAMP:** Concrete **UPPER AREA:** Shingle. **LOWER AREA:** Sand.

RAMP DESCRIPTION: Private slipway. The slip itself is concrete leading to hard packed sand. Boats can be launched at any state of the tide. The tide only reaches the bottom of the slip at high water. A large breakwater offers protection from the wind. Watch out for bait diggers leaving holes and soft ground.

FACILITIES: Remote location into a sandy bay.

Slipway, west bay

Lat. 54.7671, Long. -4.9400.

CHARGES: None

SUITABILITY: Large trailer needs a car.

ACCESS: Unknown. **TYPE OF RAMP:** Concrete but steep **UPPER AREA:** Unknown. **LOWER AREA:** Rock.

DIRECTIONS: The slipway is within the car park on the shores of Luce Bay approx 50 yards south of Ardwell Marine Shop. Public toilets are available within the car park, and Ardwell Marine Store is within 50 yards.

RAMP DESCRIPTION: Recently completed concrete ramp. Complies with all current legislation having been built under council control.

FACILITIES: Toilet facilities.

HAZARDS: Rocks under the surface can ping your prop depending on tide when launching. When out in bay not many visible landmarks to lead you back in, as already mentioned is steep need at least two people to launch. Should be ok 2 hours either side of high tide, check Ardwell marine for times, displayed on small blackboard outside.

Wall at Drummore, Drummore

Lat. 54.7014, Long. -4.9059.

01355520215

CHARGES: Nil

SUITABILITY: Large trailer needs a car.

ACCESS: All of tidal range. **TYPE OF RAMP:** Concrete **UPPER AREA:** Concrete. **LOWER AREA:** Shingle.

DIRECTIONS: Before entering Drummore you will see a sea wall on left side of road. There is a gap in this wall with a concrete slip. Occasionally the ramp will be covered in large pebbles..especially after a good blow. Sand is hard. Able to launch even on low tides. Take some ropes to aid towing out. Parking for a few cars and trailers.

RAMP DESCRIPTION: Concrete slip, moderately steep, onto hard sand.

FACILITIES: Parking for a few cars and trailers.

HAZARDS: Beware fierce tides (swirl pools) at Mull of Galloway (lighthouse)

6

Slipway, Drummore
Lat. 54.6917, Long. -4.8909.

CHARGES: Notice says there is a charge. £5.00 payment to Boathouse owner.
SUITABILITY: Large trailer needs a car.
ACCESS: ½ tidal. **TYPE OF RAMP:** Concrete **UPPER AREA:** Concrete.
LOWER AREA: Mud.
DIRECTIONS: Head south from Stranraer to the Mull of Galloway. Drummore is at the end of the A716.
RAMP DESCRIPTION: Concrete into mud basin. There is a boathouse at the top of the ramp. The boathouse is currently being renovated, making it impossible to gain access. There are however, plenty of alternative sites in the village. You will need a 4 × 4 to be able to drive onto the beach.
FACILITIES: On road parking but poor village facilities.
HAZARDS: Bombing range and fierce tides round Mull of Galloway.

Slipway, Port Logan
Lat. 54.7231, Long. -4.9576.

CHARGES: None
SUITABILITY: Large trailer needs a car.
ACCESS: All of tidal range. **TYPE OF RAMP:** Concrete to high water - Firm sand to low water. **UPPER AREA:** Sand. **LOWER AREA:** Shingle.
DIRECTIONS: From Stranraer take the A716 south. Just after the village of Chapel Rossan turn left for Port Logan.
RAMP DESCRIPTION: Slipway leads onto a wide sandy beach. The bay is the setting for the TV series 1,000 Acres of Sky, which was shot here on the mainland and not on an island at all.
FACILITIES: Free overnight parking. Parking space is for 20+ cars. Campsites available on eastern side of peninsula. Exposed coast with few safe havens but excellent sailing in good weather.

Ardwell Point, Ardwell
Lat. 54.7619, Long. -5.0029.

CHARGES: None
SUITABILITY: Large trailer needs a car.
ACCESS: No Ramp. **TYPE OF RAMP:** Concrete onto hard sand
UPPER AREA: Sand. **LOWER AREA:** Sand.
DIRECTIONS: From Stranraer, follow A 716 south, past Sandhead. Take the first road on the right and follow this straight through to the crossroads at Clachanmore to Ardwell Point. The last mile of this road is rough track, so take it easy.
RAMP DESCRIPTION: This is a steep ramp onto hard sand. A 4 × 4 vehicle is a distinct advantage here as it is a remote site and you are likely to be on your own. This does not mean that it is not possible to launch using a car, but it's your decision.
FACILITIES: Plenty of free parking. The fishing in this area is excellent.
HAZARDS: Beware of fast flowing tides, around 12 Knots!

Wig Bay, Stranraer
Lat. 54.9534, Long. -5.0693.

CHARGES: Not known
SUITABILITY: Large trailer needs a car.

ACCESS: All of tidal range. **TYPE OF RAMP:** Concrete
UPPER AREA: Concrete. **LOWER AREA:** Unknown.
DIRECTIONS: Follow road signposted The Wig. The slip is near the caravan park.
RAMP DESCRIPTION: This is an excellent ramp originally used by sea planes in WW2. Used by the local yacht club. Be aware the Sea Cat ferry creates quite a wash up the loch on arrival.
FACILITIES: Near local caravan site, bar on site, toilets. Main town approximately 2 miles away plenty of pubs.

Harbour Slipway, Ballantrae
Lat. 55.1015, Long. -5.0087.

CHARGES: Appears to be free
SUITABILITY: Large trailer needs a car.
ACCESS: ¾ tidal. **TYPE OF RAMP:** Concrete **UPPER AREA:** Harbour.
LOWER AREA: Harbour.
DIRECTIONS: Off A77 between Girvan and Stranraer.
RAMP DESCRIPTION: Good concrete ramp.
FACILITIES: Limited parking available at harbour, please park considerately. Hotels in centre of village. Fuel available in village.
HAZARDS: Rough coastline with sandy bays, good chart would be an advantage.

Girvan, Girvan
Lat. 55.2445, Long. -4.8586.

CHARGES: None
SUITABILITY: Large trailer needs a car.
ACCESS: All of tidal range. **TYPE OF RAMP:** **UPPER AREA:** Concrete.
LOWER AREA: Sand.
RAMP DESCRIPTION: Steep ramp but good tidal access
FACILITIES: Town 2 min walk with full facilities

INLAND SLIPWAYS
ALPHABETICAL BY PLACE NAME

Park Coppice Slip, Ambleside Coniston
Lat. 54.3512, Long. -3.0739.
The Warden, Park Coppice Caravan Club (01539) 441555
SUITABILITY: Small trailer can be pushed.
ACCESS: Non-tidal. **TYPE OF RAMP:** Shingle **UPPER AREA:** Unknown.
LOWER AREA: Unknown.
RAMP DESCRIPTION: Get permission to use the site. Gradient is moderate. Launching is restricted due to overhanging trees.
FACILITIES: Parking charges- Free camping or caravanning. Overnight parking available. Parking space is good. Security is good. Belongs to Coniston Old Hall Campsite. Slip water tap.

Windermere Marina Village, Bowness-on-Windermere
Nabwood, Bowness-on-Windermere, Cumbria, England LA23 3JQ
Lat. 54.3535, Long. -2.9251.
01539 446551

6

Galloway Sailing Centre, Castle Douglas

Lat. 55.0379, Long. -4.1016.
01644 420626

CHARGES: £7/day
SUITABILITY: Large trailer needs a car.
ACCESS: Non-tidal. **TYPE OF RAMP:** Long shallow concrete
UPPER AREA: Sand. **LOWER AREA:** Sand.
DIRECTIONS: R. Herman (Galloway Sailing), Parton, Loch Ken, Castle Douglas. Dumfries and Galloway, Scotland DG7 3NQ. Take the A713 north of Parton from Castle Douglas.
RAMP DESCRIPTION: Get permission to use the site. Gradient is gentle.
FACILITIES: Overnight parking available on hard standing or grass. Slip water tap available. Sailing School / Boat hire centre 10 miles north of Castle Douglas on A713 (Ayr) road. Five miles of un-crowded loch in super country. The small town of New Galloway, with it's with excellent tea shops and pubs, sits at the head of the loch. There is a beautiful RSPB reserve on the west bank, and forest walks & drives for those who like to do a bit of exploring.
HAZARDS: Skiing in the water ski zone only. Rest of loch is 10mph only.

Crossmichael Marina Lochken, Castle Douglas

4 Kirkland Terrace, Crossmichael, Castle Douglas, Kirkcudbrightshire, Scotland DG7 3AX
Lat. 54.9787, Long. -3.9839.
01556 670402

White Bear Marina, Chorley

Park Road, Adlington, Chorley, Lancashire, England PR7 4HZ
Lat. 53.6119, Long. -2.6091.
01257 481054

National Trust Car Park, Coniston

Lat. 54.3711, Long. -3.0544.

CHARGES: £5-8
SUITABILITY: Large trailer needs a car.
ACCESS: Non-tidal. **TYPE OF RAMP:** Beach **UPPER AREA:** Unknown.
LOWER AREA: Unknown.
DIRECTIONS: Access from B5285 east of Coniston then take unclassified right turn signposted Brantwood, car park is on right.
RAMP DESCRIPTION: The warden may leave well before 5.30pm so get back before 5pm or risk finding your boat and trailer locked in until next morning. Also note that there is CCTV in operation should you lose your temper with the padlocked gate. The slip opens approx 8.30am but closer to 9pm in the winter. Typical launch fee approx £5 - £8 dependant upon engine size. Slope is gentle but rocks need to be pushed out of the way.
FACILITIES: Free parking.

Coniston Sailing Club, Coniston

Lat. 54.3582, Long. -3.0715.

CHARGES: See website. Prior arrangement is strongly recommended.
SUITABILITY: Small trailer can be pushed.
ACCESS: Non-tidal. **TYPE OF RAMP:** Grass slopes; non-tidal. Suitable for small boats only. **UPPER AREA:** Unknown.
LOWER AREA: Unknown.
DIRECTIONS: Follow signs for "Coniston Old Hall".
RAMP DESCRIPTION: Sailing club launching area.
FACILITIES: Sailing club HQ with changing rooms and bar.
HAZARDS: Launching is through / past sailing club mooring area. Well sheltered from normal prevailing wind (SW).

Steam Gondola Pier, Coniston

Lat. 54.3642, Long. -3.0657.
SUITABILITY: Large trailer needs a car.
ACCESS: Non-tidal. **TYPE OF RAMP:** Concrete onto shingle.
UPPER AREA: Unknown. **LOWER AREA:** Unknown.
RAMP DESCRIPTION: Gradient is moderate.
FACILITIES: Parking charges- £6.50 per day includes parking. No overnight parking. Parking space is for 20 cars. Security is good. Slip closed after 5.30pm.

Lochview Motel, Crocketford

Lat. 55.0237, Long. -3.8466.
Steve Bean 01556 690281

CHARGES: £12 for PWC, £15 for boats per day.
SUITABILITY: Large trailer needs a car.
ACCESS: Non-tidal. **TYPE OF RAMP:** Hard core. **UPPER AREA:** Shingle.
LOWER AREA: Shingle.
DIRECTIONS: 10 minutes out of Dumfries towards Stranraer on A75. From Crocketford head south west and the hotel is on the southern shore of Loch Auchenreoch.
RAMP DESCRIPTION: Open all year round, 8.30 till late. Gives access to 100 acre fresh water lake with slipway. Insurance is required.
FACILITIES: Adjacent motel, camping and caravans. Food all day and bar. All facilities only 20 yards from the water. Accommodation: Single room £25 per person inc. breakfast. Double room £20 per person inc. breakfast. Campsite: Tent £10 per night. Caravan £6 per night. Electricity £2 per night.
HAZARDS: Some shallow areas in loch, and weed sometimes a problem in summer.

Bridge House Marina, Garstang

Nateby Crossing Lane, Nateby, Garstang, England PR3 0JJ
Lat. 53.9050, Long. -2.7885.
01995 603 207

Pier Slipway, Glenridding

Lat. 54.5444, Long. -2.9437.
Tourist Information Centre 017684 82414

CHARGES: Free
SUITABILITY: Small trailer can be pushed.

ACCESS: Non-tidal. **TYPE OF RAMP:** Cracked concrete then hard shingle with a gentle gradient. **UPPER AREA:** Concrete. **LOWER AREA:** Unknown.
DIRECTIONS: Follow the signs for the Ullswater Steamer, Glenridding and the slipway is to the left of the Steamer Pier.
RAMP DESCRIPTION: Excellent concrete slipway next to the car park. There is no concrete slipway below the water level. The ramp was built and used by Donald Campbell in 1955 when he reached 202 mph and there is a plaque close by to record this. The speed limit on the lake is 10mph however. A Lake Users Guide is available from Glenridding Tourist Information Centre. Very busy in the summer.
FACILITIES: Parking charges (2005) - £2 for 2 hours, £3 for 4 hours, £4 for 12 hours. Nearby toilet, Pier Head café. No overnight parking.
HAZARDS: Underwater rocks thrown in by unruly children! Steamers mooring at their pier.

Slipway, Keswick
Lat. 54.5946, Long. -3.1404.

CHARGES: £5 including car parking on beach
SUITABILITY: Small trailer can be pushed.
ACCESS: Non-tidal. **TYPE OF RAMP:** Pebbles, though generally firm enough for a car. **UPPER AREA:** Shingle. **LOWER AREA:** Shingle.
DIRECTIONS: From Keswick town centre, follow signs to the Theatre by the Lake. Go through the car park, and the hut for the Keswick Launch is on the right by the beach.
RAMP DESCRIPTION: Pebble beach launch, suitable for small powerboats and sailing boats.
FACILITIES: Free parking included in launch fee. Toilets and café nearby
HAZARDS: Some small islets, submerged when water level is high. Beware of hired motorboats and rowing boats, generally skippered by novices.

Derwent Water Marina, Keswick
**Portinscale, Keswick, Cumbria, United Kingdom
CA12 5RF**
Lat. 54.5983, Long. -3.1569.
01768772912

Leaplish Waterside Park, Kielder
Lat. 55.1842, Long. -2.5339.
01434 250294

CHARGES: Licence fee of £13.95 per day
SUITABILITY: Large trailer needs a car.
ACCESS: Non-tidal. **TYPE OF RAMP:** Concrete Ramp
UPPER AREA: Concrete. **LOWER AREA:** Concrete.
DIRECTIONS: Kielder Water is 25 miles NW of Hexham in Northumberland. From the A69 take the A6079 north for 3 1/4 miles, turn left onto the B6320. 1 mile before Bellingham turn left onto local roads to Kielder Water. The route is Brown Signed from the A69.
RAMP DESCRIPTION: Very wide ramp with easy gradient, suitable for all types and sizes of craft. Kielder Water is Europe's largest man-made lake.
FACILITIES: Pub, restaurant, boat club, swimming pool, toilets, large parking area (charge), shop. Nearest fuel is Bellingham (10 miles).

HAZARDS: Northumberland Water have a large number of regulations such as; 3rd party insurance, PBAs, 6 knot speed limit except for official water ski boats, inflatable boats must be at least 3m with at least 3 air chambers and must have solid floor, 2 orange smokes must be carried, 1kg fire extinguisher for motor boats, no PWCs or Jetskis.

Slipway, Leisure Lakes Slipway
Lat. 53.6534, Long. -2.8916.
01772 811866

SUITABILITY: Small trailer can be pushed.
ACCESS: Non-tidal. **TYPE OF RAMP: UPPER AREA:** Concrete.
LOWER AREA: Concrete.
RAMP DESCRIPTION: Concrete ramp into a man made lake.
FACILITIES: Changing facilities, hot showers, just turn up with your insurance details a crash hat & Buoyancy aid and let us do the rest! Concrete slip way open from 9am till dusk 7 days, 52 weeks a year!

Low Wood Marina, Low Wood
Lat. 54.4091, Long. -2.9485.
015394 39441

CHARGES: Launch fee £25 includes parking for one car and use of changing rooms and showers.
SUITABILITY: Large trailer needs a car.
ACCESS: Non-tidal. **TYPE OF RAMP: UPPER AREA:** Concrete.
LOWER AREA: Concrete.
DIRECTIONS: Leave the M6 at J36 and take the A590 and A591 towards Windermere. Continue through Windermere on the A591 and Low Wood Marina is approximately three miles on the left.
RAMP DESCRIPTION: Twin concrete ramps, most trailer boats can be launched without difficulty.
FACILITIES: Large car park, toilets, changing rooms, showers,
HAZARDS: No immediate hazards.

Bridgewater Marina, Manchester
14 Quayside Close, Worsley, Manchester, Lancashire, England M28 1YB
Lat. 53.5001, Long. -2.4121.
0161 702 8622

S. Windermere S.C., Newby Bridge
Lat. 54.2760, Long. -2.9520.
Club Sec Mrs. R. Downs 01229 65329

CHARGES: The charge is £12 and is collected by the National Trust at a gatehouse.
SUITABILITY: Small trailer can be pushed.
ACCESS: Non-tidal. **TYPE OF RAMP:** Concrete
UPPER AREA: Unknown. **LOWER AREA:** Unknown.
DIRECTIONS: 1½ml north of Newby Bridge on Windermere Rd A 592. Take 2nd entrance just before lay-by on the left.
RAMP DESCRIPTION: Gradient is gentle. Power boats are not allowed. Sailing boats with auxiliary engines are allowed to launch here. The slipway runs parallel to the one used by the sailing club. It ran into the water along side a jetty which is helpful to align the boat. Quite narrow

6

and broken up on one side. Car can get stuck here. There is a tractor available if required.

FACILITIES: Parking charges- includes launch fee. For overnight parking notify warden if leaving car overnight. Slip water tap available. Club located in Fell Foot Park ¼mile north of Newby Bridge-east shore of Lake Windermere. Café on the opposite side of the Clubhouse where you can get a reasonable meal and use the toilets.

HAZARDS: Beware of steamer docking at landing stage.

Park Foot Campsite, Pooley Bridge
Lat. 54.6093, Long. -2.8252.
Campsite reception

CHARGES: Included in parking fee.
SUITABILITY: Large trailer needs a car.
ACCESS: Non-tidal. **TYPE OF RAMP:** Shingle, very firm
UPPER AREA: Unknown. **LOWER AREA:** Unknown.
RAMP DESCRIPTION: Watch out for low trees when raising mast. Gradient is gentle. Stick to west of ramp close to fence for deepest water.
FACILITIES: Parking charges- £3 car and trailer per day. Overnight parking available. Parking space is good. Security is good. Campsite is on east side of lake ¾ mile outside Pooley Bridge. Slip water tap available.

Ullswater Yacht Club, Pooley Bridge
Lat. 54.5903, Long. -2.8418.

CHARGES: Membership fee.
SUITABILITY: Large trailer needs a car.
ACCESS: Non-tidal. **TYPE OF RAMP:** Concrete
UPPER AREA: Unknown. **LOWER AREA:** Unknown.
DIRECTIONS: Access down East side of lake on B5320 from Eamont Bridge (A6) South of Penrith.
RAMP DESCRIPTION: Get permission to use the site. Gradient is gentle.
FACILITIES: Parking space is ample.

Douglas Marine Limited, Preston
Douglas Boatyard, Becconsall Lane, Hesketh Bank, Preston, Lancashire, England PR4 6RR
Lat. 53.7015, Long. -2.8313.
01772 812462

James Mayor & Co Ltd, Preston
Boat Yard, Tartleton, Preston, Lancashire, England PR4 6HD
Lat. 53.6853, Long. -2.8243.
01772 812250

Moons Bridge Marina, Preston
Lat. 53.8179, Long. -2.7549.
01772 690627

CHARGES: Charges vary
SUITABILITY: Large trailer needs a car.
ACCESS: Non-tidal. **TYPE OF RAMP:** Concrete **UPPER AREA:** Shingle.
LOWER AREA: Concrete.
DIRECTIONS: Leave M6 at J32 (J of M6-M55), follow Garstang, left onto B5269, after railway bridge take two right turns.

RAMP DESCRIPTION: Good concrete ramp into marina, will take large trailer boats with care. Canal restrictions apply to all boats.
FACILITIES: Canal marina on Lancaster canal, chandlery, fuel, and gas.
HAZARDS: Canal restrictions only.

Blackleach Marina, Preston
Blackleach Lane, Catforth, Preston, Lancashire, England PR4 0JA
Lat. 53.8074, Long. -2.7924.
01772 690495

Howtown slipway, Ullswater
Lat. 54.5709, Long. -2.8666.

CHARGES: Free
SUITABILITY: Small trailer can be pushed.
ACCESS: Non-tidal. **TYPE OF RAMP:** Hard shingle, gentle gradient initially then steep depending on the water depth.
UPPER AREA: Unknown. **LOWER AREA:** Unknown.
DIRECTIONS: From Pooley Bridge village heading towards Tirril and Penrith, take the right fork by the church and at the crossroads turn right, signposted to Howtown. This is a narrow road with occasional passing places for 3 1/2 miles to Howtown.
FACILITIES: No overnight parking, busy during the summer. Nearby Howtown Hotel for refreshments. A Lake Users Guide is available from the Glenridding Tourist Information Centre.
HAZARDS: Underwater rocks thrown in by unruly children! Steamers on the lake.

Waterside House, Ullswater
Lat. 54.6013, Long. -2.8318.
017684 86332

SUITABILITY: Large trailer needs a car.
ACCESS: Non-tidal. **TYPE OF RAMP:** Shingle hard on the lake side
UPPER AREA: Shingle. **LOWER AREA:** Unknown.
DIRECTIONS: South of the village of Pooley Bridge next to Waterside House and the Waterside farm campsite. Address is Waterside House Campsite, Pooley Bridge, Penrith, Cumbria, CA10 2NA
RAMP DESCRIPTION: Track down to the lake side. Some rocks hidden below surface, but keep to centre line and you will be OK.
FACILITIES: Campsite nearby.

Water Edge Hotel, Windermere
Lat. 54.4212, Long. -2.9634.

CHARGES: £2
SUITABILITY: Small trailer can be pushed.
ACCESS: Non-tidal. **TYPE OF RAMP:** Shallow concrete.
UPPER AREA: Unknown. **LOWER AREA:** Unknown.
DIRECTIONS: At the northern end of Windermere next door to the Water Edge Hotel at Waterhead to the south of Ambleside.
RAMP DESCRIPTION: Public slipway suitable for dinghies only. Concrete slipway very gentle slope. Launch fee is allegedly £2 - key to barrier obtainable from Ferry Office adjacent, users are seldom charged.
FACILITIES: Large car park and toilets across road.

6

White Cross Bay, Windermere
Lat. 54.3951, Long. -2.9352.

015394 43937

CHARGES: For the use of residents only.
SUITABILITY: Large trailer needs a car.
ACCESS: Non-tidal. **TYPE OF RAMP:** Concrete running into shingle
UPPER AREA: Concrete. **LOWER AREA:** Shingle.
DIRECTIONS: White Cross Bay is approximately 15 miles from Junction 36 of the M6. Follow the direction signs to Windermere on the A591 until you reach the town centre. Stay on the A591 following signs for Ambleside. White Cross Bay is on your left hand side after approximately 2 miles.
RAMP DESCRIPTION: The slipway is for the use of holiday residents only. White Cross Bay boasts probably the finest marina and launching facilities on Windermere for sailing and watersports enthusiasts. Tractor launch at £5 per launch includes recovery. The ramp is very shallow. Most cars, including 4 × 4, would not be able to float off anything but a very shallow draught boat before being swamped. Tractor launch is a must.
FACILITIES: The modern clubhouse provides a restaurant with a varied menu, bar, fast food outlet, mini market with off licence and a family room with games and amusements for children. First class accommodation adds to the pleasure of any visit to White Cross Bay. A range of luxury pine lodges and caravans are available, sleeping between two and six people.

Ferry Nab Public Slipway, Windermere
Lat. 54.3553, Long. -2.9296.

015394 42753

CHARGES: For up to date fees and charges and terms and conditions for all facilities please visit our website at www.southlakeland.gov.uk, following the link to 'Leisure', also please visit the National Park Authority website at www.lake-distict.gov.uk for further information on boat registration and the lake byelaws. PLEASE NOTE - ALL POWER DRIVEN CRAFT MUST BE REGISTERED WITH THE NATIONAL PARK AUTHORITY BEFORE USING THE LAKE.
SUITABILITY: Large trailer needs a car.
ACCESS: Non-tidal. **TYPE OF RAMP:** Main Slipway - concrete. Dinghy Slipway - steel plates / gravel **UPPER AREA:** Concrete.
LOWER AREA: Concrete.
DIRECTIONS: Slipway is at Ferry Nab approximately 1/2 mile south of Bowness-on-Windermere. Postcode for Sat-Nav users is LA23 3JH. Access through Ferry Nab Car Park located on the B5285.
RAMP DESCRIPTION: Wide concrete ramp and a second smaller ramp suitable for sailing dinghies and tenders.
FACILITIES: Public jetties, mast hoist, tractor assisted launching if required, car & trailer parking, public toilets, showers, public phone box, fresh water, chemical toilet disposal, holding tank pump out, boat registration, permanent and holiday moorings, short and long term storage of boats / trailers.

HAZARDS: Lake User guides and charts are available at the slipway office. Lake User guides are downloadable from the National Park Authority website. There is a car ferry operating across the middle of the lake. This ferry is a cable ferry. As the ferry is travelling forwards, the cables that it pulls against are raised in the water. DO NOT CROSS IN FRONT OF THE FERRY WHILE IT IS IN MOTION! The cables rise up out of the water as it nears land. MAKE SURE you have enough FUEL! The lake is ten miles long and the distances on the water are deceptive so keep a small can with a spare gallon in. further guidance and safety advice is given in the users guide. In Emergency dial 999 and ask for coastguard, or call on Marine VHF channel 16 for 'Liverpool Coastguard' or 'Lake Wardens'

Harrow Slack, Windermere
Lat. 54.3559, Long. -2.9417.

CHARGES: £2 - Pay warden if present.
SUITABILITY: Large trailer needs a car.
ACCESS: Non-tidal. **TYPE OF RAMP:** Tarmac onto loose aggregate.
UPPER AREA: Unknown. **LOWER AREA:** Unknown.
RAMP DESCRIPTION: Use last parking area before tarmac lane ends. Watch boulders running out from shoreline near large tree stump.
FACILITIES: Parking charges- £1. No overnight parking. Parking space is busy in summer. From ferry terminal opposite Bowness, lane is about 500 metres on right after terminal.
HAZARDS: Watch your prop on the boulders.

6

7

Scotland and North England

Girvan to Amble

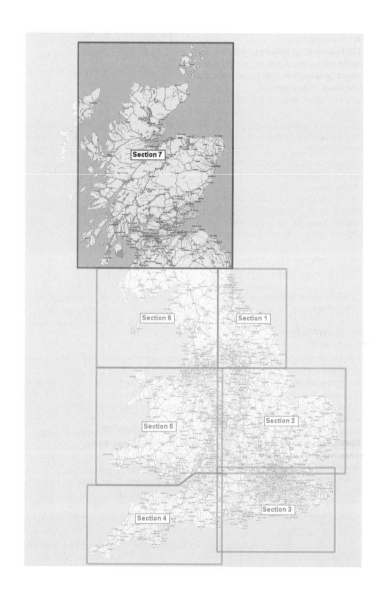

COASTAL SLIPWAYS
CLOCKWISE AROUND THE COAST

Harbour slipway, Maidens
Lat. 55.3336, Long. -4.8244.
01655 331720

CHARGES: £5.00
SUITABILITY: Large trailer needs a car.
ACCESS: ¾ tidal. **TYPE OF RAMP:** Concrete **UPPER AREA:** Rock.
LOWER AREA: Mud.
DIRECTIONS: Follow signs to harbour
RAMP DESCRIPTION: Poor design, double bend to negotiate/reverse if using car and trailer. Work in progress to improve ramp but high tide only at the moment. Call harbourmaster for key for gate, well sheltered harbour and look forward to improvements 2009
FACILITIES: Free public car park within 100 metres. Toilets 50mtrs. Excellent restaurant within 300 metres, Café within 500 metres.

Slipway, Dunure Harbour
Lat. 55.4086, Long. -4.7571.

CHARGES: £5 per day / was £35 per year now £50 (2007) payable at Dunure shop.
SUITABILITY: Small trailer can be pushed.
ACCESS: ½ tidal. **TYPE OF RAMP:** Concrete **UPPER AREA:** Concrete.
LOWER AREA: Sand.
DIRECTIONS: A719 to Dunure, head into village and there it is.
RAMP DESCRIPTION: Bend at the top, then straight down to the water. There is a 30 foot limit on boat size in the harbour.
FACILITIES: Post office, shop, parking onsite. Nearest fuel supplier is in Ayr (7 miles). Loads of locals with priceless information on the area land/sea.
HAZARDS: 30 foot boat size limit, narrow harbour entrance but markers to guide channel users.

Harbour Slipway, Ayr
Lat. 55.4683, Long. -4.6400.

CHARGES: Free
SUITABILITY: Small trailer can be pushed.
ACCESS: ½ tidal. **TYPE OF RAMP:** Concrete **UPPER AREA:** Concrete.
LOWER AREA: Concrete.
DIRECTIONS: Travel to Ayr Town Centre, following signs for Swimming pool which is located on the south side of the River Ayr at the Harbour. The slip is beside a new block of apartments.
RAMP DESCRIPTION: Often used by Swans for a nest site, and so is unusable as long as the swans return to the nest. This slip is steep with a three foot drop off the end and extremely slippery due to lack of use (swans nest) and as long as it remains in this condition is dangerous to use even with 4 × 4s. A far safer and better option is Troon marina for around £10.00.
FACILITIES: Parking is available at launch site, other facilities are all available close by.

Troon Yacht Haven, Troon
The Harbour, Troon, Ayrshire, Scotland KA10 6DJ
Lat. 55.5448, Long. -4.6781.
01292 315553

Troon Marina, Troon
Lat. 55.5453, Long. -4.6788.

CHARGES: £5 to launch, they have increased this to £7.00 launch then £7.00 recover, very high price, this was for 12ft boat, price is higher for larger vessels
SUITABILITY: Large trailer needs a car.
ACCESS: All of tidal range. **TYPE OF RAMP:** Concrete
UPPER AREA: Harbour. **LOWER AREA:** Harbour.
DIRECTIONS: Enter marina from main gates and turn left, Follow road around to slipway.
RAMP DESCRIPTION: Ramp has access for 3 boats to be launched at same time; excellent slipway can manoeuvre trailer right to water for easy launch and retrieval.
FACILITIES: All facilities of a modern marina: shops, toilets, showers, restaurant and fresh water washing.
HAZARDS: On exit from main harbour watch out for departure time of P&O ferry and also rocks off the port side when exiting harbour.

Harbour Slip, Irvine Harbour
Lat. 55.6080, Long. -4.6877.
Harbourmaster 01294 487286

SUITABILITY: Large trailer needs a car.
ACCESS: ½ tidal. **TYPE OF RAMP:** Concrete **UPPER AREA:** Concrete.
LOWER AREA: Concrete.
DIRECTIONS: From Irvine railway station, under bridge and follow road around to harbour (approximately 1 mile).
RAMP DESCRIPTION: Telephone Harbourmaster on 01294 487286 to arrange use of slip. Irvine Bridge has an air draught of 5 metres at mean high water Springs, vessels requiring bridge opened (no charge) call 'Irvine Bridge' on VHF Channel 12 or, 08708 403123.
FACILITIES: Fuel at local garages, nearest 1½km. Irvine Water Sports Club adjacent to slip, offers hospitality to visiting crews. Excellent food in nearby pubs. Try the Ship Inn, great food.
HAZARDS: Couple of obstructions close to ramp, local chart is a must. Sand bar at harbour entrance charted depth of less than 1 metre at mean low water Springs.

Stevenson Slipway, Irvine
Lat. 55.6238, Long. -4.7492.

CHARGES: Free
SUITABILITY: Large trailer needs a car.
ACCESS: ¾ tidal. **TYPE OF RAMP:** Concrete **UPPER AREA:** Rock.
LOWER AREA: Sand.
DIRECTIONS: Slipway is 2km south east of Saltcoats.
RAMP DESCRIPTION: Good angle concrete ramp. Approximately 1 foot drop onto sand at end. Useable most of tide range except for an hour either side of low tide. Exposed slipway, an onshore wind can make use

7

difficult. Can be slippy at lower parts. Good width (12ft at narrowest) Overall -good slip!

FACILITIES: Ample free parking around slipway however users should ensure suitable security measures are taken.

Harbour slipway, Saltcoats

Lat. 55.6310, Long. -4.7872.

CHARGES: Free

SUITABILITY: Large trailer needs a car.

ACCESS: ½ tidal. **TYPE OF RAMP:** Steep concrete ramp.-Steepness can make this a tricky one! Suitable for small boats. Lower parts can be slippy

UPPER AREA: Concrete. **LOWER AREA:** Rock.

DIRECTIONS: located near entrance to harbour

RAMP DESCRIPTION: Public Ramp

HAZARDS: Shallow rocky areas in harbour particularly at lower tide states

Clyde Marina, Ardrossan

The Harbour, Ardrossan, Ayrshire, Scotland KA22 8DB

Lat. 55.6420, Long. -4.8223.

01294 607077

Fairlie Quay, Fairlie

Main Road, Fairlie, Ayrshire, Scotland KA29 0AS

Lat. 55.7633, Long. -4.8549.

01475 568267

Millport, Isle of Cumbrae

Lat. 55.7530, Long. -4.9234.

CHARGES: None

SUITABILITY: Small trailer can be pushed.

ACCESS: ½ tidal. **TYPE OF RAMP:** Concrete with a gentle slope. The entrance to it is directly from the promenade **UPPER AREA:** Concrete.

LOWER AREA: Concrete.

DIRECTIONS: Five hundred yards from the Harbour along the promenade.

RAMP DESCRIPTION: Concrete. Leading down to the half-tide mark.

FACILITIES: There are very good public toilets on the harbour. All local shops, pubs, cafés and amenities. Bed and Breakfast.

HAZARDS: The stretch of water between Cumbrae and Little Cumbrae to the south can be treacherous at the turning of the tide. The wind also funnels through here making it sometimes rough water for small boats but ideal for yachting. There are rocks on the outreach from the harbour that are covered at high tide.

Slipway, Fairlie Quay

Lat. 55.7649, Long. -4.8583.

01475 568267

SUITABILITY: Large trailer needs a car.

ACCESS: ½ tidal. **TYPE OF RAMP:** Concrete **UPPER AREA:** Harbour.

LOWER AREA: Unknown.

DIRECTIONS: Slipway is situated in the Fairlie Quay boatyard 1 mile south of Largs Marina.

RAMP DESCRIPTION: The slipway at Fairlie Quay is available to half tide - but we can also crane/ hoist boats as required.

FACILITIES: There is a launch facility and secure site, with a very clean yard, access pontoon, water, and diesel and under cover storage at Fairlie Quay, 1ml south of Largs Marina. We are a very RIB and trailered boat friendly company!

Public Slip, Largs Yacht Haven

Lat. 55.7749, Long. -4.8587.

Largs Yacht Haven (VHF 80 M) 01475 675333

CHARGES: None

SUITABILITY: Small trailer can be pushed.

ACCESS: ¼ tidal. **TYPE OF RAMP:** Concrete **UPPER AREA:** Unknown.

LOWER AREA: Unknown.

RAMP DESCRIPTION: Public access slip only suitable for boats up to 20 ft and for Jetskis. It is tidal and is best about 1 hour either side of high tide depending on the size of boat launched. Concrete finger projecting from foreshore with rock armoured flanks. Descends to beach level. One user's recommendation is to view the slipway at low water, so you can see the outlying rocks which may be a hazard when you motor off the slipway beach. You may find it easier to launch/recover on a rising tide at the point where the tide is rising to the bottom of the slip thus avoiding the hazard of all the rock armour. To recover you can land on the sandy beach at low water and bring your trailer to the bottom of the slip so (again) avoiding the rocks.

FACILITIES: Free overnight parking. Parking space is for 50+ cars. Slip water tap. Adequate area for several boats to be prepared for launching at the same time. Width restricts simultaneous launching to two dinghies, or one larger boat. Security is good within the adjacent marina.

HAZARDS: The slipway has the ankle-breaking danger of the large rocks on its flanks, which are piled up higher than the slipway, and thus form a sort of reef down either side of its flanks. There are no means for a user to get on or off a boat other than scrambling over the bows.

Largs Yacht Haven, Largs

Irvine Road, Largs, Ayrshire, Scotland KA30 8EZ

Lat. 55.7745, Long. -4.8583.

01475 675333

Lifeboat slipway, Largs

Lat. 55.8005, Long. -4.8717.

CHARGES: Nil

SUITABILITY: Large trailer needs a car.

ACCESS: ¾ tidal. **TYPE OF RAMP:** Concrete/stone.

UPPER AREA: Concrete. **LOWER AREA:** Shingle.

DIRECTIONS: Situated at the northern end of Largs by the lifeboat station on Greenock Road, near the intersection of Brisbane Street.

RAMP DESCRIPTION: This slip is not useable at all states of the tidal range unless with a very light boat and trailer. The end of the slipway is a step onto very soft shingle and care must be taken not to allow the trailer wheels to go over this when launching at lower states of the tide. Do not leave any trailers on the slipway as it is used by the lifeboat. Know

7

to be used by Jetskiers. It may also be possible to use the Cumbrae ferry slipway to the south.

Public Slipway, Inverkip
Lat. 55.9058, Long. -4.8805.

CHARGES: None
SUITABILITY: Large trailer needs a car.
ACCESS: ¾ tidal. **TYPE OF RAMP:** Concrete **UPPER AREA:** Sand.
LOWER AREA: Shingle.
DIRECTIONS: From the North on the A78: Pass the Entrance to the Kip Marina and it turn in to the public lay-by 150 metres to the South. From the South on the A78: As you leave the village of Wemyss Bay heading towards Inverkip you will see signs for the lay-by and picnic point just before Inverkip turn in to the public lay-by. The Slip is at the southern end of the lay-by.
RAMP DESCRIPTION: Not suitable for large trailer sailers. The first section of the ramp is quite steep and it is easiest to use your car to get your boat down to the beach above the high water mark. Across 20 metres of fairly hard sand and shingle and then a shallow concrete ramp leads out into the Firth of Clyde. At low tide the ramp does not quite reach into the water - however the beach beside the ramp is level hard packed sand, rock and shingle and can be used by even fairly heavy craft as an alternative.
FACILITIES: Nearest Petrol station is in Wemyss Bay approximately 2miles south. Pub and shop in Inverkip village. Main Street is 100 metres from the slip. Chandlery in marina is 200 metres by car - 100 by foot, if southern gate to marina is open. Inverkip sailing club is adjacent with its own parallel slipway. It is friendly but has only the most basic facilities. Public conveniences in the lay-by are usually kept clean and tidy. Showers, laundry and other marina facilities may be available for a fee in the adjacent marina.
HAZARDS: The bay is fairly shallow and there are numerous small craft moorings just to the south of the club.

Kip Marina, Inverkip
Lat. 55.9101, Long. -4.8729.
01475 521485

CHARGES: Yes. Check at office. £10 in £10 out (2009price)
SUITABILITY: Large trailer needs a car.
ACCESS: All of tidal range. **TYPE OF RAMP:** Concrete
UPPER AREA: Concrete. **LOWER AREA:** Shingle.
DIRECTIONS: Enter Marina complex approach. Book in at administration office, follow access road adjacent pontoons. Slipway is through locked gates.
RAMP DESCRIPTION: Gets busy in summer. Popular launch site for local divers to the Clyde shipwrecks.
FACILITIES: All the facilities of a well thought-out marina. Petrol, bar, toilets, showers, phones, diving shop. Able to leave RIB in overnight, fresh water to wash down.
HAZARDS: Narrow navigable channel on low water. Busy traffic.

Kip Marina, Inverkip
Holt Leisure Parks Ltd, The Yacht Harbour, Inverkip, Renfrewshire, Scotland PA16 0AS
Lat. 55.9110, Long. -4.8734.
01475 521485

Harbour slipway, Gourock
Lat. 55.9573, Long. -4.8070.
SUITABILITY: Large trailer needs a car.
ACCESS: Unknown. **TYPE OF RAMP: UPPER AREA:** Concrete.
LOWER AREA: Unknown.

Newark Castle, Port Glasgow
Lat. 55.9342, Long. -4.6754.

CHARGES: No charge.
SUITABILITY: Large trailer needs a car.
ACCESS: ½ tidal. **TYPE OF RAMP:** Concrete **UPPER AREA:** Concrete.
LOWER AREA: Mud.
DIRECTIONS: Take M8 / A8 to Greenock. Before you reach Port Glasgow you come to Newark Castle roundabout. Take 3rd exit into Fergusons Ship Builders and bear right , this will take you round past the castle and onto the slip / jetty car park.
RAMP DESCRIPTION: The ramp is slippery as it's covered in weed, the local club does use it but it is not busy. Only one boat at a time, rocky and shallow to the left at low water so it's straight out and then head for the jetty on the right. River flow and tide can be a problem if not well practiced especially at low tide: Some rocks to the left of ramp at low water. Deep water at jetty side and deep water shipping channel 200 metres off end of jetty with marker buoys. Steel launching rails on the right hand side of the ramp at very end.
FACILITIES: Top of ramp is a park come picnic area with parking and a local fishing / boat owner's enclosure adjacent. The castle is also open to visitors.
HAZARDS: BEWARE. Reports of trailer tyres being slashed at this ramp.

Bridge Street Car Park, Dumbarton
Lat. 55.9449, Long. -4.5744.

CHARGES: None
SUITABILITY: Small trailer can be pushed.
ACCESS: ½ tidal. **TYPE OF RAMP:** Concrete **UPPER AREA:** Harbour.
LOWER AREA: Mud.
DIRECTIONS: In the centre of Dumbarton between the two road bridges. The downstream bridge is no longer open to traffic. The slipway is just off the Bridge Street car park.
RAMP DESCRIPTION: The ramp is in poor condition and only suitable for small boats and canoes. There are high walls either side of the ramp restricting the width to less than 3 metres.
FACILITIES: Car park right next to the ramp. Shops in Dumbarton.
HAZARDS: Lots of rocks downstream by the old bridge at low tide.

7

Sandpoint Marina, Dumbarton
Sandpoint, Woodyard Rd, Dumbarton, Dunbartonshire, Scotland G82 4BG
Lat. 55.9400, Long. -4.5685.
01389 762396

Pier Slipway, Helensburgh
Lat. 56.0016, Long. -4.7371.

CHARGES: None
SUITABILITY: Large trailer needs a car.
ACCESS: All of tidal range. **TYPE OF RAMP:** Concrete
UPPER AREA: Rock. **LOWER AREA:** Sand.
DIRECTIONS: The slipway is at the Pier in the centre of Helensburgh. Difficult to miss once you have found Helensburgh itself.
RAMP DESCRIPTION: The ramp is a good width and fairly steep. No problem reversing a 6 metre boat with the Landrover Discovery. The bottom half of the slip is very slippery with a thin layer of weed. Even with a 4 × 4, reversing down can be exciting when all four wheels lock up. Best to use a long rope attached to the car to pull the trailer out. There are plans to build a slipway at Rhu which may offer better facilities.
FACILITIES: Good parking at the top of the ramp. May not be very secure if leaving vehicles overnight. Helensburgh has all the usual shops and there is petrol nearby. You can tie up to the pier but it is in very bad condition. One set of steps and one ladder are usable. Watch out for the lines of the many fishermen who use the pier.

Rhu Marina, Helensburgh
Rhu, Helensburgh, Dunbartonshire, Scotland G84 8LH
Lat. 56.0124, Long. -4.7742.
01436 820238

Slipway, Rhu
Lat. 56.0269, Long. -4.7918.

CHARGES: Free
SUITABILITY: Small trailer can be pushed.
ACCESS: ¼ tidal. **TYPE OF RAMP:** Stone **UPPER AREA:** Concrete.
LOWER AREA: Shingle.
DIRECTIONS: After leaving Helensburgh, head north west along the coast, go through Rhu and turn left at signs for Outdoor centre. The centre has its own private ramp which is not available for public use, but 100 metres up is a public ramp. Only for small boats.
RAMP DESCRIPTION: Narrow road at top so best for small boats that can be handled on the trailer. The ramp is about 3 metres wide so you will need good reversing skills for a larger boat. The shingle below the ramp is firm and would take the weight of a trailer and possibly car.
FACILITIES: The lane is marked with double yellow lines but people do park on the road and any activity by traffic wardens is unlikely. The lines were put in to stop campers and caravans. The local Outdoor Centre is helpful and will give you advice.
HAZARDS: Moorings close in.

Silvers Marine (UK) Ltd, Rosneath
Silvers Marine (UK) Ltd Silverhills, Rosneath, Argyll, Scotland G84 0RW
Lat. 56.0129, Long. -4.7984.
01436 831 881

Caravan Site, Rosneath
Lat. 56.0006, Long. -4.7822.

CHARGES: Sept 2004: £7.50
SUITABILITY: Large trailer needs a car.
ACCESS: All of tidal range. **TYPE OF RAMP:** Shallow concrete ramp
UPPER AREA: Concrete. **LOWER AREA:** Concrete.
DIRECTIONS: Through Helensburgh, and Garelochhead follow road round the Gareloch to Rosneath, through town to the Caravan site. Site is on left hand side of road, approx 0.5 mile outside town.
RAMP DESCRIPTION: New ramp, shallow incline. Usually an assisted launch vehicle available. Width of ramp approx 9ft.
FACILITIES: Toilets, angling shop, parking all available at no extra charge.

Arrochar, Loch Long
Lat. 56.1946, Long. -4.7510.
SUITABILITY: Large trailer needs a car.
ACCESS: All of tidal range. **TYPE OF RAMP:** Concrete ramp.
UPPER AREA: Concrete. **LOWER AREA:** Shingle.
DIRECTIONS: Take the A83 for Arrochar. In Arrochar take the A814 towards Helensburgh. ½ miles from the above junction Teighness Stores (General Shop) is on your left hand side. The slip access is opposite the shop.
RAMP DESCRIPTION: The top of the slipway is an awkward dogleg from the road making launching a wide trailer or long rig very difficult. This slipway is best used at the bottom 3/4 of the tide so that you can drive down it and launch from the beach onto hard packed gravel. Bigger rigs or less capable vehicles are best launched from the forestry commission campsite at Ardgarten.
FACILITIES: Shop adjacent, plus further shops, cafés, toilets, hotels, petrol station, and police station in Arrochar (½ miles). There is a very good pub restaurant adjacent to the slip called the village inn.

Forestry Commission Campsite, Ardgarten
Lat. 56.1879, Long. -4.7780.
01616531981

CHARGES: £5 in addition to the overnight charge on the camp site
SUITABILITY: Small trailer can be pushed.
ACCESS: ¾ tidal. **TYPE OF RAMP:** Very poor very narrow tilts to left boulders at end no depth no way could launch with roller coaster 3 and 17 foot boat and the wardens told me not too **UPPER AREA:** Shingle.
LOWER AREA: Rock.
DIRECTIONS: Drive through the forestry commission campsite. The slipway is only for the use of those people staying on the camp site.
RAMP DESCRIPTION: Very poor slipway. Good fishing and diving is available just a few hundred yards from here.
FACILITIES: Excellent parking facilities.

7

Slipway, Lochgoilhead
Lat. 56.1701, Long. -4.9013.

CHARGES: None
SUITABILITY: Large trailer needs a car.
ACCESS: All of tidal range. TYPE OF RAMP: Beach
UPPER AREA: Shingle. LOWER AREA: Sand.
DIRECTIONS: Enter village by going over the humpback bridge at the war memorial. Follow road round till you reach the car park in the right hand side. From here the slipway is at the far end of the car park.
RAMP DESCRIPTION: The slip is only really suitable for use by 4 × 4 vehicles as it is a rock strewn beach. It is also used by the local Scout Outdoor Centre.
FACILITIES: No local petrol stations (the nearest is at Arrochar on the A82) There are a couple of pubs. Parking is at the top of the slipway in the car park. Nearest toilets are up a narrow road behind the houses. No fresh water is available at the slip.
HAZARDS: There is a sewage outfall to the right of the slip but is clearly marked. In the middle of Loch Goil is a large M.O.D. barge around which are large yellow buoys. You must stay outside these as there are cables running between them.

Holy Loch Marina, Sandbank
Rankins Brae, Sandbank, Argyll, Scotland
PA23 8QB
Lat. 55.9829, Long. -4.9483.
01369 701800

Holy Loch Marina, Dunoon
Lat. 55.9825, Long. -4.9475.
01369 701800

CHARGES: £10 covers launch and retrieval.
SUITABILITY: Large trailer needs a car.
ACCESS: All of tidal range. TYPE OF RAMP: Concrete
UPPER AREA: Harbour. LOWER AREA: Harbour.
DIRECTIONS: Holy Loch Marina is situated on the south shore of the loch, approximately ½ mile west of Lazaretto Point. 5 minutes drive north from Dunoon or Hunters Quay ferry terminals.
RAMP DESCRIPTION: 1:8 gradient concrete slipway. Restricted at very low water Springs by the pontoon. Pontoon for loading and day berths available for £10.
FACILITIES: Both diesel and petrol are available on the new fuel berth. Calor Gas and Camping Gaz are also available. Shearwater Marine's new chandlery is open daily. Roodberg slipway lift can handle craft up to 23 tonne / 60ft - on custom fit cradles. Secure car parking. Contact the marina on VHF Ch 80/37(M) Holy Loch Marina.

Isle of Bute Ferry Slip, Dunoon
Lat. 55.9232, Long. -5.1530.
Calmac office 01700 841235

CHARGES: None
SUITABILITY: Large trailer needs a car.
ACCESS: All of tidal range. TYPE OF RAMP: Concrete
UPPER AREA: Shingle. LOWER AREA: Shingle.

DIRECTIONS: Situated to the west of Dunoon. Follow A886 to Colintraive which is opposite north tip of Isle of Bute. A pain to drive to but worth it for launch into sheltered waters of Kyles of Bute.
RAMP DESCRIPTION: Use the concrete ramp onto the shingle beach to the south of the ferry slip. Bigger boats can use the ferry slipway only with permission and after the ferry has stopped running (9pm in summer).
FACILITIES: Parking available and small village of Colintraive. Toilets.

Maramarine, Maramarine
Lat. 55.9166, Long. -5.2145.
SUITABILITY: Large trailer needs a car.
ACCESS: All of tidal range. TYPE OF RAMP: UPPER AREA: Unknown.
LOWER AREA: Unknown.
DIRECTIONS: Located Tighnabruaich
RAMP DESCRIPTION: Concrete slipway which will hold up to 18tons weight

Slipway, Tank Slip
Lat. 55.8830, Long. -5.2337.

CHARGES: Free
SUITABILITY: Large trailer needs a car.
ACCESS: ¾ tidal. TYPE OF RAMP: Concrete UPPER AREA: Unknown.
LOWER AREA: Unknown.
RAMP DESCRIPTION: Steep concrete ramp, known locally as the Tank Slip
FACILITIES: Area to park and leave trailer
HAZARDS: Shore South and north of ramp Shoal

Castle Lauchlan, Loch Fyne
Lat. 56.1057, Long. -5.2078.

CHARGES: None
SUITABILITY: Large trailer needs a car.
ACCESS: ¾ tidal. TYPE OF RAMP: Hard packed shingle
UPPER AREA: Shingle. LOWER AREA: Shingle.
DIRECTIONS: Head south down the East side of Loch Fyne. At Strachur take the A886. Follow the A886 and take the B8000 towards Newton. You will pass Castle Lauchlan Caravan Site on your right hand side. ½ miles after the caravan site is the entrance to a car park. The ramp is in the left hand corner.
RAMP DESCRIPTION: Ramp is down shingle shore. Past users have removed the larger stones (please continue tradition). When launching/retrieving from 3 - 4 hours after high tide, keep parallel to the shore approximately 40 metres from top of ramp (following the river bed) heading towards the end of the small breakwater, to gain maximum water. Trim engine well up or use paddles. Watch for clumps of weed. Shallow draught boats only 2 hours before low water.
FACILITIES: Restaurant at car park (seasonal) local shops and hotels at Strachur.

Argyll Caravan Park, Dalchenna
Lat. 56.2031, Long. -5.1049.
Site Reception 01499 302285

CHARGES: £5 to park.

7

SUITABILITY: Large trailer needs a car.
ACCESS: ¾ tidal. **TYPE OF RAMP:** Concrete **UPPER AREA:** Shingle.
LOWER AREA: Shingle.
DIRECTIONS: Take the A83 south from Inverary. After 2 miles turn left into caravan / camping site, enquire at reception. Situated on the northern shore of Loch Fyne on the West coast.
RAMP DESCRIPTION: Raised concrete ramp across hard shingle. Ramp has a drop-off at the end but it is possible to launch from the hard shingle when the tide is out.
FACILITIES: Camp site nearby for tourers and tents. Can use toilets and showers on the camp site provided you are sensible. Meals available from the bar.

Beach slipway, Minard
Lat. 56.1152, Long. -5.2531.

CHARGES: Nil
SUITABILITY: Small trailer can be pushed.
ACCESS: Unknown. **TYPE OF RAMP:** Beach **UPPER AREA:** Shingle.
LOWER AREA: Shingle.
RAMP DESCRIPTION: Beach launch. Shingle /stone. Gentle slope off track from main A83

Crinan Canal, Ardrishaig
Lat. 56.0131, Long. -5.4462.
Tel: (01546) 603210
SUITABILITY: Large trailer needs a car.
ACCESS: ¼ tidal. **TYPE OF RAMP:** Concrete and stone
UPPER AREA: Unknown. **LOWER AREA:** Unknown.
DIRECTIONS: British Waterways, Pier Square, Ardrishaig, PA30 8DZ.
RAMP DESCRIPTION: You must phone ahead to use this slipway as the area is often congested. Leads into the harbour next to the canal. There is also a slipway in the village of Ardrishaig.
FACILITIES: Shops nearby, petrol 5 miles away. Parking by arrangement with British Waterways.

Bellanoch Marina, Ardrishaig
British Waterways Canal Office, Pier Square, Ardrishaig, Argyll, Scotland PA30 8DZ
Lat. 56.0747, Long. -5.5378.
01546 603210

Tarbert Harbour, Tarbert
Lat. 55.8661, Long. -5.4045.
TYC Sec 01880 820189

CHARGES: None
SUITABILITY: Large trailer needs a car.
ACCESS: All of tidal range. **TYPE OF RAMP:** Concrete
UPPER AREA: Shingle. **LOWER AREA:** Shingle.
DIRECTIONS: Head south from Lochgilphead. Ramp is next to the Tarbert Yacht Club on the south side of the harbour.
RAMP DESCRIPTION: Good concrete slipway leading onto shingle.
FACILITIES: Parking for car and trailer nearby. Toilets, chandlery, and shops in Tarbert which is a charming fishing village with good restaurants. Also a marina on the north side of the harbour.

Tarbert Harbour, Tarbert
Harbour Masters' Office, Harbour Street, Tarbert, Argyll, Scotland PA29 6TR
Lat. 55.8650, Long. -5.4105.
01880 820344

Port a Chruidh, Skipness
Lat. 55.7763, Long. -5.3157.

CHARGES: None
SUITABILITY: Portable Only.
ACCESS: No Ramp. **TYPE OF RAMP:** Sandy beach. **UPPER AREA:** Rock.
LOWER AREA: Rock.
DIRECTIONS: Turn left on metalled road just before Skipness Castle which after about 1 mile leads directly down to the launching site and small sheltered beach.
RAMP DESCRIPTION: The launch site is a Neolithic harbour and is well protected from the open sea by the rocky remains of the ancient breakwater.
FACILITIES: Limited parking. No facilities.
HAZARDS: None, but care must be taken if rounding Skipness Point close inshore at tidal flow.

Campbelltown Loch Berthing Co Ltd, Campbelltown
Kerala, High Askomil, Campbelltown, Argyll, Scotland PA28 6EN
Lat. 55.4290, Long. -5.5920.
01586 552131

Tayinloan Ferry Terminal, Tayinloan
Lat. 55.6574, Long. -5.6692.
SUITABILITY: Large trailer needs a car.
ACCESS: All of tidal range. **TYPE OF RAMP:** Large concrete
UPPER AREA: Unknown. **LOWER AREA:** Unknown.
RAMP DESCRIPTION: Calmac ferry ramp at Tayinloan, use after the ferry service has finished for the day, usually 6pm during the summer.

Slipway, Tayvallich
Lat. 56.0243, Long. -5.6250.
01546 870338

CHARGES: No charge but donations to Harbour Committee can be made at shop.
SUITABILITY: Large trailer needs a car.
ACCESS: All of tidal range. **TYPE OF RAMP:** Slip
UPPER AREA: Unknown. **LOWER AREA:** Unknown.
DIRECTIONS: Take A82 / A83 to Lochgilphead, then A816 (Oban) to Cairnbaan (approximately 2miles) Turn left and follow Crinian Canal for 3 miles. Turn left and follow road for 6 miles to Tayvallich. Slip is in centre of village by shop / Post Office.
RAMP DESCRIPTION: There is a slip in Tayvallich suitable for boats up to about 22 feet.
FACILITIES: There is also a pontoon for temporary berthing for loading / unloading. Water available.
HAZARDS: A reef extends across the centre of Tayvallich Bay but is marked by cardinal buoys.

Slipway, Carsaig
Lat. 56.0300, Long. -5.6361.
SUITABILITY: Small trailer can be pushed.
ACCESS: ¼ tidal. **TYPE OF RAMP:** Concrete ramp onto a sandy beach
UPPER AREA: Unknown. **LOWER AREA:** Unknown.
DIRECTIONS: ½ mile West of Tayvallich.
RAMP DESCRIPTION: There is a concrete ramp leading onto the beach at Carsaig facing the Sound of Jura ½ mile from Tayvallich. The beach is very shallow so the ramp is only suitable for dinghies.

Craighouse, Jura
Lat. 55.8334, Long. -5.9504.
SUITABILITY: Small trailer can be pushed.
ACCESS: Unknown. **TYPE OF RAMP:** Concrete **UPPER AREA:** Rock.
LOWER AREA: Unknown.
DIRECTIONS: Craighouse is situated in the south eastern corner of Jura
RAMP DESCRIPTION: Narrow concrete ramp across the foreshore to rocky shoreline.
FACILITIES: Beautiful remote location. Hotel in village of Craighouse.

Feolin Ferry, Jura
Lat. 55.8483, Long. -6.0909.
SUITABILITY: Large trailer needs a car.
ACCESS: All of tidal range. **TYPE OF RAMP:** Concrete
UPPER AREA: Harbour. **LOWER AREA:** Harbour.
DIRECTIONS: Western end of Jura. Roll-on roll-off ferry to Islay.
RAMP DESCRIPTION: Excellent wide concrete slipway. Used by the roll-on roll-off ferry so check times before launching.

Port Askaig, Islay
Lat. 55.8483, Long. -6.1050.
SUITABILITY: Large trailer needs a car.
ACCESS: All of tidal range. **TYPE OF RAMP:** Concrete
UPPER AREA: Harbour. **LOWER AREA:** Harbour.
DIRECTIONS: Eastern end of Islay at the ferry terminal to Jura.
RAMP DESCRIPTION: Ramp can get very shallow on Springs. It leads to sheltered harbour that is blocked by Jura ferry and very congested. Can require advance notice to clear slipway in order to launch. The ramp goes is into the harbour and is quite narrow (ok for 7 metre RIB) but straight off road so fairly easy to use. Being ferry terminal means best avoided when ferry due!
FACILITIES: Hotel in village. Petrol only available along with shop. Developments in 2003 to the ferry terminal set to change the filling station and may improve fuel supplies.

Port Ellen, Islay
Lat. 55.6260, Long. -6.1907.
SUITABILITY: Large trailer needs a car.
ACCESS: All of tidal range. **TYPE OF RAMP:** 1. Pebble beach or 2.soft sand. **UPPER AREA:** Unknown. **LOWER AREA:** Unknown.
RAMP DESCRIPTION: New concrete slipway and there are a couple of older ramps that can be used for smaller boats.
FACILITIES: Pontoon next to the slipway. Full facilities available on pontoons and fuel in village along with shops about 500 yards.

Bowmore, Islay
Lat. 55.7584, Long. -6.2894.
CHARGES: £5 to join the harbour association for the year.
SUITABILITY: Large trailer needs a car.
ACCESS: ¼ tidal. **TYPE OF RAMP:** Concrete ramp
UPPER AREA: Unknown. **LOWER AREA:** Unknown.
RAMP DESCRIPTION: Ramp is quite steep and can be slippy at bottom. Can be used all states but does get a bit shallow for larger craft on Springs. Harbour is dredged and does not dry out. Bowmore is fairly sheltered but Port Charlotte on the other side of the loch is probably better.
FACILITIES: Park in street. Petrol, fresh water, food shops and fresh water is nearby.

Port Charlotte, Islay
Lat. 55.7387, Long. -6.3772.
SUITABILITY: Large trailer needs a car.
ACCESS: No Ramp. **TYPE OF RAMP:** Shingle onto sandy beach
UPPER AREA: Shingle. **LOWER AREA:** Shingle.
DIRECTIONS: Situated at the western end of Islay to the north of Loch Indaa.
RAMP DESCRIPTION: Stone pier next to the beach access point. Camp site is not officially there now but nobody seems to mind! Can be sheltered if Bowmore exposed and vice a versa.
FACILITIES: Hotel and unofficial camping in the village. Fuel available 150 yards up steep hill!

Portnahaven, Islay
Lat. 55.6802, Long. -6.5073.
SUITABILITY: Small trailer can be pushed.
ACCESS: ¼ tidal. **TYPE OF RAMP: UPPER AREA:** Shingle.
LOWER AREA: Sand.
DIRECTIONS: Situated on the western tip of Islay.
RAMP DESCRIPTION: Concrete ramp onto the beach
FACILITIES: Slipway is next to small village

Port Wymss, Islay
Lat. 55.6763, Long. -6.5068.
SUITABILITY: Large trailer needs a car.
ACCESS: ½ tidal. **TYPE OF RAMP:** Concrete **UPPER AREA:** Rock.
LOWER AREA: Sand.
DIRECTIONS: Situated on the western tip of Islay.
RAMP DESCRIPTION: Concrete ramp across rocky foreshore to a sandy beach.
FACILITIES: Next to the village of Port Wymss and Portnahaven

Scalasaig, Isle of Colonsay
Lat. 56.0684, Long. -6.1852.
SUITABILITY: Large trailer needs a car.
ACCESS: ½ tidal. **TYPE OF RAMP: UPPER AREA:** Unknown.
LOWER AREA: Unknown.
RAMP DESCRIPTION: Gradient is gentle, Launch above half tide down shallow ramp suitable for car into harbour. Petrol and shops 150 yards.

7

Hotel 300 yards. Dinghies can also be hired from Colonsay Hotel - two North Sea Skiffs. Sailing varies from sheltered to very exposed.
FACILITIES: Car park adjacent. Fresh water from well, 100 yards.

Ardfern Yacht Centre, by Lochgilphead
Ardfern, by Lochgilphead, Argyll, Scotland
PA31 8QN
Lat. 56.1830, Long. -5.5314.
01852 500247

Craobh Marina, Lochgilphead
Craobh Haven, Lochgilphead, Argyll, Scotland
PA31 8UA
Lat. 56.2109, Long. -5.5562.
01852 500222

Marina Slip, Croabh Haven
Lat. 56.2111, Long. -5.5567.
01852 500222
CHARGES: £18.80 for RIB.
SUITABILITY: Large trailer needs a car.
ACCESS: All of tidal range. **TYPE OF RAMP:** Concrete slip and hoist.
UPPER AREA: Unknown. **LOWER AREA:** Unknown.
DIRECTIONS: Croabh Haven is on West coast - A816 - 17 miles North of Lochgilphead, 22 miles South of Oban.
RAMP DESCRIPTION: Gentle ramp in marina suitable for car, usable all states of tide. Concrete slip and hoist, all tide during working hours.
FACILITIES: Toilets are on site along with helpful staff. Limited parking on site. Ideal base for cruising and club meetings, campsite nearby. Part of marina-based village. Shops / pub / showers in village. Superb sailing area. Pay marina. All facilities in marina.
HAZARDS: Fast local streams can be dangerous, get local advice.

Kilmelford Yacht Haven, Oban
Kilmelford, Oban, Argyll, Scotland PA34 4XD
Lat. 56.2561, Long. -5.4919.
01852 200248

Yacht Haven, Kilmelford
Lat. 56.2557, Long. -5.4936.
Boatyard Ken McColl 01852 200248
CHARGES: No charge unless assisted.
SUITABILITY: Large trailer needs a car.
ACCESS: ½ tidal. **TYPE OF RAMP:** Hard gravel. **UPPER AREA:** Shingle.
LOWER AREA: Mud.
DIRECTIONS: By boatyard on A816 ½ mile southwest of Kilmelford.
RAMP DESCRIPTION: Gentle gradient, gravel hard suitable for car. Excellent sheltered cruising ground. Shingle slip only usable when launch hoist trolley rails are covered (3hours), beware of this. Very nice couple own boat yard and are very helpful.
FACILITIES: Full boatyard facilities, showers, toilets, telephone, diesel and gas. Pontoon and 3 new moorings.

Melfort Pier and Harbour, Oban
Melfort Pier Harbour, Kilmelford, Oban, Argyll, Scotland PA34 4XD
Lat. 56.2694, Long. -5.5024.
01852 200333

Melfort Pier & Harbour, Kilmelford, By Oban
Lat. 56.2701, Long. -5.5021.
01852 200333
CHARGES: £12 per night £60 per week £120 per month £600 per six months
SUITABILITY: Large trailer needs a car.
ACCESS: ¾ tidal. **TYPE OF RAMP: UPPER AREA:** Unknown.
LOWER AREA: Unknown.
DIRECTIONS: 16 miles south of Oban
RAMP DESCRIPTION: 19 Swinging moorings. Small private harbour berths -max 20ft.must be booked prior to arrival.
FACILITIES: Diesel is available nearby at Kilmelford Yacht Haven. Water/power available on pier but only accessible 3 hours either side of high water. Hot showers, onsite restaurant Melfort Mermaid open each day. Laundry, car parking. WIFI access. 16 Self-contained Harbour Houses ashore, each with sauna spa bath, log fire and spectacular views over Loch Melfort. From £90.00 per house per night.

Cuan Ferry Slip, Seil, Nr Oban, Argyll
Lat. 56.2677, Long. -5.6294.
SUITABILITY: Large trailer needs a car.
ACCESS: Unknown. **TYPE OF RAMP:** Concrete, shallow gradient, very wide (2 launches at once possible) **UPPER AREA:** Concrete.
LOWER AREA: Concrete.
RAMP DESCRIPTION: RoRo ferry slip used by Luing/Seil ferry. Permission of ferry operator required for launching.
HAZARDS: Cuan sound has notoriously fast tides, a little lee is offered by the edge of the slipway. RoRo ferry (for 2 cars)

Ardoran Marine, Oban
Lat. 56.3583, Long. -5.4912.
+44(0)1631 566123
SUITABILITY: Large trailer needs a car.
ACCESS: ½ tidal. **TYPE OF RAMP: UPPER AREA:** Unknown.
LOWER AREA: Unknown.
DIRECTIONS: Ardoran Marine is a boatyard 5 miles South of Oban on Loch Feochan, Lerags, Oban, Argyll, Scotland, PA34 4SE.
RAMP DESCRIPTION: The slip is accessible at the top half of the tide, it can accommodate up to 25 foot boats. There is also a crane for larger boats to 8 tonnes. Please note that Jetskiers are not allowed to launch here.
FACILITIES: Moorings can be rented on a daily, weekly or monthly basis or for the whole six month season from April to October, then ashore for the winter months. There are service pontoons for loading provisions and crew, with diesel, Calor gas, fresh water, and toilet and shower facilities available ashore.

7

Puffin Divers, Oban
Lat. 56.3736, Long. -5.5226.
01631 566088 - Puffin Divers

CHARGES: £3.00
SUITABILITY: Large trailer needs a car.
ACCESS: All of tidal range. **TYPE OF RAMP:** Concrete
UPPER AREA: Concrete. **LOWER AREA:** Shingle.
DIRECTIONS: Puffin Divers - Gallanach Pier near Oban, Argyll. Take the coast road south from Oban past the ferry terminal following the signs to Gallanach. Road only goes to this site.
RAMP DESCRIPTION: Owned by Puffin Divers. Overnight moorings available, also no objection to parking boat overnight in car park. Puffin Diver also offer assisted launch for a small fee.
FACILITIES: Plenty of car parking. Toilets, fresh water tap and hose on ramp. Dive shop stocking some spares and chandlery. Shoreline accommodation and campsite.
HAZARDS: Take special care in case there are trainee divers are in water - Dive support boat will fly the A flag (diver down).

Port Beag, Oban
Lat. 56.4111, Long. -5.4791.
01631 562892

CHARGES: None
SUITABILITY: Large trailer needs a car.
ACCESS: ¾ tidal. **TYPE OF RAMP:** Concrete **UPPER AREA:** Harbour.
LOWER AREA: Unknown.
DIRECTIONS: Situated at the western side of Oban near to the lifeboat station. The slipway is well signposted.
RAMP DESCRIPTION: Steep slip suitable for launching by car, usable 3 hours either side high water. Recommended as the best launching point in Oban but you must stay out of the way of the ferry. Do not use the ferry terminal slipway which is to the west, closer to the railway station, unless you have permission from Calmac.
FACILITIES: Car park ½ mile. All other facilities in Oban. No waste disposal at this slipway, go to the North Pier.

Oban Yachts & Marine Services, Oban
Isle of Kerrera, Oban, Argyll, Scotland PA34 4SX
Lat. 56.4180, Long. -5.4991.
01631 565333

Ganavan Sands, Oban
Lat. 56.4381, Long. -5.4707.
01546 602127

CHARGES: Free but may have council car parking charges for car park, see above.
SUITABILITY: Large trailer needs a car.
ACCESS: ½ tidal. **TYPE OF RAMP:** Concrete **UPPER AREA:** Concrete.
LOWER AREA: Sand.
DIRECTIONS: Head north out of Oban on the A85 to Ganavan Sands Campsite. Slipway is on beach within large council car park at the new chalet development.
RAMP DESCRIPTION: Good wide ramp but leads to shallow sandy beach which is hard to use at low water.

FACILITIES: Large council car park and slip leading to sea. May be car parking charges but this is uncertain as machines were installed but seem to be out of use.
HAZARDS: Shallows off beach but slip area all sand

Dunstaffnage Marina, Oban
Dunbeg, Oban, Argyll, Scotland PA37 1PX
Lat. 56.4488, Long. -5.4325.
01631 566555

Fisherman's Wharf, Oban
Lat. 56.4523, Long. -5.4078.
01631 710287 or mobile 07788 881811

CHARGES: Launch and park, car trailer and boat £5 per day or £10 with overnight mooring.
SUITABILITY: Large trailer needs a car.
ACCESS: All of tidal range. **TYPE OF RAMP:** Well packed sand and shingle. **UPPER AREA:** Sand. **LOWER AREA:** Shingle.
DIRECTIONS: Turn off the A85 Glasgow - Oban road in Connel village about half a mile east of Connel Bridge into the Old Shore Road. The entrance gate to Fisherman's Wharf is 50 metres in on the left and is easily identified by conspicuous port and starboard - red and green - marker buoys on either side.
RAMP DESCRIPTION: Launch from the beach. Well packed sand / shingle. 4 × 4 available to assist if required. Excellent facility on private premises just off the main road. On the doorstep to the popular dive site of the SS Breda in Ardmucknish Bay, the Falls of Lora, the shelter of Lochs Etive and Creran, plus superb sailing and fine sports fishing in the popular and well known Argyll coastal area, and the Sound of Mull.
FACILITIES: Moorings, jetty, pontoon, parking, water, air for divers, equipment washing, engine flushing, trailer storage, dinghy storage. Planning permission applied for toilets, showers, and picnic areas spring 2002.

Lochnell Arms Hotel Slip, Connel
Lat. 56.4579, Long. -5.3985.
Lochnell Arms Hotel 01631 710408

CHARGES: £10 to launch and recover.
SUITABILITY: Large trailer needs a car.
ACCESS: ¾ tidal. **TYPE OF RAMP:** Large stones cemented together.
UPPER AREA: Sand. **LOWER AREA:** Sand.
RAMP DESCRIPTION: Gentle gradient suitable for car just to the northwest of Connel Bridge by Lochnell Arms Hotel.
FACILITIES: Park nearby. Petrol 1½ miles north on A828. Showers available at the hotel for a small fee.
HAZARDS: Gives access to Firth of Lorne and Loch Etive but beware of falls under bridge. Go under at slack water just before tide turns fair.

Creran Moorings, Barcaldine
Lat. 56.5265, Long. -5.3217.
01631 720265

CHARGES: Yes
SUITABILITY: Large trailer needs a car.

7

ACCESS: ¾ tidal. TYPE OF RAMP: Hard cobbles on beach.
UPPER AREA: Shingle. LOWER AREA: Shingle.
DIRECTIONS: Located twelve miles north of Oban in Barcaldine, Creran Moorings is situated on the southern shore of Loch Creran and close to Barcaldine forest.
FACILITIES: For use by holiday makers staying in chalets.

Loch Linnhe Old Ferry Slip, Port Appin
Lat. 56.5528, Long. -5.4119.
SUITABILITY: Large trailer needs a car.
ACCESS: Unknown. TYPE OF RAMP: UPPER AREA: Unknown.
LOWER AREA: Unknown.
RAMP DESCRIPTION: Former ferry slip. Launch into Loch Linnhe opposite the northern tip of Lismore.
FACILITIES: Car and trailer parking available at the pub at the end of the pier.

Loch Linnhe Watersports, Appin
Lat. 56.5834, Long. -5.3788.
CHARGES: £5
SUITABILITY: Large trailer needs a car.
ACCESS: ¾ tidal. TYPE OF RAMP: Concrete UPPER AREA: Unknown.
LOWER AREA: Unknown.
DIRECTIONS: Lettershuna. Situated just ¼mile off A828 midway between Fort William and Oban.
RAMP DESCRIPTION: Gradient is moderate.
FACILITIES: Parking charges- £5.00/week. Overnight parking available. Parking space is for 10 cars. Security is reasonable. Excellent base for either day sailing or multi-day cruising. Moorings and Wayfarer hire also available. Slip water tap.
HAZARDS: There are strong tidal streams in the area.

Old Ferry Slipway, South Ballachulish
Lat. 56.6883, Long. -5.1829.
CHARGES: None
SUITABILITY: Large trailer needs a car.
ACCESS: ¾ tidal. TYPE OF RAMP: Concrete UPPER AREA: Harbour.
LOWER AREA: Rock.
DIRECTIONS: From the roundabout on the south side of the Ballachulish Bridge take the turning for Oban and the ramp is almost under the bridge and before you get the Ballachulish Hotel.
RAMP DESCRIPTION: Old ferry ramp. Wide and steep. There can be very strong currents when the tide is flowing. It is not accessible for approximately 1½ hours either side of low water as it dries out and then you have a sheer drop. Care must also be taken not to reverse the trailer back over the edge. Apart from this, it is an excellent slip.
FACILITIES: Hotel nearby and petrol close.
HAZARDS: Strong tides.

Lochaber Watersports, Ballachulish
Lat. 56.6802, Long. -5.1332.
01855 821391
CHARGES: None.
SUITABILITY: Large trailer needs a car.

ACCESS: All of tidal range. TYPE OF RAMP: a) Slate spoil and rocks b) concrete. UPPER AREA: Concrete. LOWER AREA: Rock.
DIRECTIONS: Slip is in car park immediately adjacent to Isles of Glencoe Hotel reached by a signposted slip road off A82. Lochaber Watersports is now clearly signposted from the A82.
RAMP DESCRIPTION: Larger ramp is best used at high water and needs a powerful towing vehicle. Smaller concrete ramp can ONLY be used at high water. Contact Lochaber Watersports for barrier key and advice.
FACILITIES: Hotel, pub, swimming pool, toilets, garage, watersports centre. Jan 2003, pontoon completely refurbished and the water connection repaired.

Old Ferry Slipway, North Ballachulish
Lat. 56.6890, Long. -5.1798.
CHARGES: None
SUITABILITY: Large trailer needs a car.
ACCESS: ¾ tidal. TYPE OF RAMP: Concrete UPPER AREA: Harbour.
LOWER AREA: Rock.
DIRECTIONS: From the roundabout on the south side of the Ballachulish Bridge take the turning for Fort William, cross bridge and turn onto B863 then turn right onto Old ferry Road and slipway is at end of the road.
RAMP DESCRIPTION: Old ferry ramp. Wide and steep. There can be very strong currents when the tide is flowing. It is not accessible for approximately 1½ hours either side of low water as it dries out and then you have a sheer drop. Care must also be taken not to reverse the trailer back over the edge. Apart from this, it is an excellent slip.
FACILITIES: Hotel nearby and petrol close.
HAZARDS: Strong tides.

Lochaber Yacht Club, Fort William
Lat. 56.8119, Long. -5.1226.
01397 703576
CHARGES: Club donation please.
SUITABILITY: Large trailer needs a car.
ACCESS: ¾ tidal. TYPE OF RAMP: Concrete UPPER AREA: Harbour.
LOWER AREA: Shingle.
DIRECTIONS: Take the A82 south of Fort William.
RAMP DESCRIPTION: The ramp owned by Lochaber Yacht Club. Visiting sailing boats are welcome but please contact the club first. Motor boats should use the slipway at Corpach.
FACILITIES: Close to Fort William with all the facilities of a large town. Parking area and trailer park

Underwater Centre, Fort William
Lat. 56.8226, Long. -5.1067.
01397 703786, Fax: 01397 704969, webenquiries@theunderwatercenter.com
CHARGES: £5 to launch and recover, £10 assisted launch and recover.
SUITABILITY: Large trailer needs a car.
ACCESS: All of tidal range. TYPE OF RAMP: Wide concrete
UPPER AREA: Rock. LOWER AREA: Shingle.

7

DIRECTIONS: The Underwater Centre, An Aird, Fort William, Scotland. Round the back of Safeways near the train station.
RAMP DESCRIPTION: Wide channel has been dug into Loch Linnhe. The slipway re-laid in 2003. Off the end of the pier is deep water and boats can be launched by crane which can be hired locally. Phone the Centre before using. Ramp is partially blocked by rubble at top and frequently by employees' cars and car park.
FACILITIES: Slipway is next door to one of the biggest diving centres in the country. Car park nearby and Fort William has extensive shops. Petrol at Morrisons. Diesel and fresh water on the end of the pier.

Slipway, Corpach
Lat. 56.8412, Long. -5.1374.
CHARGES: £20 per year. Go the security gate at the old paper mill where you can pay your money and get the key for the slipway.
SUITABILITY: Large trailer needs a car.
ACCESS: All of tidal range. **TYPE OF RAMP:** Concrete
UPPER AREA: Rock. **LOWER AREA:** Sand.
DIRECTIONS: Inbetween the old Wigans Teap paper mill and the Corpach harbour. At Corpach take the turning off the main road by the Slipway Autos and there is also a sign for Corpach Harbour. Go over the railway line and carry straight on. The slipway is to the left of the timber yard and to the right of the boat yard.
RAMP DESCRIPTION: Good concrete ramp into very sheltered water. Locked gate at the top of the ramp. Accessible all states of tide except very low Spring tides.
FACILITIES: Parking in the car park behind the signal box. Should be fine to leave car and trailer there for a couple of weeks.

Ferry Slipway, Lochaline
Lat. 56.5374, Long. -5.7753.
SUITABILITY: Large trailer needs a car.
ACCESS: All of tidal range. **TYPE OF RAMP:** Concrete
UPPER AREA: Harbour. **LOWER AREA:** Rock.
DIRECTIONS: Follow road through Lochaline toward ferry pier.
RAMP DESCRIPTION: Wide slipway with good gradient for the roll-on roll-off ferry. Avoid the Mull ferry. Times posted on pier.
FACILITIES: Petrol and air 5 minutes walk or ring Lochaline dive centre. Pub, burger van, toilets.

Craignure, Mull
Lat. 56.4691, Long. -5.7000.
SUITABILITY: Large trailer needs a car.
ACCESS: Unknown. **TYPE OF RAMP: UPPER AREA:** Rock.
LOWER AREA: Shingle.
DIRECTIONS: Launch into southeast corner of Craignure Harbour, about 100 yards from ferry terminal for Oban.
RAMP DESCRIPTION: Concrete slipway over the rocky foreshore, suitable for car. Craignure Bay is exposed to north and east but local users say the southeast corner is always sheltered. Handy for ferry from Oban and Sound of Mull.
FACILITIES: Car park adjacent.

Ferry Slip, Fionnphort, Mull
Lat. 56.3258, Long. -6.3707.
Calmac Manager
CHARGES: None
SUITABILITY: Large trailer needs a car.
ACCESS: All of tidal range. **TYPE OF RAMP:** Concrete
UPPER AREA: Concrete. **LOWER AREA:** Unknown.
RAMP DESCRIPTION: Excellent concrete slipway. Slip water tap available. Launching on ferry slip with permission, temporary moorings nearby.
FACILITIES: Plenty of parking, can be used for overnight parking. Busy slip for commercial use.
HAZARDS: Strong tides and shoals in sound of Iona.

Slipway, Derryguaig
Lat. 56.4484, Long. -6.0741.
CHARGES: Nil. I have met the locals and they seem friendly.
SUITABILITY: Large trailer needs a car.
ACCESS: All of tidal range. **TYPE OF RAMP:** Natural rock / shingle. 4 × 4 needed. **UPPER AREA:** Shingle. **LOWER AREA:** Shingle.
DIRECTIONS: Down the hill from derrygaig farm - off the shore road.
RAMP DESCRIPTION: A winding access through the rocks. You may need to reshape the beach shingle as winter storms make access from the grass difficult
FACILITIES: Nil
HAZARDS: A slip with a dog leg in. Difficult to get to the beach with a boat at high tide without catching the prop.

Loch na Keal, Mull
Lat. 56.5000, Long. -6.0054.
CHARGES: None
SUITABILITY: Large trailer needs a car.
ACCESS: Non-tidal. **TYPE OF RAMP:** Rough. Access to the beach from the road. The shingle will support a 4 × 4. Dries out at lowest tides as shown. **UPPER AREA:** Shingle. **LOWER AREA:** Shingle.
DIRECTIONS: On B8073, ¾ mile from junction with B8035 from Salen, just north of mouth of River Ba.
RAMP DESCRIPTION: Rough slip but gentle gradient. A good spot to explore the islands off west Mull. Can also camp ashore here.
FACILITIES: Fresh water from stream, other needs in Salen.

Ulva Ferry, Ulva
Lat. 56.4814, Long. -6.1498.
CHARGES: £10 per day per boat but no one around to pay when we were there!
SUITABILITY: Large trailer needs a car.
ACCESS: All of tidal range. **TYPE OF RAMP:** Steep concrete with vertical drop at end, extreme low water would be problematic
UPPER AREA: Concrete. **LOWER AREA:** Concrete.
DIRECTIONS: Follow signs for ULVA Ferry
RAMP DESCRIPTION: Steep slip dog legged to the right. Possible to launch/recover at all states of tide with care. Avoid even temporary mooring on end of ferry pier as it is in continuous use. Ample parking

7

available but its a narrow and twisty road to the slip, take care when manually moving trailers as the verges are soft and steep.

FACILITIES: None

HAZARDS: Shallow rocks on left of slip as you look down the ramp.

Tobermory Slipway, Tobermory
Lat. 56.6205, Long. -6.0679.

CHARGES: Honesty box £5.

SUITABILITY: Large trailer needs a car.

ACCESS: All of tidal range. **TYPE OF RAMP:** Wide concrete

UPPER AREA: Harbour. **LOWER AREA:** Rock.

DIRECTIONS: The ramp is next to the distillery and pub (too good to be true) at the south end of Tobermory.

RAMP DESCRIPTION: The ramp is wide but does have a turn in it. It should be possible to launch from a large trailer with care.

FACILITIES: The ramp is close to the centre of Tobermory. There are showers and laundry facilities at the mini marina and petrol and shops nearby and good parking facilities. There is also a good pontoon at the ramp.

HAZARDS: Moorings in Tobermory Bay.

Tobermory Harbour Association, Tobermory
Taigh Solais, Tobermory, Argyll, Scotland
PA75 6NR
Lat. 56.6198, Long. -6.0666.
01688 302876

Fishnish Ferry, Fishnish
Lat. 56.5148, Long. -5.8100.

SUITABILITY: Large trailer needs a car.

ACCESS: All of tidal range. **TYPE OF RAMP:** Wide concrete

UPPER AREA: Concrete. **LOWER AREA:** Concrete.

DIRECTIONS: Follow Signs to Fishnish ferry terminal

RAMP DESCRIPTION: Broad concrete slip with good parking

FACILITIES: Small café on site and ample parking behind, minimal security but this is not really a problem in the area

HAZARDS: Calmac own this slip. Ferry operates from this slip on approx 30-45 minute intervals during the day. Often a cue of waiting vehicles above slip.

Slipway, Strontian
Lat. 56.6880, Long. -5.5549.

CHARGES: None. Details about Community Moorings Committee provided on Boathouse notice board.

SUITABILITY: Large trailer needs a car.

ACCESS: All of tidal range. **TYPE OF RAMP:** Concrete

UPPER AREA: Concrete. **LOWER AREA:** Concrete.

DIRECTIONS: On the way into Strontian coming from the Corran Ferry. Slipway is just after the road becomes single track.

RAMP DESCRIPTION: Renewed in 2006 with regional and European money, this is now a first class concrete slipway, maintained by a local Committee. More than 10ft wide it is suitable for any trailer. Gives access to top of Loch Sunart and a very sheltered stretch of water.

FACILITIES: Village of Strontian is close by with shops and petrol station.

Slipway, Resipole
Lat. 56.7107, Long. -5.7192.
01967 431235

CHARGES: Launching is free if camping, £5 for visitors.

SUITABILITY: Small trailer can be pushed.

ACCESS: ½ tidal. **TYPE OF RAMP:** Concrete **UPPER AREA:** Rock.

LOWER AREA: Shingle.

DIRECTIONS: Follow the road along Loch Sunart 8 miles past Strontian on the way to Salen. Launch ramp is by the camp site. Coming from the east you will cross the Corran Ferry where there are signs stating that fuel should not be carried in cans. Never heard of this being enforced.

RAMP DESCRIPTION: Fairly narrow and there are overhead wires along the side of the road. Steep concrete slip that has recently been improved and widened slightly. Can be difficult when windy, exposed. Can be used at least 3 hours high water if not more.

FACILITIES: Local camp site for tents, tourists and static caravans/lodges for hire. Petrol at Strontian (5 miles by road from launch site). Small shop/petrol station at Strontian has fair prices. Roads are mostly single track with passing places for last leg to this site, and onwards to Salen - care needed for wide/long trailers.

Gravel slipway, Salen
Lat. 56.7158, Long. -5.7784.

CHARGES: None

SUITABILITY: Large trailer needs a car.

ACCESS: All of tidal range. **TYPE OF RAMP:** Shingle path over Estate ground. **UPPER AREA:** Rock. **LOWER AREA:** Shingle.

DIRECTIONS: Just by the small hump back bridge in Salen

RAMP DESCRIPTION: Gravel/shingle roadway across the shore to the sea. Useful for launching if you don't want to pay the fees at the jetty.

FACILITIES: Salen has a good pub. Nearby Acharacle has tea room, take away (in season) a pub, restaurant and food shops. Note: there is no diesel/petrol on sale in Acharacle. Nearest pumps are in Strontian or Kilchoan.

Salen, Loch Sunart
Lat. 56.7121, Long. -5.7778.
Mr MacCreedy 01967 431 333

CHARGES: £7 under 20 ´ to launch and £7 to recover.

SUITABILITY: Large trailer needs a car.

ACCESS: All of tidal range. **TYPE OF RAMP:** Stone Jetty

UPPER AREA: Harbour. **LOWER AREA:** Shingle.

DIRECTIONS: Follow the A861 west from Strontian for 12 miles. Single track road with passing spaces so you may need to reverse. At Salen, turn left down the steep hill by the Pub. Follow road to the stone jetty.

RAMP DESCRIPTION: Wide and steep ramp going down onto shingle at low tide. There is an alternative ramp that is free of charge 400 metres north by the old stone bridge across the stream. The track leads from the southern end of the bridge and gives access to the loch 1-2 hours around high tide.

7

FACILITIES: Petrol is now only available locally in Strontian (11 miles east) or Kilchoan approximately (18 miles west). Parking at the jetty. Yachtsmen landing at the jetty in dinghies are charges £2 per head.
HAZARDS: Marked reef in the Salen Bay.

Clan Morrison Hotel, Sunart
Lat. 56.6766, Long. -5.8886.
SUITABILITY: Large trailer needs a car.
ACCESS: All of tidal range. **TYPE OF RAMP:** Track down to the foreshore across hotel ground. **UPPER AREA:** Rock. **LOWER AREA:** Shingle.
DIRECTIONS: Follow the road from Salen west along Loch Sunart. As you come into Glenborrodale, the Clan Morrison Hotel is on the left with petrol pumps outside.(These are no longer in use)
RAMP DESCRIPTION: Track down the shore. Best to launch at high or low tide where the gradient is steepest.
FACILITIES: Hotel is closed so not sure if this slipway is available for use, but the owner still lives on site. There is a pontoon next to the slipway.

Mingary Pier, Kilchoan
Lat. 56.6887, Long. -6.0941.
SUITABILITY: Large trailer needs a car.
ACCESS: All of tidal range. **TYPE OF RAMP:** Concrete
UPPER AREA: Rock. **LOWER AREA:** Rock.
DIRECTIONS: From Kilchoan in Ardnamurchan, drive down Pier Road to Mingary Pier.
RAMP DESCRIPTION: The ramp is used by the Tobermory ferry so make sure you are not using the ramp when the ferry comes in. The ferry sailing times are clearly posted at the pier. This excellent facility is at the end of twenty miles of single track road. Make sure you know how to reverse a trailer before attempting this journey. The road can be busy in the summer.
FACILITIES: Good car parking and trailer parking, free of charge, toilets and showers ½ mile up road at local community centre. Accommodation available from Steading Holidays
HAZARDS: At low tide there are shallow rocks between the ramp and the pontoon, just to the north of the ramp.

Kilchoan Bay, Kilchoan
Lat. 56.6959, Long. -6.1185.
CHARGES: There is an honesty box at the head of the ramp.
SUITABILITY: Small trailer can be pushed.
ACCESS: ¾ tidal. **TYPE OF RAMP:** Long concrete jetty.
UPPER AREA: Rock. **LOWER AREA:** Sand.
DIRECTIONS: Ramp is opposite the shop in Kilchoan. Kilchoan at the end of 20 miles of single track road, west of Salen on the Ardnamurchan Peninsular.
RAMP DESCRIPTION: Shallow and narrow raised concrete jetty. Good for launching small craft. There is also a ramp onto hard sand that can be used for launching larger craft at high tide or allow tide to float a boat off. Goes into a reasonably sheltered bay.
FACILITIES: Shop and petrol and water at the ramp. Often used by visiting sailors. Showers available. There is a community centre approximately one mile where you can shower. Also a pub nearby. Car and boat park.

HAZARDS: There is a reef in the middle of Kilchoan Bay that should be marked by a perch. This can get washed off or damaged in storms. The ramp extends a long way and the end is marked with a perch. At low tide there is shallow water to the west of the ramp.

Beach, Portuairk
Lat. 56.7344, Long. -6.1891.
CHARGES: None
SUITABILITY: Small trailer can be pushed.
ACCESS: No Ramp. **TYPE OF RAMP:** Road goes onto hard sand.
UPPER AREA: Sand. **LOWER AREA:** Sand.
DIRECTIONS: From Kilchoan follow the signs to lighthouse and Portuairk and take the turning to Portuairk. The last bit of the road is very steep and twisty.
RAMP DESCRIPTION: A short ramp leads onto the firm sand that will easily take the weight of a car and trailer. The bay is very flat and the tide comes in quickly. The best method is to take the boat out at low tide, leave the boat on the sand and wait for the tide to come in.
FACILITIES: Sonachan Hotel is a 1 ½ mile scenic walk. Very friendly. There are good facilities in Kilchoan, about 5 miles away.
HAZARDS: The entrance to Portuairk needs to be navigated very carefully. Lots of rock but it does offer a very protected drying natural harbour.

Kentra Bay, Ardtoe
Lat. 56.7623, Long. -5.8729.
CHARGES: None
SUITABILITY: Large trailer needs a car.
ACCESS: ¾ tidal. **TYPE OF RAMP:** Large stone ramp
UPPER AREA: Rock. **LOWER AREA:** Rock.
DIRECTIONS: Situated at the end of the B8044. It can be found to the West of Fort William just off the A861 at Kentra Bay.
RAMP DESCRIPTION: Wide and fairly steep stone jetty, used by local fishing boats. Made of large stones and liable to be slippery at low tide.
FACILITIES: No overnight parking. Nice place but fairly narrow approach road. The pier is rough, and has a drop off the end at low water. There is only restricted space to park a car or trailer short term, next to the road above the pier. Longer term parking is possible at one local croft in Kentra (for a small charge).
HAZARDS: Entrance to Kentra Bay is very shallow at low water Springs.

Slipway, Ardtoe Beach
Lat. 56.7682, Long. -5.8829.
CHARGES: None.
SUITABILITY: Small trailer can be pushed.
ACCESS: All of tidal range. **TYPE OF RAMP:** Short concrete ramp on to sand. Large bay so quite a push of the trolley at low tide, but accessible.
UPPER AREA: Concrete. **LOWER AREA:** Sand.
DIRECTIONS: Follow the road to Ardtoe nearly all the way to the end. The slip is right by the sigh for the car park.

7

RAMP DESCRIPTION: Short concrete ramp on to beach. Car parking opposite for car and trailer (put 50p through the letter box of the wee cottage).

FACILITIES: Car park.

HAZARDS: Quite rocky near the shore at low tide - look out for the seaweed on the surface for a clue to their locations and proceed with care.

Slipway, Dorlin (Private)
Lat. 56.7801, Long. -5.8285.

SUITABILITY: Large trailer needs a car.

ACCESS: ½ tidal. TYPE OF RAMP: Concrete UPPER AREA: Concrete.

LOWER AREA: Concrete.

DIRECTIONS: Along the private road opposite the entrance to the car part by Castle Tioram.

RAMP DESCRIPTION: Steep concrete into the river leading in to South Channel of Loch Moidart. Would be a fantastic launch point, but it is private for the owners of the Estate, and they are apparently quite protective of it, understandably perhaps.

FACILITIES: None in Dorlin. Worth visiting the castle though - the causeway to the island is accessible except for high water +/- 1 hour.

Glenuig Beach, Glenuig
Lat. 56.8320, Long. -5.8292.

CHARGES: None

SUITABILITY: Large trailer needs a car.

ACCESS: All of tidal range. TYPE OF RAMP: Sandy beach.

UPPER AREA: Unknown. LOWER AREA: Unknown.

DIRECTIONS: Leave Fort William on A830 Mallaig road. Turn left at Lochailort to A861 after 7½ ml (Glenuig). right past hotel (pub) and beach is on right.

RAMP DESCRIPTION: Gradient is gentle. Area of soft sand would make recovery here difficult. Excellent launch site and day sail base.

FACILITIES: No overnight parking. Parking space is limited opposite beach. Car park busy in fine weather.

Jetty Slipway, Glenuig
Lat. 56.8320, Long. -5.8149.

CHARGES: None

SUITABILITY: Large trailer needs a car.

ACCESS: ¾ tidal. TYPE OF RAMP: Narrow concrete.

UPPER AREA: Harbour. LOWER AREA: Unknown.

DIRECTIONS: Take A830 Mallaig road from Fort William. Left at Lochailort onto A861 after 7½ miles. Jetty on right.

RAMP DESCRIPTION: The ramp was repaired in 2001 and is in good condition. Launch and recovery could be difficult in northwest wind. There is a road going off to the left that takes you to the beach launching area which can be a lifesaver if you miss the tide on the slip and you are desperate to get your boat out of the water.

FACILITIES: The Glenuig Inn (www.glenuig.com) offers basic chalet accommodation with the choice of bunk room, self catering and B&B plus drink and meals at the Inn. Peter and Mandy will make you very welcome and, if diving, air can be arranged.

Marine Harvest Slip, Lochailort
Lat. 56.8503, Long. -5.7109.

Rhuairidh (Rory) McInnis 01687 470220

CHARGES: None

SUITABILITY: Large trailer needs a car.

ACCESS: All of tidal range. TYPE OF RAMP: Concrete

UPPER AREA: Rock. LOWER AREA: Shingle.

DIRECTIONS: From Fort William take the A830 North towards Mallaig. Left at Lochailort to A861. After 1½miles jetty on right past the fish farm office.

RAMP DESCRIPTION: See Marine Harvest office ½ mile back up the road for permission to use A Rolls Royce of slips, but you will need to phone ahead to ask Marine Harvest to remove the concrete blocks at the top of the slip. They were placed there to stop the area being used as a camping site.

FACILITIES: Limited parking at the top of the slip.

Arisaig Marine, Arisaig
Lat. 56.9098, Long. -5.8484.

Arisaig Marine 01687 450224

CHARGES: £4

SUITABILITY: Large trailer needs a car.

ACCESS: ½ tidal. TYPE OF RAMP: Concrete UPPER AREA: Harbour.

LOWER AREA: Shingle.

DIRECTIONS: Large and smaller slipways at Arisaig Harbour. Floating pontoon at end of new breakwater.

RAMP DESCRIPTION: Main slip often used for big boat maintenance. Arisaig Marine can provide moorings. Concrete slip with rails sometimes blocked by carriage. Alternative slip is gravel. Both are fairly steep and only accessible 4 hours high water. Assisted launch is available.

FACILITIES: Fuel, hotel, post office, store, parking, WCs, train station. Arisaig Harbour. Only diesel available on site. Nearest garage in Morar or Mallaig. Limited chandlery on site with very helpful staff. Moorings can be arranged, and site has an island ferry jetty which is always in deep water. Local hotel and restaurants are excellent.

HAZARDS: Dries to mud and shingle.

Harbour slipway, Mallaig
Lat. 57.0047, Long. -5.8268.

CHARGES: None

SUITABILITY: Large trailer needs a car.

ACCESS: ½ tidal. TYPE OF RAMP: Concrete UPPER AREA: Concrete.

LOWER AREA: Harbour.

DIRECTIONS: On entering Mallaig turn right and roundabout past the boatyard, slip is on the left as the road turns round the harbour.

RAMP DESCRIPTION: Very steep, narrow but in good condition. Beach difficult, only usable when ramp is covered and with medium sized boat/trailer. Good reversing technique needed, narrow entrance and ramp.

FACILITIES: Centre of Mallaig, over-night parking available few hundred yards away.

Slipway, Letterffearn boat hire
Lat. 57.2549, Long. -5.5088.

SUITABILITY: Small trailer can be pushed.

7

ACCESS: No Ramp. UPPER AREA: Shingle. LOWER AREA: Shingle.
RAMP DESCRIPTION: At boat hire, bottle of whisky to the owner worked for us for a full week.

Kintail Lodge Hotel, Loch Duich
Lat. 57.2196, Long. -5.4219.
No need to phone , just turn up. 01599 511275

CHARGES: Free
SUITABILITY: Small trailer can be pushed.
ACCESS: ¾ tidal. TYPE OF RAMP: Concrete ramp with easy access shore to one side. UPPER AREA: Shingle. LOWER AREA: Shingle.
DIRECTIONS: Take the A87 road to Skye only as far as Glenshiel. Turn off at the Kintail Lodge Hotel and the ramp is just in front of the hotel.
RAMP DESCRIPTION: Refurbished 1985 by the army as an exercise. About two metres wide and fifty metres long. Free access.
FACILITIES: Hotel on site, garage within one mile and help and advice a telephone call away.

Slipway, Dornie
Lat. 57.2789, Long. -5.5162.

CHARGES: None
SUITABILITY: Large trailer needs a car.
ACCESS: All of tidal range. TYPE OF RAMP: Stone
UPPER AREA: Harbour. LOWER AREA: Shingle.
DIRECTIONS: On the A87, 7 miles east of Kyle of Lochalsh. Slipway is the old ferry landing just the to the east of the bridge next to Eliean Donan caste, possible Scotland's most photographed castle.
RAMP DESCRIPTION: Old stone slip for the ferry. Also try the slipway on the other side of the bridge.
FACILITIES: In the village of Dornie. Petrol station nearby.
HAZARDS: Beware of cross currents when the tide is running.

Slipway, Ardelve
Lat. 57.2780, Long. -5.5203.
SUITABILITY: Large trailer needs a car.
ACCESS: All of tidal range. TYPE OF RAMP: Stone
UPPER AREA: Harbour. LOWER AREA: Shingle.
DIRECTIONS: On the A87, 7 miles east of Kyle of Lochalsh. Slipway is the old ferry landing just the to the west of the bridge next to Eliean Donan caste, possible Scotland's most photographed castle.
RAMP DESCRIPTION: Can also launch on Dornie side down rough stone ramp (887 271) with possibility of parking on loch side or in fields by arrangement with crofters. Other possibilities are Ruaraig (813 271) opposite Balmacora Hotel, Kintail Lodge Hotel (937 196), Ratagan (920 198) (rough stone ramp near Youth Hostel). All tidal.
FACILITIES: Good stone ramp at car park, petrol, toilets, shops and camp site nearby.
HAZARDS: Look out for cross currents when the tide is running.

Ferry slipway, Kyle of Lochalsh
Lat. 57.2799, Long. -5.7119.
Harbourmaster 01599 534167

CHARGES: None
SUITABILITY: Large trailer needs a car.

ACCESS: All of tidal range. TYPE OF RAMP: Concrete
UPPER AREA: Harbour. LOWER AREA: Rock.
DIRECTIONS: The old ferry ramp, near the bridge.
RAMP DESCRIPTION: The slip is suitable for all sizes of craft and is concrete all the way down well below the low water mark. A lift or bilge keel can launch or recover at any state of tide. A small power boat has nothing to worry about. It is very exposed in southerly winds and prone to strong tides further in the channel and not directly at the slip.
FACILITIES: The recent addition of a small pontoon makes it a much more attractive prospect as owners can tie up and walk back easily to recover a trailer or wait out the tide. The pontoon is very exposed to southerlies and is not recommended for overnights if the forecast isn't too good. The public toilets also include very well kept showers (£1.00) and are open to 8.00pm. The harbourmaster, John McCrae, is very helpful and understanding of boaters needs. He can be contacted on 01599 534167 or emailed at 'john.macrae@highland.gov.uk'. Trailers and vehicles can be left near the harbourmasters office, 200m from the slip, but good security is recommended as the area is secluded and often the haunt of local youth on a weekend evening. Village of Lochalsh has all facilities with shops and petrol.
HAZARDS: Fierce tidal flow, up to 8 knots, so check the tides.

Ferry Slipway, Kyleakin
Lat. 57.2739, Long. -5.7239.
Harbourmaster 01599 534167.

CHARGES: £5 payable to the harbourmaster at Kyle of Lochalsh
SUITABILITY: Large trailer needs a car.
ACCESS: All of tidal range. TYPE OF RAMP: Stone and concrete
UPPER AREA: Harbour. LOWER AREA: Harbour.
DIRECTIONS: The old ferry slipway is gated off except by special arrangement through the Harbourmaster. The slip to be used is adjacent and runs alongside the pier wall and is more sheltered.
RAMP DESCRIPTION: Gently sloping ramp, slippy with weed at the bottom, but clean at the top. You will probably need a rope between the car and trailer to get sufficient depth.
FACILITIES: Small pontoon with limited facilities. Petrol, pubs and groceries available in the village. Water is available across the Kyle in Kyle of Lochalsh. Parking is plentiful.
HAZARDS: The maximum current under the Skye Bridge is 4 knots westwards, but this is about a mile away. The current around the slip is negligible.

Ardvasar Bay, Armadale/Ardvasar
Lat. 57.0598, Long. -5.9027.
01471 844216

CHARGES: As above
SUITABILITY: Small trailer can be pushed.
ACCESS: Unknown. TYPE OF RAMP: UPPER AREA: Shingle.
LOWER AREA: Sand.
DIRECTIONS: From Armadale Ferry Terminal take first left to Ardvasar. At entrance to village (30mph sign)go left down track to boatyard
RAMP DESCRIPTION: Hard shingle sloping foreshore at boatyard
FACILITIES: Parking for car or trailer £15/week. Toilet, showers.

7

Harlosh, Isle of Skye
Lat. 57.3816, Long. -6.5175.

CHARGES: None
SUITABILITY: Small trailer can be pushed.
ACCESS: No Ramp. **TYPE OF RAMP:** A concrete ramp provides access to a pebble beach suitable for launching small boats. The beach is useable during all states of tide. The tide never reaches the concrete ramp.
UPPER AREA: Concrete. **LOWER AREA:** Shingle.
DIRECTIONS: As you enter the town of Harlosh, the road splits into 3. The road directly ahead takes you to the ramp.
RAMP DESCRIPTION: The ramp is a rough and steep. If you are using a vehicle to launch then it will need to be an off road 4 × 4 or tractor.
FACILITIES: Limited parking.
HAZARDS: To facilitate launching on the beach large boulders have been cleared from a strip of clear beach. Be sure to remain on the "fairway" when approaching and leaving the launch area.

Meanish Pier, Loch Portiel, Glendale
Lat. 57.4567, Long. -6.7483.

SUITABILITY: Large trailer needs a car.
ACCESS: ½ tidal. **TYPE OF RAMP:** Concrete **UPPER AREA:** Shingle.
LOWER AREA: Sand.
RAMP DESCRIPTION: There is a drop off at the end of the slip, so check before launching. Bottom of slip can have weed present, near drop off. Ramp gives access to Neist Point lighthouse / Dunvegan Head.
HAZARDS: Area is remote and prone to strong tide races round headlands (Extreme care should be taken). Launch not recommended in winds exceeding 15mph.

Slipway, Dunvegan
Lat. 57.4418, Long. -6.5909.

CHARGES: Unknown, call in at the harbour master's office which is located near the slip.
SUITABILITY: Small trailer can be pushed.
ACCESS: ¼ tidal. **TYPE OF RAMP: UPPER AREA:** Concrete.
LOWER AREA: Mud.
RAMP DESCRIPTION: Steep slip which is only useable during relatively high tides. To launch at low tide requires the boat to be manhandled over mud and seaweed.
FACILITIES: There is a quay which could possibly be used however it is quite high and is heavily used by commercial vessels.

Slipway, Stein
Lat. 57.5155, Long. -6.5735.

CHARGES: None
SUITABILITY: Large trailer needs a car.
ACCESS: ¾ tidal. **TYPE OF RAMP:** Concrete slip with access to pebble beach for launching during low tide **UPPER AREA:** Concrete.
LOWER AREA: Concrete.
DIRECTIONS: Go to the village of Stein and you can't miss it.
RAMP DESCRIPTION: The slip is in good condition having been refurbished in 2005. There is a large drop at the end of the sip of approximately 1.5m so watch out when launching at low tide!

7

FACILITIES: Reasonable sized car park and boat yard at top of slip. Short distance from local dive centre.

Slipway, Salmon Farm
Lat. 57.4956, Long. -6.4396.

CHARGES: Bottle of whisky to the salmon farm,
SUITABILITY: Large trailer needs a car.
ACCESS: ¾ tidal. **TYPE OF RAMP:** Concrete onto stone on lower tide will need 4 wheel drive **UPPER AREA:** Concrete. **LOWER AREA:** Rock.
RAMP DESCRIPTION: Good ramp 3/4 tide, set in salmon farm at end of road. Car launch easy
FACILITIES: No facilities
HAZARDS: Numerous shallows, caution needed

Slipway, Uig
Lat. 57.5898, Long. -6.3715.

CHARGES: None
SUITABILITY: Large trailer needs a car.
ACCESS: All of tidal range. **TYPE OF RAMP:** Concrete
UPPER AREA: Shingle. **LOWER AREA:** Shingle.
DIRECTIONS: Left going north on A856 about a quarter mile from Uig.
RAMP DESCRIPTION: Good concrete slip with reasonable gradient. There is a drop on both sides of the slipway so care required with wide trailers, but should not be too much of a problem.
FACILITIES: Uig a quarter of a mile away with shops. Limited parking at the ramp.

Lochmaddy, North Uist
Lat. 57.6036, Long. -7.1601.

CHARGES: None.
SUITABILITY: Small trailer can be pushed.
ACCESS: All of tidal range. **TYPE OF RAMP: UPPER AREA:** Concrete.
LOWER AREA: Shingle.
DIRECTIONS: From ferry landing turn right at Morrisons shop/petrol station, then first right again, slip 200 yards down road.
RAMP DESCRIPTION: Easy sloping concrete ramp near to small harbour for local boats. Usable at all states of tide. Parking not so easy but slip not used much.
FACILITIES: Shop with petrol station nearby, café 300 yards, accommodation and pub 500 yards.
HAZARDS: The bay has reef and rocks.

Slipway, Leverburgh
Lat. 57.7667, Long. -7.0271.

SUITABILITY: Large trailer needs a car.
ACCESS: Unknown. **TYPE OF RAMP: UPPER AREA:** Unknown.
LOWER AREA: Unknown.
RAMP DESCRIPTION: Ferry slip

Slipway, Tarbert
Lat. 57.8972, Long. -6.8032.

SUITABILITY: Large trailer needs a car.
ACCESS: Unknown. **TYPE OF RAMP: UPPER AREA:** Unknown.
LOWER AREA: Unknown.

Loch Leurbost, Stornoway
Lat. 58.1322, Long. -6.4409.

CHARGES: None
SUITABILITY: Large trailer needs a car.
ACCESS: All of tidal range. **TYPE OF RAMP: UPPER AREA:** Concrete.
LOWER AREA: Concrete.
RAMP DESCRIPTION: Can be used at most tidal ranges. Next to the church so not recommended for use on Sundays.
FACILITIES: Good parking.

Slipway, Port of Ness
Lat. 58.4930, Long. -6.2235.

CHARGES: None
SUITABILITY: Small trailer can be pushed.
ACCESS: Unknown. **TYPE OF RAMP:** Concrete **UPPER AREA:** Concrete.
LOWER AREA: Sand.
DIRECTIONS: Follow signs to Port of Ness
RAMP DESCRIPTION: Good ramp with winch. BUT beware this port is into the North Atlantic and very exposed.
FACILITIES: None

Staffin Slipway, Staffin
Lat. 57.6318, Long. -6.1939.

CHARGES: None
SUITABILITY: Large trailer needs a car.
ACCESS: All of tidal range. **TYPE OF RAMP:** Concrete
UPPER AREA: Concrete. **LOWER AREA:** Concrete.
DIRECTIONS: Take A855 north through Staffin, slipway clearly signposted to right about ½ mile from Staffin.
RAMP DESCRIPTION: Long straight concrete ramp on the inner side of a breakwater.
FACILITIES: Parking and place to tie up near the slipway.

Portree Harbour (north), Portree
Lat. 57.4120, Long. -6.1919.
Harbourmaster 01478 612926

CHARGES: None
SUITABILITY: Large trailer needs a car.
ACCESS: All of tidal range. **TYPE OF RAMP:** Concrete
UPPER AREA: Unknown. **LOWER AREA:** Unknown.
RAMP DESCRIPTION: Concrete slipway by the pier. There is another slipway, northwest across the bay which is less congested.
FACILITIES: Limited parking on at the ramp.

Slipway, Sconser
Lat. 57.3144, Long. -6.1112.

CHARGES: None
SUITABILITY: Large trailer needs a car.
ACCESS: All of tidal range. **TYPE OF RAMP:** Concrete ramp next to pier.
UPPER AREA: Harbour. **LOWER AREA:** Rock.
RAMP DESCRIPTION: Ramp is next to the jetty. Used by the ferry so check the notice board for the sailing times. No ferry on a Sunday.
FACILITIES: Sconser Lodge Hotel is 100 yards away. Sligahaan Hotel recommended a few miles away. Petrol 5 miles away. Plenty of parking.

HAZARDS: Large sand bar off the entrance to the Sound of Raasay.

Slipway, Suisnish Point
Lat. 57.3320, Long. -6.0639.

CHARGES: None
SUITABILITY: Large trailer needs a car.
ACCESS: All of tidal range. **TYPE OF RAMP:** Concrete
UPPER AREA: Harbour. **LOWER AREA:** Rock.
DIRECTIONS: Southern end of Isle of Raasay.
RAMP DESCRIPTION: Good ramp, also used by the Raasay ferry so check the sailing times before launch. No ferry on Sunday. There is a second ramp 50 yards away.
FACILITIES: There is a toilet and car park. Nothing else.

Skye Boat Centre, Isle of Skye
Lat. 57.2721, Long. -5.9969.
01471 822070

CHARGES: Small charge for launch and park. Phone for details.
SUITABILITY: Large trailer needs a car.
ACCESS: All of tidal range. **TYPE OF RAMP:** Concrete
UPPER AREA: Rock. **LOWER AREA:** Shingle.
DIRECTIONS: Skye Boat Centre, Strollamus, By Broadford. Isle of Skye. Cross onto Isle of Skye via Skye bridge on A87. 8 miles north on road to Portree you will come to the small township of Strollamus. The Skye Boat Centre is on the right hand side.
RAMP DESCRIPTION: Three ramps: 1. onto beach for dinghies. 2. fairly steep ramp for RIBs. 3. 7 ton hoist and ramp for larger vessels.
FACILITIES: Chandlery shop, dive air, outboard repairs and service, boat storage. Shower and disabled toilets. Moorings and small pontoon.
HAZARDS: Shallow narrows on south side approximately 250 metres. Open water on north side.

Slipway, Broadford
Lat. 57.2473, Long. -5.9076.

CHARGES: None
SUITABILITY: Large trailer needs a car.
ACCESS: ¾ tidal. **TYPE OF RAMP:** Concrete **UPPER AREA:** Concrete.
LOWER AREA: Shingle.
DIRECTIONS: Follow A87 from Skye Bridge for 8 miles, through village of Broadford and turn right after Broadford Hotel.
RAMP DESCRIPTION: Top of ramp is fairly steep but can be negotiated by car easily. Regularly used by locals for launching RIBs, dinghies and larger motor and sailing yachts.
FACILITIES: Water and street lighting on pier. Garage, shops, pub, butcher, police and hospital are all within a few minutes walk. Also engineer and chandlery within few minutes drive.
HAZARDS: Outfall buoy, clearly marked near pier, and large military mooring situated in the middle of the bay.

Slipways, Plockton
Lat. 57.3409, Long. -5.6477.
Kyle Harbourmaster 01599 534167

CHARGES: None

7

The Good Launch Guide

SUITABILITY: Large trailer needs a car.
ACCESS: All of tidal range. **TYPE OF RAMP:** Concrete at top.
UPPER AREA: Unknown. **LOWER AREA:** Shingle.
DIRECTIONS: Can be reached from A87 or A890. It is North of Kyle of Lochalsh. Situated on south side of Loch Carron it is an excellent base to sail from, either locally or further afield.
RAMP DESCRIPTION: There are a couple of slipways; one is only suitable for dinghies. You can also launch off the beach onto shingle and mud surface. Drive to end of main sea-front, turn right and right again. Slip is on left.
FACILITIES: Can be busy in summer especially regatta days - end July and beginning of August - and parking may be difficult. Plockton is a busy harbour for cruising yachts. Hotel in Plockton.

Hotel slip, Loch Carron
Lat. 57.4032, Long. -5.4811.
CHARGES: Donation to Lochcarron Pier Trust
SUITABILITY: Large trailer needs a car.
ACCESS: All of tidal range. **TYPE OF RAMP:** Concrete
UPPER AREA: Concrete. **LOWER AREA:** Shingle.
DIRECTIONS: Opposite Loch Carron Hotel
RAMP DESCRIPTION: Straight good angle. Good level tarmac space at top
FACILITIES: Hotel, petrol, diesel and toilets

Slipway, North Strome
Lat. 57.3597, Long. -5.5530.
SUITABILITY: Large trailer needs a car.
ACCESS: All of tidal range. **TYPE OF RAMP:** Concrete
UPPER AREA: Shingle. **LOWER AREA:** Shingle.
DIRECTIONS: Take road to Strome Ferry on north shore of Loch Carron from Loch Carron Village
RAMP DESCRIPTION: Wide concrete slipway used by local commercial fish farms.
FACILITIES: Limited parking

Poll Creadha, Applecross
Lat. 57.3977, Long. -5.8136.
SUITABILITY: Large trailer needs a car.
ACCESS: ¾ tidal. **TYPE OF RAMP:** Concrete **UPPER AREA:** Harbour.
LOWER AREA: Shingle.
DIRECTIONS: Shieldaig, and then South of Applecross village
RAMP DESCRIPTION: Straight with turning area at top
FACILITIES: Facilities in Applecross village
HAZARDS: Narrow entrance from sea; leading lines sketch in Clyde cruising club guide. Submarine practice area!

Jetty Slipway, Shieldaig
Lat. 57.5195, Long. -5.6512.
CHARGES: No charge
SUITABILITY: Large trailer needs a car.
ACCESS: All of tidal range. **TYPE OF RAMP:** Concrete
UPPER AREA: Harbour. **LOWER AREA:** Rock.

DIRECTIONS: Head west on the A896 past the village of Torridon. Shieldaig is on the southern shore of Loch Torridon off the main road.
RAMP DESCRIPTION: Excellent large slipway offers good shelter. Used by local fishermen, do not obstruct.
FACILITIES: Village of Shieldaig has shops and hotel and pubs. Plenty of space for trailers and parking.

Badachro Inn, Badachro
Lat. 57.6983, Long. -5.7255.
Martin Pearson (01445) 741255
CHARGES: None
SUITABILITY: Large trailer needs a car.
ACCESS: All of tidal range. **TYPE OF RAMP:** Drivable to ½ tide.
UPPER AREA: Sand. **LOWER AREA:** Rock.
DIRECTIONS: Jetty and hard are next to the Badachro Inn on the southern side of Loch Garloch.
RAMP DESCRIPTION: Slip is located off lane leading to the Badachro Inn. Possible to launch off the hard in all but low water. Often best to put trailer on the hard at low tide and wait for the water to rise. A stone slip also exists next to the Inn but is restricted to use at high water.
FACILITIES: Showers and baths are available at the Inn as are washing machine and drying facilities. Low cost accommodation planned for 2002 and moorings are available. Very popular spot with the yachtsmen. Phone ahead to book a meal in the Inn.

Slipway, Gairloch
Lat. 57.7123, Long. -5.6792.
CHARGES: Nil
SUITABILITY: Large trailer needs a car.
ACCESS: ¾ tidal. **TYPE OF RAMP:** Concrete **UPPER AREA:** Concrete.
LOWER AREA: Rock.
DIRECTIONS: Immediately on south side after turning towards harbour.
RAMP DESCRIPTION: Reconstructed Nov 2007 following storm damage in 2005. Concrete structure replaced half existing structure. Now fitted with mooring rings. Surface excellent on slip. Transition to shore rocky but presently manageable. Trailers can be parked on the hard between burn and slip. Be mindful of "locals" assuming they own it - they don't.
FACILITIES: Café, hotel, boat club premises (toilets & showers), shops, and chandlers all immediately to hand. Harbour has pontoon, diesel, potable water and toilet facilities. Bank ATM and garage further north (< 1 km).
HAZARDS: Ref to charts - generally clear, but rock marked off point and several rocks at bays to south of Loch Gairloch

Slipway, Inverasdale
Lat. 57.7984, Long. -5.6663.
Janet Miles 01445 781408
CHARGES: Donations welcome to help cover maintenance.
SUITABILITY: Large trailer needs a car.
ACCESS: All of tidal range. **TYPE OF RAMP:** Concrete
UPPER AREA: Rock. **LOWER AREA:** Shingle.
DIRECTIONS: Follow the B8057 from Poolewe for about 4 miles. The slipway and jetty are on the right and are well signposted.

RAMP DESCRIPTION: The slipway is fairly steep. There is also a small traditional stone jetty. In January 2003 we were told that the slip is almost impossible to use as it has not been treated to remove weed growth. The Loch Ewe Action Forum cleans the slipway in the summer months so it should be usable.
FACILITIES: Parking and water tap on site. Shop and café less than half a mile away.

Aultbea, Loch Ewe
Lat. 57.8391, Long. -5.5976.
CHARGES: None
SUITABILITY: Large trailer needs a car.
ACCESS: ½ tidal. **TYPE OF RAMP:** Concrete **UPPER AREA:** Concrete.
LOWER AREA: Shingle.
DIRECTIONS: Turn off A 832 to Aultbea, Head for pier and turn right just before pier. Slip is NATO maintained.
RAMP DESCRIPTION: The ramp is straight with gentle gradient and about 3 cars wide. Some NATO anchorage points 500 metres to the northwest. Only usable about 2 hours on either side of the tide because of the amount of weed growing on the lower part of the slip.
FACILITIES: Toilets, shop, hotel and free parking

Ullapool Harbour, Ullapool
Lat. 57.8962, Long. -5.1568.
CHARGES: None
SUITABILITY: Large trailer needs a car.
ACCESS: ¾ tidal. **TYPE OF RAMP:** Concrete **UPPER AREA:** Unknown.
LOWER AREA: Unknown.
DIRECTIONS: Ullapool is situated on the West coast just off the A835 where it meets the coast at Loch Broom.
RAMP DESCRIPTION: Medium gradient concrete slipway.
FACILITIES: Free overnight parking. Parking space is limited at the slip. Bit difficult - best ask at nearby hotel.

Old Dornie, Polbain
Lat. 58.0449, Long. -5.4191.
CHARGES: None
SUITABILITY: Large trailer needs a car.
ACCESS: ¾ tidal. **TYPE OF RAMP:** Concrete, narrow (2.5m).
UPPER AREA: Harbour. **LOWER AREA:** Shingle.
DIRECTIONS: From Ullapool, head 11 miles north on A385, turn left at Drumrunie onto single track road for 12 miles to Polbain, pick up signs to Old Dornie Harbour. Carry on into harbour - ramp is on the right hand side. Grid Ref NB 983113.
RAMP DESCRIPTION: Narrow, well protected, facing north into water. Old Dornie dries completely so timing is important. Most local fishing boats are on moorings in the roads. There is another quay on the west facing Coalas Eilean Ristol channel and moorings used by the larger fishing boats; more exposed.
FACILITIES: Nearest fuel at Achiltibuie Stores, 4 miles. Summer Isles Hotel and Bar, Achiltibuie. Fuaran Bar in Altandhu.

HAZARDS: Small jetty next to ramp, submerged at high water. Strong tides with range of about 4 metres. Local advice is that inner bay moorings are buried in the sea bed and that boats anchoring may settle onto anchors; so no fisherman's anchors recommended!

Slipway, Kylesku
Lat. 58.2573, Long. -5.0184.
CHARGES: Never anyone to take money.
SUITABILITY: Large trailer needs a car.
ACCESS: All of tidal range. **TYPE OF RAMP:** Concrete
UPPER AREA: Concrete. **LOWER AREA:** Harbour.
DIRECTIONS: Drive past fishery jetty, slipway outside hotel.
RAMP DESCRIPTION: Best at high tide, slippery with weed at bottom, also steep and sharp turn, not recommended for large boats at low tide. Very small boats only at low Springs. Slipway has had repair work carried out, but has been made much narrower in process. Railings prevent easy access to most of width, still room to launch a large trailer from ¼ tide upwards.
FACILITIES: Hotel, pub, bar meals / restaurant parking toilets.

Talmine Pier, Tongue
Lat. 58.5336, Long. -4.4266.
CHARGES: None known. Highland council charge for use but nobody to take money as slip in middle of nowhere.
SUITABILITY: Large trailer needs a car.
ACCESS: All of tidal range. **TYPE OF RAMP:** Upper gravel, lower part concrete **UPPER AREA:** Shingle. **LOWER AREA:** Concrete.
DIRECTIONS: From Tongue head north and west across the Kyle of Tongue and then take the next right to Talmine.
RAMP DESCRIPTION: Steep concrete slipway leading down into a small sheltered harbour. Upper ramp is mostly gravel and is VERY steep, lower ramp is concrete. Not to be attempted with anything bar a 4 × 4 and only for small to medium sized boats. The gravel part is steep enough to drag a Jeep slowly down with wheels locked under the weight of the boat. Not easy to use a rope due to the steepness and the lack of room at the top of the ramp.
FACILITIES: Near to the village of Talmine. Plenty parking near top of slip.

Skerray, Bettyhill
Lat. 58.5422, Long. -4.3043.
CHARGES: £3.50 Highland Council, but no one to take money.
SUITABILITY: Large trailer needs a car.
ACCESS: All of tidal range. **TYPE OF RAMP:** Concrete
UPPER AREA: Harbour. **LOWER AREA:** Harbour.
DIRECTIONS: From A836 follow signs to Torrisdale and Skerray. Harbour is at end or road and ramp is in corner of harbour.
RAMP DESCRIPTION: Long straight ramp into sheltered harbour.
FACILITIES: Parking near slipway. This is a surprisingly large but almost deserted harbour in a VERY remote area. It is an area of outstanding natural beauty where you will see, golden eagles, red deer, seals, and whales. This rocky and spectacular coastline requires a great effort to

7

visit it but it is WELL worth that effort. This is the last wilderness in the UK.

HAZARDS: Rocks in left of harbour entrance.

Slipway, Bettyhill
Lat. 58.5263, Long. -4.2343.

CHARGES: None
SUITABILITY: Portable Only.
ACCESS: No Ramp. **TYPE OF RAMP:** Shingle **UPPER AREA:** Shingle.
LOWER AREA: Rock.
DIRECTIONS: Turn off main road (A836) into the village of Bettyhill. Follow signs to pier. At 'T' junction turn left down track to pier.
RAMP DESCRIPTION: Ramp is down onto shingle beach at side of pier. Rarely used pier. Final part of track to ramp past pier has hairpin bend.
FACILITIES: Limited parking. This is an area of outstanding natural beauty. Wild and isolated with small islands, abundant wild life, stunning views. It is very remote but is well worth the effort to visit.
HAZARDS: Watch out for sand bar at entrance to estuary.

New slip, Portskerra
Lat. 58.5701, Long. -3.9299.

SUITABILITY: Large trailer needs a car.
ACCESS: All of tidal range. **TYPE OF RAMP:** Concrete
UPPER AREA: Rock. **LOWER AREA:** Shingle.
DIRECTIONS: Situated in the village of Portskerra, 17 miles west of Thurso.
RAMP DESCRIPTION: Concrete slipway across the shingle foreshore and into a sheltered rocky cove.
FACILITIES: Village of Portskerra nearby.

Pier slip, Portskerra
Lat. 58.5651, Long. -3.9244.

SUITABILITY: Large trailer needs a car.
ACCESS: All of tidal range. **TYPE OF RAMP:** Concrete
UPPER AREA: Harbour. **LOWER AREA:** Shingle.
DIRECTIONS: Situated in the village of Portskerra, 17 miles west of Thurso.
RAMP DESCRIPTION: Small steep ramp next to the pier. Tight access at the top of the slipway.
FACILITIES: Pier next to the ramp and village of Portskerra nearby.

Castlehill Pier, Thurso
Lat. 58.5959, Long. -3.3793.

SUITABILITY: Large trailer needs a car.
ACCESS: All of tidal range. **TYPE OF RAMP:** Concrete
UPPER AREA: Harbour. **LOWER AREA:** Shingle.
DIRECTIONS: The slipway is at Castlehill, about 5 miles east of Thurso.
RAMP DESCRIPTION: Concrete ramp across shingle leading into a small harbour.
FACILITIES: Small harbour and the village of Castlehill and Castletown are close by.

Dwarwick slipway, Thurso
Lat. 58.6220, Long. -3.3666.
Ian Moncrief 01955 607765

CHARGES: None
SUITABILITY: Large trailer needs a car.
ACCESS: Unknown. **TYPE OF RAMP:** Concrete, good surface.
UPPER AREA: Harbour. **LOWER AREA:** Concrete.
DIRECTIONS: Take A9 North from Wick, left onto B876 Right on A836 then left into Dwarwick.
RAMP DESCRIPTION: Wide, good surface. Easy to use slip, quiet.
FACILITIES: Local shops.

Brough slip, Thurso
Lat. 58.6466, Long. -3.3444.
0845 4504486

CHARGES: Free
SUITABILITY: Small trailer can be pushed.
ACCESS: All of tidal range. **TYPE OF RAMP:** Stone
UPPER AREA: Shingle. **LOWER AREA:** Shingle.
DIRECTIONS: Head east from Thurso for 5 miles and head through Castletown and on to Dunnet. Turn left at Dunnet and take the B855 to Brough.
RAMP DESCRIPTION: Long stone pier over a shingle beach. Situated in a steep sided bay and the access road may be tricky for large boats.
FACILITIES: Situated in the bay near the village of Brough. Self catering and B&B accommodation nearby, together with a small café in season (April to September), restaurant within 3 miles.
HAZARDS: Pentland Firth can be tempestuous, strong currents.

Scarfskerry Pier, John o'Groats
Lat. 58.6524, Long. -3.2772.

SUITABILITY: Large trailer needs a car.
ACCESS: All of tidal range. **TYPE OF RAMP:** Concrete
UPPER AREA: Rock. **LOWER AREA:** Shingle.
DIRECTIONS: Head west from John o'Groats for seven miles on the A836. Turn right at the village of Mey and head for Scarfskerry.
RAMP DESCRIPTION: Concrete ramp leading across the shingle foreshore. Fairly narrow and will require careful reversing.
FACILITIES: Next to the village of Scarfskerry. Small pier right next to the slipway offers shelter and a place to tie up after launching.

Gills Pier, John o'Groats
Lat. 58.6382, Long. -3.1611.

SUITABILITY: Large trailer needs a car.
ACCESS: All of tidal range. **TYPE OF RAMP:** Concrete
UPPER AREA: Harbour. **LOWER AREA:** Unknown.
DIRECTIONS: Situated 4 miles west of John o'Groats at the village of Gills in Gills Bay.
RAMP DESCRIPTION: Excellent smooth and wide concrete slipway leading into a small fishing harbour.
FACILITIES: Small fishing village and pier next to the ramp.

Slipway, John o'Groats
Lat. 58.6445, Long. -3.0706.
Caithness Council 01955 607760 or Ian Moncrief 01955 607765

CHARGES: £3.50 (no one to take the money - see notes below).
SUITABILITY: Large trailer needs a car.

7

ACCESS: ¾ tidal. **TYPE OF RAMP:** Concrete over masonry.
UPPER AREA: Harbour. **LOWER AREA:** Harbour.
DIRECTIONS: Follow A99 North from Wick, keep going to the end of the road and you will find the slip in the harbour by the car park. John o'Groats is well signposted.
RAMP DESCRIPTION: Council ramp into harbour. Busy with sightseers in summer. Ferry to Orkney (no vehicles) leaves from inside harbour but should not cause problems. Dog leg at bottom of slip at low tide. There is no one to collect the slip fee. You are on trust and can pay at the Council Service Point in Market Square, Wick.
FACILITIES: Pub, shops, cafés, camping site, post office, toilets, tap.
HAZARDS: Pentland Firth can be exciting. Whirlpools and strong tides. Scapa Flow, sunken German battleships.

Burray Boat Yard, Burray
Lat. 58.8438, Long. -2.9163.
01856 731365

CHARGES: Phone boat yard.
SUITABILITY: Large trailer needs a car.
ACCESS: All of tidal range. **TYPE OF RAMP:** Concrete
UPPER AREA: Harbour. **LOWER AREA:** Sand.
DIRECTIONS: Turn down to the Burray village and follow the road to the Sands Hotel 1/4 of a mile and you are right there. There is a smaller slip for sports boats just past the Sands Hotel car park.
RAMP DESCRIPTION: The large ramp can accommodate boats of around 85 feet and has a storage area for these size of boats at the top of the slip. Access to the hotel and houses is also across the top of the slip. A pier is next to the slip with water and electricity.
FACILITIES: Hotel with public bar and serves meals daily, parking, toilets, electricity, water, storage, winter lay up areas, petrol, shop and post office and boat builders.
HAZARDS: The smaller slip has moored boats and buoys around it.

Stromness Marina, Kirwall
Grassethouse St. Ola, Kirkwall, Orkney, Scotland
KW15 1SE
Lat. 58.9643, Long. -3.2952.
01856 871313

Slipway, Tingwall
Lat. 59.0893, Long. -3.0445.

CHARGES: None applied
SUITABILITY: Large trailer needs a car.
ACCESS: All of tidal range. **TYPE OF RAMP:** Concrete ferry slip
UPPER AREA: Concrete. **LOWER AREA:** Concrete.
RAMP DESCRIPTION: Ferry slip - wide and even. Check ferry timetable!
FACILITIES: Toilets, parking, ferry, bus.
HAZARDS: Strong tidal flow towards Eynhallow. Various skerries (well marked). Many local storage creels.

Slipway, Kirkwall Harbour
Lat. 58.9876, Long. -2.9596.
Orkney Islands Council: 01856-873535

SUITABILITY: Large trailer needs a car.
ACCESS: All of tidal range. **TYPE OF RAMP:** Concrete
UPPER AREA: Harbour. **LOWER AREA:** Harbour.
DIRECTIONS: Located at Kirkwall Harbour.
RAMP DESCRIPTION: Public access. Excellent slipway.
FACILITIES: All facilities close by.

Kirwall Marina, Kirkwall
Orkney Marinas Limited, Grassethouse St. Ola,
Kirkwall, Orkney, Scotland KW15 1SE
Lat. 58.9873, Long. -2.9588.
01856 871313

Westray Marina, Westray
Pierowall Harbour, Westray, Orkney, Scotland
KW17 2DL
Lat. 59.3235, Long. -2.9751.
01856 852888

Tulloch Enterprises, Bressay
Utsikten Bressay, Bressay, Shetland, Scotland
ZE2 9EL
Lat. 60.1558, Long. -1.1161.
01595 820263

Skirza Pier, John o'Groats
Lat. 58.5959, Long. -3.0562.

CHARGES: None
SUITABILITY: Large trailer needs a car.
ACCESS: ½ tidal. **TYPE OF RAMP:** Concrete **UPPER AREA:** Harbour.
LOWER AREA: Shingle.
DIRECTIONS: 4 miles south of John o'Groats at the village of Skirza on the north side of Freswick Bay.
RAMP DESCRIPTION: Ramp is next to the concrete pier that can be used for loading and unloading.
FACILITIES: In the village of Skirza.

Slipway, Keiss
Lat. 58.5313, Long. -3.1161.
Caithness Council 01955 607760 or Ian Moncrief 01955 607765

CHARGES: £3.50 no one to pay at slip.
SUITABILITY: Large trailer needs a car.
ACCESS: ½ tidal. **TYPE OF RAMP:** Concrete **UPPER AREA:** Harbour.
LOWER AREA: Shingle.
DIRECTIONS: Take A99 North from Wick, Keiss is about 8 miles. Turn left into Keiss and slipway is in the harbour.
RAMP DESCRIPTION: Straight slip but can get a bit slippery. Quiet harbour (most people go straight up to John o'Groats). Payment is on trust; go to council service point in Market Square, Wick. Small or portable boats can launch any tide level.
FACILITIES: Pub, shops.

7

The Good Launch Guide

Ackergill Harbour, Wick
Lat. 58.4746, Long. -3.1011.
SUITABILITY: Large trailer needs a car.
ACCESS: ½ tidal. **TYPE OF RAMP: UPPER AREA:** Harbour.
LOWER AREA: Sand.
DIRECTIONS: Head north on the A99 from Wick and turn right after 1½ miles at the village of Ackergill. Follow the road for one mile to the sea.
RAMP DESCRIPTION: Ramp in a small harbour.

Harbour slipway, Latheronwheel
Lat. 58.2701, Long. -3.3807.
SUITABILITY: Large trailer needs a car.
ACCESS: All of tidal range. **TYPE OF RAMP:** Concrete
UPPER AREA: Harbour. **LOWER AREA:** Sand.
DIRECTIONS: 15 miles south of Wick on the A99 near the village of Latheron.
RAMP DESCRIPTION: Excellent slipway leading into a tiny stone harbour.
FACILITIES: Close to the small village of Latheron. Sheltered harbour.

Slipway, Dunbeath
Lat. 58.2451, Long. -3.4221.
CHARGES: £3.50 per day. Caithness Council. Pay at council offices!
SUITABILITY: Large trailer needs a car.
ACCESS: All of tidal range. **TYPE OF RAMP:** Concrete
UPPER AREA: Harbour. **LOWER AREA:** Harbour.
DIRECTIONS: From A9 north, cross over bridge and follow signs of on the right to Dunbeath. Follow road right to the end. Slip is in the corner of the harbour.
RAMP DESCRIPTION: Ramp has right angle turn on the access. Not used often and looks a little slippery.
FACILITIES: Parking and picnic site. Dunbeath is a quiet picturesque little harbour giving access to the spectacular cliffs of the Caithness coastline.

Slipway, Helmsdale
Lat. 58.1149, Long. -3.6469.
CHARGES: £3.50 Highland Council
SUITABILITY: Large trailer needs a car.
ACCESS: All of tidal range. **TYPE OF RAMP:** Concrete
UPPER AREA: Harbour. **LOWER AREA:** Harbour.
DIRECTIONS: In Helmsdale follow signs from A9 to Harbour. At 'T' junction at harbour turn left and slipway is at the far end.
RAMP DESCRIPTION: Straight ramp into sheltered harbour. Pretty harbour with a variety of local fishing and pleasure boats.
FACILITIES: Parking on site. Shops and fuel in Helmsdale.

Harbour Slip, Brora
Lat. 58.0111, Long. -3.8486.
CHARGES: None
SUITABILITY: Large trailer needs a car.
ACCESS: ¾ tidal. **TYPE OF RAMP:** Stone **UPPER AREA:** Harbour.
LOWER AREA: Harbour.

DIRECTIONS: Take A9 North from Inverness. In Brora look out for sign to HARBOUR. Follow sign right down harbour road. Slip in on the left at the top end of the harbour, next to the lifebuoy.
RAMP DESCRIPTION: Harbour is actually in the river Brora, there are some 'interesting' tides when the river is in full flood. Mostly used by small local fishing boats. Launching is from just outside the harbour into the river Brora mouth. Because of the amount of large rocks in the river launching is usually done as the tide rises, so if day fishing returning before the tide goes out is recommended. Larger boats can usually ONLY be slipped at high tide.
FACILITIES: Plenty of parking, shops and pubs nearby.

Pier slipway, Golspie
Lat. 57.9703, Long. -3.9806.
SUITABILITY: Large trailer needs a car.
ACCESS: ½ tidal. **TYPE OF RAMP:** Concrete **UPPER AREA:** Harbour.
LOWER AREA: Sand.
RAMP DESCRIPTION: Excellent concrete ramp leading onto a sandy beach.
FACILITIES: In the centre of the village of Golspie. Boats can tie up to the pier for loading.

Embo slipway, Dornoch
Lat. 57.9032, Long. -3.9930.
CHARGES: None
SUITABILITY: Small trailer can be pushed.
ACCESS: ½ tidal. **TYPE OF RAMP:** Concrete **UPPER AREA:** Concrete.
LOWER AREA: Sand.
DIRECTIONS: Through village, past 'Grannies Heilan Hame', through campsite towards beach. At sign for pier take right fork into small car park. Slipway is through sand dunes.
RAMP DESCRIPTION: Shallow, narrow straight ramp from car park through dunes onto beach. Small trailers can go onto beach. Beautiful sandy beach and dunes.
FACILITIES: Car parking. Camp site, toilets nearby and restaurant.
HAZARDS: Beware of Tain Bar and Gizzen Briggs if going into Inner Firth.

Slipway, Dornoch
Lat. 57.8794, Long. -4.0149.
SUITABILITY: Portable Only.
ACCESS: ¼ tidal. **TYPE OF RAMP:** Concrete **UPPER AREA:** Concrete.
LOWER AREA: Sand.
DIRECTIONS: From centre of Dornoch follow signs to beach, through campsite, past coastguard huts. Slip onto beach on right of car park at end of road.
RAMP DESCRIPTION: Small slipway onto beach through sand dunes. Shallow and not very wide. It is very shallow over the sand banks for quite a way off shore and it is pretty rough with an onshore wind. The slipway is used by the inshore rescue to launch their RIBS, do not obstruct the slipway.
FACILITIES: Car parking. Campsite has toilets. Shops and fuel in Dornoch.
HAZARDS: Beware of RAF firing range between Dornoch and Portmahomack. Also Tain Bar and Gizzen Broggs can be dangerous in an easterly wind.

7

Meikle Ferry North, Tain
Lat. 57.8541, Long. -4.1436.

CHARGES: £3.50 per day. Highland Council but no one around to pay.
SUITABILITY: Large trailer needs a car.
ACCESS: All of tidal range. **TYPE OF RAMP:** Stone
UPPER AREA: Harbour. **LOWER AREA:** Sand.
DIRECTIONS: From A9 travelling north, cross over the Dornich bridge then turn left signposted Meikel Ferry North. Follow road through golf course right to the end.
RAMP DESCRIPTION: Straight shallow ramp. Old ferry ramp not often used now. In a quiet and secluded spot. There is a colony of seals in the firth and they can often be seen on the sandbanks by Tain at low tide. It's very stony at the bottom when the tide is out (slip way ends above low water mark leaving stones and gravel) therefore probably only suitable for portable dinghies at low tide - you can't run a trailer into the water at low tide.
FACILITIES: Parking only. Shops and fuel in Tain or Dornich.
HAZARDS: Watch out for sand bars. If going into outer Dornoch Firth beware of the Tain Bar and Gizzen Briggs sandbanks in easterly gales.

Meikel Ferry, Tain
Lat. 57.8453, Long. -4.1368.
SUITABILITY: Large trailer needs a car.
ACCESS: ¾ tidal. **TYPE OF RAMP:** Concrete **UPPER AREA:** Harbour.
LOWER AREA: Sand.
DIRECTIONS: From A9 follow signs to Meikel Ferry (there is no ferry). Go past caravan site (just off A9) and follow road to the very end. You will see some houses and sheds. The slips are at the very end. Privately owned by Messrs P. Moscati of Tain Shellfish, Meikle Ferry, Tain, IV19 1NL.
RAMP DESCRIPTION: Long straight fairly shallow ramp that was once for the ferry (before they built the Dornoch Bridge). Now used by a mussel fishing boat so there may be equipment strewn about. There are two shellfish processors who use the smaller ramp for the depuration of mussels, hence the cage structure at the foot of the ramp which restricts the launch of any vessel. They also have a processing trailer on the hard standing at the top of the ramps.
FACILITIES: Plenty of parking at the ramp. Restaurant at caravan site at top of road. Fuel and shops in Tain about 3 miles away. Great for small boats and canoes. You can access the inner firth right up to Bonar Bridge. There is a large colony of seals in the Firth and they can often be seen at low tide on the sandbanks by Tain. This is a quiet and scenic area.
HAZARDS: Ropes and equipment from the mussel boats. The tide can get a bit strong at times. Beware of the Tain Bar and Gizzenn Briggs if you are going out into the outer firth. The Tain Bar can be a problem in easterly gales as the sea breaks heavily over it.

Slipway, Portmahomack
Lat. 57.8383, Long. -3.8289.
CHARGES: None for launching.
SUITABILITY: Large trailer needs a car.
ACCESS: ¾ tidal. **TYPE OF RAMP:** Concrete and stone.
UPPER AREA: Harbour. **LOWER AREA:** Sand.

DIRECTIONS: Take A9 North from Inverness, drive past Kildary, turn right onto B 9165, signposted to Seaboard Villages. In Hill of Fearn turn left onto B9165 signposted Portmahomack. Follow this road into Portmahomack, through the village and the harbour is at the end of the road.
RAMP DESCRIPTION: There are two ramps. Use the one in the corner of the harbour. The other has a sharp drop at the end and is only available for high tides. The ramp from the corner is quite shallow and leads down onto the sand/mud of the harbour. A portable or small boat can launch at any time level. A larger boat is okay for about half tidal range. It is a small fishing harbour with local boats, mainly smaller ones but a couple of larger lobster boats. There is some kelp in the harbour itself but this should not cause a problem.
FACILITIES: A picturesque little fishing village with hotels, B&Bs, restaurant, toilets, plenty of car parking. There is a tap available as well. A floating pontoon was added to the harbour in 2006.
HAZARDS: No problems about the ramp but to the west are a 'DANGER AREA' which is used by the RAF as a bombing range. This is a real spectacle when they are live firing. Just keep away from this area and you are okay. The entrance to the Dornoch Firth can be tricky in strong easterlies, the Gizzen Brigs and Tain Scalps can be dangerous and there is a large shallow sand bar at the entrance to the Dornoch Firth. The best area for fishing is around Tarbat Ness. You will often see dolphins.

Slipway, Wilkhaven
Lat. 57.8615, Long. -3.7794.
SUITABILITY: Large trailer needs a car.
ACCESS: All of tidal range. **TYPE OF RAMP:** Stone ramp
UPPER AREA: Rock. **LOWER AREA:** Shingle.
RAMP DESCRIPTION: Stone ramp in a remote spot.
FACILITIES: Parking nearby.

Rockfield, Portmahomack
Lat. 57.8228, Long. -3.8133.

CHARGES: None
SUITABILITY: Portable Only.
ACCESS: No Ramp. **TYPE OF RAMP:** Shingle **UPPER AREA:** Harbour.
LOWER AREA: Shingle.
DIRECTIONS: Take B9165 into Portmahomack, turn right at signpost to Rockfield, after 50 yards right again signposted 'Rockfield Village'. Follow this rather narrow road along to the coast and down into the village. As you come down the hill the launch site is right in front of you, along the right side of the jetty wall.
RAMP DESCRIPTION: The jetty provides shelter for launching from the shingle beach. The area is used by a few local fishermen. Rockfield is a very pretty and sleepy old fishing village nestling at the bottom of the cliffs. It is a great place for a picnic. It is also a good haven if you are caught out in bad weather in the Moray Firth. Look out for the rather spectacular, newly restored Balone Castle on the cliffs nearby.
FACILITIES: No facilities in Rockfield, but pubs and restaurants in Portmahomack about 1 mile away.
HAZARDS: Some rocks at the end of the jetty.

7

Beach Slip, Hilton of Cadbol

Lat. 57.7659, Long. -3.8953.

CHARGES: None

SUITABILITY: Small trailer can be pushed.

ACCESS: ¼ tidal. **TYPE OF RAMP:** Concrete. Small trailers can use the adjacent ramp by going in between the seat and the fence (see photo) this gives easier access to the beach. **UPPER AREA:** Shingle. **LOWER AREA:** Sand.

DIRECTIONS: Follow A9 North from Inverness, drive through Kildary, turn right on B9165 to 'Seaboard Villages'. Go through Hill of Fearn, follow signs to Balintore. Down hill into Balintore turn left on coast road, 1 mile into Hilton of Cadbol. Keep going through the village, past small harbour on right on to the end of the road. Public car park is on the right and the slip is right off the car park. Access to the adjacent slip can be gained by going between the seat and the fence.

RAMP DESCRIPTION: Small concrete ramp with a drop at the end. Most suited for small or portable boats. The ramp takes you onto the beach which is a mixture of sand, shingle and rocks. The ramp is quite steep. It is a public ramp but is rarely used. Portable boats can get onto the beach and launch at any tidal level. Winter storms can pile up shingle and make it difficult to launch.

FACILITIES: Adequate parking, visit the Hilton Chapel ruins and the replica Hilton Stone (Pictish) in the field at the end of the road. Hotel facilities in Balintore nearby. There are great picnic areas by the ramp, loads of wildlife, birds and dolphins.

HAZARDS: Some rocks about the site but no major problems. The firth is always at its worst with a south to southwest wind. If the sea is rough go over to Portmahomack as it will probably be in shelter.

Slipway, Hilton of Cadbol

Lat. 57.7627, Long. -3.8972.

CHARGES: None

SUITABILITY: Small trailer can be pushed.

ACCESS: ¾ tidal. **TYPE OF RAMP:** Concrete **UPPER AREA:** Shingle. **LOWER AREA:** Rock.

DIRECTIONS: Take the A9 going North from Inverness, drive past Kildary, turn right onto the B9165 towards 'Seaboard Villages'. Go through 'Hill of Fearn', follow signs to Balintore. Drive down into Balintore and at a 'T' junction turn left, follow coast road 1 mile into Hilton of Cadbol. The slip is at the next junction on your right behind the small bus stop.

RAMP DESCRIPTION: Ramp is used by local fishermen for small boats. The ramp can get blocked with shingle and seaweed.

FACILITIES: Some parking, hotel in Balintore nearby, public toilets in Balintore.

HAZARDS: Beware of rocks at anything less than high tide when they are hidden, you need to take a dog leg out to avoid them.

Harbour Slip, Balintore

Lat. 57.7539, Long. -3.9122.

Jack King (Harbourmaster) 01862 832833

CHARGES: Pay harbourmaster if around.

SUITABILITY: Large trailer needs a car.

ACCESS: ½ tidal. **TYPE OF RAMP:** Concrete **UPPER AREA:** Concrete. **LOWER AREA:** Sand.

DIRECTIONS: Balintore Harbour, Balintore, Easter Ross. Turn right off the A9 at Nigg roundabout (35 miles north of Inverness) on to the B9175. After 1 mile turn left and follow signs to Balintore.

RAMP DESCRIPTION: Two slipways into the sheltered harbour, one shallow, one steep. Onto relatively hard sand, launching not practical 2 hours either side of low water as the harbour dries at low water Springs but firm enough to take a 4 × 4.

FACILITIES: Petrol at Hill of Fearn (3 miles). Two pubs by harbour. Toilets adjacent to slip.

HAZARDS: The harbour has pontoons installed during the summer months, close to the steeper of the two slipways. Excellent access to the sea fishing on the eastern side of Tarbat Ness.

Ferry Slipway, Nigg

Lat. 57.6926, Long. -4.0203.

CHARGES: None

SUITABILITY: Large trailer needs a car.

ACCESS: All of tidal range. **TYPE OF RAMP:** Concrete **UPPER AREA:** Shingle. **LOWER AREA:** Sand.

DIRECTIONS: Follow A9 north out of Inverness. Turn right on B9175 (signposted to Nigg Ferry). Follow B9175 right to the slipway - about 5 miles.

RAMP DESCRIPTION: This is actually the Nigg - Cromarty Ferry slipway. The ferry runs from May to October during the day and is at the slipway every 30 minutes or so. Vehicles crossing on the ferry use the slipway and there can be cars waiting. It is okay for small boats and trailers when the ferry is running but if you are going to launch a large boat you will need to ensure that you do not impede the ferry (small 2 car ferry).

FACILITIES: Next door to a pub, however the pub owner will not let you park in his car park. Use the ferry car park instead. Good for dolphin spotting.

Slipway, Invergordon

Lat. 57.6911, Long. -4.2191.

CHARGES: No charges - public slipway.

SUITABILITY: Large trailer needs a car.

ACCESS: ¾ tidal. **TYPE OF RAMP:** Concrete / stone. **UPPER AREA:** Concrete. **LOWER AREA:** Mud.

DIRECTIONS: Take A9 North from Inverness over the Black Isle. At Alness turn right onto B817 towards Invergordon on the coast road. After about 2 miles you will see a sign for 'Public Slipway' on the right. Turn right here into car park, carry on towards Invergordon Sailing Club and ramp is adjacent to the club. Not the pier marked on the map.

RAMP DESCRIPTION: Shallow ramp from public car park into Cromarty Firth. Used by the Invergordon Sailing Club. Can be used at all tides except for the very lowest of Springs.

FACILITIES: Fuel and all facilities in Invergordon about 2 miles away. Sailing club adjacent.

HAZARDS: Safe launching into the Firth.

7

Pier slipway, Balblair
Lat. 57.6752, Long. -4.1777.
SUITABILITY: Large trailer needs a car.
ACCESS: All of tidal range. **TYPE OF RAMP:** Concrete
UPPER AREA: Harbour. **LOWER AREA:** Unknown.
RAMP DESCRIPTION: Wide concrete slipway with a good gradient. Gives access to the Cromarty Firth.

Harbour slipway, Cromarty
Lat. 57.6831, Long. -4.0380.
SUITABILITY: Large trailer needs a car.
ACCESS: ¼ tidal. **TYPE OF RAMP:** Cobble slipway into sandy harbour
UPPER AREA: Harbour. **LOWER AREA:** Sand.
RAMP DESCRIPTION: Gently sloping cobbled ramp into a harbour that dries out at low tide to expose sand.
FACILITIES: Situated in the picturesque harbour at Cromarty.

Slipway, Fortrose
Lat. 57.5788, Long. -4.1339.
Harbourmaster 01381 620311

CHARGES: £5
SUITABILITY: Large trailer needs a car.
ACCESS: All of tidal range. **TYPE OF RAMP:** Concrete
UPPER AREA: Concrete. **LOWER AREA:** Sand.
DIRECTIONS: Situated on the Black Isle north east of Inverness. Take the A832 towards Cromarty then first right when entering Fortrose. Ramp is adjacent to the old harbour.
RAMP DESCRIPTION: Long ramp that give access at all states of tide.
FACILITIES: Some parking available. You should speak with the harbourmaster or the Chanonry Sailing Club, which owns the slipway, before leaving trailers or cars in the area. Clubhouse tel: 01381 621973. Temporary membership of the sailing club available. Gives use of showers and toilets.
HAZARDS: Rock approximately ¼ east of ramp, marked with a yellow diamond on a pole.

North Kessock Old Ferry Slip, Inverness
Lat. 57.5013, Long. -4.2479.
01349 865260
SUITABILITY: Large trailer needs a car.
ACCESS: ¾ tidal. **TYPE OF RAMP:** Concrete but now in a decaying state, care required when launching in all tide states. **UPPER AREA:** Harbour.
LOWER AREA: Shingle.
DIRECTIONS: Situated just off the A9 North of Inverness across the bridge, Follow the signs for North Kessock. RNLI station was at the top of the slip but is now situated at a new purpose built station under the Kessock bridge. Note, you are not allowed to use either of their two slip ways, please observe this.
RAMP DESCRIPTION: Opposite hotel - ignore the older slip nearer (downstream) the Kessock (now blocked off) bridge. On the right hand side is a wall that protects the slip from Westerlies and there is some damage to the edge of the slipway. Update July 2009 Slip way is now in an increasing state of disrepair with quite a few pot holes, be prepared to wrestle your trailer out of them and be aware of the possible damage to you car suspension also beware of the 3 foot drop at the end of the slip.

South Kessock slip is now reopened and is in better condition. Down side is that the dolphin watch hut is situated next to it and they aren't very fond of Jetskis, also not a lot of parking space.
FACILITIES: Free overnight parking. Parking space is ample. Easy access and place to park car either at side of Main Street or in nearby car park. Dolphin café nearby is very friendly as is the hotel.
HAZARDS: Beware strong tidal currents and eddies mid-tide.

Caley Marina, Inverness
Canal Road, Muirtown, Inverness, Inverness-shire, Scotland IV3 8NF
Lat. 57.4754, Long. -4.2529.
01463 236539

Seaport Marina, Muirtown Wharf
Caledonian Canal British Waterways Scotland
Seaport Marina, Muirtown Wharf, Inverness, Scotland IV3 5LE
Lat. 57.4840, Long. -4.2462.
01463 725500

Inverness Marina Ltd, Inverness
Marina Office Longman Drive, Inverness, Scotland IV1 1SU
Lat. 57.4929, Long. -4.2321.
01463 220501

Slipway, Ardersier
Lat. 57.5731, Long. -4.0428.

CHARGES: None
SUITABILITY: Large trailer needs a car.
ACCESS: ½ tidal. **TYPE OF RAMP:** Concrete ramp surface in good condition but sometimes required to be cleared of seaweed and pebbles before using westerly winds create swell and can make launch and recovery difficult. **UPPER AREA:** Concrete. **LOWER AREA:** Shingle.
DIRECTIONS: Ardersier is east of Inverness past the Airport. Head out the A96 (towards Aberdeen) for about 3 miles and turn left signposted Ardersier and Airport. Follow the road until you come to Ardersier. Turn left onto the High St and then 1st left after the speed hump, you'll see the top of the ramp from the road.
RAMP DESCRIPTION: Long ramp that give access from mid-high tide. Very narrow and difficult to reverse over if you have a wide vehicle at the peak of the ramp, it is quite sharp and restricts your view, requires somebody to guide the driver of the vehicle
FACILITIES: There is a small car park at the top of the ramp.
HAZARDS: Sometimes lobster pots laid in bay; they are marked but can be difficult to see.

Nairn Harbour Slipway, Nairn
Lat. 57.5908, Long. -3.8613.
01667 456008

7

The Good Launch Guide

CHARGES: Owned by Highland Council and harbourmaster does come across and levy a charge - £5 to £12 I think. There are also 3 very basic (and free)concrete "slips" onto the beach sand to the west of the harbour, but none are readily accessible to vehicles, two are steep, and they usually have a drop-off where the sea has scoured the end of the concrete slab. Maybe OK for launching small dinghies from trolleys - but mostly useful for prams and buggies accessing beach!
SUITABILITY: Small trailer can be pushed.
ACCESS: ¼ tidal. **TYPE OF RAMP:** Broad asphalt slip in good condition, with gentle gradient and harbour wall rising above one side. But limited fall, with deep drop-off at end! **UPPER AREA:** Harbour.
LOWER AREA: Harbour.
DIRECTIONS: As pass through Nairn on A96, turn down into Harbour Street just West of bridge over R Nairn (signed to harbour). Slip is accessed from far (sea) side of harbour - you have to drive clockwise round 3 sides to get to it.
RAMP DESCRIPTION: Broad slipway in good condition within Nairn's sheltered harbour, which accesses from river. Very tidal, with (well marked) drop-off end - but so is river access to Firth very tidal. Depending on vessel/ trailer, probably only usable c.2-3hrs either side high water.
FACILITIES: Ample parking. Pontoons within harbour. Public toilets & café close bye. Dolphin trips. Nairn Sailing Club.
HAZARDS: Sandbanks beyond river mouth can catch the unwary. Can be bad breaking sea if northerly swell meets river flow (especially if river in spate).

Findhorn Marina & Boatyard, Findhorn
Lat. 57.6605, Long. -3.6157.
Findhorn Boatyard 01309 690099.

CHARGES: £7.50 or£10.00 depending who is behind the counter.
SUITABILITY: Large trailer needs a car.
ACCESS: All of tidal range. **TYPE OF RAMP:** Concrete
UPPER AREA: Concrete. **LOWER AREA:** Concrete.
DIRECTIONS: Follow the one way system through Findhorn past Crown and Anchor. Head towards the beach and it's on the left.
RAMP DESCRIPTION: Shallow and wide concrete slipway that is used by the boatyard. Launch anytime including low water, however bay often too shallow for many boats. Jetskis can make use of the bay at any state of tide.
FACILITIES: Launch fee includes parking and use of hose to wash down. Very beautiful village of Findhorn with fantastic pub - The Crown and Anchor Inn 01309 690243, shops and café. Findhorn YC 01309 690247. Fantastic sandy beach next to Findhorn Bay and the bay itself offers very good protected sailing. Independent lifeboat also operates from the marina www.morayinshorerescue.org. Ask about Moray Firth Watercraft Club!
HAZARDS: Moored boats. Stream at mouth of Findhorn Bay runs up to 5 knots at half tide. At 3 hours either side low water it is too shallow for passage.

Burghead Harbour Ramp, Burghead
Lat. 57.7023, Long. -3.4971.
Harbourmaster 01343 835337
CHARGES: £7/day, £33/season

SUITABILITY: Large trailer needs a car.
ACCESS: All of tidal range. **TYPE OF RAMP:** Concrete
UPPER AREA: Harbour. **LOWER AREA:** Shingle.
RAMP DESCRIPTION: Ramp is in the harbour, observe 3 knot speed limit.
FACILITIES: Car parking, food and water close by. Working harbour with chandlery.

Hopeman Harbour Ramp, Hopeman
Lat. 57.7103, Long. -3.4368.
Harbourmaster 01343 835337

CHARGES: £7/day, £33/year
SUITABILITY: Large trailer needs a car.
ACCESS: ¼ tidal. **TYPE OF RAMP: UPPER AREA:** Harbour.
LOWER AREA: Sand.
DIRECTIONS: Follow road through the village all the way down to the harbour.
RAMP DESCRIPTION: Gentle ramp, suitable for car, leads into the inner harbour. You are supposed to pay the harbourmaster in Burghead to use this ramp. Hopeman is a small well sheltered harbour giving access to the Moray Firth. 3 knot restriction in harbour. Harbour dries out at low tide.
FACILITIES: Car park and fresh water by ramp. Food, petrol in village. Beautiful beach nearby and caravan site next to the harbour.

Harbour Slipway, Lossiemouth
Lat. 57.7247, Long. -3.2837.
01343 813066

CHARGES: Expect to pay £5 per launch or £35 per year.
SUITABILITY: Large trailer needs a car.
ACCESS: ¾ tidal. **TYPE OF RAMP:** Cobble slipway then shuttered concrete. **UPPER AREA:** Harbour. **LOWER AREA:** Shingle.
DIRECTIONS: Follow signs to the harbour. Slipway is at the western most end of the harbour.
RAMP DESCRIPTION: Ramp is usable at most states of tide, lower area gives way to shingle/sand and eventually mud on low water during big Spring tides. 10.5ft in width x 100ft long. Cobble stone for 60ft.
FACILITIES: Situated in the harbour and close to the centre of Lossiemouth. Pontoon in the harbour next to the ramp. Fuel, tea room, shower, toilets and bar close by. Free car and trailer parking, toilets and showers.
HAZARDS: Harbour entrance dangerous in winds F6 & over north to southeast.

Lossiemouth Marina, Lossiemouth
Harbour Office 6 Pitgaveny Quay, Lossiemouth, Moray, United Kingdom IV31 6NT
Lat. 57.7235, Long. -3.2794.
01343 813066

Harbour Slip, Buckie
Lat. 57.6817, Long. -2.9528.
HM 01542 831700
CHARGES: £6/day

SUITABILITY: Large trailer needs a car.
ACCESS: ½ tidal. **TYPE OF RAMP:** Concrete **UPPER AREA:** Harbour.
LOWER AREA: Mud.
DIRECTIONS: Ramp is situated at the eastern end of the harbour by the lifeboat station. Drive to the eastern end of the harbour and then through the one way system to the north east corner of the harbour.
RAMP DESCRIPTION: Good concrete ramp in the harbour. All craft allowed but there is a 3 knot speed limit in the harbour.
FACILITIES: Parking and diesel on site. No petrol in harbour but Buckie is sizable town with all the usual facilities.

Harbour Slip, Findochty
Lat. 57.6981, Long. -2.9055.

CHARGES: None
SUITABILITY: Large trailer needs a car.
ACCESS: ½ tidal. **TYPE OF RAMP:** Concrete **UPPER AREA:** Harbour.
LOWER AREA: Sand.
DIRECTIONS: Head east from Buckie on the A942 to Findochty. At Findochty follow the signs to the harbour. Slipway is at the eastern end of the harbour.
RAMP DESCRIPTION: Concrete ramp into harbour. Dries out at low tide with a hard sand base.
FACILITIES: Situated in small fishing harbour, close to town centre. Parking at top of slipway and shops nearby.

Harbour Slip, Portknockie
Lat. 57.7047, Long. -2.8617.

CHARGES: £11 per launch/retrieve. Unlimited use season ticket available for £33.
SUITABILITY: Large trailer needs a car.
ACCESS: ½ tidal. **TYPE OF RAMP:** Concrete **UPPER AREA:** Harbour.
LOWER AREA: Sand.
DIRECTIONS: Head east from Buckie on the A942 to Portknockie. At Portknockie follow the signs to the harbour. Harbour is accessed via a steep a twisty road. Will need good brakes, but access should not be a problem.
RAMP DESCRIPTION: Good concrete ramp next to the harbour wall.
FACILITIES: Pontoons next to the ramp that could be used for loading and unloading. Fishing town is a short walk away. Parking at the slipway for car and trailer.

Harbour Slip, Cullen
Lat. 57.6940, Long. -2.8224.

CHARGES: None
SUITABILITY: Large trailer needs a car.
ACCESS: ¼ tidal. **TYPE OF RAMP:** Concrete **UPPER AREA:** Harbour.
LOWER AREA: Sand.
DIRECTIONS: Cullen is on the A98, midway between Elgin and Banff. If you come into town from the west, turn left immediately after going under the railway viaduct. Drive along the harbour front and the launch side is at the eastern end of the harbour.
RAMP DESCRIPTION: Concrete ramp into sandy harbour that dries out at low tide.

FACILITIES: Situated in a small fishing village. Plenty of parking nearby. Pontoons in the harbour.

Harbour Slip, Portsoy
Lat. 57.6856, Long. -2.6900.
Alisdair Galloway 01261 815544

CHARGES: £10/day, £55/6months.
SUITABILITY: Large trailer needs a car.
ACCESS: ¼ tidal. **TYPE OF RAMP:** Concrete **UPPER AREA:** Harbour.
LOWER AREA: Sand.
DIRECTIONS: Head for the village of Portsoy and the slipway is in the new outer harbour.
RAMP DESCRIPTION: Wide concrete ramp with a good gradient. Ramp extends to ¼ of tidal range but the firm sand allows launching up to ¾ of tidal range. Harbour dries out at low tide.
FACILITIES: Village shop and very quaint old harbour. Parking is OK but can be tricky at the harbour end. Speak to the harbourmaster for advice.
HAZARDS: Harbour entrance is obstructed at low water.

Whitehills Harbour Office, Whitehills
Harbour Office Harbour Place, Whitehills,
Banffshire, Scotland AB45 2NQ
Lat. 57.6794, Long. -2.5782.
01261 861291

Harbour slipway, Banff
Lat. 57.6707, Long. -2.5231.
01261 815544
SUITABILITY: Large trailer needs a car.
ACCESS: ¼ tidal. **TYPE OF RAMP: UPPER AREA:** Concrete.
LOWER AREA: Sand.
DIRECTIONS: Head for Banff and the slipway is in the outer harbour.
RAMP DESCRIPTION: Wide concrete ramp with a shallow gradient. Ramp extends to ¼ of tidal range but the firm sand allows launching up to ¾ of tidal range. Sand is too shallow at very low tide.
FACILITIES: Car park behind the harbour office, fuel nearby and plenty of shops in Banff.

Harbour slip, Gardenstown
Lat. 57.6729, Long. -2.3376.

CHARGES: £5 in/out
SUITABILITY: Small trailer can be pushed.
ACCESS: ½ tidal. **TYPE OF RAMP:** Concrete **UPPER AREA:** Harbour.
LOWER AREA: Sand.
DIRECTIONS: Head east from Macduff on the A98. Half mile outside Macduff turn left on the B9031 and go 3½ miles to Dubford. Turn left to Gardenstown. Slipway is down a steep slope (15%) in the harbour.
RAMP DESCRIPTION: Good wide slipway and good harbour. Notice saying no charge made for use of harbour or slipway but contribution appreciated.
FACILITIES: Slipway in harbour with pub in village.

7

The Good Launch Guide

Harbour slip, Pennan
Lat. 57.6792, Long. -2.2586.
SUITABILITY: Large trailer needs a car.
ACCESS: ½ tidal. **TYPE OF RAMP:** Concrete **UPPER AREA:** Harbour.
LOWER AREA: Unknown.
DIRECTIONS: Small fishing village on the B9031 in-between Macduff and Fraserburgh. Access to the harbour is down a very steep (20%) slope.
RAMP DESCRIPTION: Concrete path runs to harbour with small slipway (half tide) kept locked. Harbour master / fisherman lives nearby. Not an easy slipway to use.
FACILITIES: Penan charming very small old fishing village under steep cliffs with a 20% slope down. Very limited parking at the bottom of the hill.

Harbour Slip, Rosehearty
Lat. 57.6951, Long. -2.1174.
CHARGES: £5 per launch, £20 rover ticket? £55 yearly ticket
SUITABILITY: Small trailer can be pushed.
ACCESS: ½ tidal. **TYPE OF RAMP:** Concrete **UPPER AREA:** Concrete.
LOWER AREA: Sand.
DIRECTIONS: Head for Rosehearty Harbour.
RAMP DESCRIPTION: Narrow slipway into the harbour.
FACILITIES: Parking, toilets and chandlery nearby in small village. There is a campsite nearby. Harbourmaster lives adjacent to harbour. Slipway is popular with by divers.
HAZARDS: Beware kelp and isolated small rocks at low water, solid enough to damage a prop.

Slipway, Sandhaven
Lat. 57.6980, Long. -2.0627.
01346 518767
CHARGES: £5 in & out, £30/year
SUITABILITY: Small trailer can be pushed.
ACCESS: ¾ tidal. **TYPE OF RAMP:** Concrete **UPPER AREA:** Concrete.
LOWER AREA: Shingle.
DIRECTIONS: From Fraserburgh heading West, turn right off Watermill Road along coast for one mile, Turn right once entering the village of Sandhaven
RAMP DESCRIPTION: Shallow concrete ramp suitable for most type of vessels.
HAZARDS: Shoreline rocky but visible

Cairnbulg Harbour, Fraserburgh
Lat. 57.6804, Long. -1.9437.
CHARGES: £2.50 payable to local house
SUITABILITY: Small trailer can be pushed.
ACCESS: ¼ tidal. **TYPE OF RAMP:** Concrete **UPPER AREA:** Harbour.
LOWER AREA: Sand.
DIRECTIONS: Follow signs for Fraserburgh, then signs for Cairnbulg/Inverallochy. When you arrive in Cairnbulg follow road right thro village and you'll end up at the harbour.
RAMP DESCRIPTION: The ramp is quite good although quite slippy near lower part. The harbour is tidal so checked tides before you arrive.

Please respect harbour users and keep your speed low as possible inside the harbour.
FACILITIES: Plenty of parking available. Petrol is available from local garage.
HAZARDS: There are rocks outside the harbour which are easily seen.

Peterhead Bay Marina, Peterhead
Harbour Ofice, West Pier, Peterhead,
Aberdeenshire, Scotland AB42 1DW
Lat. 57.5031, Long. -1.7781.
01779 483600

Marina Slipway, Peterhead
Lat. 57.4948, Long. -1.7932.
CHARGES: None at the moment
SUITABILITY: Large trailer needs a car.
ACCESS: ¼ tidal. **TYPE OF RAMP:** Concrete **UPPER AREA:** Rock.
LOWER AREA: Sand.
DIRECTIONS: Head along the A982 which fronts Peterhead Bay and turn off to the Peterhead Marina.
RAMP DESCRIPTION: In the marina there is a 4 knot speed restriction which must be observed. Certain parts of the Bay are restricted but there is a notice at top of ramp giving information on the restrictions.
FACILITIES: Petrol on A982. Parking on site. Pubs in town
HAZARDS: Speed restrictions.

Boddam Harbour, Peterhead
Lat. 57.4744, Long. -1.7789.
SUITABILITY: Large trailer needs a car.
ACCESS: All of tidal range. **TYPE OF RAMP:** Concrete
UPPER AREA: Harbour. **LOWER AREA:** Unknown.
DIRECTIONS: Boddam is 5 miles south
RAMP DESCRIPTION: Good wide concrete ramp leading into the harbour.
FACILITIES: Town of Boddam next to the harbour with pubs fuel and parking. Peterhead is 5 miles away.

Cruden Bay, Cruden Bay
Lat. 57.4112, Long. -1.8451.
CHARGES: None
SUITABILITY: Small trailer can be pushed.
ACCESS: Unknown. **TYPE OF RAMP:** Concrete **UPPER AREA:** Concrete.
LOWER AREA: Sand.
RAMP DESCRIPTION: Excellent for small boats and Jetskis

Cove Bay, Aberdeen
Lat. 57.0962, Long. -2.0760.
SUITABILITY: Large trailer needs a car.
ACCESS: Unknown. **TYPE OF RAMP:** **UPPER AREA:** Harbour.
LOWER AREA: Shingle.
DIRECTIONS: Cove Bay is about 5 miles south of Aberdeen.
RAMP DESCRIPTION: Slipway into a sheltered harbour. The entire approach to the launch slope is full of small fishing boats. If you do

7

manage to squeeze a boat past then you will soon find yourself up to your axles in shingle.
FACILITIES: Town of Cove Bay is next to the slip and there is a small harbour.

Stonehaven Harbour, Stonehaven
Lat. 56.9602, Long. -2.2021.
Harbourmaster 01569 762741

CHARGES: £10/day
SUITABILITY: Large trailer needs a car.
ACCESS: ½ tidal. **TYPE OF RAMP:** Concrete **UPPER AREA:** Harbour.
LOWER AREA: Sand.
DIRECTIONS: Follow the A90 south from Aberdeen and follow signs for Stonehaven harbour.
RAMP DESCRIPTION: Two slips with easy motor access, launching trolleys may not be left on the slip whilst sailing. Medium gradient. One of the best harbours in the area.
FACILITIES: Free overnight parking but not in the harbour car park. Parking space is limited on summer weekends. Slip water tap. All the usual facilities in Stonehaven. Key for shower and toilets from the harbourmaster.

Harbour Slip, Gourdon
Lat. 56.8278, Long. -2.2863.
Stonehaven HM 01569 762741

CHARGES: £10/day
SUITABILITY: Large trailer needs a car.
ACCESS: ¼ tidal. **TYPE OF RAMP:** Concrete **UPPER AREA:** Harbour.
LOWER AREA: Sand.
DIRECTIONS: Go about 10 miles north from Montrose on the A92. Gourdon is after Johnshaven and before you get to Inverbervie.
RAMP DESCRIPTION: Large concrete slipway.
FACILITIES: No petrol in village, closest is Stonehaven. Parking, pub and village shop.

Broughty Ferry, Broughty Ferry
Lat. 56.4639, Long. -2.8716.

CHARGES: Free
SUITABILITY: Large trailer needs a car.
ACCESS: ¾ tidal. **TYPE OF RAMP: UPPER AREA:** Concrete.
LOWER AREA: Concrete.
RAMP DESCRIPTION: Wide slip, easily accessible. Useable 5 hours each side of low tide
FACILITIES: Ample parking. Shops, bars and restaurants close-by.
HAZARDS: Strong currents at times at harbour entrance.

Boat slip, Wormit
Lat. 56.4316, Long. -2.9626.
SUITABILITY: Large trailer needs a car.
ACCESS: ½ tidal. **TYPE OF RAMP: UPPER AREA:** Concrete.
LOWER AREA: Mud.
RAMP DESCRIPTION: 1/2 tide slip

Slipway, Crail
Lat. 56.2575, Long. -2.6288.
01333 450820

CHARGES: £9.60 per day.
SUITABILITY: Large trailer needs a car.
ACCESS: ½ tidal. **TYPE OF RAMP:** Concrete **UPPER AREA:** Harbour.
LOWER AREA: Unknown.
DIRECTIONS: Take the A917 to Crail and slipway is on Shoregate by the harbour.
FACILITIES: Some parking. Petrol and chandlery nearby.

Cellardyke harbour, Cellardyke
Lat. 56.2253, Long. -2.6832.
SUITABILITY: Large trailer needs a car.
ACCESS: ½ tidal. **TYPE OF RAMP: UPPER AREA:** Concrete.
LOWER AREA: Mud.
DIRECTIONS: Head for Anstruther harbour and continue east along seafront until you reach Cellardyke harbour.
RAMP DESCRIPTION: Cobbled slipway, good access, some kelp problems in winter months. Launching fees paid at Anstruther harbour. Narrow streets to negotiate but slipway and harbour are quiet.
HAZARDS: Small harbour entrance, need to be careful in moderate seas and above.

Lifeboat Slip, Anstruther
Lat. 56.2211, Long. -2.6975.
Harbourmaster 01333 310836

CHARGES: £9/day
SUITABILITY: Large trailer needs a car.
ACCESS: ½ tidal. **TYPE OF RAMP:** Concrete slip onto hard sand.
UPPER AREA: Harbour. **LOWER AREA:** Sand.
DIRECTIONS: Follow signs for Harbour. Slip behind Lifeboat Shed on middle pier. 45 degree turn at top of slip (behind wheelie bin).
RAMP DESCRIPTION: Harbourmaster Office (displaying tide tables) next to Inner Harbour Slip. If harbourmaster is not available, please make a reasonable donation to the RNLI on leaving. There is also a smaller slipway in the Inner Harbour behind harbourmaster's office on West Pier. Constructed of cobble/stone slip onto sand, ramp extends ¼ of tidal range then sand. Bollard at top of slip limits size to small boats. There is also a ramp at Cellardyke approximately ½ east. Ask harbourmaster for advice on which to use.
FACILITIES: Car park (charges in summer) on opposite side of lifeboat shed. Also car parking near the Inner Harbour.
HAZARDS: If tide is fully out, take care at port side of harbour wall due to pieces of metal in the sand.

Anstruther Harbour, Anstruther
Shore Street, Anstruther, Fife, Scotland KY10 3AQ
Lat. 56.2220, Long. -2.6989.
01333 310 836

Slipway, Elie Harbour
Lat. 56.1864, Long. -2.8188.
SUITABILITY: Large trailer needs a car.

7

ACCESS: ¾ tidal. **TYPE OF RAMP:** Concrete, is flanked rocks and you should really visit at low water first, or ask local person advice. **UPPER AREA:** Concrete. **LOWER AREA:** Sand.
DIRECTIONS: Follow signs to Harbour
RAMP DESCRIPTION: Concrete slip, there is also good beach launching.
FACILITIES: Toilets, clubhouse and food outlet
HAZARDS: Bass Rock, Isle of May and Fidra or look at your local charts to find the West Vows and East Vows

Slipway, Lower Largo
Lat. 56.2121, Long. -2.9417.
SUITABILITY: Large trailer needs a car.
ACCESS: Unknown. **TYPE OF RAMP: UPPER AREA:** Concrete.
LOWER AREA: Sand.
DIRECTIONS: Follow directions for Crusoe hotel Lower Largo
RAMP DESCRIPTION: Steep ramp into harbour opposite Crusoe Hotel. Car required.

Kinghorn Slipway, Kinghorn
Lat. 56.0693, Long. -3.1713.
SUITABILITY: Large trailer needs a car.
ACCESS: ¾ tidal. **TYPE OF RAMP: UPPER AREA:** Harbour.
LOWER AREA: Concrete.
RAMP DESCRIPTION: Slipway into the harbour

Slipway, BurntIsland Bay
Lat. 56.0596, Long. -3.2240.
CHARGES: None
SUITABILITY: Large trailer needs a car.
ACCESS: ½ tidal. **TYPE OF RAMP:** Concrete into beach.
UPPER AREA: Rock. **LOWER AREA:** Shingle.
DIRECTIONS: Follow the A921 east from the north side of the Forth Road Bridge. Slipway is to the east of the harbour.
RAMP DESCRIPTION: Fairly narrow concrete slipway with a good gradient. Slip is useable for about 3 hours either side of high water, beyond that its marginal and dries out completely for about 2 hours either side of low water.
FACILITIES: Parking available for cars and trailers. Fuel and chandlery nearby.

Slipway, Blackness
Lat. 56.0041, Long. -3.5219.
John Currie 01506 834846
SUITABILITY: Large trailer needs a car.
ACCESS: ½ tidal. **TYPE OF RAMP: UPPER AREA:** Harbour.
LOWER AREA: Unknown.
DIRECTIONS: Blackness is about 4 miles west of the Forth Road Bridge at the end of the B903.
RAMP DESCRIPTION: The slipway is located at the Blackness Boat Club and is privately owned by them. Contact John Currie on 01506 834846.

Port Edgar Marina, South Queensferry
Shore Road, South Queensferry, West Lothian, Scotland EH30 9SQ
Lat. 55.9939, Long. -3.4099.
0131 331 3330

Port Edgar Marina, South Queensferry
Lat. 55.9932, Long. -3.4091.
44 (0)131 331 3330

CHARGES: £7.50/day for 4.6-6m.
SUITABILITY: Large trailer needs a car.
ACCESS: ¾ tidal. **TYPE OF RAMP:** Concrete **UPPER AREA:** Harbour.
LOWER AREA: Harbour.
DIRECTIONS: Take A90 from Edinburgh West to South Queensferry. Come off at junction with B924. Follow into village seafront, fork right under Forth Road Bridge approach road. Shore Road, South Queensferry, Edinburgh, EH30 9SQ.
RAMP DESCRIPTION: The slipway is wide and has a gentle gradient. The fixed dock crane on the Main Pier can launch and recover boats of up to 5 tons displacement at any state of tide. Power boats launch at Hawse Piers under the Forth Railway Bridge but still pay at Port Edgar Marina. Charges; canoes windsurfers £1.40, dinghy less than 4.6m £2.55, 4.6 - 6.0m £7.50@11/2008, more than 6m £13.20. Season rates also available. Check website for latest prices
FACILITIES: There are spacious changing rooms with hot showers which are available to all marina and sailing school customers. Dinghies and other trailer based craft may be kept ashore in dinghy parks or dinghy shed. There is a well stocked and modern chandlery, with brokerage and new boat sales (The Bosun's Locker). Repairs, marine engineering, rigging and spray shop (Ferry Marine Ltd.). All users must hold fully comprehensive insurance cover for their craft and be prepared to produce proof of this on request.
HAZARDS: Keep to west side of ramp for longest length. East side is rough made ground at lower 1/4 tide.

Harbour slipway, South Queensferry
Lat. 55.9910, Long. -3.3965.
John Hawes on 0131 441 2898
SUITABILITY: Large trailer needs a car.
ACCESS: Unknown. **TYPE OF RAMP:** Cobbled 1/2tidal
UPPER AREA: Harbour. **LOWER AREA:** Harbour.
DIRECTIONS: Access to the harbour is off the High Street in the centre of South Queensferry. The slipway is immediately opposite the end of the approach road.
RAMP DESCRIPTION: Wide cobbled slipway with gentle slope on the outer wall of the harbour. The harbour is managed by the Queensferry Boat Club on behalf of Edinburgh Council. Contact John Hawes on 0131 441 2898. N.B. Access on this slip is often blocked by parked up boats/ yachts.
FACILITIES: Situated next to a small harbour.

Hawes Pier, South Queensferry
Lat. 55.9910, Long. -3.3860.
CHARGES: £1-8 depending on boat

7

SUITABILITY: Large trailer needs a car.
ACCESS: All of tidal range. **TYPE OF RAMP:** Wide tarmac with gentle slope **UPPER AREA:** Harbour. **LOWER AREA:** Harbour.
DIRECTIONS: Slipway is almost directly below the Forth Railway Bridge and directly opposite the Hawes Inn
RAMP DESCRIPTION: Slipway is the old ferry ramp and pleasure boats use the pier for evening and weekend cruises. Wide tarmac slipway running into the sea. Launching charges apply only at weekends and public holidays. Cost from £1 for a canoe, up to £8 for a boat of 6 metres plus. Pier is managed by City of Edinburgh Council.
FACILITIES: Toilets and RNLI station at head of pier.

Long Craig Pier, South Queensferry
Lat. 55.9936, Long. -3.3740.
SUITABILITY: Large trailer needs a car.
ACCESS: Unknown. **TYPE OF RAMP:** Stone slipway by pier
UPPER AREA: Harbour. **LOWER AREA:** Unknown.
DIRECTIONS: Slipway in on the pier about half a mile east of the Forth Rail Bridge
FACILITIES: Slipway is used by the Scout Centre.

Cramond slip, Cramond
Lat. 55.9807, Long. -3.3001.
CHARGES: Nil
SUITABILITY: Large trailer needs a car.
ACCESS: ¼ tidal. **TYPE OF RAMP:** Concrete **UPPER AREA:** Concrete.
LOWER AREA: Sand.
RAMP DESCRIPTION: Narrowish ramp only usable 2hrs either side high tide.

Public slipway, Granton
Lat. 55.9833, Long. -3.2227.
CHARGES: None
SUITABILITY: Large trailer needs a car.
ACCESS: ¾ tidal. **TYPE OF RAMP:** Cobbles **UPPER AREA:** Harbour.
LOWER AREA: Unknown.
DIRECTIONS: The public slipway lies just past the clubhouse of the Royal Forth Yacht Club on Granton's middle pier.
RAMP DESCRIPTION: Good wide ramp with a gentle if not a bit uneven slope but remains a good usable launch place. Also 50yds away there is a private slipway, which is steepish but thought to be all of tide, owned by the Royal Forth Yacht Club within their premises. Some sea weed growth at bottom but this is not a significant hindrance.
FACILITIES: Situated in the centre of Granton and close to Edinburgh.

Harbour slipway, Newhaven
Lat. 55.9811, Long. -3.1953.
SUITABILITY: Large trailer needs a car.
ACCESS: ½ tidal. **TYPE OF RAMP:** Cobbled **UPPER AREA:** Harbour.
LOWER AREA: Unknown.
DIRECTIONS: Newhaven is immediately to the west of Port of Leith. Slipway leads directly off the main road at the eastern end of Newhaven harbour.

RAMP DESCRIPTION: Wide, gently sloping cobbled ramp leading into the harbour.
FACILITIES: Close to the Port of Leith. Next to the world famous Harry Ramsden Fish and Chip restaurant.

Harbour slipway, Fisherrow
Lat. 55.9453, Long. -3.0674.
East Lothian Council: 01620 827477.
SUITABILITY: Large trailer needs a car.
ACCESS: ½ tidal. **TYPE OF RAMP:** Concrete **UPPER AREA:** Sand.
LOWER AREA: Shingle.
DIRECTIONS: Slipway is situated in the old harbour of Fisherrow. Harbour Master Alex Stuart 0131 665 0476
RAMP DESCRIPTION: A metal gate to the slipway is often locked and permission to use the slipway must be obtained either from the harbourmaster or from East Lothian Council.
FACILITIES: Close to the centre of Fisherrow.

Slipway, Preston Links
Lat. 55.9637, Long. -2.9774.
07968 435 946
CHARGES: None
SUITABILITY: Large trailer needs a car.
ACCESS: ¾ tidal. **TYPE OF RAMP:** Concrete. **UPPER AREA:** Concrete.
LOWER AREA: Rock.
DIRECTIONS: Port Seton Junction on the A1 10 miles from Edinburgh. West Side of Cockenzie Power Station.
RAMP DESCRIPTION: Concrete ramp, 4 hours each side of a Spring high tide.
FACILITIES: Parking, lots more when club is open.
HAZARDS: Musselburgh Sands 3 miles west.

Slipway, Port Seton Harbour
Lat. 55.9713, Long. -2.9603.
CHARGES: Ask at chandlery at end of the High Street.
SUITABILITY: Large trailer needs a car.
ACCESS: ¾ tidal. **TYPE OF RAMP:** Concrete **UPPER AREA:** Harbour.
LOWER AREA: Rock.
DIRECTIONS: Ramp is situated 100 yds west of main harbour.
RAMP DESCRIPTION: Very straight - not steep. Apart from not being a full tide range ramp this is one of the best around.
FACILITIES: Petrol, pubs, shops, parking but no toilets
HAZARDS: The ramp is quite exposed to the wind and therefore care is needed when cross winds are about. There are serious rocks to the starboard about 40-50 yards away.

Harbour Slip, North Berwick
Lat. 56.0603, Long. -2.7185.
01620 893 333
CHARGES: £8.50
SUITABILITY: Large trailer needs a car.
ACCESS: ¼ tidal. **TYPE OF RAMP:** Concrete leading to sand and flat rock mix. **UPPER AREA:** Harbour. **LOWER AREA:** Sand.

7

The Good Launch Guide

DIRECTIONS: Turn left immediately before the harbour, follow the road through the harbour flats car parking to the ramp. Just past the white flats the road narrows and turns down to the slipway. So be carefull!
RAMP DESCRIPTION: Very hard work on a making tide and an onshore wind. This is a very shallow shelving beach. Best at near high tide for launching. If launching at 1/2 tide bring waders. Coming back in is not so bad at lower tides. Have a long rope handy for towing boat and trailer to the foot of the slipway before hooking up otherwise you are in danger of bogging your vehicle down in the occasional soft sand patches.
FACILITIES: Toilets, parking. Café and chip shops nearby.
HAZARDS: Watch the rocks to the north east of the harbour.

Harbour Slip, Dunbar
Lat. 56.0053, Long. -2.5139.
01368 863206

CHARGES: £10/day and £10/day if diving.
SUITABILITY: Large trailer needs a car.
ACCESS: ½ tidal. **TYPE OF RAMP:** Concrete and stone. Additional info. 7/9/07. A new slipway is planned for the inner harbour. This will replace the current cobbled slipway. It will be concrete construction and will be longer reaching to the bridge and will allow launching and retrieving at a much lower tide state with a car rather than a 4×4. A 4×4 is presently the only realistic option at near low or the early flood tide on the sand soft mud section below the current cobbled slipway.
UPPER AREA: Harbour. **LOWER AREA:** Sand.
DIRECTIONS: Enter from the new harbour off Victoria Place by the Lifeboat Station.
RAMP DESCRIPTION: There are two slipways. One is in the outer harbour (shown in picture) at the west end of the harbour. There is another slipway in the inner harbour (Cromwell Harbour).
FACILITIES: Pubs, toilets and petrol close by. Parking available on the pier. Please keep the slipway clear as it is used by the RNLI for launching the inshore lifeboat.

Skateraw Beach, Dunbar
Lat. 55.9727, Long. -2.4218.

CHARGES: None
SUITABILITY: Small trailer can be pushed.
ACCESS: No Ramp. **TYPE OF RAMP: UPPER AREA:** Sand.
LOWER AREA: Sand.
DIRECTIONS: Take the A1 south east from Dunbar. Skateraw is about 5 km down the road and the slipway is just to the west of the Torness Power Station.
RAMP DESCRIPTION: Skateraw Harbour isn't really a harbour, no jetty, just a sheltered bay next to the Torness Nuclear Power Station, south of Dunbar. At the end of a private lane (which the public can use) is a cobbled ramp leading on to the sandy beach. Fine for dinghies. This could be an ideal place to launch slightly larger boats all that's needed is something on top of the soft sand, like a running board of some description. There are no signs about fees.
FACILITIES: There's a car park just along the top of the beach, 1 100 yards from the slip. The local council have built a low barrier to the beach, anything taller than 2mtrs will struggle to get under it

Harbour Slip, St Abbs
Lat. 55.8989, Long. -2.1301.
Peter Scott 018907 71708 (Home)

CHARGES: £10/day
SUITABILITY: Large trailer needs a car.
ACCESS: ¾ tidal. **TYPE OF RAMP:** Concrete **UPPER AREA:** Harbour.
LOWER AREA: Rock.
DIRECTIONS: Follow Road down to harbour slip way to the left of breakwater.
RAMP DESCRIPTION: Entrance to slip way is extremely tight and requires very hard turn down slip which limits the length of boat to 20 foot. The ramp can be slippery and is steep at lower end with a three foot drop at low tide. Bottom area of slip in good condition and provides good access to harbour area and fishing grounds beyond. The inner harbour dries out completely at low water. Contact the harbourmaster, Peter Scott, before using as the ramp is closed off in bad weather and launching can be difficult in north and north easterly winds. Site is very popular with divers.
FACILITIES: Nearest petrol in Coldingham village, pubs and local caravan campsite at Scoutscroft. Toilets 50 yards from harbour. Car park available at high season and weekends £5/day, near breakwater. No trailers to be parked in the car park. Overall parking very tight and best to get there very early and avoid on bank holiday week ends. Space for storing trailers at the side of the slip is limited to about 4 trailers for mid sized day boats. Compressed air on site and overnight moorings available.

Harbour and Beach, Eyemouth
Lat. 55.8705, Long. -2.0887.
Harbourmaster, 01890 750223

CHARGES: £9/day inc. harbour dues
SUITABILITY: Large trailer needs a car.
ACCESS: ½ tidal. **TYPE OF RAMP:** Concrete **UPPER AREA:** Harbour.
LOWER AREA: Harbour.
DIRECTIONS: Harbour ramp is situated at the southern end of Harbour Road. The beach ramp is just the west of the harbour entrance.
RAMP DESCRIPTION: Concrete ramp into the harbour. Be careful of the large drop off at the end of the ramp. Take extra care if launching around half tide or lower.
FACILITIES: Shops in Eyemouth including chandlery. Parking available and showers and toilets in the fish market. Harbour may be installing pontoons.
HAZARDS: Speed restriction in the harbour.

Amble Marina, Morpeth
Amble, Morpeth, Northumberland, England NE65 0YP
Lat. 55.3365, Long. -1.5861.
01665 712168

Dock Road, Berwick-upon-Tweed
Lat. 55.7612, Long. -2.0009.
01289 307404

CHARGES: None

SUITABILITY: Large trailer needs a car.
ACCESS: ¾ tidal. **TYPE OF RAMP:** Concrete **UPPER AREA:** Rock.
LOWER AREA: Rock.
DIRECTIONS: Ramp is on the southern side of the estuary, just upstream of the lifeboat station.
RAMP DESCRIPTION: Concrete slipway. Ends in a steep drop so be careful at low tide. Pay harbour dues if staying in the harbour. Nothing to pay for day use.
FACILITIES: Café and pub are 10 minutes walk away. Limited parking at the slipway, popular with fishermen.
HAZARDS: Keep clear of shipping entering and leaving the harbour.

Harbour slipway, Holy Island
Lat. 55.6682, Long. -1.7958.
Harbour Master 01289 389248

CHARGES: £2/day or £5/week
SUITABILITY: Large trailer needs a car.
ACCESS: All of tidal range. **TYPE OF RAMP:** Flat soft mud.
UPPER AREA: Sand. **LOWER AREA:** Sand.
DIRECTIONS: Holy Island is cut off by tides that cover the Causeway 2 hrs before and 3 hrs after high water. Berwick-on-Tweed lies 10M to the north-west; the Farne Islands lie 6M to the south-east. The slipway is owned by the Local Authority and used by the fishermen. It is over by the fishing shacks but outside the harbour wall that protects The Ouze.
RAMP DESCRIPTION: The Harbour Master, Mr Tommy Douglas (01289 389248) must be paid £2/day or £5/week. His house is the one closest to the water tower. Then you may proceed past the "NO VEHICLES BEYOND THIS POINT" sign to the grassy area before The Ouze. Vehicles and trailers may be left nearby on the grass. Light boats can be hand launched across the sand directly into The Ouze high water +/-2hours.
FACILITIES: For accommodation there is a choice of one hotel, two pubs, and a handful of B&Bs. Either pub may serve as evening HQ and restaurant. Other facilities are: Post Office, telephone, souvenir shops, off licence and public loo with cold water washing sink. Provisions are all but unavailable.

Slipway, Seahouses
Lat. 55.5825, Long. -1.6515.
Harbour Office on 01665 720033

CHARGES: Pay harbourmaster.
SUITABILITY: Large trailer needs a car.
ACCESS: ¾ tidal. **TYPE OF RAMP:** Concrete **UPPER AREA:** Sand.
LOWER AREA: Mud.
DIRECTIONS: From Seahouses take the road down to the harbourside past the lifeboat station (on left). Before road to breakwater follow road to the right, look for wooden cabin on right. Slip is adjacent to the cabin.
RAMP DESCRIPTION: Used by local divers visiting the Farne Islands. In busy periods the slip is in constant use. Out of season the slip is kept locked. In season the slip remains locked till 08.30 and secured 18.00. A launching fee is payable to the harbourmaster per boat and passenger. A registration plate is then issued. PWCs are not welcome at this harbour.
FACILITIES: Petrol, pubs, cafés, all in town approximately 500 metres away. Trailers can be left on the beach or on the nearby car park.
HAZARDS: Rather evil smelling mud at end of slip.

Beadnell Boat Launch, Beadnell
Lat. 55.5498, Long. -1.6276.

CHARGES: £280 for an annual pass £20 for day launch. £10 for assisted launch, £5 for an unassisted launch.
SUITABILITY: Large trailer needs a car.
ACCESS: No Ramp. **TYPE OF RAMP:** Concrete railway sleepers over sand connect the beach launching area to the public car park.
UPPER AREA: Concrete. **LOWER AREA:** Sand.
DIRECTIONS: Car park and launch site is just to the south of Beadnell point.
RAMP DESCRIPTION: The Beadnell Bay slip is open again thanks to local resident Richard Patterson. The facility is open 7 days a week between the hours of 8am and 6pm, outside of these times the access to and from the beach is locked. Weekday launches are by appointment only except for during the school holidays. The slipway can accommodate boats up to 10m long and 3m wide.
FACILITIES: Trailers are parked on the beach above the high water line; the sand is flat and firm enough for larger boats. There is a pay and display car park with public toilets. The tractor driver operates from an office attached to the toilet block and male and female showers are available for a small fee.
HAZARDS: Flat sandy beach, other beach users, rocks underwater to the north end of the beach, alongside the headland.

Public Slipway, Amble
Lat. 55.3372, Long. -1.5879.
01665 710306

CHARGES: £7.25 per day or £50.00 per annum
SUITABILITY: Large trailer needs a car.
ACCESS: ½ tidal. **TYPE OF RAMP:** Concrete **UPPER AREA:** Mud.
LOWER AREA: Mud.
DIRECTIONS: Follow the A1068 north towards Alnwick, turning off between Amble and Warkworth. Site is adjacent to the marina to the left (just upstream) of the marina outer wall.
RAMP DESCRIPTION: The top of slip is hard concrete, but only usable about 3 1/2 hours around high water. Below the ramp it is really soft mud. The harbourmaster's office (located east of the marina) is often empty, so you should phone ahead to arrange payment. The ramp has a wooden roundabout just on the green above it. You have to drive round the roundabout the wrong way in order to straighten up and reverse down the ramp without getting stuck on the wooden centre. Boats up to about 22 ft manage it but that is the limit unless you can manhandle the trailer around this centre island.
FACILITIES: Marina services are available if you take a day berth (subject to availability) marina telephone: 01665 712168. Petrol is available from garage on the main road, diesel only at the marina. Park about 50 metres away in the public car park (free). The car park is a secluded and not in view of the launch site nor the main road.
HAZARDS: Keep well over towards Fish Quay when leaving or entering as river badly silted to half the width. There are some small buoys marking channel, keep between these and Fish Quay. 4 mph speed limit in the harbour. No Jetskis allowed.

7

INLAND SLIPWAYS

ALPHABETICAL BY PLACE NAME

Loch Sheil, Acharacle
Lat. 56.7442, Long. -5.7882.

CHARGES: None.
SUITABILITY: Large trailer needs a car.
ACCESS: Non-tidal. **TYPE OF RAMP:** Gravel track.
UPPER AREA: Shingle. **LOWER AREA:** Shingle.
DIRECTIONS: Track to the loch is next to the Sheil Hotel opposite the Acharacle Garage.
RAMP DESCRIPTION: Road down to the loch side that continues into the loch. Shallow gradient so you may have to go some way out to get the boat off the trailer. Popular with fishermen on the loch.
FACILITIES: Shops, tearoom, hotel and pub in Acharacle. Nearest fuel available in Strontian or Kilchoan. There is no fuel for sale in Acharacle.)

Loch Lomond Marina, Alexandria
Riverside, Balloch, Alexandria, Dunbartonshire, Scotland G83 8LF
Lat. 56.0030, Long. -4.5800.
01389 752069

Ardbrecknish, Ardbreaknish House Hotel
Lat. 56.3438, Long. -5.1327.

CHARGES: Launch / recovery £8.00
SUITABILITY: Large trailer needs a car.
ACCESS: Non-tidal. **TYPE OF RAMP:** **UPPER AREA:** Concrete.
LOWER AREA: Shingle.
RAMP DESCRIPTION: Boat launch facilities good gentle sloping ramp fine when loch is at normal height but care should be taken when loch is low
FACILITIES: Boat launching and boat hire + outboard motor and tackle shop, toilets, fishing, permits and advice
HAZARDS: Be careful when sailing near the shore and islands lots of boulders and crannogs most are marked but not all

Loch Lomond Castle, Arden
Lat. 56.0235, Long. -4.6249.
Loch Lomond Castle Lodges 01389 850215
SUITABILITY: Large trailer needs a car.
ACCESS: Non-tidal. **TYPE OF RAMP:** Concrete **UPPER AREA:** Concrete.
LOWER AREA: Unknown.
DIRECTIONS: Loch Lomond Castle Lodges is situated at Arden, some 19 miles north of Glasgow. The driveway leads off the A82 Glasgow to Inverness main road, 2 miles north of the roundabout and junction with the A811 to the east. Coming from the south - follow the M74 to Glasgow and continue through Glasgow on the M8 as far as the Erskine Bridge (toll). After crossing the Erskine Bridge, take the A82 (Cranlarich) for 11 miles. Driveway and signboard are visible on the right.
RAMP DESCRIPTION: Concrete ramp into the loch with pontoon nearby.

FACILITIES: Slipway is part of a holiday complex with chalets for sales and rent. There is also a Leisure Club with indoor heated swimming pool, fitness suite, sauna and solarium. Also a restaurant with views of the loch.

Glen Mallin, Arrochar 6 miles
Lat. 56.1294, Long. -4.8183.
01301702885
SUITABILITY: Large trailer needs a car.
ACCESS: ¼ tidal. **TYPE OF RAMP:** Cobbled **UPPER AREA:** Unknown.
LOWER AREA: Unknown.
DIRECTIONS: A814 Garelochhead to Arrochar road about 1 mile after the Finnart oil depot follow the road you'll see a jetty with 3 cranes on it, the road narrows and theres a small boarded up cottage on your right hand side about 100 yards after that theres a long layby the slipway is straight across from the layby. if you miss it you can turn at the jetty car park its got a big enough turning circle.
RAMP DESCRIPTION: Slip way is wide enough for a van and trailer to get access and egress
FACILITIES: None
HAZARDS: Large M.O.D shipping from time to time, also large ocean going tankers unloading at Finnart.

Duncan Mills Slip, Balloch
Lat. 56.0083, Long. -4.5908.

CHARGES: None. But powered boats must be registered and will have to pay for the number plates. See http://www.lochlomond-trossachs.org/
SUITABILITY: Large trailer needs a car.
ACCESS: Non-tidal. **TYPE OF RAMP:** Concrete **UPPER AREA:** Concrete.
LOWER AREA: Concrete.
DIRECTIONS: Access to the slipway is made from Balloch Road on the west side of the river and is located next to the Maid of the Loch Paddle Steamer.
RAMP DESCRIPTION: The new slipway in Balloch opened in June 2000. At the time of writing this slipway is the quietest on the loch and the most accessible, it is also the most secure for overnight parking of cars and trailers. The building next to the slip is the new headquarters of the Water Borne Rangers and you will have to register your boat if you have not done so already.
FACILITIES: The slipway is run by the Park Authority by the Ranger Service. The slipway closes at 10pm (in summer - earlier in winter) but offers secure parking and chain down points for your trailer. There are jetties for getting passengers on and off and the slipway offers deep water for bigger boats.
HAZARDS: Speed restrictions apply until past the yellow marker buoys.

Slipway, Balloch
Lat. 56.0048, Long. -4.5826.

CHARGES: None
SUITABILITY: Large trailer needs a car.
ACCESS: Non-tidal. **TYPE OF RAMP:** Concrete **UPPER AREA:** Concrete.
LOWER AREA: Concrete.

7

DIRECTIONS: From the northern most bridge in Balloch head east and take the first turning left and then turn left again before a car park with a height restriction bar on it. Follow the road down to the river.
RAMP DESCRIPTION: Wide slipway along the river bank. Popular with Jetskiers.
FACILITIES: Limited parking at the slip, best to use nearby car park.
HAZARDS: Moored boats in the river.

Balmaha, Balmaha
Lat. 56.0840, Long. -4.5421.
SUITABILITY: Large trailer needs a car.
ACCESS: Unknown. **TYPE OF RAMP: UPPER AREA:** Unknown.
LOWER AREA: Unknown.

Stewartfield Slipway, Broxburn
Lat. 55.9397, Long. -3.4665.
CHARGES: None
SUITABILITY: Large trailer needs a car.
ACCESS: Non-tidal. **TYPE OF RAMP:** Concrete **UPPER AREA:** Concrete.
LOWER AREA: Mud.
DIRECTIONS: On the Union Canal. Turn into Church Street from East Main Street Broxburn. Between the church and Somerfields supermarket. Gate at bottom on road. If locked, key can be obtained from the Sports Centre (deposit required).
RAMP DESCRIPTION: Has a tendency to silt up. Watch which way you go. To go east head west and vice versa as the canal is looped into an 'S' at this point. Suitable up to 25 ft.
FACILITIES: Good tarmac turning area. Supermarkets available in town (200 m) Toilets are situated opposite Church Street on East Main Street.

Slipway, Dores - Loch Ness
Lat. 57.3825, Long. -4.3338.
Dores Inn 01463 751203
CHARGES: No charges - public slipway.
SUITABILITY: Large trailer needs a car.
ACCESS: Non-tidal. **TYPE OF RAMP:** Concrete **UPPER AREA:** Concrete.
LOWER AREA: Shingle.
DIRECTIONS: Take B862 from Inverness (along South of Loch Ness), at Dores turn right into car park of Dores inn. Ramp is in public car park adjacent.
RAMP DESCRIPTION: Concrete ramp from car park. Ramp is straight and shallow, giving easy access.
FACILITIES: Dores Inn (01463 751203) next to ramp does food and beer. See council sign at ramp for rules.
HAZARDS: No Jetskis. Keep clear of buoyed area to left of ramp. 5 mph speed limit by the beach. Beware of swimmers.

Falkirk Wheel, Falkirk
Forth Clyde Canal Just SW of Falkirk Falkirk
Lat. 56.0015, Long. -3.8426.

Watersports Centre, Kenmore
Lat. 56.5787, Long. -4.0048.
CHARGES: From £5 per day

SUITABILITY: Small trailer can be pushed.
ACCESS: Non-tidal. **TYPE OF RAMP:** Concrete
UPPER AREA: Unknown. **LOWER AREA:** Unknown.
DIRECTIONS: Follow the main A827 road from Aberfeldy. Coming into Kenmore take the left fork to follow the south shore of Loch Tay. The Water Sports centre is 1/4 mile on right but you must use the lodges car park on the left of the road.
RAMP DESCRIPTION: Very steep ramp means all but light dinghies need reversed down but ramp is narrow. Little space to manoeuvre at bottom as there is a replica Crannog (house on stilts) immediately to the east (right) of the ramp and large boulders lie under the surface near the ramp.
FACILITIES: Loch Tay Water Sports Centre provides changing & shower facilities free with launch fee and has a coffee shop on the site. It is situated in the picturesque village of Kenmore, next to the safest bathing beach in Perthshire at the East end of Loch Tay. This is the heart of Scotland just 6 miles away from Aberfeldy.

Loch Tay Boating, Kenmore
Lat. 56.5849, Long. -3.9986.
01887 830291
CHARGES: £8.50/day
SUITABILITY: Large trailer needs a car.
ACCESS: Non-tidal. **TYPE OF RAMP:** Concrete
UPPER AREA: Unknown. **LOWER AREA:** Unknown.
DIRECTIONS: Follow the main A827 road from Aberfeldy. Coming into Kenmore follow the Loch Tay Boating Centre signs along to the car park on the left. Turn left as if to enter the car park and follow Pier Road.
RAMP DESCRIPTION: Weekly rates; Up to 17 feet £40.00. Over 17 foot. £47.00. Day rates; Up to 10 Hp £6.50. Over 10 Hp £8.50. £6-00 for launch and recovery with our tractor if needed. All boats either on moorings or launched from this slip must be insured for third party risks. Jetskiers are not allowed to use this slipway.
FACILITIES: Loch Tay Boating Centre is situated in the picturesque village of Kenmore, next to the safest bathing beach in Perthshire at the East end of Loch Tay. This is the heart of Scotland just 6 miles away from Aberfeldy.

Auchinstarry, Kilsyth
Lat. 55.9670, Long. -4.0498.
CHARGES: None
SUITABILITY: Large trailer needs a car.
ACCESS: Non-tidal. **TYPE OF RAMP:** Concrete **UPPER AREA:** Concrete.
LOWER AREA: Mud.
DIRECTIONS: Situated to the south of Kilsyth. Take the B802 to Auchinstarry and immediately after the bridge over the canal, turn left down a gravel track that will take you to the slipway.
RAMP DESCRIPTION: One of the best access points for the Forth and Clyde canal. About 9 miles and only 3 locks from the Falkirk Wheel which is well worth a visit.
FACILITIES: Plenty of parking. There is a British Waterways office nearby and often boats in the basin so it should be safe to leave cars and trailers here. Pontoon in the basin for narrow boats. Short walk into Kilsyth. Idyllic spot to stay.

7

Manse Road Basin, Linlithgow

Lat. 55.9745, Long. -3.5987.

CHARGES: None

SUITABILITY: Large trailer needs a car.

ACCESS: Non-tidal. **TYPE OF RAMP:** Concrete **UPPER AREA:** Concrete.
LOWER AREA: Concrete.

DIRECTIONS: From Edinburgh and the east leave the M9 at junction 3 northbound and follow the A803 into Linlithgow. The Canal Basin is signposted from the roundabout at the east end of the High Street in Linlithgow. Take the B9080 towards Winchburgh. Immediately after going under the railway bridge at the lights turn sharp right up Back Station Road , 300 yards further on bear left over the canal bridge. The basin is on the right. From Falkirk and the north leave the M9 at junction 4 and follow the A803. Drive through the town to the roundabout. From Glasgow and the west leave the M8 at junction 4 and follow the A706 into Linlithgow. Turn right at the T-junction onto the High Street and through the town to the roundabout. From Carlisle and the south leave the M74 at junction 13. Follow the A73 into Lanark and join the A706 to Linlithgow.

FACILITIES: Toilets, parking, tea room, petrol station nearby, 5 minutes walking distance to the east of canal basin (follow the towpath under the bridge and keep a lookout to your left). Linlithgow Union Canal Society (LUCS) administers the Canal Centre and operates boat trips from Manse Road Basin every weekend from Easter until the first week in October with two boats from 2pm. You can cruise the calm and peaceful canal to the Avon Aqueduct in comfort on board the "St Magdalene". Or journey the town stretch on "Victoria", a replica of a Victorian steam packet boat. During July & August open weekdays with one boat. Charters and private bookings can be arranged at other times. The Canal Museum has a sales counter, a short audio-visual presentation, admission is free.

Ardlui Marina, Loch Lomond

Ardlui, Loch Lomond, Argyll, Scotland G83 7EB
Lat. 56.3041, Long. -4.7205.
01301 704333

Cameron House Marina, Loch Lomond

**De Vere Cameron House, Loch Lomond,
Dunbartonshire, Scotland G83 8QZ**
Lat. 56.0135, Long. -4.6067.
01389 722508

Ardlui Hotel, Loch Lomond

Lat. 56.3037, Long. -4.7201.
01301 704 243

CHARGES: £6.00 each way

SUITABILITY: Large trailer needs a car.

ACCESS: Non-tidal. **TYPE OF RAMP: UPPER AREA:** Unknown.
LOWER AREA: Unknown.

DIRECTIONS: Situated at the northern tip of Loch Lomond.

RAMP DESCRIPTION: Part of the marina. Phone before travel to check you can use it. Use of slipway only: £6.00 in £6.00 out. Boat slipped for you with tractor: up-to 5 metres: £16.50, 5 - 6 metres: £20.00, 6 - 7

metres: £27.50. You must register your craft. There is no actual charge for registration. You are however, obliged to display registration numbers on each side of your craft, which needs to be of a specific size. So rather than you making your own number plates, you can buy a couple from the registration office for £5.

FACILITIES: 100 berth marina facilities offer all year round quality berthing in the most sheltered of positions. Berthing is available on either floating pontoons, floating pier, swinging moorings, or in our secure boat yard for those of you wishing to store your boat out of the water. All pontoon, pier and boat yard berthing are equipped with electricity and fresh water hook-up.

HAZARDS: Speed limits operate on the Loch.

Lochore Meadows, Lochore Meadows

Lat. 56.1482, Long. -3.3352.
01592 414300

CHARGES: £6 per day (2006 prices) including safety cover. The slip and park are also open to the public during non business hours free of charge; however there will be no safety cover.

SUITABILITY: Small trailer can be pushed.

ACCESS: Non-tidal. **TYPE OF RAMP:** Concrete surrounded by pontoons.
UPPER AREA: Concrete. **LOWER AREA:** Shingle.

DIRECTIONS: From M90 heading north, take exit no 3 onto A92 heading East for Cowdenbeath. Take next left onto A909 still heading for Cowdenbeath. Go straight through Cowndenbeath and turn right onto B981 for lumphinnans. Follow the road through Lochgelly which becomes the B920. Just after Glencraig at the mini roundabout before Crosshill take a left into the park. It is signposted from Cowdenbeath as Lochore Meadows Country Park. After turning into the park take the first left towards the outdoor centre. The slip is round the back of the centre as you approach it.

RAMP DESCRIPTION: 2 slips available beside the outdoor centre situated at the side of the loch. Suitable for dinghy sailing, kayaks or small craft only.

FACILITIES: It is the main centre for outdoor and environmental education in Fife and comprises a nature reserve, park centre, outdoor pursuits centre, adventurous play area, picnic and barbecue areas and nature trails. Activities in the park include windsurfing, horse riding, orienteering and fishing in addition to a 9-hole golf course and putting green. The ruins of Lochore Castle and remains of the Mary Pit coal workings are also in the park which is open to the public throughout the year.

HAZARDS: All danger marks within the loch are buoyed.

Slipway, Milarrochy Bay

Lat. 56.0999, Long. -4.5606.

CHARGES: None

SUITABILITY: Portable Only.

ACCESS: Non-tidal. **TYPE OF RAMP:** Concrete **UPPER AREA:** Concrete.
LOWER AREA: Shingle.

DIRECTIONS: The road to Balmaha can be quite busy on holidays and weekends with day trippers.

RAMP DESCRIPTION: The 'slipway' is very short and it has a bend right at the start with trees to one side and a short drop to the other, certainly one for the more experienced. The area is very shallow even when the water is high enough to get up to the slip, underfoot the shingle will break up very easily. 25m of rope needed between the car and the trailer to get the boat out for the sake of finding a grip. Milarrochy is popular with Jetskis; the eastern end of the loch is somewhat windier and is also frequented by windsurfers and the Loch Lomond Sailing Club. The slipway is manned by the Park Authority; they will check your registration and also limit cars accessing the shore.

FACILITIES: There is nowhere to tie up to whilst cars are parked and trailers retrieved, fine on a calm day but on Lomond they are rare and the onshore wind blows straight on to the shoreline for most of the year. Recommended for canoeists, windsurfers and Jetskis only.

HAZARDS: There is a speed limit of 6mph to 150 metres off shore but it is open water.

Great Glen Water Park, North Laggan
Lat. 57.0463, Long. -4.7981.

CHARGES: £5
SUITABILITY: Large trailer needs a car.
ACCESS: Non-tidal. **TYPE OF RAMP:** Concrete **UPPER AREA:** Concrete.
LOWER AREA: Shingle.
DIRECTIONS: Great Glen Water Park, Loch Oich. Turn right before Lagan Swing Bridge into the Great Glen Water Park. Slipway is halfway up the park, past the Loch Side Lodges.
FACILITIES: Pub, toilets, washroom.

7

Index of Place Names